B.R. 519 C (Restricted)

GEOGRAPHICAL HANDBOOK SERIES

FOR OFFICIAL USE ONLY

PACIFIC ISLANDS

VOLUME IV

WESTERN PACIFIC

(New Guinea and Islands Northward)

August 1945

NAVAL INTELLIGENCE DIVISION

PREFACE

IN 1915 a Geographical Section was formed in the Naval Intelligence Division of the Admiralty to write Geographical Handbooks on various parts of the world. The purpose of these handbooks was to supply, by scientific research and skilled arrangement, material for the discussion of naval, military, and political problems, as distinct from the examination of the problems themselves. Many distinguished collaborators assisted in their production, and by the end of 1918 upwards of fifty volumes had been produced in Handbook and Manual form, as well as numerous short-term geographical reports. The demand for these books increased rapidly with each new issue, and they acquired a high reputation for accuracy and impartiality. They are now to be found in Service Establishments and Embassies throughout the world, and in the early years after the last war were much used by the League of Nations.

The old Handbooks have been extensively used in the present war, and experience has disclosed both their value and their limitations. On the one hand they have proved, beyond all question, how greatly the work of the fighting services and of Government Departments is facilitated if countries of strategic or political importance are covered by handbooks which deal, in a convenient and easily digested form, with their geography, ethnology, administration, and resources. On the other hand, it has become apparent that something more is needed to meet present-day requirements. The old series does not cover many of the countries closely affected by the present war (e.g. Germany, France, Poland, Spain, Portugal, to name only a few); its books are somewhat uneven in quality, and they are inadequately equipped with maps, diagrams, and photographic illustrations.

The present series of Handbooks, while owing its inspiration largely to the former series, is in no sense an attempt to revise or re-edit that series. It is an entirely new set of books, produced in the Naval Intelligence Division by trained geographers drawn largely from the Universities, and working at sub-centres established at Oxford and Cambridge. The books follow, in general, a uniform scheme, though minor modifications will be found in particular cases; and they are illustrated by numerous maps and photographs.

The purpose of the books is primarily naval. They are designed first to provide, for the use of Commanding Officers, information in a comprehensive and convenient form about countries which they may be called upon to visit, not only in war but in peace-time; secondly, to maintain the high standard of education in the Navy and, by supplying officers with material for lectures to naval personnel ashore and afloat, to ensure for all ranks that visits to a new country shall be both interesting and profitable.

Their contents are, however, by no means confined to matters of purely naval interest. For many purposes (e.g. history, administration, resources, communications, etc.) countries must necessarily be treated as a whole, and no attempt is made to limit their treatment exclusively to coastal zones. It is hoped therefore that the Army, the Royal Air Force, and other Government Departments (many of whom have given great assistance in the production of the series) will find these Handbooks even more valuable than their predecessors proved to be both during and after the last war.

J. H. GODFREY
Director of Naval Intelligence
1942

The foregoing preface has appeared from the beginning of this series of Geographical Handbooks. It describes so effectively their origin and purpose that I have decided to retain it in its original form.

This volume has been prepared for the Naval Intelligence Division at the Cambridge sub-centre (General Editor, Dr H. C. Darby). It has been mainly written by Mr A. E. P. Collins, Dr J. W. Davidson, Dr Margaret Davies and Mr Adrian Digby, with contributions from Dr J. P. Harding, Dr Phyllis Kaberry and Dr P. W. Richards. The maps and diagrams have been drawn mainly by Miss S. H. Collins, Miss K. S. A. Froggatt, Miss F. Hands and Mrs Gwen Raverat. The volume has been edited by Dr Raymond Firth, Dr J. W. Davidson and Dr Margaret Davies.

E. G. N. RUSHBROOKE
Director of Naval Intelligence
August 1945

CONTENTS

PART TWO: THE JAPANESE MANDATED ISLANDS

SUMMARY OF CONTENTS OF HANDBOOK ON PACIFIC ISLANDS

LIST OF MAPS AND DIAGRAMS

LIST OF PLATES

Chapter I

INTRODUCTION

Plan of this Volume: Source Literature and Maps: Place-names

PLAN OF THIS VOLUME

The term Western Pacific has been used in this Handbook to describe the area west of the international date line and east of the Philippines, Indonesia, and the east coast of Australia; the northern and southern boundaries of the area covered are approximately lat. 30° N and 30° S. The islands of the southern and eastern parts of this area have been described in vol. III of the Handbook. This volume describes the remainder of the area—i.e., New Guinea and its adjacent islands, and the islands and groups to northward as far as the Bonin islands. All these islands have been directly affected by the present war. Large parts of New Guinea and many of the islands further north have been the scene of land fighting; everywhere ports and major settlements have been subjected to bombing from the air; and the normal pattern of life has been disrupted, for both natives and non-natives, as a consequence of military operations. Even where fighting has for some time been over, as in Papua, conditions have not yet returned to normal. This volume, therefore, does not in general attempt to describe the present situation, which is everywhere subject to rapid change, but deals with conditions immediately before the outbreak of war. At some points, however, it has seemed necessary to refer to developments subsequent to 1941, and a summary of war-time changes in New Guinea is given in Appendix III. (For an outline of military operations in the Pacific, see vol. I, Appendix VI.)

A general outline of the characteristics of the region—physical, cultural and economic—has been given in vol. III (pp. 1–9). Here, it is necessary only to add an explanation of the arrangement of the present volume. The area described can be divided into three parts: (i) New Guinea and the islands near to it and linked with it economically and politically and, to some extent, culturally; (ii) the Caroline islands, Marshall islands and Marianas, which have been administered since the war of 1914–18 by the Japanese under mandate from the League of Nations, and where the native peoples are Micronesian; and (iii) the minor American and Japanese territories in the northern part of the area (Guam, Wake island, the Bonin islands and Marcus island).

The New Guinea area is unique within the Pacific islands region, in that it contains the large land mass of the mainland of New Guinea. On this account it differs in many ways from all other parts of the region. For example, the population of Papua and the Territory of New Guinea—somewhat over a million—is more than twice that of the Hawaiian islands, which have the next largest population. An even more important difference is the far greater difficulty of establishing communications in New Guinea, as compared with the smaller islands, where no point is at any considerable distance from the coast. As a consequence, many of the New Guinea peoples have as yet had little contact with Western civilization, and the economic resources of the country are less fully explored than are those of almost any other part of the Pacific.

The Caroline islands, Marshall islands and Marianas cannot be so sharply differentiated from other areas in the Pacific. In respect of physical geography, their most notable characteristic is the predominance of atolls in the Marshalls and Carolines; but in this they do not differ from the great belt of islands which stretches south-eastward across the Pacific between the Marshall islands and the Tuamotu archipelago. In respect of their native population, they are to be distinguished by the fact that the people are Micronesian; but the Caroline islanders and Marshall islanders do not differ markedly, either physically or culturally, from the Micronesians of the Gilbert islands, immediately to the east, while in the Marianas the Micronesian characteristics have been to some extent overlaid as a result of past immigration of Spaniards and Filipinos. The primary reason for treating the three groups of islands as a unit is that the most powerful outside influence in them all during recent times has been not that of any European people, but that of the Japanese.

The remaining islands treated in this volume—the Bonin and Volcano islands, Marcus island, Guam, and Wake island—have little in common except that they all lie near the northern fringe of the Pacific islands region and that they are all of greater importance strategically than economically.

For convenience of reference, two general maps of the Western Pacific showing respectively main shipping routes (Fig. 1) and political organization (Fig. 2) are reproduced here from vol. III.

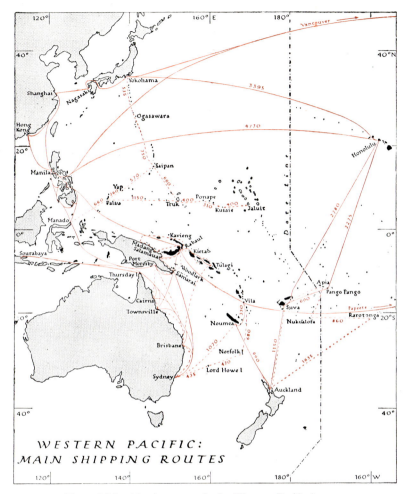

Fig. 1. Main shipping routes in the Western Pacific in 1939

Distances are approximate, in nautical miles. The main through routes are shown by a solid brown line; the principal short-distance routes linking mainland territories with neighbouring islands or groups are shown by a pecked brown line. Trans-Pacific services from Australia and New Zealand, and many local services, are omitted. West of New Guinea only main trends are shown. Based on official and commercial sources.

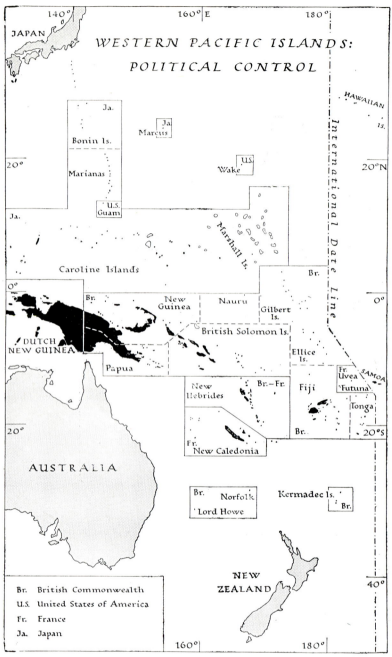

Fig. 2. Political control of the Western Pacific islands in 1939

The lines separating the various groups do not necessarily indicate extent of sovereignty. The open rings (as in the Marshall islands) represent major atolls.

Source Literature and Maps

The literature of the islands treated in this volume is extensive, but it is of very uneven quality and much of it is concerned with subjects highly specialized. The most useful general sources include: the *Pacific Islands Year Book* (wartime edition, 1942); *The South Seas in the Modern World*, by F. M. Keesing (1942); and (for coasts and anchorages) the Admiralty *Pacific Islands Pilot* and *Japan Pilot*. Useful handbooks have been issued by the governments of the Territories of Papua and New Guinea. In normal times the governments of Australia and of Japan printed detailed annual reports on the administration of the Territory of New Guinea and of the Japanese mandated islands respectively for presentation to the League of Nations; the government of Papua also printed an annual report. The most useful periodicals covering the area are *Oceania*, an anthropological journal, and the *Pacific Islands Monthly*, a topical paper. Detailed bibliographical notes are given at the ends of chapters.

Much survey and cartographical work still remains to be done in the Western Pacific. The maps in this volume therefore differ considerably in their accuracy. Many are based primarily on Admiralty charts, but much detail (especially in regard to areas away from the coast) has been added from other sources. The most important of these are maps produced by Lands Departments and other government bodies in normal times or by military agencies as a result of wartime surveys. In some cases sketch maps in scientific periodicals, etc., have also been drawn upon. Details of maps and charts for the area covered by this volume are given in Appendix I.

Latitude and longitude have been taken from Admiralty charts and *Sailing Directions*; in some instances they are only approximate, since precise observations have not been made. Reference to the *Sailing Directions* will show that some islands are reported as being several miles out of their charted positions. Altitudes also are often only approximate. Sources of apparently equal authority frequently show discrepancies; and, since many altitudes have been calculated from observations at sea, they probably include the height of the vegetation. Except where specially stated, British units have been used throughout this volume. Heights are given in feet, depths in fathoms, distances on land and also between islands in statute miles. On maps, scales are given in both miles and kilometres (or component parts of these).

For the commoner physical and social features on the maps a series of conventional symbols has been used. The general key to these symbols is given in Fig. 3. When other symbols are used a special key

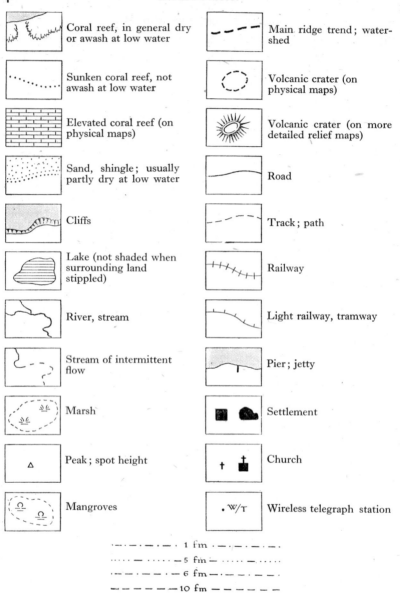

	Coral reef, in general dry or awash at low water		Main ridge trend; watershed
	Sunken coral reef, not awash at low water		Volcanic crater (on physical maps)
	Elevated coral reef (on physical maps)		Volcanic crater (on more detailed relief maps)
	Sand, shingle; usually partly dry at low water		Road
	Cliffs		Track; path
	Lake (not shaded when surrounding land stippled)		Railway
	River, stream		Light railway, tramway
	Stream of intermittent flow		Pier; jetty
	Marsh		Settlement
	Peak; spot height		Church
	Mangroves		Wireless telegraph station

·—·—·—·— 1 fm ·—·,—·—·—.

····· — ····· —5 fm — ······ —······

·—— ·—— ·— 6 fm —·—— ·· —— ·

—— —— —— —10 fm —— —— —— ——

Fathom lines (datum as source charts)

Only a small proportion of coral reefs (including sunken reefs) are shown, namely those of major importance to navigation, or to a presentation of the structure of islands.

The approximate position of an anchorage is shown on some maps by an anchor symbol.

Fig. 3. Key to general symbols used on maps

is given for the map, or maps, concerned. Mercator's projection has been used for all maps.

PLACE-NAMES

The treatment of place-names in the islands covered by this volume is complicated by several factors. In the New Guinea area the number of separate languages makes far more difficult the task of discovering correct forms, with the result that systematic study has not yet gone beyond a very elementary stage. Much work similarly remains to be done in the Japanese mandated islands. There are, further, in all parts of the areas covered, a great number of alternative names. Thus, in the Territory of New Guinea native, German and English names often exist for the same feature; and in the Japanese mandated islands a native name, several European names, and a Japanese name may in some cases be found.

The main principles adopted in this volume are:

1. In general, local official names (as used on government maps or in official documents) have been adopted. But certain exceptions have been made in respect of Japanese-administered territories. Thus, the name Bonin islands has been used instead of the official Japanese name for the group, Ogasawara guntō; and Marcus island has been adopted in place of Minami Tori shima.

2. Descriptive geographical terms are normally given in their English form in the text and in maps. The most important exceptions are in the Bonin islands, where Japanese geographical terms are used when Japanese place-names are adopted.

3. Since the same native name often applies to a physical feature and to a nearby settlement, names of all physical features are given on the maps in italic lettering and names of settlements in roman lettering.

4. The system of orthography followed is in general that of the Permanent Committee on Geographical Names, the R.G.S. II system.

5. Japanese names are transliterated according to the modified Hepburn system.

6. In spelling, the forms on local official maps have been generally used for the New Guinea area; Admiralty charts and *Sailing Directions* have been followed generally for the Japanese territories and for Guam and Wake island. Much supplementary material has been obtained for many islands from official maps and reports prepared in the course of present military operations.

Further details regarding place-names are given in Appendix II.

PART ONE

NEW GUINEA AND ADJACENT ISLANDS

Chapter II

GEOLOGY AND PHYSICAL FEATURES

Recent Exploration : Physiographic Regions of Eastern New Guinea : New Britain :
Bismarck Volcanic Belt :Ninigo-New Ireland Arc :Vulcanism :Bibliographical Note

RECENT EXPLORATION

New Guinea is one of the largest islands in the world. Until recently
little was known to Europeans of its interior, and even now much of
it has not been scientifically surveyed and accurately mapped. While
there are still considerable gaps in our knowledge of the topography,
recent years have seen a gradual filling in of the map so that the
general trends of the mountain ranges and drainage pattern are now
determined. The last twenty years have seen most progress in surveying and until the outbreak of the present war it was largely as a result
of the patrols and travels of men connected directly or indirectly with
the administration of Papua and the mandated territory that this
advance was made.

The first modern surveys, which partly covered the coasts of New
Guinea, New Britain and their off-lying islands, were undertaken by
the British Admiralty and the German Admiralty in the late nineteenth century. As sporadic British and German colonization affected
pockets of land behind the small ports the coastal fringe gradually
became known. Little work was carried out in the interior of German-
occupied New Guinea, although the anthropologist Thurnwald had
reached the Sepik headstreams by 1914. Survey work, directed towards delineation of physical and geological features and having as a
primary aim friendly contacts with native peoples, is now a well-
established tradition in mandated New Guinea and Papua. The
earliest of such surveys was undertaken by Sir William MacGregor
in 1890 (p. 132). This was an ascent of the Fly river, and the basin of
this great southward-flowing stream, navigable for much greater
distances than any apart from the Sepik river, attracted the attention
of later patrols. In 1924 Leo Austen ascended the Fly river head-

Plate 1. Mount Yalbu from mount Keluwere

This mountain is about 11,000 ft. high and lies on the north-west flank of the Purari plateau. Typical high-plateau vegetation is seen in the foreground.

Plate 2. View looking towards mount Tafa

These ranges lie to the east of Ononge in Papua and form part of the main cordillera known in that area as the Wharton range.

Plate 3. The Wahgi-Nabilya watershed

These peaks form part of the Kubor range which bounds the northern margin of the Purari plateau.

Plate 4. The Wahgi valley near mount Hagen

In its upper course in the central plateau the Wahgi meanders through a broad valley. Note the gravel terraces and hillocks of solid rock rising out of the alluvium which fills the valley floor.

streams as far as the gorges by which they leave the main cordillera. Between 1890 and 1926, when the exploration of the central ranges began, the knowledge of the coastlands and of the lower basins of the larger rivers increased. The eastern valleys and much of the interior of south-east Papua became known as a result of the search for gold (pp. 129–30). By 1921 geological information was available in sufficient detail to allow E. R. Stanley to construct a provisional distribution map of the rock types of Papua, for which much additional information has since become available.

By 1930 the exploration of the central ranges had been initiated and in succeeding years large areas of the ranges were penetrated, though the small size of most parties did not allow of intensive surveys. In 1926–7 C. H. Karius and Ivan Champion worked on the headstreams of the Fly and Sepik rivers, and accomplished the first crossing of the broadest part of New Guinea, from south to north. It began to be realized that much of the central mountain and plateau country might be open grassland and not densely forested. The existence of large plateaux and relatively open wide valleys leading towards them was confirmed by Michael Leahy. In the period 1930–4 Leahy, often accompanied by his brothers, covered the ranges from behind Salamaua up to mount Hagen, and obtained a fine photographic record of his travels. In 1934 K. L. Spinks and E. W. P. Chinnery published the results of several years' work in the central ranges. Their maps of the mountains, from the upper Ramu valley westward to mount Hagen (incorporating part of Leahy's work) and those from mount Lawson to mount Joseph further south-east along the Papuan border, gave a reasonable picture of the drainage of central New Guinea. The first survey to be carried out largely from the air was one of the Fly-Sepik headstreams, made in 1935 by Stuart Campbell. In 1936 Ivan Champion and J. G. Hides examined the basins of two great Papuan rivers, the Kikori and Purari, up to the border where their headstreams lie. As a result of the present war much progress has been made in aerial photographic surveys, not only in New Guinea but in the little-known mountain interior of New Britain and in the off-lying islands.

Great progress has been made, often under hazardous conditions, but there are still large stretches of country (especially those intervening between the valley ways which are largely used by the surveyors) of which little is known. The southern plain of Papua is not wholly explored away from the main rivers. There is little accurate knowledge of the main ranges between long. 142° and 144° E. The landward sides of many of the northern ranges, such as the Torricelli, Prince Alexander, and Adalbert ranges, are poorly known.

PHYSIOGRAPHIC REGIONS OF EASTERN NEW GUINEA

The major physiographic outlines and drainage pattern of New Guinea are known (Fig. 4). Knowledge of the geology of the country

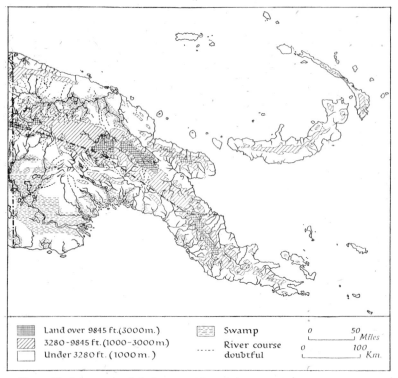

Land over 9845 ft.(3000m.)	Swamp	0 50 Miles
3280-9845 ft.(1000-3000m)	River course	0 100
Under 3280 ft. (1000 m.)	doubtful	Km.

Fig. 4. Drainage and relief of eastern New Guinea and the off-lying islands

Only the more extensive lowland swamps are shown. Based on: (1) G.S.G.S. map, no. 3860; (2) *Schetskaart van Nieuw-Guinea*, 1 : 2,990,000 (Batavia, 1938).

is, however, still very incomplete. Parts of the country where the presence of oil has been suspected have been intensively studied. Such parts include the southern fringe of Papua and the Vogelkop, in Dutch New Guinea. In the latter region a specially careful survey has been made since 1936; nearly 40,000 sq. miles of territory have been covered. As a comprehensive account of the geology of New Guinea is not possible, a more generalized description of the main

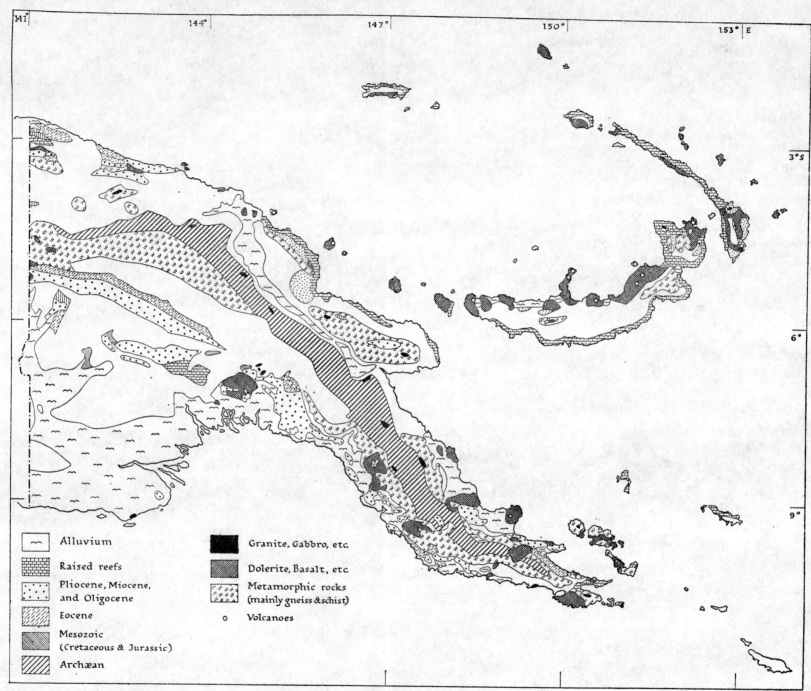

Legend

~	Alluvium
	Raised reefs
	Pliocene, Miocene, and Oligocene
	Eocene
	Mesozoic (Cretaceous & Jurassic)
	Archæan
	Granite, Gabbro, etc.
	Dolerite, Basalt, etc.
	Metamorphic rocks (mainly gneiss & schist)
o	Volcanoes

Fig. 5. Geology of eastern New Guinea and the off-lying islands

Only active volcanoes are shown. The geological formations of the unshaded areas are not known. The Archaean formations may be equated with the Pre-Cambrian of the geological Table (p. 9). Based on: (1) T. W. Edgeworth David, *Geological Map of the Commonwealth of Australia*: 1 : 2,990,000 (Canberra, 1931); (2) E. R. Stanley, *The Geology of Papua* (Melbourne, 1923).

physiographic regions will be given. Since these are controlled in large measure by relatively recent geological history, it is simpler to explain structural forms rather than individual rock outcrops.

Figs. 5 and 6 and the accompanying Table summarize the location and nature of the principal geological formations. In describing the physical geography of the seaboard descriptive terms such as 'Daru coast' or 'Moresby coast' are used, but it must be noted that the term is comprehensive. It does not necessarily refer to the immediate surroundings of a settlement or to the local usage for administrative or other purposes.

Geological Formations and Associated Rocks in the New Guinea Area

Geological formation	Representative types of rocks
Holocene (Recent)	Active volcanoes: living coral. Peaty swamps in river flood-plains. Raised coral reefs are widespread at elevations up to 2,000 ft. Gold-bearing gravels and conglomerates: laterites 24 to 36 ft. thick.
QUATERNARY Pleistocene	Raised coral limestone: cape Vogel, Vanimo and Wewak. Consolidated river deposits. Traces of ice erosion in Owen Stanley range. Lavas and debris (ash).
CAINOZOIC (TERTIARY) Pliocene ⎫ Mio-Pliocene ⎬Neogene Miocene ⎭	Shell sandstones, limestones and marls. Lignite. Igneous lavas and debris. Oil-bearing beds of marls and lignites with sandstones and coral limestone. About 10,000 ft. thick. Some metamorphosed rocks with intrusive igneous rocks and associated mineral deposits (e.g., copper at Laloki). Also volcanic debris, marls, sandstones and conglomerates with some oil and brine. Over 15,000 ft. thick.
Oligo-Miocene ⎫ Oligocene ⎬Palaeo- ⎩ gene Eocene ⎭	Limestones about 3,500 ft. thick. Lavas. Limestones with conglomerates derived from a former land surface to the north. Coral limestones and hard sandstones.
MESOZOIC (SECONDARY) Cretaceous (Upper)	Marls on Dutch side of border of mandated territory, etc.
PALAEOZOIC (PRIMARY) Devonian (Middle) PRE-CAMBRIAN	Limestones of Tauri river (Papua). Gneisses of Owen Stanley and Bewani ranges.

The islands in the New Guinea area form the eastern end of the great arc of fold mountains which extends through the Himalaya and Malaya into the Pacific. This zone of uplift and folding has provided the core around which the vast island of New Guinea has been built. The New Guinea region has been divided into eight distinct physiographic provinces (Fig. 7). They are concentric to the north-eastern part of the Australian continent and are: the southern littoral, the southern foothills, the main cordillera, the central intermontane trough, the northern chain, the northern littoral, the active volcanic arc and the outer island festoon. The two last-named regions are best represented in New Britain and in the smaller islands which

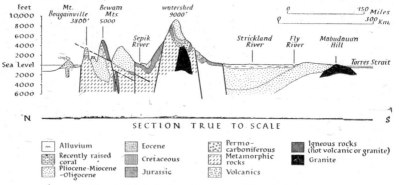

Fig. 6. Geological section across New Guinea

The section runs from north to south across the greatest width of New Guinea. There are divergencies from the general north-to-south direction to include outstanding peaks. The volcano north of mount Bougainville represents the active volcanic arc. Based on T. W. Edgeworth David, *Geological Map of the Commonwealth of Australia*: 1 : 2,990,000 (Canberra, 1931).

surround the Bismarck sea. These physiographic provinces are of ancient origin but have been partly re-emphasized in recent geological time (late Neogene), as is shown by the Pliocene marine limestone caps of the Carstensz Toppen of Dutch New Guinea, which are now over 16,000 ft. above sea level.

The stable core underlying much of southern New Guinea is an area which has been little affected by the cycles of rapid Tertiary sedimentation and mountain-building characteristic of the rest of New Guinea. The central cordillera (a complex of mountain ranges), which forms the backbone of the land mass, runs continuously for nearly 2,000 miles. It stretches from the Vogelkop ('bird's head') of Dutch New Guinea, southwards through the Bintini isthmus and swings round Geelvink bay into the Nassau range (or Snow mountains) and the Star mountains. Thence it widens around the central plateau of British New Guinea and passes south-eastwards as the Owen Stanley range of Papua from which it continues eastwards, though only its higher points are above sea level in the drowned chain of the Louisiade archipelago. North of the central cordillera is the

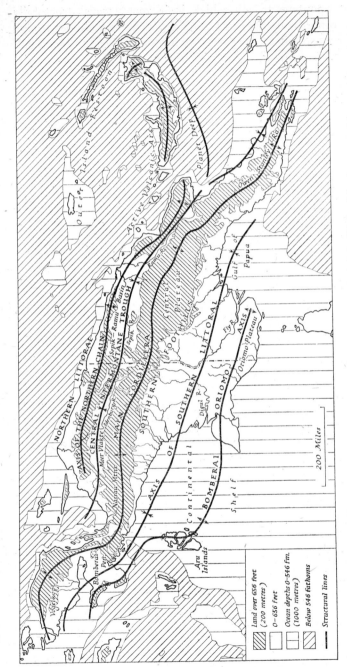

Fig. 7. The physical features of New Guinea and the off-lying islands

The axes of major upfolds and downfolds are shown by heavy lines. The arrows show the direction of slope from the crests of the anticlines or into the downfolds. Based on: (1) S. W. Carey, 'The Morphology of New Guinea', *Australian Geographer*, vol. III, no. 5, p. 4 (Sydney, 1938); (2) G.S.G.S. map, no. 3860.

central intermontane trough which is in many ways structurally-analogous to the great valley of California. This New Guinea trough extends for 1,000 miles from Geelvink bay on the west to Huon gulf on the east. The trough is drained by the Rauffaer, Idenburg, Sepik, Ramu and Markham rivers.

Bordering this trough on its northern side are the coastal ranges which include the Van Rees, Gauttier, Foya, Karamor and Bonggo mountains of Dutch New Guinea, the Bewani mountains of the border and the Torricelli, Prince Alexander, Adalbert, Finisterre and Saruwaged mountains of the mandated territory. New Britain is included in this structural unit. The outer island festoon includes, within the area discussed in this volume, the Ninigo, Hermit and Admiralty groups, Lavongai (New Hanover) and New Ireland and its off-lying islands. This belt of islands, together with those of the active volcanic arc, are more fully described below in the chapters on coasts and individual islands (Chapters III, XII, XIII).

The Southern Littoral

The whole of this region is a continuously sinking zone, but nevertheless there are regional differences, for the central sector (the Daru area) faces the flooded shelf of the more stable region known as the

Fig. 8. The lowland area of southern New Guinea

The broken line is the 546-fathom (1,000-metre) contour. Based on: (1) S. W. Carey, 'The Morphology of New Guinea', *Australian Geographer*, vol. III, no. 5, p. 4 (Sydney, 1938); (2) G.S.G.S. map, no. 3860.

Australian shield with which it was formerly linked, whilst the eastern and north-western section face great oceanic depths, and subsidence, although slow by human standards, is more rapid here.

The western area, in the west of Dutch New Guinea, is a region of subsidence with long penetrating estuaries. While off-shore reefs are numerous, there are no raised reefs. This coast is similar to that of the Port Moresby area.

The Daru Coast. The central area, the Daru coast, embraces from east to west, the great delta plains of the Turama, Awarra-Bamu, Fly-Strickland, Digul, Eiland and Lorentz rivers. It covers 100,000 sq. miles and is one of the most extensive swamps in the world (Fig. 8). Backed by high non-resistant mountains subject to heavy tropical rain, the rivers carry heavy alluvial loads and are building out their deltas over the slowly subsiding continental shelf to the south. In many places the shore is slightly higher than the immediate hinterland. This may not rise above sea level for as much as 20 miles inland. Mangrove, sago and nipa swamps are characteristic, and towers as much as 30 in. high, raised by crabs, obstruct the drainage seaward and in a small way assist in the accumulation of sediments and help to build up the land surface. As an area of slight though progressive subsidence, it is free from recently raised corals (older raised reefs of Miocene age are found in the Kikori region and near the junction of the Purari and its north-south tributary, the Aure river). West of Bramble cay, in the south-west of the Gulf of Papua, the shore is very swampy and usually without a beach. It is difficult to make landings west of this reef. Near Merauke, on a coast facing south-westward, are found a few miles of sandy beach. North of the marshy Fly river delta and further east, heavy seas ride in across the Gulf of Papua during the south-east monsoon season from May to November, and wide sweeping beaches are found with bars across the estuary mouths.

Underlying the region from near the mouth of the Digul river to near Daru (south of the Fly river delta), a distance of some 300 miles, is the Oriomo plateau, which is buried in alluvium and limestone except at its eastern end, where the low granite knob of the coastal Mabudauan hill rises to 630 ft. This underlying ridge is sufficiently high to raise the surface on an average nearly 200 ft. above the surrounding marshlands. The plateau is a monotonous tract of open grassland with some eucalyptus and pandanus scrub. It is bounded on the north by the jungle and marshes of the Fly and Digul rivers. The surface is broken occasionally by hollows formed by solution of the limestone, and the native peoples utilize the rich soil at the bottom of these cup-like sink holes (known as *kwipi*) for their gardens. The Oriomo plateau has played a substantial part in determining the shape of the existing shoreline and hinterland; at present it probably separates a more active sinking zone near lake Murray and the confluence of the Strickland and Fly rivers from another actively sinking zone in the Torres strait region.

Structurally the plateau is similar to the adjacent Aru islands, which are the remnants of a low plateau, and to the Bomberai peninsula in Dutch New Guinea, for all three have in common an underlying stable core capped by limestone, although they differ in that the Bomberai peninsula rises higher than the Oriomo plateau and attains nearly 5,000 ft. It would appear that there has been a stable axis joining these areas and to the north of it a sinking zone known as the Papuan geosyncline, which is gradually filling up with sediment. It is comparable, though on a smaller scale, with the geosyncline occupied by the Indo-Gangetic plain between the newer Himalaya range and the older Deccan plateau. The stable shield of Australia lies to the south, and while its exact northern boundary is unknown it is probably near the mouth of the Bamu river.

The Eastern or 'Moresby' Coast. This extends from approximately 145° to 150° E and embraces the southern shores of central and eastern Papua (Fig. 9). Much of it fronts on to the deep Coral sea and the shore consists of rocky headlands at the seaward ends of ridges, joined by wide sweeping beaches, and not by the wide marshes found further west. Headlands of this type are cape Possession, cape Suckling and Redscar head. Where the outermost ridges lie seaward of the main foothills extensive and marshy coastal plains are developed between the two; plains of this type are the Kunimaipa river basin, the Inawafunaa river basin (north of Yule island), and the plains of Galley reach and Hood bay. As the coast is continuously subsiding and there is no off-shore shelf to allow mud accumulation, drowned, and only partly silted-up estuaries are the rule. Such are Kerema inlet, Hall sound, Fairfax harbour (and its seaward continuation, Port Moresby harbour), Bootless inlet and the numerous inlets of eastern Papua and the Louisiade archipelago. The conditions which allow sediments to be deposited clear of the coast in deep water have allowed intermittent fringing and barrier reefs to develop. Raised coral reefs extending inland from the beach are never found. The so-called raised coral reefs of the Bluff and Ie hills behind Kerema are relatively old and do not belong to the comparatively recent 'raised coral' formations.

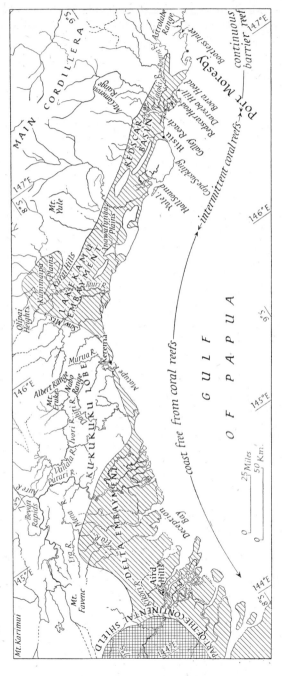

Fig. 9. The coastlands of the Gulf of Papua

This map covers the northern and eastern shores of the gulf between the mouth of the Turama river in the north-west and the Astrolabe range in the south-east. Coastal plains and embayments are shaded. The continental shield on the western margin is largely composed of dolerites and basalts. It is low-lying and much of it is covered by thick alluvial deposits. Based on: (1) S. W. Carey, 'The Morphology of New Guinea', *Australian Geographer*, vol. III, no. 5, p. 8 (Sydney, 1938); (2) official sources.

The rivers of the Moresby coast are all navigable to some extent and this characteristic feature of a subsiding coastline contrasts strongly with the interrupted river courses of a rising coastline such as the Finsch coast, which lies north of the Torricelli mountains of north-east New Guinea.

THE SOUTHERN FOOTHILLS

Behind the southern littoral the foothills rise from the plain. They are composed for the most part of folded and faulted Neogene rocks, or more rarely, as in the Port Moresby area, of Palaeogene and Cretaceous rocks. The foothills belt varies considerably in breadth. In Dutch New Guinea, the southern fall of the Nassau range section of the cordillera is extremely sharp (16,000 ft. to sea level in some 35 miles), and as the watershed is close to the plains there is practically no foothills zone. East of the Strickland river the profile becomes more gradual and the land gradually ascends from the alluvial plains through the foothill ridges to the main cordillera. Thus from Kikori, at sea level, the limestone ridges rise to 300 ft. on the lower Sirebi, a tributary of the Kikori river, 2,000 ft. in the middle Sirebi, 5,000 ft. in the upper Sirebi and so progressively to ridges of 8,000 ft. near mount Murray and 13,000 ft. at mount Hagen in the main New Guinea axis. This succession of gradually rising foothills and plateaux ascending from the coastal plain to the central cordillera contrasts with the abrupt rise of the great Nassau range from the western plain.

Among the foothills of western Papua are three main types of surface form produced respectively by Miocene limestones, by younger Neogene sediments, and by Pleistocene volcanoes.

East of the 'delta embayment' Neogene sedimentary rocks outcrop once more and greatly affect the landscape; the sandstones, conglomerates and limestones form broken lines of escarpments and ridges, whilst the clay beds produce rolling lowlands densely covered with jungle and forest. There has been much faulting, and this, together with the recent development of the land forms, has been responsible for a number of T-shaped river junctions—e.g., the Era-Mena, Aure-Purari, Vailala-Ivori, Vailala-Dahiti and Matupe-Sori junctions. Some of the faults have produced scarps, as is shown in the steep slopes of the Kereru and Albert ranges. Extending north-west from the Murua river there is a series of valleys controlled by the faults and scarps. River courses may be interrupted by falls. The most conspicuous is the valley of the upper Dahiti river which follows the gentle arc of the faulted face of the Nabo outlier of the Albert range

Plate 5. Mount Keluwere

This mountain (13,700 ft.) lies to the south-west of mount Hagen. The upper slopes have a scanty cover of alpine grasses and much bare rock is exposed at the summit.

Plate 6. View from mount Keluwere

Note the peaks rising from the grassy plateau; they are believed to be the uplifted remnants of ranges reduced by erosion.

Plate 8. Typical scenery in the Morobe District

This view shows part of the difficult country of deeply entrenched valleys and interlocking hill spurs which lies between the Morobe goldfield and Huon gulf.

Plate 7. The Rouna falls

This view was taken during the dry season. The Laloki river here drops 210 ft. over the scarp edge of the volcanic plateau.

for 20 miles; the trench continues over a low col on to the Murua river and is carried on by a tributary trending to the south-east. For a great part of the course the Ivori fault forms the boundary between the high country and the foothills (and in addition, the boundary between the mountain peoples and the coastal peoples).

The Pleistocene volcanoes such as mount Favenc, mount Murray, the Bosayi mountains, the Aird hills, mount Karimui and mount Suauru, which lie mainly north of the Kikori river, take the form of dome-like stumps of mountain clusters and are usually surrounded by a plain of volcanic detritus. The Great Papuan plateau is such a plain which was raised some 2,000 ft. and tilted in recent geological times (Fig. 10). It falls southward and slopes to sea level. The Wawoi falls, at approximately 7° s, stand where the river of that name drops 120 ft. over a mass of detritus. Originally the Great Papuan plateau extended much further to the north-east, but rapid denudation has reduced its area. In the centre of this plateau stand the Bosayi mountains, domed masses which culminate in mount Leonard Murray which is nearly 8,000 ft. high. The Bosayi (Leonard Murray) mountains have been compared with a great octopus. The peaks form the head, and the radiating spurs the arms. The rapid rise of the mountains from the southern plains, the very heavy rainfall experienced as a result, and their isolation cause overestimates of their true height of 7,800 ft. For 15 miles around the drainage forms a deeply etched radial pattern which is particularly well developed on the north-east side. At the head of the Omati river and east of the Turama river is another volcanic dome and 20 miles to the south is a basalt lava plateau 200–300 ft. high. These, as well as the lava capping of the Darai hills on the western side of the Turama river, may be the tilted and dissected detrital spread of the volcanic dome at the Omati headwaters. Mount Favenc, a volcanic cluster some 6,000 ft. high, is similar to the Bosayi mountains. The lavas outpoured from this centre cap the ridges for some 30 miles around. Like the Bosayi debris, this material covers the youngest series of Pliocene coals, but more subsequent dissection has taken place here than in the Bosayi area. The rivers draining the Favenc area are full of volcanic boulders up to 10 ft. in diameter.

Contemporaneous with the activity which produced the Favenc and Bosayi volcanoes was that which formed the Aird hills. These rise abruptly from delta swamps a few miles south-east of Kikori but, lying further south than their contemporaries in an area of subsidence, form only a horseshoe-shaped ridge some 3 miles across, and 298 ft.

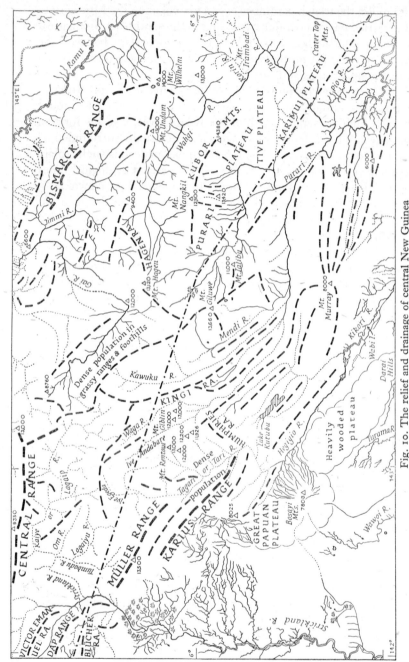

Fig. 10. The relief and drainage of central New Guinea

The trends of the major ridges are shown by heavy pecked lines. Much of this area is unsurveyed and probable river courses are shown by broken lines. Heights of peaks are approximate. Scale, 1 in. = approximately 40 miles. Based on official sources.

in maximum height. This represents the crown of the old volcanoes and the surrounding volcanic outcrop is now lost beneath deltaic muds. It is probable that mount Suauru which rises out of the Tive plateau and reaches 8,744 ft., and mount Karimui with its girdling plateau, also belong to the Bosayi-Favenc group.

Limestones play a very important part in the topography of the Strickland-Purari foothills. South of the Müller range section of the main cordillera lie mainly limestone formations. To the south the limestones are covered by the wide alluvial spreads of the Turama, the Bamu and the Fly. East of the Kikori, where the supporting continental shelf terminates, these limestones of Oligocene to Lower Miocene age are buried by thick deposits of more recent rocks and so do not appear in the first rows of foothills. North-eastwards the limestones are replaced by a great thickness of tuffs which were showered from a volcanic girdle which flanked the Owen Stanley massif during the Mid-Tertiary period.

Within the limestone region nearly all the prominent ridges and some extensive plateaux are of limestone, but there are also large valleys floored with younger rocks. Overland transport is often extremely difficult as sheer limestone walls are found along fault-lines and deep gorges along streams. On the plateaux the limestone surface is broken by sink holes (solution pits) 200 to 300 ft. deep, with sides of jagged limestone. Knife-edged limestone blocks lacerate the feet and legs of travellers. At approximately 8,000 ft. in the country of the Fly headstreams there are crevices 50 to 100 ft. deep spanned only by a few moss-covered roots or a fallen tree. Other obstacles include sudden sharp descents and equally sharp climbs, into and out of a series of large pot holes varying from 50 to 150 yd. across and from 80 to 200 ft. deep, typical sink holes of limestone country. These depressions, running in chains, and gradually working to a lower level, are the only visible indication of the direction of flow of the subterranean streams. The terrain appears from the air to be a mass of needle-pointed pinnacles, although the general level is that of a plateau. Similar country exists in the foothills of the Whiteman range in New Britain (Fig. 11). North of the limestone belt of western Papua is a zone of grassy upland valleys which lead generally northwestward into the central plateau, e.g., the valleys of the Tari-Furoro, Mendi, Kagoli and Wahgi rivers.

The Kukukuku Lobe. East of the limestone area is the rugged mountainous area of the Nabo, Albert, Stanniforth and Armit ranges which form the great southward lobe, known as the Kukukuku lobe (Fig. 9),

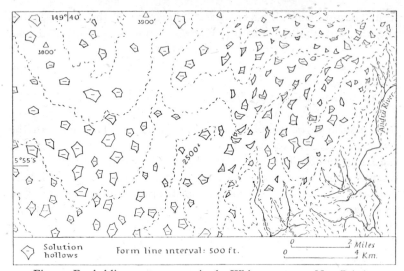

Fig. 11. Eroded limestone country in the Whiteman range, New Britain

The form lines show the approximate configuration of slope. The positions of solution hollows are indicated from an aerial survey of surface depressions. Their areas are approximate. Based on official sources.

which separates the lowlands of the Delta embayment from those of the Lakekamu embayment. In the basin of the Era river to the west of the lobe the foothills are 40 miles from the coast, whereas at Kerema and cape Cupola (south of the mouth of the Matupe river) the hilly lobe pushes the shoreline outwards. Behind Kukipi the Lakekamu coastal plain retreats towards mount Lawson and to the mountainous border of the mandated territory. The Kukukuku lobe behind Kerema contains some of the most rugged country of Papua. The grain of the country runs from north-west to south-east, somewhat obliquely to the Gulf of Papua coast. A line drawn from the head of Kerema bay, north-westward to Bevan rapids on the Purari river, divides the more isolated coastal hills on the south-west from the lowest foothills on the north-west. The coastal hills have large areas of flat, often swampy, country through which run sandstone and mudstone ridges which are usually under 500 ft. in height, although one line from the Bluff through the Ie hills and Pollard's peak approaches 1,000 ft. The lower foothills containing the Saw mountains, Ingham and Matupe hills, and the Nabo and Selubwe ranges, are a rugged mountain area consisting of sandstones, tuffs and limestones rising to nearly 4,000 ft. They are deeply dissected by precipitous valleys clothed in dense jungle. There is a distinct step, probably due to a fault, between the lower foothills zone of the Nabo range and the upper foothills zone which rises to 6,000 or 8,000 ft. In this zone are the Albert mountains rising to mount Eruke (8,500 ft.), the Stanniforth and Armit ranges and the highlands between the headstreams of the Tauri river.

The most broken country is found in the transition belt between the upper and lower foothills. Here the streams are entrenched in rugged canyon-like valleys and their courses are frequently interrupted by falls. Below the transition belt the valleys soon open out while in the highlands the valley floors, at heights of from 3,000 to 4,000 ft., are again more open. The sides of the valleys, open to the dry north-west monsoon, are grassy, while those exposed to the south-east monsoon are covered with scrub and pine.

The Lakekamu Embayment. East of the Kukukuku lobe is the Lakekamu embayment which has a north-west to south-east coast, but is hemmed in on the three other sides by highlands. The shape is defined by faults; on the west is the scarp of the Saw mountains, on the north-west the Olipai heights and foothills which are formed mainly of conglomerate; in rising they merge into the broken Kukukuku country. On the north and north-east is the great scarp of mount Lawson and the Chapman range, which rises over 10,000 ft. from the Kunimaipa plain and extends to mount Yule. The floor is divided into three areas: the Kunimaipa, Inawafunaa and Redscar basins. The Kunimaipa basin is isolated from the others by the Kurai range and its continuation; they form a level-topped barrier which rises to 2,000 ft. and runs from south-west to north-east for 20 miles from near mount Yule. The basin has a swampy south-eastern part with gravel terraces rising towards the Chapman scarp while the north-west is hilly with rugged ridges rising to 2,000 ft. These ridges are of tilted conglomerates which are locally 10,000 ft. thick.

Along the coast of the Gulf of Papua south-east of the Lakekamu estuary are ranges of hills separated from the main foothills of the interior by embayments of the coastal plain. The first group includes the Popo, Lesi, Apinaipi, Oiapu and Maiva hills which have all been formed by Pliocene folding. There is a second group of hills from the Mekeo foothills to the coast between cape Suckling and Hisiu on the west side of Redscar bay. Each of the hills in these two groups is formed by an anticline (or upfold) and surrounded by a section of the coastal plain. Redscar head, Dareeba hill and Boera head are formed of limestones and tuffs. They have been islands during relatively recent submergence but are now isolated hills joined by the coastal plain. Port Moresby, Fairfax harbour and Bootless inlet are formed by the sea flooding in through breaks in the coastal ridges which run from north-west to south-east.

From the Mekeo district near mount Yule to the Astrolabe range and on south-eastward to behind Rigo, the main foothills flank a rugged area which rises to over 10,000 ft. This rough jungle-clad country has been produced by the very deep dissection of a thick sheet of consolidated volcanic detritus. Mount Yule is a striking isolated remnant of this same sheet. These uplands are mostly shrouded in cloud but in early morning the landscape often reveals ridges of a razor-edge sharpness. South and east of mount Yule in the Mekeo country the volcanic outcrop dominates the landscape, gradually dropping by scarps and bluffs until it is lost under the coastal plain.

The Laloki headstream, which drains the undulating tableland north of the Astrolabe range, tumbles over the lip of the volcanic plateau at Rouna falls (Plate 7) where the volcanic rocks dip gently inland and form a scarp across the upper part of the valley. At the foot of the bluff the valley is littered by loose blocks carried from the scarp. The larger of the Hombron bluffs, which rises to slightly more than 2,000 ft. behind the coast, is a miniature mount Yule which has, by dissection, become almost isolated from the main volcanic plateau. Between the Laloki river and Port Moresby the country is carved from older sediments and is more open, and above the river valleys has stretches of xerophytic vegetation. Conspicuous among these lowlands is a zone of craggy hillocks made up of Lower Tertiary sediments which have been baked and hardened by an invading igneous mass. The main volcanic mass continues eastward and parallel to the coast. This coastal side of the volcanic outcrop has a steep craggy scarp, but the north side has a gentler inland slope which is drained by the Rouna river and by the Musgrave tributary of the Kemp Welch river. South-eastward near this latter river the scarp swings inland and the landscape changes completely. The coast trends roughly west to east and is largely low alluvial land until the Cloudy mountains, which lie west of Samarai, rise to about 4,450 ft. North of these dissected mountains a low isthmus leads eastward to Milne bay.

THE MAIN CORDILLERA

This cordillera consists of two great crescentic arcs with their convex sides to the north. They rise to over 15,000 ft. and there is a structural

Plate 9. The watershed of the Tiviri and Watut rivers

The mountains between the Lakekamu embayment and Huon gulf protrude grassy summits above the foothill forests. Trees are confined to watercourses.

Plate 10. The Bulolo river

The course of the deeply incised upper river is governed by protruding spurs. Native tracks out of the valley often follow ridge crests such as that shown here.

Plate 11. Dogura mission, Goodenough bay

Much of the coastland of Goodenough bay is free of forest. The mission lies on one of the broad terraces by which the hills rise steeply from the bay.

Plate 12. Foothills north of Finschhafen

These raised reef terraces are characteristic of the north-east coast of the Huon peninsula. Forests are confined to the bottoms of gullies.

deep on the north side. The western curve in Dutch New Guinea is known as the Nassau (Snow mountains) and Oranje ranges and over-looks on the northern side the crescentic basin of the Rauffaer, Idenburg and Sobger valleys. The eastern crescent is formed by the Victor Emanuel range, by the Central and Müller ranges, which enclose the undulating central plateau, and by the Kratke and Owen Stanley ranges. This chain overhangs the great curved trough of the Sepik-Ramu-Markham systems. Between the eastern and western mountain crescents there is an important gap between the Star and Victor Emanuel ranges and here the headwaters of the Sepik, Sobger and Strickland rivers have their sources.

These mountain chains have old rocks at their cores, as have those of smaller continental islands which girdle the Pacific. They were, however, upthrust relatively recently, for the highest point of all, Carstensz Toppen at over 16,000 ft. in the Nassau range, is composed of Lower Neogene sediments of marine origin. The peaks and ridges of the main cordillera have largely identical summit heights. Along the flanks of the mountains there has been intense recent erosion and the country has been cut up into deep canyons with rugged slopes.

The character of the central cordillera provided many surprises for the first surveyors. Late in 1927 Karius and Champion crossed the Strickland-Sepik divide and noted 'huge mountains rising tier above tier, dome shaped, peaked, or bluff and table topped'. They found an intricate system of valleys and grassy plateaux, with many villages and native gardens. The rock formations on the plateaux show a striking contrast with those of the southern watershed. Exposures of white limestone, which are characteristic of the sides of the southern moun-tains, are replaced by brown or red rocks, exposed where landslides have occurred on the mountain-sides. The valleys appear to be very fertile, as evidenced by the many large gardens dotted about everywhere, and the population is large as compared with the sparse population on the southern slopes.

At the eastern end of the main cordillera a striking drainage pattern occurs. The rivers run for long distances parallel with the ridges. For example, the Yodda, Chirma, Upper Waria and Bulolo-Watut rivers form a rough line from south-east to north-west parallel with the Huon gulf coast. Some of these valleys meet end-on. For example, the Yodda and Chirma rivers unite to form the Mambare which cuts at right angles across the ridges. These valleys are a considerable asset, for in them is found the greater part of the alluvial gold and the climate is suitable for European settlement and plantation development. (Fig. 12 shows a typical section of the Bulolo goldfields.) The wide open sections such as the Yodda valley from Kokoda northwards to Yodda provide many aerodrome sites.

In eastern New Guinea the series of mountain ranges varies considerably in width. Near the Dutch frontier in the Star mountains where the Fly, Digul, Sepik and Sobger rivers rise, the highlands are only 35 miles across from northern to southern flank and the same is true 350 miles to the east in the area of the lower Watut river. Between these two narrow areas the cordillera widens until it is 150 miles from north to south, and it is in this wide sector that the Great Central plateau occurs. The northern scarp of the plateau is the line of the Schrader, Bismarck and Kratke ranges which also form the southern rim of the Ramu valley. On the southern side, the plateau is flanked by foothills which are much cut by rivers draining to the Gulf of Papua. The plateau itself consists of wide terraced valleys at elevations from 5,000 to 6,000 ft., separated by ridges up to 14,300 ft. high. The greater part of the southern plateau in the area of the Bismarck and Hagen ranges is drained by the Wahgi-Tua rivers, which form the Purari headwaters ; but some of the area is tapped by the northward-flowing Yuat, a tributary of the Sepik, and by the Strickland river (Fig. 10).

The country bounded on the north by the mount Hagen and Kubor ranges and on the south by the basin of the Purari river has been termed the Purari plateau. It forms the eastern portion of the great central plateau and east of it the bounding ranges again coalesce as one main range. Signs of the extensive uplift which has affected the whole of the main cordillera are visible here and there is much block faulting. The Kubor mountains which rise to 14,300 ft. are capped like Carstensz Toppen with limestone. Though they rise gradually from the Purari swamps their northern slopes to the Wahgi river are steep (Plate 3). The Hagen range rises to over 14,000 ft. and has precipitous slopes of volcanic rocks which may have been upthrust subsequent to the late Neogene elevation of the plateau. Compass bearings taken on mount Hagen are affected by magnetic minerals in the rocks. Lava flows from the range are found in peripheral river valleys such as that of the Gai river to the west. These rivers have carved deep gorges through relatively soft tuffs and volcanic breccia. Twenty miles south of the Hagen range the plateau slates are overlain by 300 ft. of breccia. A similar spread lies east of mount Hagen in the wide swampy upper valley of the Wahgi river. North-east of the Hagen range metamorphosed rocks occur in the Jimmi river valley and these hard fine-

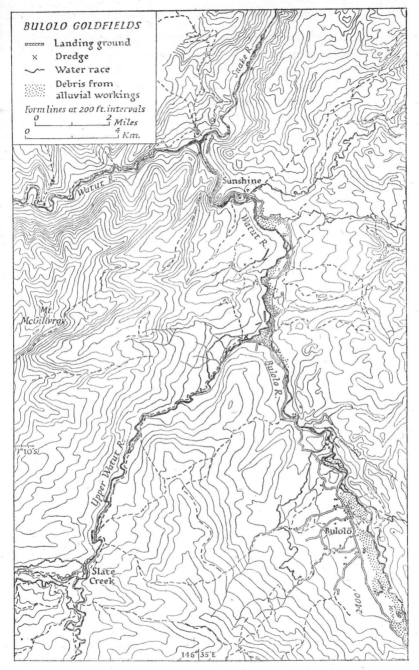

Fig. 12. Part of the Bulolo goldfields (Bulowat area)

Foot tracks are shown by pecked lines. The double lines indicate a motor road following the main valley. Out-lying mining settlements are largely served by airways. The Watut river flows westwards from this area and then northwards to join the Markham river. Based on official sources.

grained materials are frequently used by the native peoples for their polished stone axes.

The central plateau area is characterized by grassy uplands on the valley floors, and the same vegetation is seen in valley bottoms in the goldfield region of the Bulolo-Watut rivers. It was noted in 1933 that the central ranges around the Langimar headstream of the Watut river were split by rocky crags and precipices. The valley bottoms were floored with granite and conglomerate and quartz veins were plentiful. Some yielded traces of gold. Bare walls of laminated sandstone and volcanic agglomerate (breccia) lined the streams. Basalt as well as granite occurred in the igneous series and, as evidence of further disturbance, the beds of former streams were found hundreds of feet above the existing river beds. The country was mainly grass-covered with some timber on the tops of the ridges, which varied in height from 5,000 to 8,000 ft. The valley soils tended to be heavy clay where they had weathered from schist and basalt. The country north-west of the upper Watut rises sharply 4,000 ft. above the valley in rugged masses of slate and porphyry. These old rocks yield in the uplands stone for implements and gold, where they form the basement beds of the Morobe goldfields to the east.

In some cases gravel spreads appear along valleys on the plateau side of the bounding central ranges. Such deposits have been noted in the wide upper valleys of the Wahgi above the junction of its east-bank tributary, the Korin. The Wahgi there meanders through a gravel deposit up to 500 ft. thick in places. The generally level appearance suggests that, above the miles of limestone gorge through which the river runs to join the Purari, there was at some time a huge lake. The rivers on either side, rushing down from the mountains, probably filled up the lake with gravel, and subsequent erosion has produced a series of level alluvial stretches of grass country cut through by streams. It is possible that at some future date these lacustrine terraces may be equated with stages in the uplift of the foothills and in the acceleration of erosion in the limestone ranges through which lies the Wahgi gorge which taps the former lake basin. Extensive alluvial fans occur where lateral streams join the main valley (Plate 4).

Conditions at higher levels have also been recorded, e.g., for mount Keluwere, south-west of mount Hagen. The lower slopes have some scrub and scattered timber which at 9,500 ft. give way to stunted bushes and clumps of alpine grasses. The ground, like many patches of the plateau lower down, is waterlogged at this level. Small water-holes persist to 12,000 ft. and these become ice-covered overnight. The weather is often very clear, and mountains 100 miles away are visible. This mountain (Plate 5) is 13,700 ft. high and falls away 3,000 ft., down an almost precipitous slope on its south-west side. The accordance of summit levels in the country east-north-east of mount Keluwere is well shown on Plate 6.

The main ranges pass south-eastward through Papua as the Owen Stanley range. This is generally at a lower elevation than the mountains which bound the central plateau, although round 148° E is a series of high peaks of which mount Obree reaches 10,264 ft. The Owen Stanley range shares the geological characters of the main cordillera. The pre-Cambrian core is well developed and is bordered by belts of country with largely schistose and other metamorphic rocks (Plate 9). West of Goodenough bay an area of basalt and dolerites is exposed in the mount Dayman country where the rocks have welled up through the narrowing Pre-Cambrian core.

The metamorphic belt is continued as the Cloudy mountains south of Milne bay and further east through the off-lying chains of islands of which Sariba, Sideia and Moresby are the larger links. On the mainland and in the islands granites may form outstanding summits— e.g., Bohoboho (3,360 ft.), south of the head of Milne bay.

The islands of the Louisiade archipelago are composed of slates and schists which dip steeply and are deeply eroded. Quartz veins traverse the metamorphosed rocks and gold has been found. Tagula, the largest island, has ten peaks varying in height from 1,330 to 2,645 ft., and its deep cliffed inlets and much evidence of large-scale subsidence are typical of the group (p. 296). The Tagula barrier reef is unusual in that several of its component islets are of schists and volcanic material and represent merely the tips of former ranges.

The Central Intermontane Trough

This trough runs from Geelvink bay to Huon gulf and lies between the northern ranges and the main cordillera. It owes its origin to earth movements rather than to river erosion, and it is probable that the area is still sinking. There are 'islands' of older consolidated sediments set in a sea of swamp land. Two main sub-regions lie within the belts: in the west is the Meer Vlakte ('lake plain') and in the eastern half the Sepik-Ramu valley. The Markham valley forms a third sub-region which carries the trough eastward towards the Planet deep.

The Meer Vlakte is the great central plain of Dutch New Guinea and contains the middle basins of the Rauffaer and Idenburg rivers which unite to form the Mamberamo river. The floor is an almost flat plain, crescentic in plan, with the concave side to the south, and under 200 ft. in height. The plain is mountain-locked and on the northern margin the Mamberamo river escapes through a narrow gap in the Van Rees range. Geelvink bay is a drowned plain continuing the line of the valley to the west.

The Sepik-Ramu valley is another crescentic depression similar to, but larger than, the Meer Vlakte. It is not wholly enclosed on the seaward side, for the Ramu and Sepik rivers enter the sea through a breach in the northern mountains which is roughly 90 miles wide. On the south the scarp rises steeply to over 15,000 ft., though the main cordillera here has a wider foreland than the ranges south of the Meer Vlakte. On the north there is a gentle slope for 50 miles to the crest of the Torricelli mountains, which are only 5,000 ft. high. On the north these mountains drop sharply to a narrow coastal plain. The northern mountain boundary of the Sepik river basin may be divided into three zones. The most southerly, or plains zone, is a belt of low-lying flat country about 20 to 25 miles wide which flanks the river.

Formed by alluvium from the Sepik and other rivers draining the mountains, this zone, of recent origin, is liable to flooding. Much of the land adjoining the river is swamp (p. 81). The middle zone is overlooked by escarpments. Northwards the rocks dip more steeply and become folded and faulted and the zone merges into the third or foothills zone. In this last zone, the topography is dominated by older rocks as in the broken country of West Wapi. Between the Torricelli ranges and the Sepik river is a lofty escarpment which commences in West Wapi and runs to the south-east. This scarp is of sandstone and has a precipitous fall of 1,000 ft. It overlooks to the north a broad area of gentle slopes which extends almost to the mountains and is drained by meandering streams. The escarpment is well peopled on its plateau-like crest.

The Wapi zone of the foothills has been described as a heavily forested and well-peopled region. Like the main Torricelli range, it is a region of considerable instability and in 1935 much earthquake destruction occurred and the devastation of villages was severe. It is customary to build along ridge tops, and in 1935 many houses slipped down the hillsides. The rivers afterwards carried great loads of mud down to the Sepik plain.

The Ramu valley in the eastern part of the basin is similar to the Sepik valley, though a much smaller area lies below 100 ft. than in the Sepik basin (p. 82). The divide between the Ramu and Markham valleys is relatively low (1,345 ft.). The Markham valley, a broad valley with, like the Sepik, grass-covered swamps with scattered forest clumps, drains south-eastward to the Huon gulf and the trough passes then into the Planet deep which is a structural depression similar to Geelvink bay. The trough form of the Sepik-Ramu area has been modified by faulting in the Markham valley, but there is a superficial similarity in the high mountain flanks above the broad valley. The submarine slopes have a similar fall down to the Planet deep.

An additional group of lesser valleys each with a wide, low-lying valley floor have their courses both in the main cordillera and along parts of the trough. In this category are the valleys of the Sobger and upper Idenburg in Dutch New Guinea and of the Gogol, which flows into Astrolabe bay south of Madang. The Gogol valley, an important depression lying in a downfold of the rocks, runs between the Adalbert and Finisterre mountains. Its valley lies parallel with that of the upper Ramu river. The north wall of the trough is a fault scarp and when viewed from the south-west the scarp face stands like a rampart above a vast plain of low, rounded country. This scarp is a part of the northern chain, which rises as it passes towards the Finisterre range. It drains westward into the upper Ramu valley along many parallel streams.

The Northern Chain

This mountain chain runs parallel with the main cordillera, but the continuous trough of the Sepik, which is about 100 miles across, lies between them. The northern chain is neither so wide, so lofty nor so continuous as the main cordillera. The Finisterre-Huon peninsula sector lies nearer the main ranges across the narrower Markham trough. The ranges making up the chain are: the west-east line of the Van Rees, Gauttier, Foya, Karamor and Bonggo mountains of Dutch New Guinea; the Bewani, Torricelli and Prince Alexander mountains, lying between the frontier and the Sepik river outlet; and the Adalbert, Finisterre and Saruwaged ranges between the mouth of the Ramu river and the Huon gulf.

The altitude of the ranges north of the Sepik trough does not exceed 5,000 ft., but in the Karamor range some peaks reach nearly 7,000 ft. and in the Finisterre and Saruwaged ranges of the Huon peninsula some peaks exceed 13,000 ft. In the region of the Sepik delta for some 70 miles the northern range falls beneath recent sediments and its crests are below sea level. Each of these ranges has a core of schistose and andesitic rocks but is flanked by foothills which are made up of more recent Pliocene rocks which have intricate folds and sharp faults. The Prince Alexander range and the mountains of the Huon peninsula carry raised reefs at considerable elevations as their most recent deposits.

THE NORTHERN LITTORAL

Unlike the southern littoral which is still sinking, the northern coast is one of active elevation. The Finsch coast between the Sepik delta and the Dutch frontier has at the headlands coral terraces raised up to 200 ft. above sea level. The coast zone between Aitape and the Torricelli mountains and the lower valleys of the Danein and Mima rivers behind Matapau, show recent uplift of a few feet. This rising land affects the navigation of the rivers and even fair-sized streams like the Hawain, Anumbe, Danmap and the Raihu are scarcely navigable by canoes because the rising land has increased the velocity of the streams (particularly near their mouths) and has reduced their depths.

Raised coral reefs, symptomatic of recent uplift, are found along the north coast of Dutch New Guinea. Round Humboldt bay and Sentani lake (south of Hollandia) to the south and west of the Cyclops mountains, recently raised coral terraces are found standing generally between 200 and 300 ft. above sea level, but in some cases up to 1,500 ft. These extensive limestone terraces reach inland for 30 miles almost to the foot of the Bewani mountains. At the time of formation of these terraces the Cyclops and Bougainville mountains were islands; the relatively narrow Sentani lake, a relic of the former marine strait, still contains sharks. To the south-east of the Sepik delta, headlands and terraces of raised coral are distributed continuously from cape Gourdon, cape Croisilles, Sek harbour (Alexishafen), Madang and Astrolabe bay almost to Lepsius point. Fig. 13 shows a series of raised reefs in the latter area. Then comes a stretch of rocky coast, but near cape King William the raised coral reappears and continues beyond Finschhafen to cape Cretin (Plate 12).

The Morobe coast between Salamaua and Morobe is a drowned littoral and there is a complete absence of raised coral from the mouth of the Markham river to cape Vogel, north of Goodenough bay. Raised coral reappears round the shore of Milne bay and overlies most of the bounding northern peninsula. Although the south side of Huon gulf is sinking, the islands and coast of the most southerly peninsulas of Papua, like the remainder of the northern littoral of British New Guinea, are rising (Plate 11).

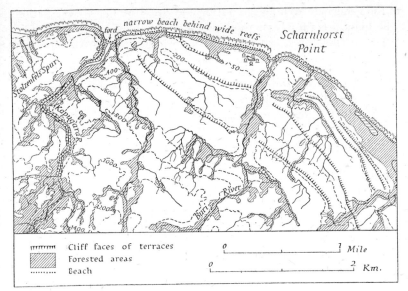

Fig. 13. The raised coral reefs of the Scharnhorst point area

This section of the coast of mandated New Guinea lies in lat. 5° 59′ s, long. 147° 29′ E, on the north coast of the Huon peninsula. Terraces are shown at heights of 50, 200, 400 and 600 ft. and form lines at 50 and 200 ft. and subsequently at intervals of 200 ft. The faces of the terraces maintain equal heights over considerable distances. The restriction of forests to valley bottoms is evidence of the porosity of the raised reef surfaces, as human interference with the vegetation cover is not important in this lightly peopled coastland. Based on official sources.

In the off-lying islands there is considerable variation in the heights of the upper coral limestone terraces. On the northern coasts of Murua the raised reefs reach elevations of 200 ft. The raised reefs of the low-lying Trobriand islands overlie Tertiary volcanic and sedimentary rocks. Kiriwina, the largest of the group, has raised reefs along all but the southern coast. A continuous belt of weathered coral rises from 50 to 100 ft. from the shore. On the rich soil in its crevices the native peoples have their gardens. On the southern shore the belt is more broken. This coral belt surrounds the former lagoon of a large atoll. The upraised floor is now covered with 3 to 6 ft. of clayey loam and a good deal is swampy. The southern isthmus of Kiriwina is wholly of raised coral and the soil is more sterile. Kaileuna island and the Lusançay group of the Trobriands have much volcanic ash, and the latter group has been elevated about 200 ft. Five distinct elevations seem to have occurred in Misima island in the north-west of the Louisiade archipelago during and since the Pleistocene period. The highest coral terrace there reaches 1,000 ft.

Four major physical units may be distinguished on the northern littoral. They are, from south to north:

(i) An almost continuous fringe of faulted and folded hills, the foothills of the northern chain.

(ii) A belt of marshy alluvial coast plains between the foothills and the coast. These plains vary very much in width and the belt is not always continuous.

(iii) Elevated coral reefs which take the form of isolated headlands west of the Sepik delta and of more or less continuous terraces between the Sepik delta and Dampier strait, which lies between the Huon peninsula and New Britain.

(iv) The Quaternary volcanoes of the off-shore island arc between Wewak and Dampier strait. Between Morobe and the Louisiade archipelago they appear as the outermost mainland belt.

Along the Finsch coast, to the north of the Torricelli mountains, the coastal plain becomes narrower eastwards. Behind Aitape it is 10 miles wide; but 50 miles further east at Matapau the mountains reach to the sea, and from here to the Sepik delta there is practically no coastal plain or foothill belt. Intermittent raised coral headlands and off-shore coral islands are scattered along the belt but there are no extensive coral terraces. In the Sepik-Ramu delta the coastal plain extends again and merges with the great interior plain of the Sepik-Ramu basin.

From the Sepik delta to Dampier strait (a distance of some 250 miles) the coastal plain is replaced by an almost continuous terrace of raised coral which is set against the foothills. From the mouth of the Markham river to Morobe the rocky inlets of the Huon gulf coast show features associated with a drowned littoral (Fig. 14).

Flanking the shore for about 300 miles between Morobe and East cape in the extreme south of Papua is an extensive downfold which is mainly occupied by the sea and along which earth movements have not yet ceased. A long narrow submarine trough, which is probably the continuation of this downfold and is flanked on either side by island festoons, extends from Goodenough bay for a further 300 miles in a south-south-easterly direction. The D'Entrecasteaux and Louisiade groups flank it on the east. Instability and volcanic activity are a feature of both groups. The final stages of volcanic activity in

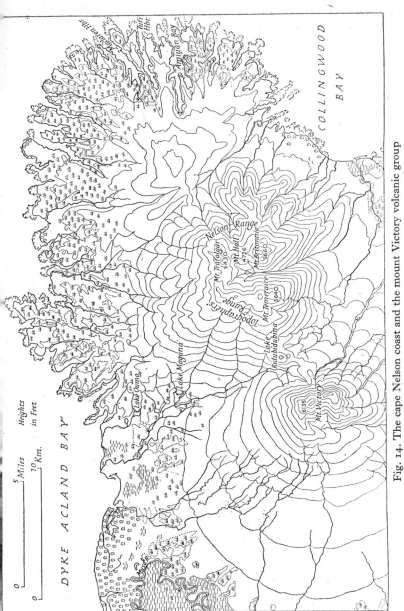

Fig. 14. The cape Nelson coast and the mount Victory volcanic group

Form lines are shown at 200 ft. and subsequently at 400 ft. intervals. The areas enclosed by the dotted line are free of forest. Secondary growth and savannah are indicated by those grassland symbols which lie outside the dotted lines. The remainder of the area is forested or swampy. The coast of the cape Nelson peninsula between Dyke Acland and Collingwood bays is typical of the drowned coasts of south-eastern New Guinea. Drowned river valleys (rias) are characteristic. Based on official sources.

Fergusson island are shown in Fig. 15. The rocks exposed at cape Vogel show a great thickness, and there appears to be a partial parallel between this area and the volcanic masses of the Gulf of Papua. The volcanic rocks of mount Victory, mount Lamington and the Hydrographer's range are probably the equivalent of the Favenc, Karimui

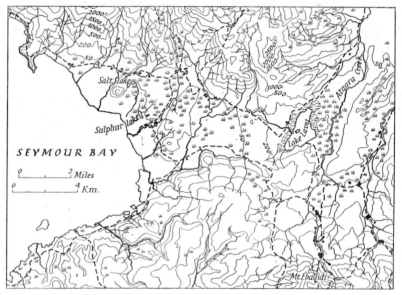

Fig. 15. The northern isthmus, Fergusson island

The final stages of volcanic activity are shown in Sulphur lake and in adjacent hot springs not indicated on the map. The isthmus eastwards from Seymour bay and along Ataara creek is swampy, and villages and foot-trails keep to its margins or to hillsides. Based on official sources.

and Bosayi mountains and of the Aird hills. In this zone the headlands are for the most part volcanic and behind the heads of Collingwood, Dyke Acland and Hercules bays are wide stretches of coastal plain with extensive swamps. Between these coastal plains and the mountains there is a fringe of folded foothills.

NEW BRITAIN

This island, which was not crossed in the western part until 1909, is structurally related to the northern littoral of the mainland and was probably once joined with it. Exclusive of the Gazelle peninsula, which forms a separate unit, the characteristic features are: (i) a rising south coast with an ascending series of raised coral reefs; (ii) an axis of uplift along the centre; and (iii) a belt of active vulcanism associated with subsidence along the north coast (Fig. 16).

To the south of the island lies the Planet deep and to the north a subsiding area. Between these two is a great upfold. There are two types of mountains—the central mountains, such as the western Whiteman and central Nakanai ranges, and the volcanic peaks along the northern coast.

The southern littoral is low and reef-bound with off-shore coral islets and ascending coral terraces inland. From cape Büsching in the

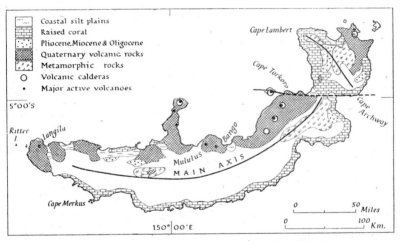

Fig. 16. Geology and physical features of New Britain

The Gazelle peninsula in the north-east of the island is a distinct structural unit. Its axis diverges from the direction of the main axis of the island. The line between cape Torkoro and cape Archway probably represents a major fault. Based on T. W. Edgeworth David, *Geological Map of the Commonwealth of Australia*: 1 : 2,990,000 (Canberra, 1931).

west to Put Put on the Gazelle peninsula the raised coral extends almost continuously. The greatest uplift occurs in the south-eastern half, where the highest of several terraces reaches 1,500 ft. above sea level. At cape Merkus in south-western New Britain and in the Arawe islands the raised coral islets are extremely numerous and closely set and navigation is very intricate (Figs. 17–18). From cape Merkus eastwards to cape Anukur the cliffs average 200 ft. in height. Apart from mount Tangi in the volcanic cluster east of Dampier strait, which is structurally a part of the northern volcanic belt, the southern foreshores have a monotonous skyline which becomes steadily more elevated towards the north-east. Kwoi peak in south-eastern New

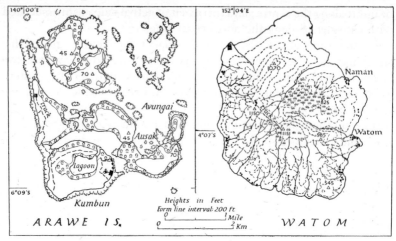

Fig. 17. Types of islands lying off New Britain

The Arawe islands are low-lying coral islets situated west of cape Merkus. Watom, which shows a crescentic volcanic rim, lies west of the Rabaul peninsula. The low-lying interiors of the Arawe islands are largely forested. Watom is forested except for the grasslands which probably cover porous volcanic deposits. Based on official sources.

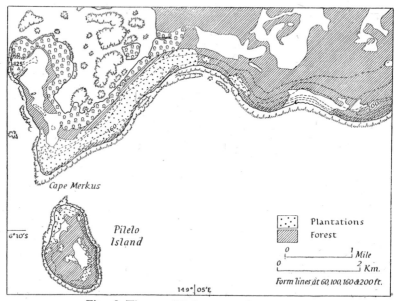

Fig. 18. The cape Merkus coast of New Britain

The map shows a characteristic portion of the steep southern coast of New Britain, which is one of active elevation. The narrow coastal ridge is of coral and much of it is covered by coconut plantations. Based on official sources.

Britain stands as an isolated smooth cone on the plateau about 7 miles north-westwards of cape Kwoi.

The fold mountains of the Whiteman and Nakanai ranges reach 6,000 ft. They are really the same range but have a wide intervening section at lower heights, through which runs the track from Talasea to Gasmata. These mountains have a core of old rocks very similar to the northern ranges of the mainland, but they have a considerable thickness of young sedimentary rocks round the core. Wide exposures of eroded limestone with innumerable potholes are characteristic (Fig. 11). Volcanic rocks have been added and have had a considerable effect on the topography.

The low relief of the north coast is broken by a large number of sharp volcanic peaks which may reach 7,000 ft. in height. These volcanoes are all of the explosive type and catastrophic eruptions have

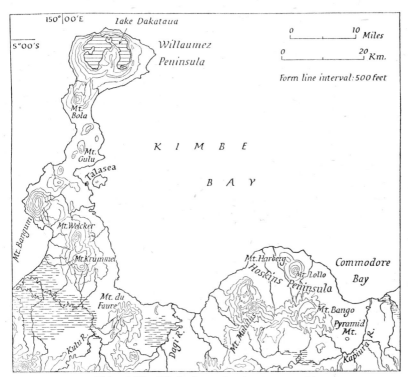

Fig. 19. The Kimbe bay volcanic arc: west side

The shores of Kimbe bay are flanked by a fine series of volcanoes, which form part of the volcanic arc of northern New Britain. The seaward slopes are steep. Lake Dakataua lies within a caldera. Based on official sources.

occurred in recent times. Geysers and hot springs are abundant; and, although many of the volcanoes do not appear to be active, nowhere in the zone can activity be considered wholly extinct.

In the western end of New Britain is a cluster of volcanic mountains along a north-south fissure. Of these volcanoes Langila (the only active cone), Tangi (3,340 ft.), Talawe (3,345 ft.), the Gutailis peaks and mount Momolo are the most conspicuous. Between this cluster and the Whiteman range much of the broad isthmus is low undulating country. Limestone outcrops with many sink holes suggest that it has probably been covered recently with upraised coral reefs. The red soil characteristic of the volcanic areas is absent. Willaumez peninsula which projects for 30 miles has many volcanoes, with at least twenty lofty cones (Fig. 19). At the northern end is the great explosion crater of lake Dakataua which is 5 miles in diameter and has a rim from 600 to 1,200 ft. high. Within the crater lake are younger cones, e.g., the active mount Benda, and mount Doko which is 600 ft. high. Outside the crater rim lies mount Bulu, or Bola (3,820 ft.). Hogu reef

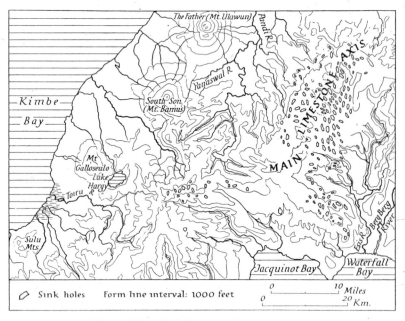

Fig. 20. The Kimbe bay volcanic arc: east side

The Father and The South Son are among the highest volcanoes in New Britain. Eroded limestones of the northern end of the Nakanai range appear on the east side of the map. Based on official sources.

and Kimbe island, probably the crowns of off-shore volcanoes, form part of the mount Mululus group in the Hoskins peninsula.

In eastern New Britain is another fissure with the magnificent active cone of Ulawun (The Father, 7,546 ft.), Likuranga (The North Son, 3,240 ft.), Bamus (The South Son, 7,376 ft.) and mount Galloseulo (3,848 ft.) (Fig. 20). Lake Hargy, east of mount Galloseulo,

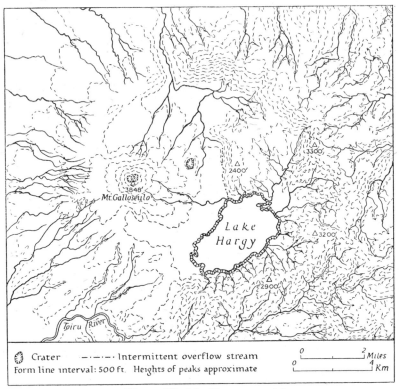

Crater —·—·—· Intermittent overflow stream
Form line interval: 500 ft. Heights of peaks approximate

0   2 Miles
0   4 Km

Fig. 21. The lake Hargy crater lake

This shows in greater detail part of the area shown on Fig. 20. The lake overflows to the northward in the rainy season. A high crater rim surrounds the lake; it is broken to the west by the cone of mount Galloseulo. Based on official sources.

fills another great crater (Fig. 21). In Lolobau island the main fissure runs through the long axis and carries three volcanoes. The highest reaches 3,058 ft. The two low off-shore islands, Banban and Muli, are volcanic remnants. This fissure continues eastward to cape Archway forming the southern structural boundary of the Gazelle peninsula.

The Gazelle peninsula has raised coral on the south-west overlooking the isthmus between Open bay and Wide bay (possibly a former strait). Volcanic deposits are found on the north-east. The peninsula is upfolded from north-west to south-east from cape Lambert through the Baining mountains and mount Sinevit to cape Archway. The Gazelle peninsula coast differs from that of the rest of New Britain for it is straighter and slopes up more steeply from the sea. There is coral tilted at 5–10° towards the sea for several miles and rising to 2,000 ft. inland of the coast. The valley east of the coral scarp of the west coast is carved out of young Tertiary rocks and to the east lies an underlying core of older rocks which are responsible for the rugged country round mount Sinevit. Tertiary rocks reappear east of the central massif. The tilted coral is continuous round the Baining mountains and the north coast west of Ataliklikun bay. In the south-east of the peninsula the raised reefs continue from the isthmus northward round the upfolded area until they are lost at Put Put, beneath the volcanic debris of the Rabaul volcanoes (Fig. 52).

Rabaul is the centre of young volcanic rocks, which seem to be spread on a very low flattened cone extending for some 10 miles south-west from Rabaul. Within the area of this cone lies the great volcanic lake which is occupied by Simpson harbour, Karavia bay and Matupi harbour (Fig. 22). Rabaul lies on the north side of Simpson harbour. Except where the cone is breached by the sea it falls steeply to the centre from 600–700 ft., but its outer slopes are fairly gentle. Within the area of the same major cone are other signs of volcanic activity—e.g., the dormant craters of The Mother (Plate 15) and South Daughter, on Crater peninsula, and The North Daughter, north of Rabaul. The active volcanoes Tavurvur (Matupi) and Rabalankaia lie within these three. Vulcan crater (Plates 13–14), which has been formed recently, is now joined by ash deposits with the mainland on the south side of Simpson harbour. As in the Willaumez peninsula and Lolobau island there is the association of fissure line and a group of old volcanoes, a great explosion crater off the centre of the line and a group of active craters near the explosion crater.

THE BISMARCK VOLCANIC BELT

This volcanic arc runs along the north side of New Guinea and New Britain between long. 143° E and 152° E. The islands of this belt are entirely of volcanic origin and the vulcanism is mainly of the explosive type. Seismic sea waves (tunami) are not uncommon, and when these

Plate 13. Blanche bay from Talili gap

Vulcan crater is seen in eruption on the left. The Blanche bay caldera rim, with higher dormant volcanoes, bounds the horizon. The low-lying land projecting below these cones is Matupi island.

Plate 14. Vulcan crater from Blanche bay

The slopes are of pumice. Material eroded from the slopes by gully erosion is fairly frequently replaced. The crater has a relatively wide mouth.

Plate 15. The South Daughter from the air

This dormant volcano lies to the south-east of Blanche bay and is linked by a forested isthmus to The Mother. Matupi island is seen to the right. The steep western shore of Blanche bay and the highest point of the Karas range (3,500 ft.) are seen on the horizon.

Plate 16. A harbour in the Vitu islands, New Britain

Harbours enclosed within low spits of land are frequently used in this group of steep volcanic islands. Note the inter-island schooners anchored in the harbour.

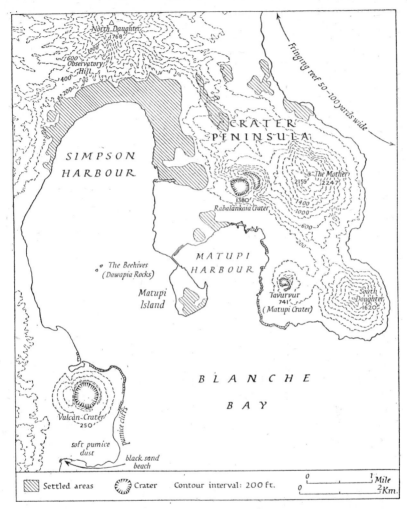

Fig. 22. The Blanche bay volcanoes

Two series of volcanoes are represented. The outer group includes the three
dormant cones, The North Daughter, The Mother and The South Daughter.
The inner active volcanoes are Rabalankaia, Tavurvur and Vulcan; the last, an
ash cone, is the most recent. The Beehives are volcanic remnants which rise steeply
out of Simpson harbour. The whole area is a great caldera. Settlement is restricted
by steepness of slope to land below 200 ft. in height, with the exception of official
quarters east of Rabaul. Based on official sources.

disturbances occur extensive pumice fields may float up to the surface of the ocean. The eastern part of this arc has already been described (pp. 37–9). West of New Britain the islands are arranged *en echelon*. The volcanic islands Sakar and Ritter belong to one such line in Dampier strait. Sakar is a lofty volcano, with a breached summit and a conical base 12 miles in circumference. Ritter is an active volcano 350 ft. high and, though the cone is otherwise regular, it has a broken rim.

Umboi (Rooke island), on the west side of Dampier strait, is a large volcanic island 27 miles long and almost 16 miles across from west to east at its maximum extent. The island is a cluster of many volcanic peaks, the highest of which is 4,500 ft. above sea level. These volcanoes are alined obliquely to the general trend of the volcanic arc. Prolongation of the line to the north-west and south-east takes it through Hein islet (95 ft. high) and the Tolokiwa and Siassi groups. Tolokiwa is an active volcano, 5 miles across at the base and 4,521 ft. high.

The next volcanic arc passes through Long and Crown islands and north-west of them is continued in a north-westerly direction as a submarine ridge. Crown island is a truncated cone nearly 2,000 ft. high and 10 miles in circumference. Long island (4,278 ft.) has a steep mountain rim surrounding an upland lake which occupies a caldera. The lake covers an area of 20 sq. miles. Local traditions suggest that the eruption which formed the crater now occupied by the lake took place about three centuries ago. The native population of Long and Crown islands was wiped out and recolonization took place only three generations ago. To the north-west lies Karkar island, a truncated cone rising nearly 5,000 ft. from a base 40 miles in circumference. The outer crater has a precipitous slope of 1,000 ft. which encircles a smaller but active cone. Bagabag island, rising to 1,970 ft. on the same volcanic line, lies 12 miles to the south-east of Karkar. This island is flanked by a barrier reef 1½ miles off-shore which, according to Darwin's theory of reef formation, indicates that it is sinking.

Manam (4,265 ft.) is the principal volcanic island on the next line and is a very active volcano, with a blunt cone rising from a base which is 12 miles in circumference. Aris (Boisa) is 4 miles to the north-west and appears to be a worn volcanic stump with an irregular flattish summit 705 ft. high.

In the Schouten group, off the Sepik delta, are three parallel rows of volcanoes. In the first row, is the very active cone of Bam (1,969 ft.

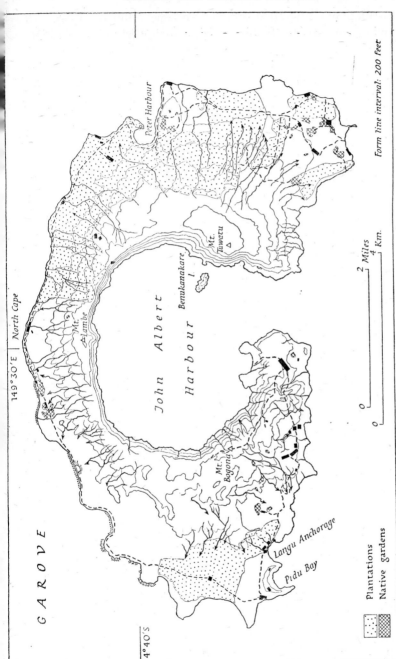

Fig. 23. Garove

This island, which is the most easterly of the Vitu group, is a volcanic remnant whose crater has been breached by the sea. Within the crater, the steep slopes of the land are continued under water and anchorage is impossible. Much land on the more gentle outer slopes of the crater is alienated for plantations. Areas indicated in solid black are occupied by native villages. Based on official sources.

high), Blupblup, a steep weatherbeaten cone, Motmot, a denuded volcanic cone only 197 ft. high, Viai, a conical island 525 ft. high, Koil and the northerly Wogeo, the largest island of the group. Parallel to and 20 miles to the north of the central volcanic arc of the Schouten islands is a submarine ridge 100 miles long which, rising 4,000 to 6,000 ft. above the ocean floor, almost reaches the surface. The third row is to the south of the Bam-Vokeo line and it consists of older volcanoes which have been very much reduced and which have cappings of raised coral. To this group belong Mushu, Kairiru, Valif and Tendanye. A central crater lake and a thermal spring are said to be found on Kairiru. Kadovar (Blosseville island) is an extinct volcano of the Schouten group which does not appear to belong to any of the three arcs already mentioned.

In addition to the above southern components of the Bismarck volcanic arc there is a cluster of submarine volcanoes which form a line from the Admiralty islands to Willaumez peninsula and include Sydney shoal, Circular reef, Sherbourne shoal, Albert, Victoria, Ottilien and Whirlwind reefs, and in the Vitu group the islands of Narage, Undaga, Mundua, Vambu, Garove and Unea. These are entirely of volcanic origin and probably all geologically recent, although only the final stages of volcanic activity are shown in the form of geysers and thermal springs. Garove, the largest island in the Vitu group, is about 7 miles long and has a horse-shoe form (Fig. 23). The island is a mere shell of hills about 900 ft. high round a large explosion crater 3 miles in diameter. Its valleys are deeply cut and from a distance there appear to be several islands. Narage island, lying 25 miles to the north-west of Garove, has more geysers and hot springs than the other islands of the group. It is of sugar-loaf shape, 1,033 ft. high, and 3 miles in circumference. The island is surrounded by a reef which extends a considerable distance along the eastern coast and is breached to the northward.

THE NINIGO - NEW IRELAND ARC

This arc, the outermost in the New Guinea region, includes the Admiralty group, New Ireland, the Solomons and the New Hebrides and probably the Ninigo and Hermit groups. It is analogous to New Britain and the northern ranges of New Guinea in that the islands of this arc are essentially of continental rather than of volcanic origin. Their axes are composed of relatively old rocks mantled by Upper Tertiary sediments and volcanic products. These axes have fairly active volcanoes. The Ninigo and Hermit groups may not belong to this arc for they are apparently built on a volcanic foundation with no continental rocks. Submarine volcanoes are still active in the neighbourhood of these groups. The Ninigo islands actually consist of six atolls which lie in a line running from south-west to north-east. The fifty islets which lie on these atolls are low and flat, and the straits separating the atolls are of considerable depth. To the south-east of the Ninigo islands and 90 miles west-north-west of the Admiralty group lies the Hermit islands atoll which encloses four 'high' islands and itself supports thirteen coral islets. The high islands vary in height from 364 ft. in Maron to 800 ft. in Luf. They are mainly steep-sided and are encircled by barrier reefs.

The Admiralty group is relatively low-lying and is composed mainly of raised coral and volcanic rocks. There may, however, be a core of older rocks in the main island, Manus, which belongs, like New Ireland, to the continental type of island. The highest point of Manus is mount Dremsel (2,356 ft.) which lies in the south-centre of the island. Steep slopes lie to southward and northward of the mount Dremsel ridge. Three roughly parallel ranges appear to run from

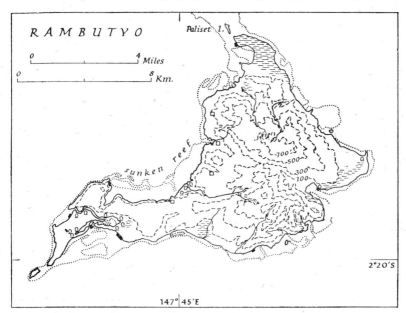

Fig. 24. Rambutyo, Admiralty islands

Form lines are shown by pecked lines. Reef villages are shown by solid black and inland villages by open squares. Based on official sources.

north-west to south-east obliquely to the main axis. They are deeply
cut by longitudinal valleys of which the Harlu river valley, flowing to
the north coast, is typical. The southward-trending Watani river west
of mount Dremsel flows transversely to the main axis. Raised coral
terraces are found up to 700 ft. on Rambutyo (Fig. 24) and elsewhere
in the group. A group of small coral islands in the Admiralty islands
is shown on Fig. 25. Volcanic activity is not yet extinct in the group
for there are hot springs on Lou and Baluan (quiescent volcanoes) and
on Mbuke and the south side of Manus.

New Ireland, which is nearly 200 miles long, averages only 7 miles
in width except in the south where it expands to 30 miles. It is exceed-
ingly mountainous with the Schleinitz mountains (in the northern
part of the island) attaining 4,100 ft. and the Rossel mountains (in
the south) reaching 6,430 ft. North of cape St George the mountains
are reported to be about 7,000 ft. high. Older igneous intrusive rocks

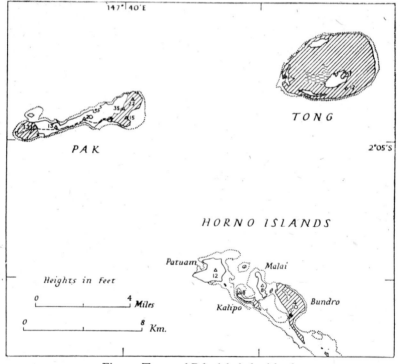

Fig. 25. Tong and Pak, Admiralty islands

The Horno islands lie on the reef which extends north-westwards from Rambutyo
(Fig. 24). The shaded areas are forested. Plantations cover the unshaded areas of
these coral islands. Based on official sources.

form part of the central area together with limestone ridges. Much of the southern region has not yet been thoroughly explored. The coastal areas are veneered with limestone of more recent date. Interbedded with these limestones are more recent volcanic deposits which give, in combination with limestone, a soil suitable for coconut plantations. To the south-east of the Schleinitz mountains is the extensive Lelet plateau which has a mean height of about 2,600 ft. The raised coral limestone terraces on the south coast of New Ireland are probably the equivalent of those on the south coast of New Britain.

VULCANISM

Volcanic activity has played an important part in the evolution of New Guinea. At present there are few vigorously active volcanoes, and most of those which have been active in recent times are now quiescent.

The more active volcanoes include mount Victory (5,967 ft.), on the north side of Collingwood bay in Papua, and Manam (4,265 ft.) and Bam (1,960 ft.), off the coast of north-east New Guinea. In the Rabaul area of New Britain there are the volcanoes of Matupi, Tavurvur, Vulcan, Ghaie and Watom island (Fig. 17). The active volcanoes on, or off, the north coast of New Britain are The Father (or Ulawun— 7,546 ft.), The South Son (or Bamus—7,376 ft.), mount Bango (2,376 ft.), Lolobau island (600 ft.), mount Bulu (3,819 ft.), Langila (approximately 4,000 ft.), the Sulu mountains (1,884 ft.), the volcanoes west of Talasea in the Willaumez peninsula, and Ritter island (350 ft.)

The eruption of Tavurvur in 1937 led to the proposal to remove the capital from Rabaul (p. 238). Renewed quiescence induced a feeling of security and the proposals were not proceeded with until 1941, when in June Tavurvur again began to belch out masses of dust and ashes. These were carried over Rabaul by the prevailing south-easterly winds. In September 1941 the Australian government decided to move the capital to Lae.

Many of the volcanoes have erupted catastrophically with the destruction of a large part of the volcanic cone, thus producing a caldera (a large flat-floored crater) such as that from which rises mount Galloseulo (Fig. 21). It was as a result of such an eruption that the magnificent harbour of Rabaul was formed. The eruptions are often accompanied by seismic sea waves. In 1887 the eruption of the Ritter island volcano raised a tunami 40 ft. high which wiped out villages over a radius of 70 miles.

In the more unstable parts of New Guinea earthquakes can rapidly change the landscape, e.g., the severe earthquake of September 1935 caused great devastation in the Torricelli mountains, for parts of hillsides slid into the valleys and, besides leaving great scars which exposed bare rock, dams of rubble blocked the valleys and, on breaking, caused floods and much loss of life.

BIBLIOGRAPHICAL NOTE

A general account of the main physiographic divisions of New Guinea and New Britain will be found in a paper by S. Warren Carey, 'The Morphology of New Guinea', *Australian Geographer*, vol. III, pp. 3–31 (Sydney, 1938). The first general description and map of the geology of New Guinea was produced by Evan R. Stanley, 'Report on the Salient Geological Features and Natural Resources of the New Guinea Territory . . .', *Report to the League of Nations on the Administration of the Territory of New Guinea* (1921–2), Appendix B (Melbourne, 1923). Subsequent annual reports on Papua and the mandated territory provide additional information, as does the general account of the mandated territory contained in the *New Guinea Handbook* (Canberra, 1937).

Regional descriptions include: Leo Austen, 'Recent Explorations in the North-West District of Papua', *Geographical Journal*, vol LXVII, pp. 434–41 (London, 1926); C. H. Karius, 'Exploration in the Interior of Papua and North-East New Guinea: The Sources of the Fly, Palmer, Strickland and Sepik Rivers', *Geographical Journal*, vol. LXXIV, pp. 305–22 (London, 1929); E. W. P. Chinnery, 'The Central Ranges of the Mandated Territory of New Guinea from Mount Chapman to Mount Hagen', *Geographical Journal*, vol. LXXXIV, pp. 398–412 (London, 1934); K. L. Spinks, 'Mapping the Purari Plateau, New Guinea', *Geographical Journal*, vol. LXXXIV, pp. 412–16 (London, 1934); K. L. Spinks, 'The Waghi River Valley of Central New Guinea', *Geographical Journal*, vol. LXXXVII, pp. 122–5 (London, 1936); Michael Leahy, 'The Central Highlands of New Guinea', *Geographical Journal*, vol. LXXXVII, pp. 229–62 (London, 1936); A. J. Marshall, 'Northern New Guinea', *Geographical Journal*, vol. LXXXIX, pp. 489–506 (London, 1937); L. E. Cheesman, 'The Cyclops Mountains of Dutch New Guinea', *Geographical Journal*, vol. XCI, pp. 21–30 (London, 1938); Stuart Campbell, 'The Country between the Head-waters of the Fly and Sepik Rivers in New Guinea', *Geographical Journal*, vol. XCII, pp. 232–58 (London, 1938); Ivan Champion, 'The Bamu-Purari Patrol, 1936', *Geographical Journal*, vol. XCVI, pp. 190–206, 242–57 (London, 1940); L. E. Cheesman, 'The Mountainous Country at the Boundary, North New Guinea', *Geographical Journal*, vol. XCVIII, pp. 169–88 (London, 1941). The work of Hermann Detzner is described briefly in the *Geographical Journal*, vol. LXXXVII, p. 228 (London, 1936); his journeys are fully described in *Mitteilungen aus den Deutschen Schutzgebieten*, Band XXXII, pp. 1–19; Band XXXVII, pp. 112–30 (Berlin, 1920, 1929).

Raised reefs are described in W. M. Davis, 'Coral Reefs of the Louisiade Archipelago', *Proceedings of the National Academy of Sciences of the United States*, vol. VIII, pp. 7–13 (Washington, 1922). The most comprehensive geological map of British New Guinea is T. W. Edgeworth David, *Geological Map of the Commonwealth of Australia (with Memoir)* (Sydney, 1932). The memoir cites some of the earlier geological papers dealing with New Guinea. More detailed geological maps for Dutch New Guinea include J. Zwierzycki, *Geologische Overzichtskaart van den Nederlandsche-Indischen Archipel*, sheet XX (*Aroe, Kei en Tenimbareilanden*), sheet XIII (*Vogelkop*) (Batavia, 1928, 1932). Earth movements are discussed by J. Zwierzycki, 'Notes on the Morphology and Tectonics of the North Coast of New Guinea', *Philippine Journal of Science*, vol. XXIX, pp. 505–13 (Manila, 1926). The Rabaul eruptions are described in: E. Stehn and W. G. Woolnough, *Report on Vulcanological and Seismological Investigation at Rabaul* (Canberra, 1938); and in N. H. Fisher, 'Geology and Vulcanology of Blanche Bay and the Surrounding Area, New Britain', *Geological Bulletin*, no. 1 (Canberra, 1939). A wider field is covered in H. H. Fisher, 'Report on the Volcanoes of the Territory of New Guinea', *Geological Bulletin*, no. 2 (Canberra, 1939).

For maps, see Appendix I.

Chapter III

COASTS AND NAVIGABLE RIVERS

Coasts of New Guinea—South Coast: South-east Coast: North Coast
Coasts of New Britain—South Coast: Gazelle Peninsula Coasts: North Coast
Main Navigable Rivers of New Guinea—Fly River: Sepik River: Ramu River
Bibliographical Note

The total length of the coastline of New Guinea, together with that of its off-lying islands, is approximately 5,000 miles. Except in the areas west and north of the Gulf of Papua there are few extensive and monotonous coastal plains. The coasts of the south-east of Papua and of mandated New Guinea have mainly narrow coastal plains, which at some points expand inland for 5 to 10 miles behind the heads of bays, but at others are interrupted where mountain ranges trend seaward. Mangrove swamps line most sections of the coast; fringing reefs, though never continuing without a break for many miles, are common off-shore.

There are marked physiographic differences between the northern, southern and south-eastern coasts of New Guinea. The southern coast is still sinking and fronts on to a relatively shallow sea. Between the Dutch border and cape Cretin at the south-east tip of the Huon peninsula, the north coast shows many signs of recent elevation, and earth movements are still a feature. The coast between the Huon peninsula and Samarai, here referred to as the south-east coast, is mainly a subsiding coast which fronts on to a major submarine trough, the Planet deep. The most southerly section of this coast, from cape Vogel to Samarai (Ward Hunt strait to China strait) is a minor region of elevation. The off-lying island groups to the east of these straits, such as the D'Entrecasteaux, Trobriand and Louisiade islands and Murua, also have recently elevated coasts. The coasts of these archipelagos, which lie off the south-east of Papua, are dealt with in the description of individual islands (Chapter XIV). Descriptions of the coasts of isolated off-lying islands are included here. Off Papua such islands share the physiographic characteristics of the mainlands which they adjoin. The islands which lie off the north of New Guinea are volcanic and belong to a distinct series, viz. the volcanic arc south of the Bismarck sea which is better represented in and off northern New Britain.

THE COASTS OF NEW GUINEA

In the following description the coasts of the New Guinea mainland are treated in the following order:

(i) The south coast—(a) the Daru coast (west of 145° E); (b) the Moresby coast (east of 145° E).

(ii) The south-east coast—(a) Samarai to cape Vogel; (b) cape Vogel to cape Cretin.

(iii) The north coast—(a) cape Cretin to Hatzfeldt harbour; (b) Hatzfeldt harbour to Vanimo.

THE SOUTH COAST

From the Dutch border at the Bensbach river outlet to 145° E in the east of the Gulf of Papua, the coast is low and swamp-covered. It is sinking slowly under an encroaching shallow sea. Sedimentation appears to keep pace with subsidence on the west side of the Gulf of Papua. The east side of the Gulf of Papua, the so-called Moresby coast, has no great delta plains and, though it is also subsiding, it lacks sedimentation on so great a scale.

The Daru Coast. The shoreline of the Daru coast is low and has an extensive mangrove fringe backed inland by sago and nipa swamps. Off the coast mud shoals may extend for several miles out to sea from a flat alluvial shore on which firm beaches are rare. Several relatively short sandy beaches lie along the coast south of the Fly river mouth, notably near the Pahoturi river outlet (opposite Saibai island) and on both sides of the mouth of the Binaturi river, about 15 miles west of Daru island. Coral reefs occur around the coasts of off-lying islands and as isolated patches up to 5–10 miles off-shore. South of Daru the complicated series of reefs, which are grouped as the Warrior reefs, runs outhwards parallel to the northern end of the Great Barrier Reef, which lies well to the east of them. These coasts are little known and navigation is difficult because of the shallow seas off-shore, and the constant changes in the trends of the mud banks which form the coastline and in the position of off-lying shoals. The streams south of the Fly delta rise in the low savannah-covered Oriomo plateau. They are, from west to east, the Bensbach, Morehead, Wassi Kussa, Mai Kussa, Pahoturi, Binaturi and Oriomo. These rivers are wide and sluggish, and their slight gradients allow navigation by ships' launches for as much as 50 to 100 miles upstream.

They cut through nipa swamps and bordering rain forest in their lower basins.

Daru island has few undulations over a surface 6 miles long and 2 miles wide. The government station and boat jetty lie on the south coast. Its mangrove fringe is ¾ mile wide on the average, and the interior has fairly open forest with tall trees. The islands of the Fly river have mainly muddy beaches and mangrove fringes, though sandy beaches may occur. Mibu, the most southerly island, is characteristic, much of the interior being nipa swamp. The mainland coast of the Fly outlet, on both sides of the mass of islands lying within the wide funnel, is similar in character to the island coasts. At some points villages are placed on sites which take advantage of slightly higher ground rising out of the mangrove fringe and the sago swamps which back it.

North-east of the Fly delta and at the head of the Gulf of Papua are the poorly drained swamps between and around the deltas of the Awarra-Bamu, Turama, Kikori and Purari rivers. The Kikori is navigable by launches for about 90 miles and the Purari for about 140 miles. Extensive sago and nipa swamps, fringed with mangroves along the coasts and lower rivers (and pit-pit along the Aramia), extend for over 20 miles inland on this coast. The plains are liable to be flooded periodically. Slightly higher land has rain forest and the dense blanket of swamp and forest is broken only at the mouths of streams. The delta channels are frequently clogged by sand and mud as are their entrances from the sea. The Aird hills which rise out of the swamps of the Kikori delta form one of the few conspicuous points behind this coast. They lie 23½ miles north-west of cape Blackwood, the most southerly point of the mud islands which form the Kikori delta.

Between the large delta of the Purari river, which empties into the Gulf of Papua through several shallow channels, and the outlet of the Vailala river, the character of the coast begins to change. The first of the coastal hills, which from here southwards to Samarai alternate with swamp plains, appears behind the coast. In this case the hill, Flat Top, is only 200 ft. high. It lies just west of the swampy lower Vailala basin. For a further 23 miles the coast trends eastward to Kerema bay. Thence it turns south-east, to form the east side of the Gulf of Papua; it maintains this general trend to Hood point, south of Port Moresby. Between Hood point and Samarai the trend is again west to east.

The Moresby Coast (Fig. 9). From Kerema to Samarai gradual subsidence is again characteristic, but the outlying chains of the main mountain axis are never far from the coast. Hills, peninsulas and headlands alternate with swampy plains. The rivers have drowned and only partly silted estuaries (as distinct from the Daru coast deltas), and are shorter and on the whole less readily navigable than those which flow to the Daru coast. This limited sedimentation allows for more continuous development of fringing and barrier reefs. The lowland embayments of the lower basins of the larger rivers have mangrove fringes and sago and nipa swamps. The basin of the Lakekamu is the best example and here the river is fairly widely used, notably to transport supplies intended for the Morobe goldfields. Other streams are navigable as far as the foothills of the main cordillera for boats drawing only 6 ft. Such streams are the Maipura, Tauri, Biaru, Ethel (emptying into Hall sound) and Aroa, and the Laloki, which flows into the mouth of Galley reach, the inner arm of Redscar bay. There are many sandy beaches along this coast. The largest stretch lies between Yule island and the western limit of this coast section at 145° E. There are few breaks in this beach. Lesser developments of sandy beach lie near Port Moresby, where they are fronted by reefs. Both fringing and barrier reefs extend south-eastward from Caution bay, immediately south of Redscar head, to well south of Port Moresby and around Hood point towards Samarai.

Kerema bay, the drowned outlet of the Matupe river, lies between low hills and backs on to the foothills of the Nabo range. The government station and mission at Kerema is placed on a low peninsula on the south side of the bay. To the east of Kerema bay the coast plain widens out and is known as the Lakekamu lowland embayment. The coastal plain continues southward to Hall sound, an inlet which is partly barred on the seaward side by Yule island and several small coral-rimmed satellites. It is broken by such higher points as Wedge hill behind Rocky point. Yule island, with the government station of Kairuku as its main settlement, is 43 miles long from north-west to south-east and rises to 526 ft. Its seaward side has a reef varying in width from 600 yd. to 1 mile, but the inner side facing the swampy shores of Hall sound is clear of reefs. Both shores are fringed with coconuts and the north of the island is well wooded.

Cape Suckling, to the south of Yule island, backs on to a hilly interior and has reefs off-shore. The reefs continue off Redscar bay and Caution bay which lie between cape Suckling and Port Moresby. These are open bays and far less useful to shipping than the hill-lined harbour on which Port Moresby stands. This is the best harbour on the New Guinea mainland (Fig. 53). There are fringing reefs off-shore, as elsewhere along this coast, but native canoes cross them at high tide in all seasons. The hills which run out to sea—e.g., in the promontory on which Port Moresby stands—or lie in narrow belts parallel to the Moresby coast, are usually from 300 to 750 ft. high. They have deep gullies with strips of forest, but trees are generally interspersed with grasslands in this relatively dry area. There is usually a narrow coastal flat from $\frac{1}{4}$ to $\frac{1}{2}$ mile wide between the hills and the shore. Intermittently this is bordered by mangrove swamps.

South-east of Port Moresby the coastal lowland is squeezed out as the steep grassy slopes of the Astrolabe range come down to the sea from crests varying from 3,000 to 4,000 ft. Detached hills line the coast south of the Astrolabe range, behind Rigo and Hood point and there are no good anchorages along the straight coastline. Immediately south of Rigo government station, for example, the heavily wooded Round hill (665 ft.) flanks the shore and comes out to sea as Round point. At Hood point the coast turns eastwards. Hood bay, immediately east of the point, receives the north-south Kemp Welch river from the deeply dissected hills behind the head of the bay (Plate 21). On the east of Hood bay lies Hood lagoon, a shallow stretch of water enclosed by sand-spits.

From Hood point to Samarai the south coast of Papua is fronted by a series of barrier reefs, which lie from 5 to 10 miles off-shore. These reefs are broken by passes, which lead to sheltered all-weather anchorages such as Cloudy bay (in which Abau island lies), Losoa Dudu and Port Glasgow. The coast is undulating and is largely fringed with shore coral. Coves with sandy beaches are rare. Most of the coast is heavily wooded, although at several points as, for example, behind cape Rodney, isolated grassy hills project from the forest cover. The coast plain widens out south-east of Abau, which is backed by Table mountain, but a line of isolated hills lies between the shore and this lowland embayment. From Kwaipomata point to Port Glasgow, and more particularly east of Eagle point (the most westerly projection of the Cloudy mountains peninsula), the hills rise steeply out of the sea. The south coast of the Cloudy mountains peninsula is not only steep but deeply indented, and behind Eagle point several steep-sided submerged river valleys (rias), with narrow intervening peninsulas, point westwards. The Cloudy mountains peninsula is separated from the remainder of Papua by a narrow and relatively low isthmus which has Mullens harbour at its western

and Milne bay at its eastern end. The shores of Mullens harbour
are low-lying and densely wooded, especially along the margins of
its numerous creeks. Many rocky islands lie off the Cloudy mountains
peninsula. These include Rogeia and Sariba, which lie south-west
of and east of Samarai (p. 236). China strait, in which these islands
lie, has reefs at its north-eastern entrance and there are strong
tide-races through it. These tide-races make voyages in native craft
difficult between the Engineer group, to the east, and Samarai and
the Milne bay neighbourhood, to the west.

THE SOUTH-EAST COAST

Samarai to Cape Vogel. The mountains behind the south coast of
Milne bay drop steeply to a narrow thickly populated coastal plain,
which broadens gradually towards the head of the bay. It is almost
wholly fringed with coral. There is relatively deep water off-shore.
To westward the coastal plain is bordered by a shallow sea with
several small reefed islands. The north shore of Milne bay is bounded
by the long narrow peninsula, which has the Stirling range as its
spine, and which gradually narrows towards East cape, its narrow
terminus on Goschen strait. There is little coral along this northern
side of the bay. East of Giligili, one of several large plantations
around the head of the bay, muddy beaches extend for 8 miles,
interrupted occasionally by low wooded rises. Further eastward there
are sandy beaches. The hills of the East cape peninsula are from 3,000
to 4,000 ft. high in the west, and although they are considerably
lower in the east, the peninsula is much narrower here and gradients
inland from the coast are still steep.

From East cape to the head of Goodenough bay the coast trend is
parallel with the main range, which lies relatively near the coast.
The south-east coast as a whole is characterized by open bays backing
on to the main range and by large intervening peninsulas, where
high volcanic areas break across the general trend of the coast. This
coastline from East cape to Bibi, at the north-west corner of Goodenough bay, is the longest and least indented south-east to north-
west stretch. The only major projecting points are cape Ducie and
cape Frere. Both are largely free of forest, as are several stretches of
the mountain hinterland up to 1,500 ft. Shingle and sand beaches
are almost continuous except round these rocky capes, but the coast
is too exposed to allow of many safe anchorages. On the north side
of the bay shore reefs are found, but on the south-west side they

are present only in Awaiama bay, between cape Frere and cape Ducie. The coast plain rises sharply and the cloud-capped dissected main cordillera with peaks such as mount Thompson (5,900 ft.) and mount Simpson (9,975 ft.) are visible from the bay. The cape Vogel peninsula lies along the north shore of Goodenough bay. The neck adjoining the mainland is relatively low, and the Ruaba river flows across it and into the bay at Bibi. The peninsula has mount Borabora (1,083 ft.) as its central point, and the hills lose height southward and eastward. Those fringing the Goodenough bay coast are from 300 to 400 ft. high. The coastal hills form rolling country with a largely grassy surface. Dense forests are limited to the margins of the short rivers. There is a considerable amount of coral off-shore, especially around cape Vogel. The chief off-lying island is Baniara, off the north coast of the bay. It has a government station and a small jetty on its west coast.

Cape Vogel to Cape Cretin. From cape Vogel the coast trends north-westward and bears many signs that it is gradually sinking. Off-shore slopes continue the relatively sharp slopes of the land into the Planet deep. Instability—notably along the Huon gulf coast, where earth tremors are not infrequent—and active vulcanism—in the area behind cape Nelson—are features of this stretch of coast. Between cape Vogel and Wanigela at the head of Collingwood bay there is a narrow mangrove-fringed coastal plain and little coral off-shore. The plain is widest near the head of Collingwood bay around the lesser Moi Biri bay. East of this bay, Flat Dark hill rises to 250 ft. out of a plain which runs in-shore for over 10 miles. The north-west coast of Collingwood bay has scattered reefs off-shore, and the mount Victory volcanic mass rises boldly from an indented shoreline (Fig. 14). The coast of the cape Nelson peninsula has an intricate series of narrow rocky ria-like bays, whose mouths are flanked by the cliffed headlands of the intervening peninsulas. There are muddy beaches at the heads of each narrow bay and fringing reefs around the headlands. Rivers are short and fast flowing from the ridges which run along the peninsulas. In the centre of the peninsula the cones of mount Trafalgar (5,083 ft.) and mount Victory (5,967 ft.) rise out of the mass of steep densely wooded volcanic hills.

From cape Nelson the coast turns westwards along Dyke Acland bay, until it comes against the eastern flanks of the Hydrographer's range and trends northwards. From Porlock bay, at the western end of the cape Nelson peninsula, black sandy beaches, backed by wide mangrove and sago swamps, continue along the southern coast of Dyke

Acland bay. There are many shoals and coral patches off-shore. The south shore has wide swamp-covered plains which front the coast for over 30 miles and at their widest extend for 15 miles inland. Wide areas along the Musa river are periodically flooded. The river is navigable for boats drawing not more than 4½ ft. for 70 miles upstream as far as Garagarata. On the west side of Dyke Acland bay the coastal lowlands are interrupted by spurs with long sweeping slopes and deep ravines which run eastward from the Hydrographer's range. Two minor anchorages, Port Harvey and Oro bay, are found here. Port Harvey is flanked by sandy cliffs 30 ft. high but has a sandy beach at its head. Oro bay has a sandy beach on its north side which continues northward with few interruptions to Caution point (lat. 8°15′ s, long. 148°10′ E), about 3 miles north of the sluggish Opi river outlet.

At cape Endaiadere the coast turns and trends north-westward for a short distance to Buna, from which point it turns westwards along the south side of Holnicote bay. Cape Endaiadere, like cape Ward Hunt at the further extremity of Holnicote bay, has shore reefs and there are scattered coral patches from 1 to 5 miles off-shore along the bay. The bounding coast is low-lying, with a dense fringe of mangroves and well-developed sago and nipa swamps around the mouths of the larger streams. The scattered hills which lie behind the coast are relatively low and mainly well wooded. Buna itself lies on the seaward edge of a sago swamp (though there are many coconut plantations in the area), and has an anchorage about 200 yd. off-shore between sandbanks and coral patches. A reef runs 2 miles northward from Buna. Cape Ward Hunt rises from the north-west corner of the bay as a prominent well-wooded bluff, 150 ft. high at the coast, rising to about 600 ft. inland.

From cape Ward Hunt the coastal trend is mainly north-westward to the Markham river outlet, but minor deviations around inlets are common north-west of Morobe as are off-lying islands. The coast plain is very restricted after the border between Papua and the mandated territory is crossed at 8° s, being hemmed in first by the eastern foreland of the main cordillera west of Morobe and then by the Kuper and Herzog mountains west of Huon gulf. The coast fringe consists of alternating sand beaches around the heads of inlets and cliffed headlands fringed with coral. Generally, as this is the most actively sinking section of the south-east coast, there are considerable depths of water off-shore. There are few extensive swamp flats at the mouths of rivers; even considerable rivers like the Waria, south of Morobe, flow through deeply dissected hills, which fringe them right down to the coast. The largest swamps are developed at the outlet of the Mambare river, 6 miles west of cape Ward Hunt. This river has a considerable delta and, though low in the dry season, is navigable for 80 miles to Tamata by launches. The Mambare, and further north-west the Gira, bring down considerable masses of silt, which discolours the sea water and reduces depths off-shore. The coast from cape Ward Hunt to Morobe is low and wooded.

Morobe harbour is a good, well-sheltered anchorage lying behind the peninsula on which the settlement stands. The south-north fringe of the wooded Luard islands continues the line of the peninsula northwards. Rolling hills backed by mountains, such as the Grasberg and Adolf mountain, lie to westward. There are anchorages with 16 fathoms depth within the harbour, and prior to 1942 vessels drawing less than 14 ft. used the small stone jetty at the head of the harbour. The indented coastline between Morobe and Salamaua is fringed in turn by the Hosken, Straggling and Longuerue islands. There are many interconnecting reefs and sheltered anchorages between there and the steep-faced coast to westward. Salamaua (p. 243, Fig. 57), the main port for the Morobe goldfields, lies on the neck of a hilly peninsula which encloses a wide bay. The coast north-west of the port is deeply indented and has some fringing reef as far as the mouth of the Markham river. South of this estuary, which has many shoals, lies the Laby swamp with the long Herzog lagoon parallel to the shore and the steep bounding Herzog mountains on the west. The Markham river is relatively fast flowing and its valley forms a natural routeway north-westward over the low divide to the upper basin of the Ramu river. There is a good deal of marginal sago swamp near its mouth, but much of the shore is free of forest both southwards and eastwards around Lae, a scattered settlement between 2 and 3 miles from the Markham outlet (p. 241, Fig. 56).

East of the mouth of the Markham river the coast trends eastward to cape Cretin. Near Lae it is unindented, with narrow shingle and black sand beaches below low cliffs. Good depths of water are found close in-shore. Off-shore, coral reefs are not continuous between Lae and cape Cretin, but they are well developed 9 miles east of the steep and prominent bluff of cape Arkona (near Hopoi) and for 8 miles west of cape Cretin. The narrow wooded coast plain narrows towards the east as the Rawlinson range foothills push out towards the coast west of Hanisch harbour and around its head. Hanisch harbour has an anchorage in a depth of 24 fathoms in the north-east of the harbour. It is a well populated inlet. Further east there is some shelter in the lee of small islands, but generally along this coast there is little shelter in the south-east trade season and the winds pile up much surf, especially in the afternoon. Navigation between the off-lying islands is difficult as, for example, among the four low wooded islets known as the Tami islands which lie 5½ miles south-east of cape Cretin. Cape Cretin is a bold headland, whose wooded slopes are continued westward in the flat ridge of Lugaueng (1,150 to 1,300 ft. high). The Bugaim river flows into a small bay lying east of the cape.

The North Coast

Cape Cretin to Hatzfeldt Harbour. This is the southern portion of the gradually rising north coast of New Guinea. From cape Cretin north-westward to the plains fringing the Ramu and Sepik outlets the coastal plain is almost wholly replaced by series of coral terraces. There is much heavy surf off-shore and beaches are difficult to approach. Only the head of Astrolabe bay is relatively free either of fringing or barrier reefs or, on land, of elevated coral reefs. Sand beaches are frequent behind the fringing reefs. The slopes seaward from the mountains of the Huon peninsula, and their north-westward continuation, the Finisterre range, are some of the most abrupt in New Guinea and there is little level land around the entire fringe of the peninsula.

From cape Cretin to Finschhafen the coast is bordered by the south-north chain of the Gingala islands, which are connected by reefs. They consist of six small wooded islands and two islets. Their seaward sides and the mainland shore have coral cliffs from 8 to 10 ft. high. Langemak bay, south of Finschhafen, is bordered by similar cliffs along its southern shore. The cliffs are backed by hills rising to approximately 1,300 ft. and flank sandy beaches bordered by coral patches. The Babui river, which flows into the bay, is swift and cannot be forded. Coral cliffs and fringing reefs continue along the north side of the bay, on the seaward side of the peninsula (2 miles long) which shelters Finschhafen, around its northern point, and for about 100 yd. along its inner side. Further south, within the harbour, there is a narrow sandy foreshore passing into clay and mud towards the head of the bay. There is a shore reef on the west side of the bay. Three minor basins, separated by narrow shallow channels, lie within the bay. The shores are densely wooded, and the sandy bottom of the anchorage is good holding ground. The Bumi river, which has a bar across its mouth, flows into the western entrance to the harbour. From its outlet there are coral cliffs to northward. The Sattelberg (3,182 ft.) lies behind this coast. From Finschhafen north-westward along Vitiaz strait the steep rocky shores are known as the Rai coast. To Sareuak bay, half-way along this coast, coral cliffs are almost continuous, and elevated coral terraces are prominent on land. Fringing reefs are almost negligible. Indentations are few but there are several small coves with sandy beaches. A typical section of coast, that in the neighbourhood of Scharnhorst point, is shown in Fig. 13. The varying groups of coral terraces differ in their development. There are usually from one to four with steep faces from 50 to 100 ft. high, separated by from 100 to 1,000 yd. of fairly flat land. Forests are largely confined to river courses.

Long island, which is separated from the Rai coast by Vitiaz strait, is a huge volcanic cone about 14 miles in diameter which has very steep slopes, especially on its western and southern sides. There are two prominent peaks, Reamur (4,278 ft.) and Cerisy (3,727 ft.), giving the impression from a distance of two separate islands. Much of the rest of the surface is lower than 1,000 ft. The friable brown soil is very porous, being largely disintegrated volcanic rock, so that creeks are non-perennial and there are no swamps. Forests are rather stunted with little undergrowth and kunai patches are common on the eastern side of the island. There is a large interior crater lake, lake Wisdom, with a very active and probably new island crater within it. Reef patches which break off-shore are found 1 mile west-south-west of the main village of Bok, on the south-east shore, and 1 mile off the north-west tip of the island. Tongues of submerged reef extend to within 1 mile of the headlands on the east side. Approaches are otherwise clear, but there are no good all-weather anchorages. The eroded south-east shores have vertical or overhanging rock faces 60 to 80 ft. high. An eruption which occurred within the last 150 years appears to have exterminated the then large population. In 1940 there were 232 native inhabitants and no whites or Asiatics. Crown island, to the north-west of Long island, has a broad fringing reef and is a mountainous mass of volcanic rock rising to approximately 1,860 ft.

Astrolabe bay, where the mainland coast turns north, is deep and open. From cape Tiwalib, at its south-east margin, to the mouth of the Kabenau river there is a rocky coral coast with a few sandy beaches as, for example, at Bau plantation, Bongu and Marakum. The land rises gently for about a mile from the coast and thence very sharply. Melanua harbour (Konstantinhafen), a small well-sheltered bay (with depths of 12 to 30 fathoms) on this southern coast, also has a sandy beach at its head, as have Bogadjim and Erima across the head of the bay. At Bogadjim, landings could be made, prior to the Japanese occupation, at the jetty and at the north end of the settlement. Erima, 2½ miles northward, was an unloading place for mail steamers. At Madang (pp. 244–5) the shoreline consists of a submerged coral shelf averaging 10 yd. in width, backed by a sharp bank about 8 ft. high. Ragetta island continues northward the protection afforded to Madang harbour by the bounding Schering peninsula. The only good sandy beach surrounds the northernmost minor bay on the town side of the inner harbour.

The low bank fringed with coral persists northwards to Sek harbour (Alexishafen). Between the barrier reef and the coast is a lagoon studded with reef and islets which extends to cape Barschtsch, north of Sek. Sek lies 8 miles north of Madang and the harbour is entered through Ottilien pass, a clear channel more than 30 fathoms deep between Sek island and the mainland. There is an anchorage about 200 yd. west of Sek island in 12 to 16 fathoms. There are small beaches near these anchorages, but for the most part a low bank abuts directly on to the shore; the inner harbours are fringed with mangrove swamp. A rough coral shore extends from Sek to cape Croisilles and is backed by a narrow lowland with much swamp forest. There are beaches at the mouth of the Rempi river and at Matukar plantation 2 miles north of the river of that name. There are many coconut plantations along the west shore of Astrolabe bay, which is backed by the southern outliers of the Adalbert range. Cape Croisilles is fairly low and is bordered by reefs.

Karkar and Bagabag are separated from the cape Croisilles coast by Isumrud strait. Both are volcanic, wooded and rugged. Their narrow coastal lowlands are well planted with coconuts and some cocoa below the steep slopes, which in the Karkar cone reach 4,920 ft., and in Bagabag 1,968 ft. Karkar lies 10 miles north-east of cape Croisilles and has great depths close in-shore except where there are shore reefs—e.g., from Kurum, the main settlement at the south-west corner, to Kulili, on the north coast. The south-east and north-west shores have little shelter from seasonal winds and the only anchorages are at Kulili, Kurum and Dogowan nearby. Kurum takes 200-ton vessels, and by the cocoa and coconut plantations at Dogowan

700-ton vessels may tie up. Native gardens are numerous within about 4 miles of the shore. Further up-slope heavy forests clothe mount Ulumam, which has a deep crater with a partly wooded bottom and a small smoking cone. There were about 9,300 natives on Karkar in 1940, together with six white planters and three missionaries. Bagabag lies about 12 miles south-east of Karkar and is almost encircled by a narrow submerged reef from $\frac{3}{4}$ to 2 miles off-shore. There is an opening opposite New Year bay, the only recognized anchorage. New Year bay is deep (15 fathoms at the head of the bay) and is protected in all weathers. It has been used by a vessel of 4,000 tons. Spurs descend from the central cone on either side of New Year bay which is on the south-east side of the island. Reefs project about $\frac{1}{4}$ mile from points on the east coast and there are numerous detached reefs off the west and north-west coast. The native population in 1940 was about 400.

The mainland coast north-west of cape Croisilles is fairly regular and has no prominent indentations apart from Eitel Friedrich and Hatzfeldt harbours. Grassy hills alternate with narrow expanses of wooded plain behind the shore which is composed either of sharp coral cliffs rising 10 to 12 ft. above high water or, at the heads of small bays, of black sandy beaches. Most of the coast is fringed with coral. Hatzfeldt harbour is sheltered on the east by the wooded Pataki island and the settlement lies on the east side of the harbour. The short Deigun river flows into the head of the harbour, which has several shallow anchorages. The coastal hills lose height west of the harbour and the coast turns north-westward to Bogia (Prinz Albrecht) harbour where there is anchorage in a depth of 10 fathoms.

Hatzfeldt Harbour to Vanimo. From Hatzfeldt harbour the coast continues its south-east to north-west trend along Stephan strait. The shoreline is regular and the interior slope to the forested Adalbert range steep. Manam and Aris (Boisa) lie across Stephan strait. Recent investigations have shown that Manam lies 12 miles north-east of Hansa point (about 4 miles north-east of its charted position). It is actively volcanic, being a great cone 4,268 ft. high, with a glow visible from the mainland. The only gentle slopes are found on the west of the island, although slopes to about 1 mile inland are nowhere excessive. There is fairly dense forest to about 3,700 ft. and short coarse grass to about 3,800 ft., succeeded by a waste of black ash. The coast is rocky, the only small beaches being in the west and south-west. On the east side lava flows fall steeply into the sea. In the eruption of 1919 the coast track which encircles the island was overwhelmed on this east side. The shoreline passes so steeply under the sea that off-shore anchorages are very restricted. There is a small harbour at Tabele which will shelter 500-ton vessels at all seasons. Vessels of about 50 tons can hang on to the under-water shelf at several points as, for example, off Bedua or Tabele (in the north-west monsoon season) and off Bieng, near cape Bremen (in the south-east trade period). Aris (Boisa) is an extinct steep-sided crater about 700 ft. high which is also surrounded by very deep water. It lies roughly 5 miles north-west of Manam. There is a small village of about 100 inhabitants on the east side, with an anchorage for small vessels.

From Condor point on the north side of Hansa bay to the outlet of the Lamu river, the coast trends north-westward and the coastal plain increases in width. There are patches of kunai grass among the forests behind the coastal mangrove fringe. Around the Ramu and Sepik outlets the low marshy plain continues for about 50 miles. Much of it, together with the lower river courses, has pockets of black mud fronted with fringes of mangrove and nipa palms. Both river entrances are difficult to pick out from the sea, and, although the Sepik has no bar, that across the more southerly Ramu mouth has average water depths of only 12 ft. Great sand-spits, which come out to sea as cape Girgir, lie along the north of the Sepik outlet. To the west of this cape the coast trends westward and encloses the crescentic Karau lagoon which curves behind the coast for 20 miles and has Casuarina point at its eastern end.

The Schouten islands lie more or less parallel to the coast which adjoins the Sepik mouth and from 15 to 25 miles off it. There are six islands fairly evenly spaced, usually in the form of single volcanic cones. They are Bam, which is steep-to with no anchorages; Blup-blup, connected by a line of rocks with Motmot islet; the almost precipitous Kadovar; Viai; Koil, with a detached reef running west-ward from its south-east extremity; and Wogeo (Vokeo). All these islands are high and wooded. The reef $1\frac{1}{2}$ miles west of Kadovar breaks in any swell.

Cape Girgir has long sand-flats 5 miles to seaward which have been accumulated by deposition of silt from the Sepik. The coast west of cape Girgir is very low, but as it passes westward it starts rising gradually inland to hills from 300 to 1,000 ft. high, which form the foothills of the Prince Alexander range. The range is well wooded, as is the Torricelli range which continues the same chain westward. Both ranges are regions of instability, and earth tremors are fairly common. The whole coastline from cape Girgir to the Dutch border shows signs of a recent uplift of a few feet. It is mainly free of off-lying dangers, but heavy surf breaks along it in the north-west monsoon season. The general trend of the coast is west-north-west to the Dutch border. There are no major promontories; indentations and good anchorages are few. Coastal streams are short and their swift flow allows only of navigation by canoes. The foreshore is of black sand to the west and of white sand further east; the bordering coastland is often swampy except where foothills run out to sea. Near Matapau, roughly equidistant from Wewak and Aitape, and at several other points, grass-covered hills rise directly from the shore. There is very little fringing coral east of Lapar point, near Aitape, but reefs are common west of it.

Wewak lies on Dallmann harbour; it is sheltered from the full force of the north-west monsoon by the islands of Kairiru and Mushu, and by the northward trend of the coast to cape Pus, which stands on its north-western side. Mushu (Gressien island) lies on the north side of Mushu strait opposite cape Pus and is 8 miles long in a north-south line and 3 miles across. There are several small bays on the southern coast. The island is well populated and mainly low-lying. Kairiru lies a short distance north of Mushu and rises gradually to a flat topped mountain 3,346 ft. high. It is heavily wooded with little flat land, although there are several plantations along the south coast. The west coast of Dallmann harbour is broken for about a mile to enclose Victoria bay, which is a good anchorage except in the north-west monsoon season. Another small bay lies on the south coast of Kairiru. Valif and Tendanye, about 10 miles west-north-west of western Kairiru, are densely wooded and rise only to 150 ft. This maximum is attained at the south end of Tendanye, where there is also a small bay. Valif is heavily fringed by reefs, which extend for nearly a mile off-shore on its southern side.

The coast between cape Pus and Aitape is steeply cliffed at several points and hills rise to between 600 and 800 ft. within a few miles of the shore. About 17 miles south-west of cape Pus, mount Turu rises to 3,938 ft. out of the general level of the Prince Alexander range, and further westward mount Sapau (4,593 ft.) breaks the generally even crest line of the Torricelli mountains. There are long stretches of good sand beach from 75 to 100 yd. wide both east and west of Aitape, and cliffs with rock-strewn beaches, such as those at Lapar point, are fairly rare. The coastal plain is undulating and patches of kunai grass are found among the rain forests. The plain reaches its maximum width of 10 miles at Aitape. There is often a line of casuarina along the shore. The Torricelli mountains fall to the coastal lowland in a series of terraces.

Aitape lies west of Seleo island and is protected by two more small islands, Ali and Tamara. There are several plantations with landing grounds and jetties in the area. The three off-lying islands are bordered by reefs and are difficult to approach, though sandy beaches lie behind the reefs. Tamara, on which there is a mission station, has the best anchorage and the greatest elevation in this otherwise low-lying group, a hill 260 ft. high, at its north-western end.

West of Aitape the Sissano lagoon lies behind long sand-spits with a fringe of casuarina and mangrove. Its inner shore has some high timbered dunes but much of its shore is swampy and there is a good deal of dead forest. The coast has few distinctive features between here and Vanimo, apart from Baudissin point a few miles west of Sissano lagoon and Laitere, which has a smaller lagoon. The entrance to Vanimo harbour is about $1\frac{1}{4}$ miles wide and lies west of cape Concordia. This point has off-lying reefs for about 600 yd. northward and is a densely wooded hill 330 ft. high. The head of the harbour is shallow although depths of 17 fathoms are found at the entrance. The coast is more rocky and the hinterland higher between Aitape and the Dutch border. Cliffs are well developed and conspicuous points such as mount Bougainville, a flat topped cone 3,957 ft. high, 16 miles west of cape Concordia, and mount Hartmann, 6 miles south-south-west of it, are clearly visible from the coast. There is an anchorage in Bougainville bay. The entrance is a mile wide and the bay has depths of 10 to 12 fathoms. Steep cliffs mark the entrance to the bay.

THE COASTS OF NEW BRITAIN

The coasts of New Britain are about 1,000 miles in length. They are treated below in three sections: (i) the south coast; (ii) the coasts of the Gazelle peninsula; and (iii) the north coast. The south coast fronts on to the steep submarine slope into the Planet deep; it is a rising coast, with an ascending series of coral reefs. The north coast is an area of active vulcanism, associated with subsidence; the coastal lowlands are much broken up by large, steep-sloped volcanic masses. The coasts of the Gazelle peninsula are more regular, and on the whole they slope more steeply into the sea than those of the remainder of New Britain. Simpson harbour, on which the town of Rabaul is situated, is one of the best harbours in the Western Pacific.

THE SOUTH COAST

The south-west coast of New Britain in the neighbourhood of mount Tangi is described with the north coast (p. 77), with which it is structurally more closely connected. Cape Büsching, south-east of the southern entrance to Dampier strait, is selected here as the westerly terminus of those sections of the south coast which possess common characteristics. Cape Büsching lies to the south of the flats at the mouth of the Itne river. This drains the south of the relatively low belt of land which continues northwards to the northern coast. The coastal lowlands between cape Büsching and cape Merkus, to the south-east, are broader than such strips on the northern littoral. The intervening capes, such as cape Peiho, have fringing reefs which may extend seawards for as much as 1½ miles. The bays are shallow with many coral patches. The lower rivers have considerable mangrove swamps, and the southern foothills of the Whiteman range are a fair distance away from the coast. Marjie bay, lying east of cape Peiho, has the swamps of the lower Adi river at its head. Between the eastern side of this bay and cape Merkus lie a considerable number of low-lying islands, the Arawe group. Kaptimati, 6 miles south-west of cape Merkus, lies furthest off-shore. The islands lying between it and the mainland have low ridges at their cores and for the most part are densely forested. There are several coconut plantations in the group. On the seaward sides of the islands cliffs are common, whilst the inner islands have wide shallow reefs. Fig. 17 shows a typical group. Arawe island proper, and Pilelo lying south-west and south of cape Merkus, have the same general features. Both have wide mangrove swamps, but a good deal of the land has been cleared and there was a mission station on each island. Arawe harbour, lying between the islands and the mainland, has three entrances, all of which may be used by large vessels. They are Pilelo passage (between cape Merkus and Pilelo), Arawe passage (between Pilelo and the eastern Arawe islands) and Kumbun passage (between the Arawe group and Kumbun). On the mainland, Arawe plantation has 500 yd. of sandy beaches. Such beaches are uncommon. There is more frequently about 150 yd. of fringing reef, and coral extends in-shore up to the outer limits of the forest or mangrove swamps.

At cape Merkus the emergent coral limestone typical of the south coast backs the shore in the form of a flat-topped ridge 150 to 250 ft. high and up to ¼ mile wide. There are breaks in the fringing reef, but the whole coast has heavy surf in the south-east trade season and in-shore navigation may be difficult. For 28 miles eastward to Möwe harbour the south coast curves in a more northerly direction towards the Whiteman range of central New Britain. Several fair-sized rivers flow to the coast, among them the Pulie river, up which vessels drawing 6 ft. may travel a fair distance. Crocodile plantation marks the west side of the Pulie outlet. Except at river mouths the coast rises fairly steeply from the shore. The raised coral cliff (or in its absence a steep coastal slope) is maintained along this section and cliffs may reach 300 to 400 ft. Möwe harbour lies between the three small islands Ganglo, Bugid, and Geglep, and the cliffs of the mainland (Plate 17). These islands have ridges about 250 ft. high bounded by narrow coastal flats. The mainland shore is similar apart from the low-lying area opposite Geglep around the small Guimere lagoon. Aliwa plantation lies around the south shores of this lagoon. From Möwe harbour the coast runs south-eastward for 3 miles to cape Anukur and then eastwards towards the mouth of the Andru river. Low uneven country flanks it for some distance inland, and there is a well-developed fringing reef. Short stretches of sandy beach lie behind the reef. The low coastal plain is interrupted occasionally by hills. That behind cape Bali, 3 miles east of cape Anukur, is about 400 ft. high. From the mouth of the Andru river to the Johanna river, north of Kablumgu point, the coast is reefed but not cliffed. Cliffs reappear east of the Johanna river where they are about 200 ft. high. Off-shore islands are small and low-lying with projecting reefs, and like the mainland are densely timbered. About 4 miles inland the coast plain merges into the gradual slopes of the Whiteman range, where sink holes become increasingly common on the limestone slopes and the rain forest thins out. Just east of Kablumgu point the cliffs are broken at the entrance to Ablingi harbour which has dense mangrove swamps around its head and gently shelving shores. Ablingi island, off the south-east of the harbour entrance, and the coast to eastward have high cliffs; those at the southern point of Ablingi island rise to 200 ft.

The coast continues its eastward trend with some loss of height on the shoreline to Gasmata (Thilenius) harbour. This lies within a convex curve of islands: Anato, on the north-west, Gasmata (which has a government station), Dililo, and Awrin island on the north-east. The west entrance to the harbour lies between Anato and Gasmata islands and the main entrance between Awrin and a small peninsula pointing southwards from the mainland. Coral patches are common in the harbour area, as are small islands (Plate 20). A track follows the coast to Linden harbour, passing through Ring Ring and Linden-hafen plantations to the mouth of the Amgen river, which flows alongside the large Lindenhafen plantation. A 2-mile tramway runs southward through the centre of the plantation to a jetty on the east side of the harbour. The main anchorages, with depths of 13–17 fathoms, lie behind the west-to-east line of the islands of Siwot, Walunguo, Lue and Baronga. Passages into the harbour run between these islands, which have off-lying reefs. The harbour shores on the mainland have fewer or even no reefs. Behind the plantations, the mainland is densely timbered especially on hill spurs, which here run close to the shore.

From Linden harbour to cape Beechey and on to cape Cunning-ham on the south side of Jacquinot bay the coast trends north-eastward. In the 60 miles from Linden harbour to cape Beechey, fringing reefs are common, especially in the first 20 miles. Sandy beaches may occur behind the reefs, and except around the heads of bays the coast slopes steeply inland and eventually rises sharply in the peaks of the central range, which are known as the Nakanai mountains behind cape Beechey. Montague harbour, lying roughly half-way to cape Beechey receives the considerable Ania river from the central range, here relatively narrow between the northern Commodore bay and the south coast. A track runs across the island between the two bays, following the west side of Montague bay. The western shores of the open Montague bay are steep, but the head and eastern side are low-lying and marshy. East of this bay the fringing reef is not continuous and off-lying islands are rare along the remainder of the south coast. There are fairly extensive marshy flats at the heads of bays and along such streams as the Melkoi river, which comes to the sea 3 miles due west of cape Beechey. Between its outlet and the headland lies Rano plantation, at the seaward end of a hill spur. A coast track runs throughout the narrow lowland of the littoral, eastwards from Linden harbour, and terminates eventually at Rabaul.

Cape Beechey and its hinterland to northward have some of the steepest seaward slopes in New Britain, but before cape Cunningham is reached the mountains recede from the coast. The large Tolu river has its delta on this coast. Lau, 4 miles to the east of this delta, has a beach of black sand and no reef, but north-eastward the fringing reef is continuous, except across river mouths. Drina, south-west of cape Cunningham, has an anchorage behind the reef, and a consider-able plantation flanks the shore. It utilizes the small 100-ft. platform

of raised coral. This raised reef, with a characteristic fall inland to
heavily forested and ill-drained land, is a common feature in this
section of the south coast. For 4 miles between Drina and cape
Cunningham the fringing reef is broader and there are coral islets
off-shore. Cape Cunningham is the eastern terminus of a rectangular
peninsula with relatively low shores which lies between the mouth
of the Drina river and Jacquinot bay. Palmalmal plantation covers
much of its northern coast. The names cape Cunningham North
and cape Cunningham South are given by some authorities to the
seaward corners of the peninsula.

Jacquinot bay is a wide bay open to the east and bounded by cape
Cunningham North and cape Jacquinot, 14 miles to the north-east.
Katnalgaman anchorage lies on its north-eastern side, within the
shelter afforded by the cape Jacquinot peninsula. The coast of the
main bay has a broad fringing reef, with small off-shore islands
backed for the most part by steep slopes. Sandy beaches are best
developed along the Palmalmal plantation coast. The north side has
dense mangrove swamps backed by steep limestone hills. From cape
Jacquinot the coast trends eastward for 28 miles and then north for
18 miles to cape Cormoran. The open Waterfall bay lies immediately
east of cape Jacquinot. It receives the waters of the large Esis and
Berg Berg rivers at its head and the pyramidal Kwoi peak rises to
1,800 ft. north-east of the bay. The fringing reef is not well developed
along the head of the bay, although round the Mocklon islands off
the south-east border of the bay coral patches are common. Fringing
reefs are common around Rondahl harbour immediately east of
Waterfall bay and are continuous to cape Orford, where the coast
begins to turn north. High hills rise steeply from the sea here and
cliffs backed by steep slopes force the coast track 2 miles inland
between cape Orford and cape Cormoran.

Wide bay, between cape Cormoran and the south-east of the
Gazelle peninsula, is a deep indentation about 20 miles across and
20 miles deep. Its southern coast trends south-east to north-west
and its head is joined to that of Open bay on the north coast by the
low isthmus which separates the Gazelle peninsula from the remainder of New Britain.

THE COASTS OF THE GAZELLE PENINSULA

The head of Wide bay is known as Henry Reid bay. This receives
the Henry Reid and Powell rivers which have a joint delta (Fig. 52).
The east coast of Henry Reid bay is occupied by two plantations.

Further eastward the north coast of Wide bay trends from west to east, and, as it cuts transversely across the high eastern axis of the Gazelle peninsula, its slopes are very steep. High mountains lie close to the shore as far east as cape Archway, where the east coast begins. Low cliffs, separated by lower stretches with rough beaches, continue to Sum Sum plantation, except at the intervening Eber and Adler bays where there are good though exposed sand beaches. Put Put harbour, further north, is suited only to small vessels and has a rocky southern shore and a mangrove fringe along the north shore. A large plantation of the same name borders the coast on both sides of the harbour. At Put Put the raised coral limestones which have bounded the coast from the head of Wide bay to this point, and which reach to almost 2,000 ft. inland, disappear under the debris of the former Rabaul volcano. From Put Put to cape Gazelle, a distance of 18 miles, there is a fringing reef which dries at low tide but has 3 ft. of water over it at high tide. There are breaks in the reef at the mouths of the Warangoi river, which drains the greater part of the north-east quadrant of the Gazelle peninsula, and of the Kabanga river. The reef is also absent for a few miles south of cape Gazelle. Sandy beaches sometimes strewn with rocks lie behind the reef, and behind this is a flat never much more than a few hundred yards in width. From the Warangoi outlet northwards lies the relatively well developed north-east coast of the cape Gazelle-Blanche bay area. Roads available in the dry season for motor traffic, and many plantations with jetties, lie along the coast. The triangular area between Blanche bay and Put Put is much lower than the rest of the peninsula.

The Duke of York islands lie 5 miles north-east of cape Gazelle. They are low and thickly forested, except where clearings have been made round coastal villages and in the large plantation area of the south-west of Duke of York island, the largest of the group. The remaining islands of the group are Mioko, Utuan, Ulu (Mauke), Kerawara and Kabakon, to the south of Duke of York island, and Makada, off its north-west coast. There is much off-lying reef in the group and low cliffs are frequent, especially along the north coast of Duke of York island. A break in the cliffs in the north-east of this island leads to the small but well-sheltered Balanawang harbour (Port Hunter). Mioko harbour lies off the south coast of Duke of York island and within the shelter of the fringe of lesser islands to southward. It is deep, and although there is a fair amount of reef, sandy beaches, free of reef, are common on those coasts of the off-lying islands which fringe the harbour. On the main island, north-east of Mioko harbour and east of Mangrove creek, is a densely peopled peninsula. Kerawara harbour lies between Ulu (Mauke) and the two reef-free islands of Kabakon and Kerawara, which have steep southern shores faced with low cliffs from 20 to 60 ft. high. Makada harbour, between Makada and the north-west shore of Duke of York island, is shallow and only takes vessels of less than 200 tons. Its shores are sandy. The two small Gredner (Pigeon) islands lie between the Duke of York group and Blanche bay. They are low-lying and much of their surface is under coconuts. An oval barrier reef surrounds the two islands.

From cape Gazelle to Raluana point the coastland is almost entirely planted. In some places, there are low cliffs—for example, at Kokopo, where they are 50 ft. high—and shallow bays with anchorages such as Kokopo harbour ; but between Lesson and Raluana points the coast runs uniformly west-north-westward, paralleled by the coast road. The salient features of Karavia and Blanche bays and of the port of Rabaul are shown on Figs. 22 and 54. Within the explosion crater of a great volcano whose broken rims surround the bays (except on the south-east side, which has been blown away) there is shelter in all weathers. The beaches are of sand and mud, much of it worn-down volcanic debris from active minor volcanoes around the bay. Soft mud lines the foreshore at Rabaul and on the north-east shore of Matupi harbour. Low cliffs occur round some parts of the coast of Blanche bay. Karavia bay is deep and anchorages are difficult. It has a rocky foreshore with a coral facing which is otherwise lacking in Blanche bay. Hills rise steeply from within 1,000 yd. of the shore on all sides, except at Rabaul where the coast flat is wider. The crests of the former crater lie close to the shore, and only short streams enter the bay.

The steep cone of The South Daughter, with Praed point at its foot, marks the northern side of Blanche bay. From Praed point to Tawui point the coast is well peopled, especially in the northern half. For a mile north of Praed point, there is a sandy beach along the steep eastern slopes of The South Daughter. Similar conditions are found along the steep coast of The Mother to northward. Thence to Nordup (Nodup) rocks are common. Nordup lies 5 miles north of Praed point. North of Nordup the beach narrows but the interior slopes more gradually. Northwards to Tawui point the coast is high and bold with cliffs rising from a narrow coral fringe to a height of 150 ft.

From Tawui point, the most northerly cape in New Britain, the coast has cliffs and a rocky beach for 2 miles. The eastern and southern shores of Talili bay have sandy beaches with only occasional patches of shore reef for 6 miles. The southern shores are lined with coconut plantations set on undulating hills. At Kabagada point which marks the western limit of Talili bay white cliffs rise from the beach. From this point to cape Liguan the shore is rocky with many isolated coral patches and a broad fringing reef $\frac{1}{4}$ to $\frac{1}{2}$ mile wide.

Watom island (Fig. 17), lying 4 miles north of Liguan bay, is a volcanic cone rising to 1,115 ft. It has rocky shores, steep gullied slopes and an encircling reef. Watom is largely forested except around the broken crater rim and along planted sections of the coast. The eastern and western shores have many native villages. Urara island, $2\frac{1}{2}$ miles west of cape Liguan, is low-lying and has a fringing reef. Though there is much swamp this small island is densely populated.

The Rembarr range runs out to sea at cape Liguan and forms the north-eastern rim of Ataliklikun bay, a large bay with 25 miles of coast. The broad fringing reef off cape Liguan continues along the coast for 4 miles to Kabaira bay. Here there is over a mile of sandy beach with only scattered coral patches. To southward there is a low foreshore with a muddy beach. Both the south-east and north-west sectors of the bay have mud and mangrove patches. The head of Ataliklikun bay is backed by low-lying, slightly undulating land. There is a sandy beach at Vunalama, a plantation which is centrally placed on the west side of the bay. Here the steep north-western mountains of the Gazelle peninsula lie behind the shore. North of Ramandu mission the coast turns westward, and apart from minor indentations maintains this direction for 20 miles to cape Lambert. There are both fringing and barrier reefs off this coast, the barrier reef being 3 miles off-shore at Ramandu and 7 miles off-shore north of cape Lambert, where it encloses the Talele islands, a group of reefed islets. The barrier reef is interrupted by several passages, and deep water lies between it and the shore. For 3 miles between Ramandu and New Massara the coast is comparatively low-lying with flat sandy beaches. The next 6 miles to Lassul (Byning) bay are steep and cliffed; the northern spurs of the Baining mountains run out to sea here. Lassul bay has flat sandy beaches backed by large plantations west of the bay. Westward to cape Lambert the Gavit range rises to about 3,000 ft. behind the coast, and its spurs produce cliffed headlands which alternate with sandy beaches. This coast is almost wholly under plantations, which are placed in and between the lower valleys of short northward-flowing rivers. The Namburg river, which flows along the eastern flanks of the Gavit range, has a fairly deep mouth. The coast at and between cape Lambert and cape Pomas (2½ miles south-westward) is high and steep.

The west coast of the Gazelle peninsula, from cape Pomas to Open bay, is 57 miles long. Broken coral reefs flank the shore for most of this distance and tend to lie up to a mile off it. The barrier reef terminates about half-way between cape Pomas and the head of Open bay. This is a rough and mainly infertile coastline, and most of the settlements lie a short way inland on the coast track or up the larger rivers. There are sandy beaches at Seraji, Stockholm and Pondo plantations. Otherwise, rocks and, to the south, swamps lie along the shore. South of Stockholm plantation, the coast hills have steep limestone slopes with largely subterranean drainage and sink holes are common. Those streams which reach the coast have falls just above their mouths. In the south of this section level grass-covered plains, with some coastal swamp, lie around Powell (Tavana-tangir) harbour. The Toriu river to northward has extensive swamps at its mouth, as has the winding Sai river at the head of Open bay.

THE NORTH COAST

The south-west shore of Open bay is stony, and reefs project at right angles from the points. Mangrove swamps back the shore. There are fringing reefs off Rangambol point; but south-west of it the shores of Hixon bay are sandy, or at its head (along the delta of the Pandi river) muddy. There are extensive swamps inland. The Pandi river flows between the coastal volcanic arc and the central limestone axis of New Britain. The first of the coastal volcanoes, The North Son (3,248 ft.), lies on the west side of Hixon bay. The coast track, broken by the Pandi deltaic flats, follows the coast north of this volcano. This is a rugged coastline, which rises steeply from the sea and has extensive fringing reefs. Cliffs back cape Deschamps north-west of The North Son, and the coast turns south-westward as an almost unbroken line along the east side of the great Kimbe bay (Fig. 20). The volcanic cones of The Father, or Ulawun (7,546 ft.), The South Son, or Bamus (7,376 ft.), and mount Galloseulo (3,848 ft.) rise from the coastal lowlands with their narrow sandy beaches. Surf breaks heavily along this exposed coast, especially in the north-west monsoon period. From Sule, on the east side of Expectation strait, the coast-lands are fairly low, although the major volcanoes rise steeply out of the heavy forest cover. West of mount Galloseulo the belt of lower land is narrower and extensive reefs lie off-shore.

Lolobau (Namisoko) island lies 8 miles west of cape Deschamps, across Expectation strait. It is mainly formed out of an old crater with a broken rim. Several newer cones lie within this rim—notably Sile crater (2,720 ft.), the main peak, and Giwu peak in the east of the island. Crater lake, an area of fresh water a mile in diameter, lies behind the south coast. There is an almost continuous barrier reef off-shore with short breaks on the east side and many detached coral patches on the west. A track follows the coast except on the east of the island, where it is interrupted by the deep gullies of many short streams and the sharp slopes of Giwu peak. In 1940 the island had a population of 171.

South-west of mount Galloseulo the coast is swampy as far as Lara point, at the east side of Bangula bay. Here the volcanic Sulu range runs close behind the coast and east of the wide mangrove flats around the head of Bangula bay. Reefs are extensive on the west side of this bay and off the coast west of it. Here Saddle mountain (702 ft.) rises behind the shore. The Saddle mountain ridge runs out into the north-east side of Commodore bay at cape Reilmitz. The north-west boundary of Commodore bay is at cape Hoskins, 15 miles west of cape Reilmitz. The head of the bay is set 6 miles back from a line joining the two capes, and a good deal of the intervening bay is filled with coral patches. There are discontinuous fringing reefs and several miles of sandy beach around the bay. The marshes of the lower Kaplura and Bilomi rivers lie in the extensive coast plain south of the bay. To westward the Hoskins peninsula contains the active cone of mount Bango (2,375 ft.); to northward mount Lollo (2,683 ft.); and to north-westward mount Mululus (4,282 ft.), mount Mataleloch (3,457 ft.) and mount Otto (2,204 ft.). This series of steep cones rises out of densely forested undulating coastlands. Wide reefs and large detached patches of coral lie off-shore and in Stettin bay to westward. In Stettin bay the Fisch, Möwen and Grabo reefs, each about 4 miles off-shore, are most outstanding. Wulai island, 5 miles north-west of cape Hoskins, has a circular barrier reef within which there is said to be anchorage for a vessel of up to 3,000 tons. Megigi plantation, $7\frac{1}{2}$ miles south-west of cape Hoskins, has no fringing reef and is fronted by $1\frac{1}{2}$ miles of sandy beach. Much of the east coast of Stettin bay lacks a fringing reef. The head of the bay is low-lying and swampy, especially along the meandering Dagi river. The line of mountains, running from south to north, which comes to the coast as the mount Du Faure massif rises at the south-west of Stettin bay. From here for 17 miles to Garua harbour fringing reefs are almost continuous and there is a fair amount of detached reef. The line of volcanic cones which forms the spine of the Willaumez peninsula is shown on Fig. 19. Coast plains are small and interrupted throughout the peninsula. Garua harbour is 3 miles long from east to west and 2 miles wide. It is protected from south-east winds by Garua island, which lies ½ mile off the government station of Talasea, on the mainland. There are reefs on its south and east sides and shoals north and west of it. The mainland shore in the neighbourhood of Talasea has deep water off-shore and a sandy beach 100 yd. wide. The shores of the harbour are undulating, and its northern shores have extensive reefs. There is a good anchorage off Talasea in depths of 8 fathoms. North of Garua harbour the coast is rugged and lacks well-developed reefs. Wangore bay, 7½ miles northward, is a deep anchorage and well sheltered in the north-west monsoon season by the 600–700 ft. rim which surrounds the great crater lake of Dakataua. The shores of Wangore bay rise steeply to the crater rim. The northern coast of the Willaumez peninsula has similar characteristics. The crater rim is less than 500 ft. high west of the rocky cape Hollmann.

The Vitu islands, lying 40 miles north-west of cape Hollmann, are volcanic islands with an incomplete coral capping. Garove (Fig. 23) and Unea are the main islands. Garove is the broken rim of an old crater and is shaped like a horse-shoe. John Albert harbour, the cliffed crater, is too deep for anchorage to be feasible. The entrance is deep and reef-faced. Vessels may tie up to the cliffs or lie off the few flats which have sandy beaches. Balangori bay, inside the western cape at the entrance, is most frequently used by ships. Broad fringing reefs or rocky shelves follow the coast to Peter harbour which, behind its protecting off-shore reefs, is the best harbour on Garove. Depths of 30 to 100 ft. are found here, and the land rises steeply from the shore, especially round the inner harbour. Here there is a small flat with a jetty serving the plantation on the north side of the harbour. The north shore of Garove has a narrow fringing reef, except at Tortoiseshell bay where there is a narrow, steep, black sand beach. From Senta bay to Widu harbour the coast is rocky. Lava cape is cliffed and has a reef running out from it. There are black sand beaches between this point and the West Entrance cape of John Albert harbour.

The circular island of Unea lies 20 miles south-west of Garove.

It is about 4 miles in diameter. A curved ridge runs parallel to the west coast and carries the peaks Penata (500 ft.) and Monoto (475 ft.). To eastward lies a planted lowland a mile wide which runs across the island from north to south. This is Bali plantation which is served by a mile of tramway running southward to the jetty at Bali harbour on the south-west coast. This is the only alienated land on Unea. The difference between the social situation here and on Garove with its widespread plantations is discussed on p. 147. To the east of Bali plantation the land rises rapidly to the central peak of mount Kumbu (1,936 ft.) and to other more easterly peaks. Dense forests clothe the slopes except where native gardens are planted. The villages lie mainly between 200 and 600 ft., usually with their gardens up-slope. Unea is completely encircled by a fringing reef which on the south-west is up to 1,600 yd. wide. There are cliffs on the east and west, and on the south coast except round Bali, where there is a deep and partly sheltered harbour. On the north-west coast lie Tambaram and Papua bays, the latter backed by swamps. Makari mission, which has a short jetty, lies west of the swamp at the head of the bay. The hilly island of Mundua lies 4½ miles north-west of Garove. Several smaller islands and reefs lie west of it. Mundua itself has reefs all round the coast; these are especially wide off the north and south sides of the island.

The west coast of Willaumez peninsula runs from cape Monts to Riebeck bay and is deeply indented and steep, especially off mount Bangum on the north side of this bay. There are no useful anchorages and the whole coast is exposed to the full force of the north-west monsoon. The head of Riebeck bay is wholly fringed with mangrove swamps, developed largely on the mud flats of the Sulu delta. Off-shore reefs fringe the north-west and north-east shores of the bay on both sides of the delta. Eleanora bay, with an irregular reef-bordered coast, lies between Riebeck bay and Rudiger point. The Kapuluk river flows into its head east of Linga Linga plantation. The bays between Eleanora bay and Rein bay are shallow and full of reefs and small low-lying islands. There is much swamp land along this low-lying coast, especially around and between the Molo and Via river outlets, 4 to 10 miles south-west of Rudiger point. West of Rein bay the coast is again hilly and densely timbered. Fringing reefs are wide and there are some sandy beaches. Inland the land slopes steadily up to volcanoes such as mount Andewa (about 3,200 ft. high), south of cape Raoult. Between Rein bay and cape Raoult the coastal area slopes fairly gently into the sea, and there are large

Plate 17. An auxiliary vessel leaving Möwe harbour

The view is taken from the New Britain shore and shows part of the line of three steeply ridged islands which protects the harbour.

Plate 18. A native village, Aromot island

This small well-wooded island is part of the Siassi group which lies between New Britain and the Huon peninsula.

Plate 19. Cape Gloucester, New Britain

Reefs are not well developed off this coast. Kunai grasslands are common and there
are coastal and riverine strips of forest.

Plate 20. Gasmata, New Britain

Coral patches are common both in the inner reaches of the harbour, shown here,
and between the islands which form the seaward fringe.

stretches of kunai grass. East of the head of Rottock bay lie the mud flats of the lower Tamo river.

From cape Raoult to cape Gauffre narrow fringing reefs flank the coast, widening around the points of land which jut out from the head of Rottock bay. The coast plain is very restricted here and the rivers flow down deep gullies from the steep mountains. Borgen bay is partly free of reef and has 2 miles of sandy beach at its head. The coastal flat here is only 150 yd. to a mile wide and rises inland to rugged hills. Detached coral patches lie between Borgen bay and cape Gauffre, which is extensively reefed and surrounded by coral which runs northward for 2 miles in a broad belt. The coast is swampy for a mile on either side of the cape. Between Borgen bay and cape Gloucester reefs are infrequent and there are several coast flats fronted by sandy beaches. The land is undulating up to the great 6,600 ft. cone of mount Talawe, and within the main belt of forest kunai patches are common. Grasslands are frequent behind cape Gloucester (Plate 19) where there are good landing beaches. Casuarina groves line sections of this coast.

From cape Gloucester to cape Büsching the west coast of New Britain rises steeply and regularly from Dampier strait. Numerous short streams drain radially from the mount Talawe-mount Tangi volcanic axis. The forest cover is generally dense but tends to thin out on the rolling slopes of the volcanoes. For the first $1\frac{1}{2}$ miles west of cape Gloucester the coast line is very regular and most of the shore lacks a fringing reef. Shingle and black sandy beaches are a feature of this west coast though they tend to be narrow around the slight projections. The fringing reef reappears as a narrow belt around the coast west of mount Talawe. It is absent at Grass point, which lies west of mount Tangi and is the most westerly point in New Britain. There are negro heads (black coral masses) in the beach at Gimo, half-way down the coast. There are deep-water channels between the detached coral reefs of Dampier strait and the shore. The coasts which lie off mount Tangi are partly cliffed and expose to the sea red soil eroded from volcanic rock for heights of 50 to 100 ft. West of cape Bach, where the coastal lowland begins to spread out towards cape Büsching, there are extensive mangrove swamps backed by the red soils of the undulating interior. A track runs close to the shore right round this western part of New Britain.

The islands which lie off western New Britain in Dampier strait are Umboi (Rooke island), the Siassi islands, Tolokiwa, Sakar and Ritter. Umboi lies 14 miles west of Grass point and 30 miles north-east of Scharnhorst point in New Guinea. It is about 27 miles from north-west to south-east and its greatest breadth is 16 miles. The island is volcanic and has several isolated cones with a maximum height of approximately 4,500 ft. just east of the centre of the island. The coasts are mainly steep and the volcanic slopes are trenched by deep radial valleys. There are lakes in two of the extinct craters but the interior as a whole is little known. The east of the island has a narrow coastal lowland, the south-east is swampy, especially around Marien harbour, and the south-west coast is fairly low for a short distance inland. The island is densely forested, although some grass stretches are found on the northern and southern slopes of the island. The whole coast is reefed and coral may extend over 400 yd. off-shore. There is relatively little coastal settlement; the one mission and the villages lie a few miles up the main streams or on the lower mountain slopes.

The Siassi islands are a well-peopled group of small wooded islands, lying south of Umboi and separated from it by a maze of reefs. The main island, Tuam, lies 10 miles south of Umboi. It is about 1½ miles long from north-west to south-east and rises to 100 ft. Tolokiwa, 16 miles north-east of cape King in Umboi, is a circular volcanic cone 5 miles in diameter. Deep water lies off-shore, and the coast has narrow flats covered like the remainder of the island, with dense forest. There is a broad fringing reef which extends from ½ to 1 mile off the west and south-west coasts. Ritter island is a volcanic remnant lying between Umboi and Sakar, 5 miles to northward. It is 350 ft. high and uninhabited. Sakar lies 16 miles north-west of Dorf point in New Britain. It is a high volcanic island and rises steeply and regularly to the central crater. This is 3,275 ft. high and is occupied by a lake. The island is about 4 miles in diameter and much of the north coast is free of forest. Alaro on the west coast is the main settlement. There is a broad fringing reef with anchorages in the coves for small schooners. Many short streams with dense forest in their deep gullies drain outwards from the central peak.

THE MAIN NAVIGABLE RIVERS OF NEW GUINEA

A number of the larger rivers of New Guinea are navigable for considerable distances from their mouths. They are specially important as means of communication owing to the dense swampy forests of the lowlands, which make land communication very difficult or almost impossible in many areas. The most important of the navigable rivers are the Fly, in western Papua, and the Sepik and Ramu, in north-east New Guinea.

THE FLY RIVER

The Fly river was first ascended by the Italian explorer D'Albertis in 1876. D'Albertis used a steam launch and continued up the Palmer river beyond its confluence with the Fly. He reached a point 500 miles from the Fly estuary. The foothills below the source of the main stream were reached by Dr. (later Sir) William MacGregor, then Governor of British New Guinea, in 1890. Recent surveys of the headstreams of the Fly have been made largely from the air.

The Fly river is navigable for vessels drawing less than 8 ft. for nearly 500 miles during the whole of the year. It is tidal for a distance of about 150 miles from its mouth. At the entrance to the estuary the river is 33 miles wide, and at the inner (north-western) end of Kiwai, the largest of the fertile islands in the estuary, it is 7 miles wide. Large sandbanks are constantly forming in the mouths of the river, especially during the south-east trade season. Navigation of the lower river is very difficult during the 3 days before and after the full moon as the tides are constricted in the narrow funnel of the estuary and pass upstream in the form of a bore, which is dangerous to moored craft in the south-east trade season. Along the lower course and well above the tidal limit are wide stretches of mangrove swamps and flooded forests. The Fly river transports vast loads of alluvium and its silt is carried southwards along the coast past Daru.

The river falls only 60 ft. in the last 512 miles of its course. The lower course of the Fly river winds for over 600 miles from its mouth in a tortuous course across the huge flat alluvial plain of the Western Division of Papua. Its banks are fringed with dense tropical jungle; the only break in their monotony occurs in the mid-Fly area around Everill junction, where the jungle is replaced by vast areas of swampy grasslands intersected by numerous small lagoons and lakes of which lake Murray is most notable. At 120 miles above the junction with the Strickland, the river winds and curves through grass country which gradually becomes higher and ribbed with low ridges as the foothills are approached. Coconut trees have been observed up to 410 miles inland.

The river floods are an impediment to navigation, for the water can rise more than 30 ft. Floods are most frequent during the period from October to April, and individual floods last from 2 to 14 days. In the country around the Fly and Palmer rivers immediately south of the foothills, much of the terrain is too wet to allow forests to develop.

Above the junction with the Palmer, the Fly becomes faster and shallower. Here begins a gradual ascent from the swamp plains towards mount Austen and the Hindenburg range. Fifteen miles above Palmer junction, the river bed is 250 ft. above sea level. Further north the country rises rapidly among limestone ridges running mainly from east to west. The river cuts through each transverse range by means of a gorge. That through the Williams range is over 1,000 ft. deep, and only 200 yd. across at the top. North of the Williams range two headstreams of the Fly flow parallel to the range at the foot of its steep northern slope. On the north side this transverse valley is bounded by the precipitous southern slopes of the Melokin range, and the ascent of this line reveals a further parallel valley between it and the very steep Hindenburg range. The five main headstreams of the Fly river proper flow from its slopes into the valley which runs across the southern ends of the outlying spurs. The Hindenburg divide between the Fly and Upper Sepik is often as little as a mile wide.

THE SEPIK RIVER

The Sepik was first studied in 1886 by Schleinitz, who reached Malu, 250 miles upstream. In 1887 the river was ascended for 380 miles and in 1910 for 520 miles. On the latter occasion Malay canoes were used on the upper reaches. In 1914 a vessel of 50 tons reached a point 450 miles from the mouth. The headwaters were discovered by Thurnwald in 1914. For a few years immediately preceding the Japanese invasion the Sepik basin was under administrative control as far as Yesan, 270 miles from the coast.

The mouth of the Sepik is about a mile wide and is bordered by sandbanks. River alluvium is carried well out to sea—as far as the islands of Kadovar and Bam. There is no tidal bore. The course may be navigated for 300 miles by vessels drawing 13 ft., and the river bed rises only 26 ft. in this distance. Above this the river widens to form a long narrow lake approximately 9 ft. deep. Seasonal differences of 20 ft. may be recorded in the level of the lower river, and habitations are not common along its banks in the middle and lower basin. In the lower course floating masses of logs and vegetation may form considerable islands. These are carried into midstream from the backwaters but eventually break up there or in the breakers at the deep river mouth. Round the meanders near the mouth, and for

Plate 21. The Kemp Welch river

This river rises in the Owen Stanley range and flows southward through dense forest to Hood bay.

Plate 22. The Strickland river

The Strickland is the main tributary of the Fly and, like it, flows through extensive and deep alluvial deposits.

Plate 23. Tropical rain forest, Dutch New Guinea
This view was taken between Lomira and lake Kamakawallar.

about 6 miles upstream, there are swamps and many casuarina trees. From this point, for about 170 miles, the black, alluvial plains carry a covering of high grass. For the first 60 or 70 miles the grass is interspersed with bulrushes. Forest occurs in isolated patches. Beyond the grassland plains, the forest gradually becomes denser over a stretch of 20 miles, until it closes in upon the river and lines its banks. From this point, the river is bordered by forest for about 100 miles. Cut-off meanders are numerous on this reach of the river, specially east and west of Ambunti, where the river cuts through the northern periphery of the Hunstein range.

Beyond a point about 300 miles from the mouth, swampy forest increases, and the river carries much floating timber which obstructs navigation. It retains this character for about 250 miles, over which distance there is a rise in the river bed of about 180 ft. The rise is greatest in the upper 30 to 40 miles, where there are many rapids. This section and the lower course of the river have a general trend from west to east, but the upper course trends from south-east to north-west. The river is diverted eastwards by the Papoea mountains.

A comparatively straight section follows from 8 miles below the junction of the Hollander with the Sepik to the Hoffnung confluence. Here, for 18 miles, the Sepik is relatively straight and the river bed wider, so that gravel beds are exposed in the drier months. Here there are still sago swamps and young forest growth appears on the banks. Between the Hollander and Hoffnung rivers, at Mountain Gate, the river breaks through a low barrier, and there are rapids with a fall of about 6 ft. This may denote a recent fault. For 5 miles above and below this barrier the trees have been overwhelmed by floods and the forests have much decayed timber. The forest disappears as a continuous cover as the river valley leads into the foothills. The mountains close in on it at the Zweifel gorge where the bed is 500 ft. above sea level. Navigation here and above the gorge is hampered by the great speed of the river. The average fall of the stream is 4 in. in 100 ft. Whirlpools are frequent and the active erosion of the river banks tends to cause landslides. Gravel beds are common in the stream's course.

The upland section of the Sepik river, above the Zweifel gorge, is a good deal longer than that of the Fly river. The Sepik is flowing against the south-western flank of the Thurnwald range and is hemmed in by a less continuous range on the south. Before the valley reaches the gathering ground of its headstreams—i.e., in the straight section west of the Thurnwald range and more southerly Donner mountains—the river is deeply entrenched among jungle-covered hills which slope upwards more or less uniformly to 7,000 ft. There has been little clearing of the jungle and the upper part of this section is practically unpopulated.

The uppermost basin is dominated not by jungle but by wide grasslands. In contrast to the last section, the valley is relatively open and only lightly etched into the plateau. This falls in terraces to the main river and its headstreams. The milder relief has its response in the greater intensity of agriculture and in a fairly dense population. The alluvial cover of the terraces provides sites for gardens; at greater elevations the plateau soil is thin and supports grass. The most easterly headstream of the Sepik, the Takin, has its source between the south-west end of the Victor Emanuel range and the 11,000-ft. mount Effel. At heights of over 4,000 ft. its terraced valley is well peopled. The source is 700 miles from the Sepik mouth.

THE RAMU RIVER

The Ramu is shorter than either the Fly or the Sepik; it is more difficult to enter and is easily navigable by launches for only a short distance upstream. In 1923 E. R. Stanley ascended the river for 199 miles, but in many places navigation was difficult. Stanley found that the river was 220 yd. wide 2 miles from the mouth. It did not begin to narrow till a point more than 100 miles upstream had been reached. Then, at a series of rapids, its width decreased to 70 yd. The maximum width of the river was 400 yd., and the average over the distance covered 234 yd.

The general trend of the Ramu, after its headstream from the east end of the Purari plateau flows into the main valley, is first from south-west to north-east, between the Bismarck range and the mountains which prolong the Finisterre range round Astrolabe bay. In this section there are many parallel east-bank tributaries which flow from east-north-east to west-south-west. The watershed with the Markham river is only about 1,350 ft. high, and at Dumpu (due south of Madang, across the mountains) the river bed is at about 1,000 ft. The lower course trends generally from south to north, but in detail there are many changes of direction and the last 200 miles to the sea has a long series of meanders. The river mouth is fairly narrow and tidal influences do not extend more than a mile inland. The main tributary is the Japon (Ramuta) river, which joins the Ramu east of the Keram hills and 114 miles from its estuary. The course of the Japon coincides with that of the lower south-east to north-west section of the main stream. Upstream from the Japon-Ramu confluence, at the south end of the Keram hills, there is a great meander; and in the flood season the Ramu waters overflow north-westward into the Keram (Töpfer), a tributary of the Sepik.

The whole lower course of the Ramu is subject to floods and changes in the stream bed, so that villages are built on knolls above the sago and bamboo swamps. These are a feature of the lower alluvial lands. The soil on the knolls is of considerable fertility, but along the river the marginal sands and flood gravels support only pandanus and pampas grass. Stanley's party noted that the first riverside village was 104 miles upstream. Richer ferruginous loams cover the banks further upstream, and between 100-Mile island and Atemble the flood plain begins to rise very gradually and increases in width and fertility. Atemble lies well below the mountain-girt upper valley. Here sago swamps persist, mainly where creeks and tributaries join the main stream.

BIBLIOGRAPHICAL NOTE

The most detailed information on the coasts and navigable rivers of New Guinea is contained in recent official reports, which are not generally available. The fullest published accounts of the coasts are in the Admiralty *Pacific Islands Pilot*, vol. i (6th ed., London, 1933; with supplement, 1944); and the United States Hydrographic Office *Sailing Directions for the Pacific Islands*, vol. ii (Washington, 1940; with supplement, 1942). An account of the Fly and Sepik rivers is given in C. H. Karius, 'Exploration in the Interior of Papua and North-East New Guinea: The Sources of the Fly, Palmer, Strickland and Sepik Rivers', *Geographical Journal*, vol. LXXIV, pp. 305–22 (London, 1929). The Sepik basin is discussed by W. Behrmann, *Im Stromgebiet des Sepik* (Berlin, 1922); some details of the lower Ramu basin and of the area between it and the Sepik are included. The exploration of the lower Ramu river is described in E. R. Stanley, 'The Ramu River', *Report to the League of Nations on the Administration of the Territory of New Guinea* for 1921–2, pp. 77–83 (Melbourne, 1923).

For maps see Appendix I.

Chapter IV

CLIMATE

The climate of the New Guinea area, like that of the East Indies, is transitional in character. In the Ninigo and Admiralty groups, lying in lat. 1° to 3° S, conditions are equatorial; but south-east Papua possesses a climate resembling that of the neighbouring coasts of northern Queensland. As in the surrounding regions, there is a seasonal change in the direction of the winds. Seasonal variations in temperature are everywhere negligible, and diurnal ranges are greater than those between monthly means. Seasons are distinguished primarily by the changes in the winds and by the resultant variations in rainfall. From May to October, prevailing winds are south-easterly; from December to March they are from the north-west. They are nearly always light or moderate; gales (apart from occasional squalls) are almost unknown. The temperature averages about 80° F. throughout the year; it is usually damp heat. Visibility at sea is invariably good except during rain. Overcast skies occur on perhaps 5 days a month during the least cloudy months, as compared with about 10 days on the south coast of England. Much rain, as judged by English standards, falls in all months. It is heaviest from November to March in localities exposed to the north-west monsoon, and from May to September at stations exposed to the south-east trade and backed by high ground.

PRESSURE AND WINDS

During the southern winter, New Guinea, a large land mass in low latitudes, records the lowest average barometric figure (1006 mb.) of any island in the tropical Pacific. The island lies within a low pressure system which extends over the north of Australia and the southern East Indies and attracts the outflowing monsoons of south-east Asia. These winds change direction in passing the equator and reach New Guinea as the north-west monsoon. Although still low in comparison with other parts of the Pacific, New Guinea and the Bismarck archipelago have their highest pressures in July when the whole area is under the influence of the south-east trades. May and November, at the change of seasons, are months when doldrum conditions with considerable atmospheric instability are characteristic. Seasonal barometric variations are nowhere great and it has been estimated that, in the mandated territory, 1008·5 mb. is the mean and 3·5 mb. the extent of the variation from it. The following monthly figures (+ 1000 mb.) show the averages recorded at Kokopo during the period 1902–12:

J	F	M	A	M	J	J	A	S	O	N	D	Year	Variation
7·5	7·5	7·4	8·2	9·0	9·3	9·0	9·3	9·3	9·3	8·2	7·5	8·2	1·9

Barometer readings are commonly relatively high at 0900 hr.; they fall to a minimum at 1600 hr., rise to a second peak at 2200 hr., and fall to an early morning minimum at 0400 hr.

Barometric and most other readings are not yet available for more than a few years for stations well inland in New Guinea, but it may be noted that as much of the interior consists of high mountains, decreased barometric pressure and a more rarified atmosphere will be found there. Some indication is given by the experience of aviators; it has been estimated that the length of runways must be increased above that needed at sea level by 15% at 2,000 ft., by 25% at 3,000 ft., and by 50% at 5,000 ft.

Papua and the mandated territory are outside the typhoon and hurricane belts and gales are very rare at ground level. Winds greater than 35 m.p.h. (force 7 on the Beaufort scale) have not yet been recorded at sea level in the mandated territory, although on 28 August 1939 a wind of 60 m.p.h. (force 11) was registered at 18,000 ft. by pilot balloons above Rabaul. Squalls are fairly common, especially during the less steady north-west monsoon half-year (December–May), and in May and November over-turning of large masses of unstable air produces afternoon thunderstorms. Fig. 26 shows in diagrammatic form, wind directions, constancy and force in the region. Except where indicated, the percentages refer to winds of 1–12 m.p.h. (Beaufort force 0–3). It should be noted that most of the New Guinea land mass and the greater part of New Britain lie south of 5° s, the median line for each small diagram. Fig. 26 shows the south-east trades predominating from May to November, the north-west monsoon, dominant for the remaining months, the gradual displacement of one wind system by the other and considerable variation in wind direction at the change of seasons. The greater constancy of the south-east trade is noticeable, especially in the

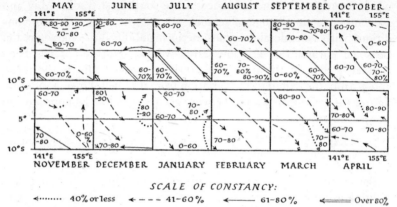

SCALE OF CONSTANCY:

◄·········· 40% or less   ◄ ─ ─ ─ 41–60%   ◄─────── 61–80%   ◄════ Over 80%

Fig. 26. Direction, force and relative constancy of average surface wind drift

Each rectangle covers the area occupied by New Guinea and the Bismarck archipelago. The months are arranged in two series. The upper group includes the
months in which the south-east trades, and the lower, the months in which the
north-west monsoon winds are dominant. April and November, at the change of
seasons, have winds from both directions. When the symbol % is added, the figure
refers to winds of Beaufort force 4 or higher. Other figures refer to winds of force
3 or less. The south-east trades stand out as the strongest and most constant winds.
Based on U.S. Hydrographic Office, 'Climatic Features of the Pacific Islands
Region', *Naval Air Pilot*, no. 184, charts 3–14, pp. 11–16.

months of June–September. While winds of 13–18 m.p.h. (force 4),
or over, occur over New Guinea and New Britain in each of the
months May to October, only winds of 1–12 m.p.h. (force 0–3) are
experienced during the season of the north-west monsoon.

The south-east trades begin to blow over Papua and the south of
the mandated territory in mid-April and the area affected gradually
increases, as does the wind force, until in July the whole area is swept
by them. In August as much as 80% may be winds of 13–18 m.p.h.
(force 4). Fig. 26 records conditions at coastal stations. Greater
velocities (20 to 35 m.p.h.—force 5–7) are recorded between approximately 1,500 and 2,000 ft. Wind force then decreases until the south-
east trades cease to be felt at about 7,500 ft. The south-east trade is
more intermittent north of 5° s, for example, in the Admiralty group
and the New Guinea coast north of the mouth of the Sepik. On the
other hand, just south of 5° s, in the Bismarck archipelago, the trade
wind may blow steadily and strongly for a fortnight without a break.
Locally, as in Dampier and Vitiaz straits, between New Britain and
New Guinea, and in St George's channel, between New Britain and
New Ireland, the south-east trade may be deflected by the configura-

tion of the coasts to become a more southerly wind. Kokopo, standing on an embayment in the Gazelle peninsula coast on the west side of St George's channel, shows a fair proportion of south winds during the months May to November, although, as is shown by the following Table, the larger percentage of south winds recorded there come during the season of the more intermittent north-west monsoon.

Percentage Frequency of Wind Directions at Kokopo, 1902–5

	N	NE	E	SE	S	SW	W	NW	Calm
J	4	3	1	8	35	9	5	30	4
F	2	2	1	3	20	8	11	41	14
M	4	5	1	5	36	13	4	22	10
A	1	3	1	8	23	12	1	40	9
M	2	2	3	54	22	3	0	8	5
J	0	1	2	78	11	1	0	1	6
J	0	2	2	81	8	1	0	0	5
A	1	1	2	74	13	2	0	1	4
S	1	2	3	76	10	3	0	0	3
O	2	5	1	67	13	5	0	4	5
N	1	4	1	64	13	5	0	5	7
D	3	3	4	31	19	7	2	20	11

Source: C. Braak, 'Klimakunde von Hinterindien und Insulinde', *Handbuch der Klimatologie*, Band IV, Teil R, p. 112 (Berlin, 1931).

This station lies in latitude 4° 20′ s and towards the eastern margins of the area included on Fig. 26 in a region where winds with a southerly component are dominant for the greater part of the year.

The north-west monsoon blows to heights of over 12,000 ft. as against 7,500 ft. for the south-east trade. It frequently brings alternating calms and violent squalls which may last for three hours, though they are usually much shorter. January shows the greatest monthly total for most north-coast stations. The highest wind velocities recorded in New Guinea occur during the Papuan *guba*, a severe squall which develops either late at night or early in the morning during this season. It approaches from the north-west and brings heavy rain to the narrow belt of land along its course. In an average year the *guba* occurs five or six times.

At coastal stations in New Guinea, New Britain and New Ireland, land and sea breezes may be dominant for several consecutive days during the north-west monsoon season. This should be taken into account in an analysis of wind direction records for a station such as Kokopo. The five or six weeks during April and May and during November and December, which witness the seasonal change of winds, are also periods in which the juxtaposition of air masses over land and sea may locally control the movement of air and produce winds of up to 15 m.p.h.

Along the coasts of New Guinea, New Britain, New Ireland and Manus, land and sea breezes may at times be dominant from 10 miles out to sea to a short distance inland, and up to 1,500 ft. They rarely blow at more than 10–15 m.p.h. (force 3–4). Damper air tends to blow in from the sea from mid-morning to sunset, and cooler air to flow seawards during the night. Land breezes are usually of slight strength and normally both they and the normal monsoon or trade winds die down between sunset and sunrise, specially on clear nights. The strength of surface winds is normally greatest in the early afternoon and least in the hours before dawn. The following units of the Beaufort scale for Kokopo illustrate this:

Daily Variations in Wind Strength at Kokopo, 1902–5

Hr.	J	F	M	A	M	J	J	A	S	O	N	D
0700	1·2	1·3	1·1	1·9	1·7	2·0	2·0	2·1	1·8	1·5	1·5	1·2
1300–1400	3·7	3·8	3·4	3·5	4·0	3·8	4·1	4·1	3·7	3·5	3·2	3·0
1900–2100	1·4	1·6	1·4	1·5	2·2	2·6	2·6	3·0	2·2	2·1	2·1	1·3

Katabatic (gravity) winds may blow locally down steep mountain slopes. They are often recorded along the faulted foothills which fringe the Markham valley, in interior valleys which fringe the main cordillera of New Guinea, and near the volcanic arc of northern New Britain. Unless they have been strengthened by the normal seasonal wind, gravity winds have slight force.

TEMPERATURE

At sea level in New Guinea and the Bismarck archipelago maximum temperatures are rarely above 95° F. and minimum temperatures seldom below 70° F., though 97° F. and 64° F. have been recorded at Port Moresby on 31 December 1926 and 11 June 1923 respectively, and 60° F. has been recorded several times at Buna. Mean maxima are about 88° F. and mean minima about 75° F., giving an average of 82° F. for coastal stations:

Station	Mean Maximum (° F.)	Mean Minimum (° F.)
Port Moresby	86	75
Samarai	88	75
Daru	85	75
Kikori	87	72
Cape Nelson	86	75
Madang	88	75
Kokoda	88	68

It will be noted that Kokoda, the only interior station, has the greatest range.

While, as elsewhere, the thermometer falls about 3° F. for every 1,000 ft., seasonal temperature variations are still small at high altitudes, as is shown on Fig. 27. On the highest mountains tempera-

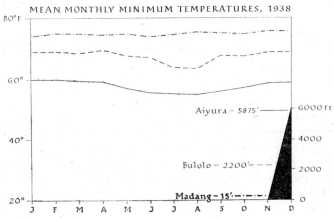

Fig. 27. Mean monthly minimum temperatures for Aiyura, Bulolo and Madang, 1938

Whilst the temperature regimes show little seasonal variation there is a distinct decrease of temperature as the altitude increases. Based on statistics in B. G. Challis, 'Climatic Notes on New Guinea', *New Guinea Agricultural Gazette*, vol. v, no. 3, pp. 19–23 (Canberra, 1939).

tures often fall below freezing point. Sharp frost has been experienced on mount Keluwere and snow is frequently reported on the peaks of the main cordillera. As yet, large expanses of perpetual snow have not been reported in eastern New Guinea, and there is nothing comparable to the snowfields which cap the higher Nassau range of Dutch New Guinea. Diurnal variations are larger in the south-east trade season; the highest figures are usually recorded then—e.g., a range of 22·3° F. at Hatzfeldt harbour in August, and of 15·8° F. in

October at Kokopo. Monthly variations at these stations are much smaller:

	J	F	M	A	M	J	J	A	S	O	N	D	Year	Range
Hatzfeldt harbour: (1886–9)	80	80·5	79·7	79·9	80		77·9	78·1	79·4	80·2	80·6	80·1	80·1	79·9	2·7° F.
Kokopo: (1902–12)	79	78·7	78·7	79·2	79·3	78·7	78·1	78·1	78·7	79·2	79·2	79·3	78·8	1·2° F.

Source: C. Braak, 'Klimakunde von Hinterindien und Insulinde', *Handbuch der Klimatologie*, Band IV, Teil R, p. 108 (Berlin, 1931).

At stations nearer the equator, such as Kavieng in New Ireland (2° 30′ s) and Lorengau in Manus (2° 02′ s), the annual range is similar, though temperatures are slightly higher, varying from 80° F. in the trade wind season to 82° F. in the period of the north-west monsoon.

HUMIDITY

Humidity is very high at all seasons throughout New Guinea, New Britain and their off-lying islands. The mean relative humidity for twenty Papuan stations is 80·5%, but Kikori, at the head of the Gulf of Papua, and Orangerie bay station, on an exposed coast, each register 89%. It has been noted that the south-east trade winds extend up to approximately 7,500 ft. as against about 12,000 ft. in the case of the north-west monsoon. Very low humidity percentages have been recorded at 2,723 ft. on the Sattelberg, when dry air from above the trade wind limits falls at night to the level of the station. On the night of 6–7 September 1912, the relative humidity at the mission station at 2100 hr. was 41% and at 0600 hr. 28%. Sir William MacGregor noted the dryness of the air above the afternoon cloud belt during his crossing of the Owen Stanley range which was made in the trade wind season. Throughout the area percentages vary between 75 and 95, although few stations register the consistently high figures of Kikori. Relative humidity figures for Buna and Rigo have on occasion dropped to 71% and 69%. Seasonal differences are slight, though it has been suggested that as a general rule the air is drier in the south-east trade season. The averages for the mandated territory are 81% at 0900 hr., 75% at 1500 hr., and 88% at 2100 hr. Exceptions to this generalization are coasts which face south-east. Limited records suggest that within the forest belts, which are altitudinally zoned on the slopes of the New Guinea mountains, certain variations in humidity may in future be more fully recognized. In lowland swamp forests and jungle and in the rain forests which may extend upwards to about 7,500 ft., the free movement of air is checked and

relative humidity is higher than it is either in savannah or in partly
cleared forest, or on wide exposures of pure limestone where edaphic
controls preclude the growth of tall trees and dense undergrowth,
or in grass-covered expanses of the higher mountains and plateaux
which lie above the tree limit. The widest contrasts in humidity are
to be expected between the enclosed upland valleys of the central
cordillera of New Guinea and the saturated moss forests (where there
is a continuous dripping of moisture), which lie above the rain forests.

Relative humidity figures for the morning hours are almost always
greater than those for the afternoon, and the lowest percentages seem
to occur between noon and 1500 hr. Yearly averages for 1912–13 at
the mission station on the Sattelberg (2,723 ft.) and at Finschhafen
(sea level) show this, together with the greater evening humidity:

	0600 hr.	*1400 hr.*	*2100 hr.*
Sattelberg:	91	89	92 %

	0700 hr.	*1400 hr.*	*2100 hr.*
Finschhafen:	88	75	89 %

Sattelberg faces south-east, and in the period July–September its
averages are 4% higher for each of the hours quoted above. At a
series of more widely separated stations the mean morning and
afternoon figures are:

Average Relative Humidity (%)

Station	0900 hr.	1500 hr.
Madang	84	76
Port Moresby	75	74
Rabaul	76	72
Salamaua	84	75

Readings taken at 1400 hr. tend to show greater falls in humidity
from the monthly means. For 1902–5 the figures at Kokopo were:

	J	F	M	A	M	J	J	A	S	O	N	D
Monthly means (%)	84	85	83	84	82	82	82	81	80	79	79	84
Means of readings at 1400 hr. (%)	74	77	75	76	71	72	72	72	70	68	72	75

(Note the drier south-east trade season of this northward-facing station.)

In a single year considerable variations may be recorded both
from these annual means, and month by month. In 1938 the percentages for Kavieng (2° 30′ s), Madang (5° 75′ s) and Lorengau (2° 02′ s)
were:

Station	J	F	M	A	M	J	J	A	S	O	N	D	Average	Maximum
Kavieng (10 ft.)														
0900 hr.	91	91	91	91	95	91	91	87	91	91	87	87	90	95
1500 hr.	87	83	87	91	91	87	91	88	92	92	87	87	89	92
Madang (15 ft.)														
0900 hr.	83	95	87	83	83	91	95	91	91	91	91	91	89	95
1500 hr.	72	79	75	75	75	75	75	75	79	79	79	83	77	83
Lorengau (20 ft.)														
0900 hr.	87	87	87	87	83	86	91	95	91	91	83	91	88	95
1500 hr.	76	83	76	76	69	72	69	80	88	92	83	91	80	92

Source: B. G. Challis, 'Climatic Notes on New Guinea', *New Guinea Agricultural Gazette*, vol. v, no. 3, pp. 21–4 (Canberra, 1939).

It will be noted that in the months July–December at Kavieng, and October–December at Lorengau, afternoon figures are equal to or higher than those of 2100 hr. This afternoon accumulation of moisture may be related to their more nearly equatorial position as compared with Madang.

CLOUD COVER

Inland and at most leeward coast stations the clearest skies are to be seen in the early morning. High cirrus may then be the only cloud-type recorded. By 0900–1000 hr. cumulus clouds begin to accumulate and during the afternoon may cover the greater part of the sky or frequently be replaced by thunder clouds. Over coasts towards which the wind is blowing it is more usual for the early morning to be cloudy. The following figures, while omitting the earliest morning observations, give some suggestion of increase in cloud cover as the day advances.

Daily Variations in Cloud Cover at Kokopo, 1902–05
(tenths of sky covered)

Hr.	J	F	M	A	M	J	J	A	S	O	N	D
0700	5·7	8·0	5·9	5·5	5·2	6·5	6·6	6·3	5·8	5·2	5·3	6·2
1300–1400	6·3	8·2	6·3	6·2	5·4	6·4	6·6	6·5	6·2	6·1	6·4	6·7
1900–2100	7·2	7·6	7·1	6·5	5·6	6·3	7·1	6·7	6·4	6·4	6·4	6·9

Source: C. Braak, 'Klimakunde von Hinterindien und Insulinde', *Handbuch der Klimatologie*, Band IV, Teil R, p. 117 (Berlin, 1931).

It is rare for the sky to be completely overcast by low-level clouds throughout the day except at such very humid centres as Kikori. During the north-west monsoon season overcast skies commonly result from the accumulation of middle-level clouds.

A provisional survey of the area in January, as representing north-west monsoon conditions and in July, a characteristic south-east trade month, suggests that in January the grading is on the average from 7-tenths to 8-tenths on the north and east coasts of New Guinea to 9-tenths in the interior highlands and in the basin of the Kikori river. A narrow coastal belt south of the Fly river delta and across the Gulf of Papua southward from the Lakekamu outlet has less than 7-tenths of the sky cloud-covered. The north coast of New Britain and the Kavieng district of New Ireland has 7-tenths to 8-tenths covered, and the south coast of New Britain and remainder of New Ireland 6-tenths to 7-tenths. The Papuan areas which in January registered less than 7-tenths record 4-tenths to 5-tenths in July. The north coast of the Gulf of Papua has 5-tenths to 7-tenths; but inland the cloud cover soon reaches 7-tenths to 8-tenths, the figure for the Owen Stanley range, the remainder of the main cordillera and the mountains of the Huon peninsula. A narrow strip of the north coast of New Guinea, eastwards to approximately 145° E, has 5-tenths to 6-tenths as has northern New Britain and the north-west half of New Ireland. Southern New Britain and the rest of New Ireland have rather more than 6-tenths of the sky cloud-covered, and a broad belt down the east side of New Guinea from the Dutch frontier behind the north coast down to the south-east tip of Papua has 6-tenths to 7-tenths in July.

Seasonal variations in cloud cover are shown in the following Table, which shows least cloud at Hatzfeldt harbour in the trade-wind season, least at Kokopo at the change of seasons, and least at Sattelberg (which receives the full force of the south-east trades), in the north-west monsoon period. The figures represent the means of daily observations made at 0700, 1400, and 2100 hr.

	J	F	M	A	M	J	J	A	S	O	N	D	Year
Hatzfeldt harbour (1886–9)	7·2	8·1	7·4	6·7	5·3	5·1	6·1	5·9	5·6	5·5	6·8	6·8	6·4
Sattelberg summit (1895–8)	7·1	6·5	7·0	7·0	7·6	7·9	7·4	7·7	7·0	6·6	7·2	6·9	7·2
Kokopo (1902–5)	6·4	7·9	6·4	6·0	5·4	6·4	6·8	6·5	6·1	5·9	6·1	6·6	6·4

These are average conditions. The following Table gives a better representation of the occurrence of overcast days per month and of the rarity of clear days, this latter being typical of the whole area. The greater cloudiness of Sattelberg summit, which is almost entirely cloud covered in the afternoon, may be accounted for by its height of 3,182 ft. (as against 213 ft. at Kokopo observatory):

Number of Overcast Days

	J	F	M	A	M	J	J	A	S	O	N	D	Year
Sattelberg summit (1895–8)	9·8	6·5	12·3	12·2	14·0	18·5	13·7	17·7	12·2	9·3	11·7	8·1	146
Kokopo (1902–5)	8·1	16·3	9·1	6·9	3·5	6·6	9·9	9·7	7·1	6·3	6·3	8·1	97

Number of Clear Days

	J	F	M	A	M	J	J	A	S	O	N	D	Year
Sattelberg summit (1895–8)	0·3	0·0	0·2	1·0	0·7	1·0	0·2	0·8	1·2	0·8	0·8	0·2	7
Kokopo (1902–5)	0·3	0·3	0·0	1·0	1·1	0·3	0·5	0·3	1·0	2·3	0·8	0·0	8

Overcast days are those with more than 8-tenths and clear days those with less than 2-tenths of the sky covered.

Thunder-clouds accumulate over the land in mid-afternoon and New Guinea records some of the highest totals for such storms in the Pacific. At the change of seasons thunderstorms are common in the early mornings over the seas off New Guinea and the Bismarck archipelago. The greater frequency of thunderstorms in the north-west monsoon period, a widespread phenomenon, is brought out in the following totals for Sattelberg mission station (for 1912–13) and for Kokopo (averages for the period 1902–5):

Days with Thunder

	J	F	M	A	M	J	J	A	S	O	N	D	Year
Sattelberg mission (2,723 ft.)	15·7	8·4	4·4	7·6	3·9	5·6	0·5	1·5	3·0	1·0	8·6	8·8	66
Kokopo (213 ft.)	7·4	6·2	7·2	6·8	4·2	1·0	3·2	2·7	4·8	5·2	10·1	10·8	70

FOG

Sea fogs are unknown in the New Guinea area. Between about 3,000 and 7,000 ft. mists cover mountain slopes in the early morning and may pass down-slope, reducing visibility on the coastal hills, until they are dissipated, usually well before mid-day. Mountain stations thus record high totals of days with mist. The following figures for Sattelberg mission (2,723 ft.) for 1912–13 illustrate this:

J	F	M	A	M	J	J	A	S	O	N	D	Year
7·9	17·2	10·3	20·3	19·1	19·8	25·0	27·0	23·3	19·1	16·7	13·3	219

In the rainiest months, which vary regionally, visibility is most frequently reduced by heavy rains, although such conditions do not last for many hours. January, July and August have the greatest totals of such storms on the average. The figures for Sattelberg mission show that the greater number of mist days occur during the south-east trade season. At and off the coast in this season a haze may accompany the wind and may infrequently reduce visibility below 5 miles. On the high plateau of the interior smoke hazes are produced locally as a result of the native practice of burning grass in the dry season.

RAINFALL

Regional Variations

Fig. 28 is an attempt to represent a real distribution of rainfall, and

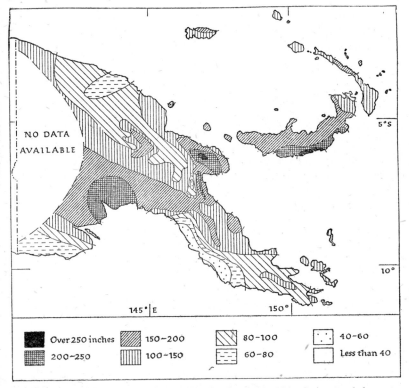

Fig. 28. Provisional map of rainfall distribution in New Guinea and the
Bismarck archipelago
Based on official sources.

for lack of information as to conditions in the interiors of the larger islands is necessarily provisional. Wide valleys parallel to the east coast of New Guinea, such as the middle and upper Ramu and the goldfield valleys, are known to be rain shadow areas. The high enclosed plateaux are also relatively dry, but it is probable that much of the central mountains may have higher falls than are here shown. It has been suggested that exposed slopes at 5,000 ft. may record about 300 in., and that at 6,000 ft. higher totals are likely. Above this level there is probably a diminution in rainfall at the rate of 50 in. for each of the 6,000–7,000 ft. and 7,000–8,000 ft. levels. Heights of 10,000–13,000 ft. have, it is suggested, only about 180 in. This remains to be proved.

Fig. 28 reveals the higher mountains of the Huon peninsula and the swamp plains and foothills behind the head of the Gulf of Papua as the areas of greatest rainfall in New Guinea. Across Dampier strait, southern New Britain (and especially the coast east of Gasmata) are equally wet. That is, the highest totals are recorded on coasts and mountain sides exposed to the steady south-east trades. Areas reputed to have roughly 150–200 in. are the southern slopes of the central highlands of New Guinea (probably too low an estimate) and the Western Division of Papua north of the Fly river delta. This belt traverses New Guinea between the Purari delta and Huon gulf and pushes a long tongue down the main cordillera. Where the northern boundary of Papua comes to the east coast, the Mambare basin and its bounding mountains record 150–200 in. Ioma in this area averages 161 in. Most of New Britain, with the exception of the Gazelle peninsula and the south coast, has similar figures, as has central New Ireland.

The driest area in New Britain is the north-east of the Gazelle peninsula with less than 100 in. of rain. In New Guinea averages may fall well below this figure. The Bulowat goldfields district has the lowest rainfall in the mandated territory—Bulolo (2,200 ft.) has an average of 56 in.; the higher Edie Creek station has 105 in. Much of the 'tail' of Papua has less than 100 in. of rain and the east coast of the Gulf of Papua has a considerable area behind the coast, between Kairuku and Kalo, with less than 60 in. For example, according to one source, Kemp Welch government station has an average rainfall of 56 in. and Kairuku one of 50 in. The lowest figures are recorded at Port Moresby and Rigo. Port Moresby is reported to have an average of 38 in. and Rigo one of 43 in.

Yearly rainfall totals for a number of Papuan stations are given in Table I (p. 104). These show wide variations from year to year. The years 1930–2 are outstanding at most stations as a drier period, although at Kikori, Kokoda and Ioma, stations with high average totals, the 1931–2 totals were above the mean of the period 1922–39. In the year from 30 June 1929 to 30 June 1930, rainfall totals were above average except at Cape Nelson. A similar series of records for the mandated territory would show the same wide variations; and the same possibilities of water shortage exist in the dry season of a year such as 1930–1 at Rabaul as at Port Moresby. Relatively, the greater annual discrepancies are found in the drier areas.

Annual totals of rain days fluctuate similarly, as is shown in Table II (p. 105). The figures in Tables I and II may also be compared to assess the intensity of rainfall. In 1935–6 Kikori recorded 239 in. and Daru 75 in. In the abnormal year 1930–1, Samarai recorded 46 in. against an average of 100 in., and Losuia, in the Trobriand islands, 21 in. against an average of 149 in. Both had 176 rain days in that year. Generally speaking the areas with highest averages have greater intensity of rain, but local factors of exposure should be taken into account in comparing individual stations. For example, such figures as are available for Kairuku show lower totals of rain days than for the drier Port Moresby station to the south of it, although fluctuations run roughly parallel. The difference in totals and intensity of rainfall is probably related to the exposed position of Kairuku, at the southern tip of Yule island, as compared with that of Port Moresby, on an enclosed bay with hills and islands to seaward.

At most centres in New Guinea and the Bismarck archipelago, the morning hours have least rain. Over the surrounding seas the early morning and late evening have most rain, but inland and over leeward shores the characteristic heavy showers come in the afternoon and at night. In interior mountainous districts rain commonly begins shortly before sunset and may fall continuously for three or four hours. Over windward shores rain comes mainly between 2200 hr. and 0800 hr. The Table on p. 98, for stations in the mandated territory, shows the greater frequency of night rain. The first four stations lie in Astrolabe bay and are thus partly sheltered. (Most of the figures are averages of readings over a period of two years; ' day ' is the period from 0600 hr. to 1800 hr. and ' night ' that from 1800 hr. to 0600 hr.)

The greater amount of night rainfall is brought by the monsoon or trade which is blowing in from the sea. Kokopo, the exceptional

Average Day and Night Rainfall in the Mandated Territory (inches)

Station	Position	Day	Night
Melanua	5° 30′ S, 145° 50′ E	24·0	94·5
Madang	5° 10′ S, 145° 48′ E	20·1	116·9
Erima	5° 24′ S, 145° 45′ E	9·4	93·3
Bogadjim	5° 25′ S, 145° 45′ E	23·2	99·2
Sattelberg	6° 30′ S, 147° 49′ E	86·2	111·8
Kokopo	4° 20′ S, 152° 15′ E	42·5	31·1

Source: C. Braak, 'Klimakunde von Hinterindien und Insulinde', *Handbuch der Klimatologie*, Band IV, Teil R, p. 93 (Berlin, 1931).

station in the above Table, has its rainy season in the period of the north-west monsoon (Fig. 29). This wind, and the south wind which may blow at this season, are land winds at a station so placed, and the greater proportion of the rain therefore falls by day.

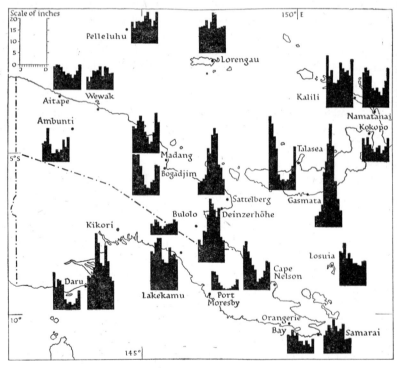

Fig. 29. Rainfall regimes of selected stations in New Guinea and the Bismarck archipelago
Based on official sources.

Seasonal Distribution of Rainfall

Fig. 29 shows differing rainfall regimes and some regional variations in seasonal distribution of rainfall, Fig. 30 a series of rainfall

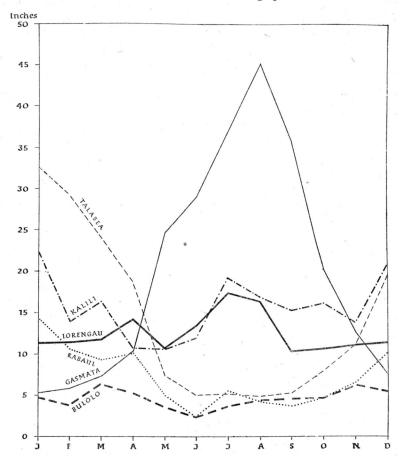

Fig. 30. Average monthly rainfall totals and annual regimes of stations in the Mandated Territory of New Guinea

Figs. 30–1 show that in spite of the variety of regimes there is a general correspondence of monthly totals at the change of seasons (April–May and November). Based on various sources.

regimes for the mandated territory, and Fig. 31 a similar series for Papua.

A primary contrast according to relationship to rain-bearing winds is obvious at most stations. Talasea on the northern coast and

Gasmata on the southern coast of New Britain provide the most extreme contrast on Fig. 29. The mountains of the Huon peninsula and their westward continuation, the Finisterre range, shelter the Astrolabe bay area from the south-east trade. Hence Madang and Bogadjim have their dry seasons in the southern winter, and Sattelberg and Deinzerhöhe, on the windward side of the Huon peninsula in relation to the south-east trade, have heavy rain when that wind prevails. The off-lying Tami islands have greater totals than the

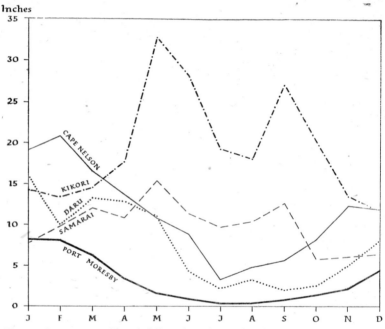

Fig. 31. Average monthly rainfall totals and annual regimes of stations in Papua
Based on various sources.

coastal station at Deinzerhöhe: from May to October 173 in. out of the yearly total of 253 in. falls on the Tami group (Table III). The north-west monsoon season of both these Huon gulf stations is only relatively dry. Pellelehu in the Ninigo group and Lorengau at the north-east corner of Manus have the more evenly distributed rainfall which is to be expected in view of their position on relatively small islands and their more equatorial regime, but they show maxima in the trade season. Maxima in the north-west monsoon season occur at north-coast stations in the area. The graph of Ambunti in the heart of the Sepik basin suggests that regimes which show maxima in the north-west monsoon season prevail for some distance inland, as does the graph for Bulolo. The figures for other goldfield centres such as Edie Creek, and for Aiyura in the upper Ramu valley show similar maxima (Table III). The goldfield observatories in the Bulowat area show more evenly distributed rainfall than most stations. Aitape and Wewak in New Guinea, and Kalili and Namatanai in New Ireland, provide contrasts which can best be explained in terms of local relationships. The first pair would be expected to show maxima in the north-west monsoon season. Both are partly sheltered from this wind by a northward pointing coast to the west. Wewak, the apparently abnormal station, is also protected on its seaward side by the islands of Kairiru and Mushu. Though August is fairly dry there, the months of greater rainfall are those in which the south-east trade blows along the coast. Namatanai is sheltered from, and Kalili exposed to, the south-east trade in spite of broad similarity of coastal alinement. Kalili, like Lorengau, shows no dry season. Madang is the only station in the mandate which records monthly maxima at the change of seasons. The differing regimes shown in Fig. 30 show a marked tendency to group around rather low averages in April–May and in November.

The Papuan stations graphed on Fig. 31 show a general tendency for north-west monsoon maxima. These winds blow across the Gulf of Papua and on to the northern slopes of the mount Victory volcanic area. They give Port Moresby and cape Nelson, which are sheltered during the trade period, the most marked seasonal differences in Papua. Daru, an island station backed by hundreds of miles of low-land, much of it swamp covered, and Lakekamu behind the north-east corner of the Gulf of Papua have similar regimes. Samarai and Kikori, each with the greatest monthly total at the May change of season, are exposed to the full force of the south-east trades, but lacking mountain barriers to the north have no markedly dry season as has Gasmata. Of the Papuan stations, those of the ' tail ' of New Guinea show greater rainfall in the north-west monsoon period (Fig. 29, and the figures for Buna, and the interior stations Ioma and Kokoda in Table IV). Off this part of New Guinea, island regimes show no dry season, peaks in May and a greater rain total in the first half of the year. The head of the Gulf of Papua, which has the heaviest totals in Papua, has most rain in the months May to October, and the figures for May are higher than those for any other month (Fig. 29, Kikori; and figures for Kerema in Table IV).

BIBLIOGRAPHICAL NOTE

Data for Papua and the mandated territory are published in the Territory of Papua *Annual Report* (Melbourne, to 1927; Canberra, from 1928); and the Commonwealth of Australia *Report to the Council of the League of Nations on the Administration of the Territory of New Guinea* (Melbourne, to 1927; Canberra, from 1928). The number of stations for which data was available was increasing yearly till the outbreak of war. A summary based mainly on observations made during the German occupation of the mandated territory will be found in C. Braak, 'Klimakunde von Hinterindien und Insulinde', *Handbuch der Klimatologie*, Band IV, Teil R (Berlin, 1931). More recent statements of conditions in the latter area include two papers by B. G. Challis: 'Rainfall Notes', *New Guinea Agricultural Gazette*, vol. IV, no. 1, p. 39 (Canberra, 1938); and 'Climatic Notes on New Guinea', *New Guinea Agricultural Gazette*, vol. V, no. 3, pp. 8–27 (Canberra, 1939). There are, in addition, some details of applied meteorology by the same author: 'The value and uses of meteorology', *New Guinea Agricultural Gazette*, vol. VI, no. 1, pp. 55–62 (Canberra, 1940).

CLIMATIC TABLES

I. Papua: Yearly Rainfall Totals, 1922–39 (inches)

Station	1922-3	'23-4	'24-5	'25-6	'26-7	'27-8	'28-9	'29-30	'30-1	'31-2	'32-3	'33-4	'34-5	'35-6	'36-7	'37-8	'38-9	Average 1922-39
Port Moresby	39	54	43	26	32	37	29	58	18	28	42	54	28	44	34	35	36	37·5
Rigo	28	—	53	35	50	48	37	74	18	37	43	59	32	31	31	31	39	40·7
Kemp Welch R.	—	58	64	40	68	52	47	87	32	51	62	101	58	58	64	60	52	59·3
Misima	156	88	119	79	140	138	115	142	63	75	162	151	120	125	139	142	146	116·5
Samarai	131	72	93	73	101	106	97	125	46	84	57	105	133	88	151	121	—	99·6
Buna	128	128	124	117	116	111	143	128	131	100	110	116	112	88	151	123	156	120·7
Kikori	190	205	206	108	289	229	234	268	175	228	63	255	259	239	—	210	289	221·6
Orangerie bay	131	84	104	86	96	137	66	165	43	83	—	106	139	104	98	92	110	103·9
Kerema	143	139	155	114	140	147	147	195	105	144	113	154	161	135	141	152	158	147·0
Cape Nelson	151	151	133	99	127	201	175	117	74	126	86	143	105	129	164	127	156	127·1
Losuia (Trobriands)	—	129	200	139	245	160	120	194	21	111	12	183	149	177	208	165	170	148·9
Kokoda	112	—	143	140	173	175	119	147	134	136	121	124	109	99	88	131	102	133·9
Daru	80	88	84	55	61	71	73	77	62	47	82	99	76	75	91	80	102	76·7
Kairuku	—	—	—	36	57	44	44	59	23	39	55	41	39	37	55	81	48	47·2
Ioma	—	125	129	—	126	193	151	—	153	179	133	181	170	148	162	150	121	151·5
Doubina	—	—	89	—	73	49	63	57	40	51	40	—	58	48	48	48	89	55·3
Conflict Is.	—	—	—	35	—	80	78	82	26	36	47	82	65	65	87	77	88	71·5

Figures in italics represent rainfall for 11 months only; the remainder are for the year 1 July–30 June.
Compiled from data in the Territory of Papua *Annual Report* for 1922–39 (Melbourne, 1925–7; Canberra, 1928–40).

II. *Papua : Yearly Totals of Rain Days*

Station	1922-3	'23-4	'24-5	'25-6	'26-7	'27-8	'28-9	'29-30	'30-1	'31-2	'32-3	'33-4	'34-5	'35-6	'36-7	'37-8	'38-9	Average 1922-39
Port Moresby	111	83	123	79	90	105	80	99	55	70	84	130	86	106	83	104	108	93·9
Rigo	—	—	—	107	128	—	119	141	56	107	120	168	120	102	90	91	*102*	112·0
Kemp Welch R.	—	94	130	—	145	132	122	148	77	117	130	197	136	138	130	125	112	127·5
Misima	209	*161*	*156*	208	—	—	181	198	126	161	170	177	191	—	177	—	205	176·4
Samarai	237	220	231	197	250	253	201	245	176	193	161	193	202	183	200	190	—	208·9
Buna	217	180	208	212	174	168	142	162	124	108	138	140	—	135	118	169	193	160·8
Kikori	275	225	—	—	—	211	266	301	245	255	278	276	252	228	210	208	*202*	245·2
Orangerie bay	216	133	*165*	160	158	195	155	202	113	145	—	185	188	188	172	202	194	173·2
Kerema	192	229	*158*	164	202	211	219	260	171	220	231	207	242	231	201	*187*	234	209·8
Cape Nelson	221	191	211	180	—	—	130	146	131	161	126	189	172	171	188	177	—	173·1
Losuia (Trobriands)	—	—	—	—	—	—	206	209	176	251	197	203	202	—	224	239	209	207·0
Kokoda	102	151	—	—	*174*	—	*180*	—	204	—	236	265	190	226	*160*	*192*	—	209·7
Daru	—	—	—	134	—	*189*	175	194	138	143	80	202	222	—	185	181	164	166·2
Kairuku	—	—	—	—	—	66	82	76	50	84	78	116	—	95	75	—	92	81·4
Ioma	—	—	—	—	—	—	65	—	119	—	*149*	—	—	—	157	—	134	124·8
Doubina	—	—	—	80	111	—	124	122	59	108	*97*	—	126	113	80	122	170	144·4
Conflict Is.	—	—	—	—	—	—	*136*	169	—	110	126	198	178	145	151	180	180	157·3

Figures in italics represent rainfall for 11 months only; the remainder are for the year 1 July–30 June.
Compiled from statistics in the Territory of Papua *Annual Report* for 1922–39 (Melbourne, 1925–7; Canberra, 1928–40).

III. Mandated Territory: Mean Monthly Rainfall (inches)

Station	J	F	M	A	M	J	J	A	S	O	N	D	Total	Three wettest months			Three driest months			No. of years' observations
Gasmata (New Britain)	5·4	5·8	7·3	10·4	24·7	29·0	36·9	45·1	35·8	20·3	12·8	7·7	241·3	Jly	Aug	Sep	Jan	Feb	Mar	19
Lindenhafen (New Britain)	7·2	6·4	6·1	11·0	27·3	33·9	39·4	44·6	34·9	19·5	13·5	8·3	252·2	Jly	Aug	Sep	Jan	Feb	Mar	19
Palmalmal (New Britain)	7·3	8·7	8·4	10·6	20·0	15·8	29·3	41·6	16·8	13·8	9·8	10·3	191·1	May	Jly	Aug	Jan	Feb	Jne	7
Talasea (New Britain)	32·7	29·4	24·1	18·9	7·5	5·1	6·0	4·8	5·4	13·8	11·1	19·7	177·1	Jan	Feb	Mar	Jne	Jly	Aug	21
Tobera (Gazelle peninsula)	9·7	8·1	10·4	9·6	4·0	3·1	6·0	6·0	3·2	4·8	8·5	8·1	81·5	Jan	Mar	Apr	May	Jne	Sep	8
Kokopo (Gazelle peninsula)	10·0	7·0	10·4	7·0	5·2	6·0	5·6	6·7	3·3	4·9	6·4	10·3	80·9	Dec	Jan	Mar	Jne	Sep	Oct	12
Rabaul (Gazelle peninsula)	14·3	10·6	9·5	9·7	5·1	3·4	6·6	4·3	3·7	5·2	6·4	10·3	88·1	Dec	Jan	Feb	Jne	Aug	Sep	25
Keravat (Gazelle peninsula)	11·9	9·7	10·6	10·6	9·5	5·9	6·6	5·7	7·3	9·1	9·6	9·6	105·5	Jan	Mar	Apr	Jne	Jly	Aug	9
Notre Mal (Gazelle peninsula)																				
Pondo (Gazelle peninsula)	32·3	18·6	21·0	12·3	8·2	7·6	7·6	7·9	6·4	6·7	9·3	16·6	153·9	Jan	Feb	Mar	Jly	Sep	Oct	10
Watmabara (Duke of York Is.)	36·6	24·8	19·3	15·0	8·1	7·8	9·4	9·4	8·2	6·7	8·8	19·2	173·3	Jan	Feb	Mar	May	Jne	Sep	12
Kavieng (New Ireland)	13·1	10·7	10·4	10·8	7·7	8·5	10·9	11·0	8·5	9·6	8·3	9·4	119·0	Jan	Feb	Apr	Jne	Sep	Nov	15
Kalili (New Ireland)	12·0	11·3	11·5	11·3	10·5	8·7	9·2	9·7	7·3	8·9	9·2	10·7	120·2	Jan	Feb	Jly	Jne	Sep	Oct	22
Namatanai (New Ireland)	22·6	13·7	16·2	10·6	11·9	11·9	19·2	17·0	15·3	16·1	9·8	20·8	187·8	Jly	May	Dec	Apr	Jne	Nov	15
Lorengau (Manus)	15·2	17·3	16·1	13·8	8·6	7·5	8·8	6·7	5·3	8·7	11·4	17·1	136·7	Dec	Feb	Mar	Aug	Sep	May	21
Pelleluhu (Ninigo Is.)	9·1	11·4	11·7	14·2	9·1	13·3	11·8	16·3	10·4	7·2	9·7	11·4	149·6	Jly	Aug	Apr	Feb	May	Oct	21
Peter Haven (Garove)	16·3	6·7	9·3	9·6	10·5	9·5	17·3	13·3	10·3	7·2	9·7	11·4	118·7	Jly	Jan	Aug	Feb	Jne	May	9
Aiyura (New Guinea)	6·2	7·4	9·4	12·1	4·2	3·4	3·4	3·9	4·9	5·9	7·1	9·3	87·3	Mar	Apr	Dec	Jne	Jly	Aug	5
Edie Creek (New Guinea)	6·2	7·5	12·0	7·2	4·2	6·0	3·4	6·5	8·7	5·9	7·1	13·3	129·0	Mar	Nov	Dec	May	Jly	Aug	5
Bulolo (New Guinea)	4·7	3·9	6·4	11·1	3·6	2·4	4·6	4·5	4·6	4·7	6·3	13·3	87·3	Dec	Aug	Jly	Jne	May	Jan	8
Sattelberg mission	5·0	5·9	6·8	5·4	20·0	17·9	25·8	28·7	26·2	12·9	18·8	5·6	104·7	Aug	Sep	Jly	May	Jne	Jan	13
Madang (New Guinea)	12·4	11·6	15·0	8·6	14·8	10·0	7·8	4·8	5·9	9·7	11·3	6·7	176·5	Mar	Apr	Nov	Aug	Sep	Jly	21
Bogadjim (New Guinea)	17·3	17·1	17·2	17·0	8·5	4·1	2·8	2·7	5·2	6·1	12·9	14·4	141·4	Jan	Feb	Apr	Jly	Aug	Sep	16
Finschhafen (New Guinea)	2·8	3·2	4·5	12·4	12·5	17·2	18·4	18·8	13·2	14·9	9·4	12·4	118·3	Jly	Aug	Feb	Jan	Feb	Mar	10
Deinzerhöhe (New Guinea)	10·0	7·5	13·9	13·5	20·8	27·6	25·5	22·9	19·8	23·3	11·1	9·7	130·2	Jne	Jly	Aug	Jan	Feb	Mar	7
Hatzfeldt harbour (New Guinea)													206·5	Jne	Jly	Oct	Dec	Jan	Feb	17
Tami Is. (New Guinea)	15·8	14·8	0·8	14·8	4·8	3·1	6·9	3·5	4·8	6·1	12·2	11·6	108·3	Jan	Feb	Apr	Jne	Jan	Sep	8
Urti Kurum (Karkar)	11·4	7·6	1·7	17·9	32·4	30·9	31·6	26·2	29·1	23·4	17·3	14·2	253·2	May	Jne	Jly	Jan	Feb	Mar	13
Wewak (New Guinea)	5·7	3·5	5·7	8·0	7·9	8·1	9·8	5·8	9·7	9·2	6·9	7·0	115·1	Mar	May	Oct	Jly	Aug	Feb	10
Aitape (New Guinea)	10·0	10·6	10·5	9·5	7·9	6·3	7·0	6·6	5·0	6·3	8·0	10·2	98·0	Sep	Feb	Mar	Jan	Sep	Feb	18

Sources: (1) B. G. Challis, 'Climatic Notes on New Guinea', *New Guinea Agricultural Gazette*, vol. v, no. 3, pp. 26–7 (Canberra, 1939);
(2) C. Braak, 'Klimakunde von Hinterindien und Insulinde', *Handbuch der Klimatologie*, Band IV, Teil R, pp. 17, 89 and 108 (Berlin, 1931).

IV. *Papua: Mean Monthly Rainfall (inches)*

Station	J	F	M	A	M	J	J	A	S	O	N	D	Annual Total	Three wettest months	Three driest months	No. of years' observations
Port Moresby (govt. station)	8·1	8·0	6·3	3·4	2·0	0·9	0·3	0·4	0·7	1·4	2·1	4·3	38	Jan Feb Mar	Jly Aug Sep	15
Kemp Welch	9·0	6·5	7·6	7·5	4·9	1·3	1·0	0·9	1·7	2·0	4·4	5·3	52	Jan Feb Mar	Jne Jly Aug	12
Samarai	7·7	9·7	12·0	10·8	14·8	11·4	9·6	10·4	12·6	9·1	6·1	6·4	117	Mar May Sep	Oct Nov Dec	11
Buna	13·3	12·3	10·7	9·4	7·6	7·2	3·0	4·0	7·9	9·1	12·9	14·7	113	Nov Dec Jan	Jne Jly Aug	12
Kikori	14·2	13·4	14·5	17·7	32·6	28·1	19·3	18·2	27·0	20·1	13·5	11·7	230	May Jne Mar	Nov Oct Dec	8
Orangerie bay	8·0	7·5	10·1	7·4	8·8	5·1	5·	3·5	5·3	3·9	2·8	6·2	74	Jan Jne Mar	Aug Oct Nov	10
Kerema	9·4	9·8	8·9	10·0	16·0	12·4	8·	11·4	10·6	11·1	8·1	7·1	123	May Mar Aug	Nov Oct Dec	13
Cape Nelson	19·2	20·9	16·5	13·6	10·7	8·8	3·3	4·7	5·1	8·1	12·3	11·9	135	Jan Feb Mar	Jly Aug Sep	12
Losuia (Trobriands)	14·7	14·0	15·0	11·5	13·9	11·6	9·3	9·3	8·7	10·1	10·1	10·3	140	Jan Feb Mar	Jly Sep Oct	13
Kokoda	14·8	13·8	13·5	13·8	8·2	8·1	5·8	7·0	8·4	8·4	14·9	12·8	131	Nov Jan Feb	Jne Jly Sep	12
Daru	15·8	9·8	13·2	12·7	10·9	4·4	2·6	3·2	2·0	2·5	4·7	8·0	90	Jan Dec Apr	Sep Oct Aug	15
Ioma	18·2	16·1	19·1	12·1	11·2	8·5	6·9	6·6	10·8	11·3	18·0	21·7	161	Dec Jan Mar	Jne Jly Aug	11
Lakekamu	16·8	15·8	20·4	22·6	22·6	13·2	11·9	11·6	18·3	15·0	15·6	11·3	197	Mar Apr May	Jly Aug Dec	11

Source: M. Staniforth Smith, *Handbook of Papua*, 4th edition, pp. 76–7 (Melbourne, 1927).

Chapter V

VEGETATION AND FAUNA

Vegetation—Types of Vegetation: Forestry: Cultivated Plants: Vegetation of the Bismarck Archipelago
Fauna— Mammals: Birds: Reptiles and Amphibia: Insects
Bibliographical Note

VEGETATION

New Guinea has a very rich flora and there is perhaps no land area of the same size in the world with more luxuriant vegetation or a greater wealth of plant species. For this there are several reasons, of which the chief are the predominantly hot, moist climate, the great area of the island, the topography, which ranges from swampy coastal plains to high mountains with permanent snowfields, and the soils, which vary from recent alluvium and disintegrated coral, to igneous and old sedimentary rocks. Though there are large areas in which, in spite of the sparse and primitive population, the whole aspect of the vegetation has been transformed by human activities, by far the greater part of the island still bears natural vegetation as little affected by man as any in the world. Since much of New Guinea is entirely unexplored, the flora and vegetation are still very incompletely known; though many thousands of species of plants have been found, many more must remain to be discovered.

The flora has much in common both with that of Australia, especially the north-eastern part, and with that of the islands to the west. Many species range from Australia through New Guinea as far as the Malay peninsula and beyond. In past geological periods waves of plant migration have swept southwards over the island from south-eastern Asia, and on a smaller scale probably northwards from Australia. Because of the large proportion of Asiatic elements in the flora, New Guinea is reckoned botanically as part of the Indo-Malayan region, but owing to the large number of endemic species not shared with the neighbouring countries, which show that it has been an independent centre of plant evolution of some importance, it is often regarded as a separate sub-region or province, termed Papuasia.

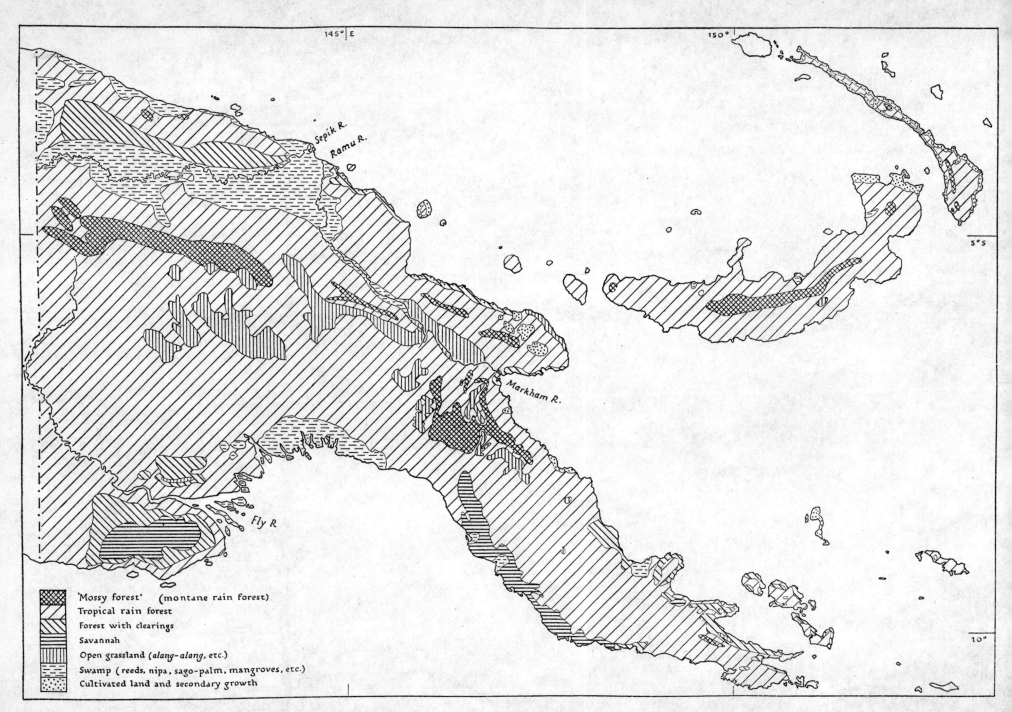

Fig. 32. Provisional vegetation map of eastern New Guinea and the Bismarck archipelago

No data are available for the areas which are not shaded. Based on a folded map in Allied Geographical Section, South-west Pacific Area, Directorate of Intelligence, Allied Air Forces, *Vegetation Study, Eastern New Guinea*.

Types of Vegetation (Fig. 32)

Approaching New Guinea from the sea the first vegetation seen is usually a fringe of beach forest or an interminable line of mangrove swamp. On sandy beaches are found the goat's-foot convolvulus (*Ipomoea pes-caprae*) and other herbaceous plants and bushes found in similar situations all over the Western Pacific, sometimes including the strange-looking *Tacca pinnatifida*, with its lurid, almost black, inflorescences. Behind this low-growing vegetation stand coconut palms or a wall of beach forest in which gigantic trees of *Barringtonia* and *Calophyllum inophyllum* are often conspicuous, leaning seawards. Commonly on the north coast, and less often on the south, pure stands of the graceful *Casuarina equisetifolia* are seen, especially on sandy spits near river mouths.

Mangrove forests, which occur mainly on sheltered muddy shores, cover enormous expanses on the south coast, especially near the deltas and estuaries of the great rivers. The chief trees here are the stilt-rooted *Rhizophora mucronata*, *Bruguiera* and *Avicennia*, with their peculiar cigar-like aerial roots growing up vertically through the mud, and *Xylocarpus granatum*. A little further up the estuaries where the water is brackish rather than salt there are pure growths of *Nipa fruticans*, a stemless palm with leaves 20 ft. or more long. There are vast areas of these nipa swamps also, especially along the Gulf of Papua from the Purari delta to that of the Fly.

Higher up, the rivers are bordered by beds of wild sugar cane and other reeds growing to a height of 10 to 30 ft., with swamps of sago palm (*Metroxylon*), pandanus and other plants behind them, often covering many square miles. The sago palms are of great importance to the natives, as they provide the staple diet for many tribes.

Where the river banks are better drained the rain forest may come down right to the water's edge, a thick curtain of creepers, many with brightly coloured flowers, hiding the forest interior. Like the Malayan rain forests, the lowland forests of New Guinea are composed of a vast number of different kinds of evergreen trees with their crowns in a series of superimposed layers or storeys, the average height of the tallest being about 150 ft. The trunks are smooth and straight and many have plank buttresses growing out as flanges from the base. Great lianas, some with stems as thick as a man's thigh, rise up everywhere or hang down in festoons; smaller climbers, attached like ivy by aerial roots, cling to the tree trunks. Shrubs and small palms, together with seedling trees, form most of the undergrowth, which is not as a rule dense or difficult to penetrate. The branches of the trees are loaded with epiphytic orchids and ferns, most of them growing so high up that they are difficult to see from the ground (Plate 23).

Generally in the rain forest of the lowlands and foothills no one species of tree predominates over the rest, but in some places the composition is less mixed; for instance, in the Hydrographer's range in Papua, there are large areas of forest in which two trees, the leguminous *Afzelia bijuga* and *Anisoptera polyandra*, one of the Dipterocarpaceae (the most important family of timber trees in Malaya and the Philippines) form over 90% of the timber volume. On the banks of the large rivers, especially in Papua, where the ground is usually well drained but is flooded when the water is high, the forest may consist of almost pure stands of *ilimo* or *erima* (*Octomeles sumatrana*), a tree 180–200 ft. high, providing a very useful light timber much valued by the natives for making canoes; in some places trees of this species are planted by the natives and handed on to their heirs. Another type of rain forest differing from the normal in several respects is found on upraised coral limestone (*korang*) in the north-west of Dutch New Guinea. Doubtless many other variations from the normal type of rain forest remain to be discovered.

In the more thickly populated areas there are considerable areas of secondary rain forest, thickets of brambles, *alang-alang* (kunai) grasslands and other types of secondary vegetation, all of which arise by the destruction of the virgin forest. The natives practise shifting cultivation, clearing, felling and burning the trees to make gardens for taro, sweet potatoes and yams. After taking one or two crops the land is abandoned and in a remarkably short space of time quick-growing soft-wooded trees such as *Trema* and *Macaranga* spring up, soon growing into a young secondary forest very much denser than the original primary rain forest. Left to itself the secondary rain forest would no doubt revert after many years to forest much like the original, but if the land is again cleared before there has been time for the humus destroyed in the last period of cultivation to be restored to the soil, *alang-alang* (*Imperata*) and other grasses tend to invade the ground, gradually converting it into grassland. Grasslands produced in this way cover large areas and are very like natural savannahs in appearance. In the Markham and upper Ramu valleys, for instance, there are hundreds of square miles of open grassland in which occasional old trees of *Alstonia scholaris* and other evergreen forest species are the only evidence that the land was originally forest-covered. These grasslands are burnt by the natives at frequent intervals in order to drive game when hunting; a re-invasion by trees is impossible as long as the fires recur.

Though the greater part of the low country is covered with rain forest or its derivatives, there are dry belts, some of considerable extent, in the rain shadow of the mountains where the rainfall is so low that except in the river valleys rain forest gives way to dry evergreen forest or open treeless savannahs. In the Port Moresby dry belt, for example, a longitudinal belt which extends from Hula north-west to Maiva, there are gum (*Eucalyptus*) forests very like those of the drier parts of Queensland. The chief trees are four species of eucalyptus which grow about 50 ft. high; in addition there are paper-barks (*Melaleuca*) and other characteristically Australian trees. Except near the coast, where it has been mostly exterminated, the valuable sandalwood tree is common. In the gullies where the soil is comparatively moist the forest is similar to rain forest, but contains, in addition to various rain-forest trees, deciduous species such as *Bombax malabaricum*. In the Owen Stanley range eucalyptus forest ascends to over 5,000 ft. On the raised reefs of the north-eastern coast of New Guinea, between cape Cretin and Astrolabe bay (Fig. 13), there are no eucalyptus forests, and the vegetation consists of completely treeless grassland which, unlike the grasslands of the Ramu and Markham valleys, seems to be natural and not due to recurrent fires.

The mountains of New Guinea have an even more interesting flora than the low ground. They are the home of the finest orchids and of many magnificent species of rhododendron with showy red, white or yellow flowers. Here, too, are found some of the strangest forms of plant life in the island, such as the pitcher plants (*Nepenthes*), and *Myrmecoidia*, fantastic-looking plants in which the stem is swollen into a huge spiny tuber, honeycombed by cavities inhabited by ants.

Up to a great height the mountains are forest-covered like the lowlands; as the altitude increases the character of the forest changes. In the steeply sloping and much broken country from about 1,000 to 4,500 ft. is found the 'foothills forest', which differs from the lowland rain forest in having buttressed trees and fewer lianas and epiphytes. One of the chief trees is a species of oak (*Quercus Jung-huhnii*); with it are found a few conifers and many other trees not seen at lower levels. The ground cover consists largely of ferns and species of *Elatostemma*, small herbs belonging to the nettle family. When the cloud belt is reached between 4,500 and 7,500 ft. a new type of vegetation, the 'mid-mountain forest', begins. Here the most characteristic tree is the hoop pine (*Araucaria Cunninghamii*), which because of its preference for growing on ridges stands out conspicuously everywhere on the sky-line. The total number of tree species is much less than in the lowlands. In addition to the hoop pine there are several other conifers, two species of oak and many other trees not found in the lowland and seldom in the foothills forest.

At a height varying according to local conditions from about 5,000 to 8,000 ft. the lower limit of the 'mossy forest' is often reached. Here the average temperature is about 50° F. and there is unceasing mist and drizzle. The trees are only about 20 ft. high, with bent and crooked trunks which like everything else are covered with a thick blanket of soaking wet moss. Tree ferns and conifers are found here, as well as many orchids and rhododendrons, whose large and often brilliantly coloured flowers are the chief attraction in this otherwise uninviting region.

At about 10,000 to 11,000 ft. the mist belt gives way to a drier and more sunny climate, the forest now consisting mainly of the conifers *Podocarpus, Libocedrus, Dacrydium* and *Phyllocladus*. These coniferous forests do not usually form a continuous belt, but grow in blocks separated by stretches of grassland over which tree ferns and shrubs are scattered. Similar grasslands usually occur above about 12,000 ft., where trees cease to grow. Though these high mountain grasslands at first sight look quite natural, they are possibly brought into existence by fires started by the mountain tribes when hunting the wallaby.

The true climatic limit above which trees cannot grow is probably reached at about 14,000 ft. Above this height are found low scrub, bare stony ground with scattered bushes and grasses, or sometimes little but lichens and mosses and, in flatter places, bogs. Many of the plants at these great heights are singularly beautiful and the rhododendrons often make masses of bright colour. From a botanical point of view the high mountain flora is of great interest because the gentians and other plants found there belong to genera usually confined to much higher latitudes.

FORESTRY

The New Guinea forests contain many fine timber trees, among which may be mentioned red cedar (*Cedrela toona*, var. *australis*), 'New Guinea walnut' or *damoni* (*Dracontomelum mangiferum*), *mellila (Afzelia bijuga), nona (Pterocarpus indicus)* and *taun* or *okamu (Pometia pinnata)*, but as in most rain forests the extremely mixed nature of the stand makes exploitation difficult. For example, a sample plot of 105 acres at Veimauri in Papua had 437 trees of timber size belonging to 69 species, but of the 6 species, forming 45% of the timber volume, only two were first-class timbers; other valuable species were present only in very small numbers. The mountain forests with their large proportion of coniferous woods are potentially much more valuable than the lowland rain forests, but their inaccessibility makes them uneconomic to work.

Until recently the only timber exploitation in New Guinea was carried on by a few small sawmills mostly organized by missions, except in the Morobe goldfield where most small settlements were constructed entirely out of local timber (chiefly red cedar and two species of *Araucaria*), using machinery imported by air. However, about 1937 Australian sawmillers began to take an interest in New Guinea as a possible source for timber, and a demand arose for timber concessions. A new sawmill was set up at Lae and two new ones in New Britain. About 1923 the Australian Commonwealth Inspector General of Forests visited and reported on the forests of Papua and the Territory of New Guinea, recommending the establishment of a forestry service. In 1938 a forestry service was created in the Territory of New Guinea, as a branch of the Department of Lands, Mines, Survey and Forests. It is under the control of the Secretary for Lands.

CULTIVATED PLANTS

The natives of New Guinea have a great love for flowers and plants with ornamental leaves. Round villages and along tracks shrubs such as 'crotons' and hibiscus, and trees such as the scarlet-flowered *Delonix (Poinciana regia)* and the variegated *Erythrina* are commonly planted and make splashes of bright colour. Various trees, especially *Alstonia scholaris*, are grown to provide shade.

All the common crop plants of the Western Pacific, such as yams, taro, sugar cane, etc., are cultivated. Tobacco is widely grown and at one time it was thought that there might be an indigenous species peculiar to the island. Recent work has shown, however, that all the varieties of tobacco cultivated in New Guinea belong to the two species grown in other countries, both of which are of American origin. Tobacco probably reached New Guinea through Amboina or the Philippines, where it had been introduced by early Spanish or Portuguese voyagers.

The native sugar-cane varieties are of particular interest. As well as the cultivated sugar cane (*Saccharum officinarum*), there are two closely related wild species, *S. robustum* and *S. spontaneum*. The original home of *S. officinarum* was probably in the Indo-Malayan region, of which New Guinea forms a part. For these reasons it would be expected that there might be native varieties with special characteristics which would make them useful to cultivate elsewhere. Several expeditions, the first in 1893, the most recent in 1937, have been sent to New Guinea to look for such varieties. One of the varieties found by an early expedition, Badila ('New Guinea 15') is still extensively grown in Australia. The aim of the recent American expeditions has been to find varieties with characteristics which might make them valuable in plant breeding, rather than to find varieties which could be used as they are.

VEGETATION OF THE BISMARCK ARCHIPELAGO

New Britain, New Ireland and Lavongai originally had vegetation similar to that of the Solomons and the adjoining parts of New Guinea, but it is now much altered by human influence. At one time the whole of these islands was covered by luxuriant rain forests, except on newly deposited volcanic ash, where trees had not had time to establish themselves. To-day most of the old forests has been destroyed by shifting cultivation and by fires which sweep over large areas during dry years; in its place low secondary forests, which contain few valuable timber trees, and open stretches of *alang-alang* grass have grown up. In New Britain small areas of virgin forest still remain, but in New Ireland and Lavongai there is little besides occasional very fine individual trees to give evidence of the former magnificence of the forests.

The relics of old forest in New Britain resemble the rain forest of New Guinea, but some trees—e.g., *Afzelia bijuga*—are much less common than on the mainland. On steep slopes in New Britain, New Ireland and Lavongai is found a 'foothills' type of forest like that in New Guinea, except that the oak *Quercus Junghuhnii* is absent. In New Britain there is a unique type of rain forest in which the top storey is formed by a single species, the superb tree *Eucalyptus deglupta* (sometimes called *E. Naudiniana*), which is nearly related to the giant gums of Australia. The eucalyptus, locally known as *kamerere*, grows to a height of well over 200 ft. and the trunk is often over 20 ft. in diameter at breast height. Below the crowns of the *kamerere* trees, and hiding them from view, there is the usual mixture of evergreen trees characteristic of rain forest. *Kamerere* timber has been exploited by the Roman Catholic mission; it is useful for general constructional purposes and much of Rabaul is built of it. This unusual type of forest, the only one in New Britain of great economic value, is unfortunately found only in small patches of which there are few now remaining: the only strip of virgin *kamerere* forest left in 1923–4 was on the Powell and Henry Reid rivers north of Wide bay. *Kamerere* forest grows in valleys where it is flooded annually, but not permanently water-logged. It frequently consists of trees all of approximately the same age; this is because it owes its existence to fires, which destroy the old rain forest, making openings in which the *kamerere* seedlings come up like wheat. The seedlings grow rapidly, and in forests burned in 1916 there were young *kamerere* trees 70 ft. high less than ten years later.

FAUNA

The fauna of New Guinea, which is very rich, is closely related to that of Australia and is quite distinct from that of those islands of the East Indies which lie west of Lombok.

MAMMALS

There are over a hundred species of mammals; but apart from the bats and rats and mice none of them is of the kind of mammals familiar in Europe or Asia. There are no monkeys, cats, dogs, weasels, deer, hedgehogs, or rabbits. The Australian and New Guinea mammals are more primitive than these, and belong either to the marsupials or to the monotremes. These groups were formerly widely distributed, but have become extinct in other parts of the world in competition with the more modern mammals which have evolved outside this area and have never reached it. The monotremes are the most primitive of mammals and lay eggs; they are represented in New Guinea by two species of spiny ant-eater (or echidna). The larger of the two weighs up to 30 lb. and has thick black fur, in which a few short spines are hidden. Both species are ant-eating terrestrial animals, using their powerful claws to open up ant-hills.

There are several families of pouched mammals or marsupials. The kangaroo family includes five species of small wallaby. Four of them inhabit the drier, more open, parts of the island, and the other is found in the dense forests of the mountain ranges. More striking, perhaps, are the tree kangaroos which appear to have originated in New Guinea as they are not found anywhere else except in north Queensland. While they are kangaroo-like in general build, they have much more powerful front legs and shorter hind legs with strong curved claws, and have a longer, less tapering banded tail. They are the largest of the New Guinea mammals. The phalanger family is represented by several species ; the spotted cuscus is the largest and is about the size of a large cat, with a long tail, naked and prehensile at the end. The coat is close and woolly and mottled and variegated in an extraordinary pattern of white, black and red blotches. No two individuals are alike. There are several other species of cuscus and of the closely related ring-tailed opossums. Perhaps the most interesting of the phalangers is the Papuan flying phalanger, the only New Guinea species of an Australian genus. It is about the size of a squirrel, with a short round head, large eyes and ears, and a long bushy tail, and is one of the most attractive animals imaginable. It glides from tree to tree by spreading a membrane which stretches from fore-foot to ankle along the flanks of the animal.

The rat bandicoots are marsupials which live on insects. There are several species of them in New Guinea and they appear to take the place in the ecological scheme occupied by the hedgehog in Europe. Most of them are about the size of a large rat.

There seems to be only one carnivorous mammal in New Guinea, the dasyure; this is also a marsupial, and is known in Australia as the native cat. The dasyure is something like a large mongoose in appearance.

The bats of New Guinea are many and varied. The island is particularly rich in fruit-bats, of which the 'flying foxes' are the largest and most abundant. One species of 'flying fox' has a wing spread of about 3 ft. They live entirely on fruit and travel long distances at dusk to find their feeding places. There are several species of the curious tube-nosed bat. These are fruit-eating bats with the nostrils elongated to form prominent tubes. There are a great many species of small insectivorous bats, most of which are inconspicuous, nocturnal and elusive, and not easily studied. The horseshoe bats, the leaf-nosed bats and the free-tailed bats are, however, easily identified.

The rats and mice are the only terrestrial mammals belonging to orders higher than marsupials which have reached New Guinea;

but of them there are a great many genera and species. Several of the rats are very large and reach a head and body length of over a foot. The genus *Mallomys* is confined to the mountain ranges of New Guinea. There are several species, and they are the largest rats in the world. *Mallomys hercules* and *Mallomys rothschildi* are very striking animals; they may reach a length of 18 in. without the tail, and have very long black fur, and long coarsely-scaled, parti-coloured tails. Several of the New Guinea rats are aquatic in habit; most of these are large and one has lost its external ears.

In the estuaries of the larger rivers is found the dugong or sea-cow, related to the manatee. These are completely aquatic animals and never leave the water, except when accidentally stranded. They differ from whales in being vegetable feeders. They are gregarious and browse under water on sea weeds and other plants, coming in to feed with the flood tide and returning with the ebb. Their thick mobile lips are furnished with bristles, and they have claws on their flippers. They suckle their young from teats on the breast. The slight resemblance to a human figure with a fish-like tail has often given support to the belief in mermaids. They are harmless and inoffensive creatures, and have been reduced in numbers by the natives who spear them easily with harpoons.

BIRDS

New Guinea is noted for the richness and specialization of its birds. Most of them are, like the mammals, of Australian origin, but there are also many forms which have come from the Malayan region. The birds of paradise and the cassowaries have arisen on the island. There is a high proportion of handsome and brightly coloured forms; these may have been favoured by the comparative absence of predators. In addition to the many species of birds of paradise, there is an abundance of brightly coloured parrots, cockatoos and lories. Many of the pigeons, including the crowned pigeons, are very beautiful, and so are the numerous kingfishers, honey-suckers, the gay pittas and some remarkable flycatchers. On the other hand the thrushes, warblers and shrikes, which are dull-coloured birds on the whole, are represented by comparatively few species.

The birds of paradise are related to the crow family and have their headquarters in New Guinea and the immediately adjacent islands; only a few species extend westwards to the Moluccas or southwards into northern Australia. The females are more or less soberly coloured, but the males are resplendent with colour and have specially developed feathers which can be erected and are often vibrated. The largest is the emerald bird, about the size of a jay. The head and neck is covered with thick short feathers like velvet pile, bright straw colour above and emerald green beneath. From under the shoulder on each side springs a dense tuft of golden-orange plumes about 2 ft. in length, which the bird can raise to enclose most of its body. The two central tail feathers are nearly 3 ft. long and have a long, thin, wire-like appearance. The king bird of paradise is one of the smallest and most brilliant species; its two middle tail feathers are webbed only at the tip and are coiled into a beautiful spiral disk of a lovely emerald green colour.

Birds of paradise live chiefly in the lowland forests up to about 3,000 ft. above sea level. They are very shy and great patience is required to watch them; but the sight of these wonderful birds sporting themselves in a patch of sunlight is unforgettable. Little is known about their habits except what has been gathered from the stories of the natives. The males are described as congregating in a tree and holding dancing parties, vying with each other while the females keep in the background. Since the early days of the Portuguese voyagers the skins of birds of paradise have been a coveted article of commerce, and their numbers have suffered in consequence. Recently efforts have been made to protect them.

REPTILES AND AMPHIBIA

New Guinea is rich in reptiles. There are over 70 species of snakes, many of which are poisonous. There are eight species of *Typhlops*, a subterranean snake living on worms. There are eight species of boas and pythons, mostly less than 6 ft. long, and there are about 60 species of Colubridae, of which about half are poisonous. There are no vipers. Among the many species of lizard there are many nocturnal geckos with fragile tails and dilated toes for climbing. There are almost as many agamas which are rather similar in appearance, but are diurnal. Most, but not all, are arboreal, with very long non-fragile tails; and many of them can change their colour according to that of the background or as a sign of anger or other mood. There are seven species of *Varanus*, large carnivorous lizards either terrestrial or aquatic in habit. There are a great many species of skinks. These have long fragile tails as a rule, and many of them are without limbs. They may be either terrestrial or arboreal. Of the tortoises and turtles found in New Guinea, there are about a dozen species found in the rivers, and the green turtle, the loggerhead turtle and the leathery turtle are found in the sea. In the lower parts of the rivers and in the sea there is also one species of crocodile.

There are over 80 species of amphibia, all of which belong to one or other of five families of frogs; many are arboreal.

INSECTS

There is a rich invertebrate fauna, with many insects. The insects include numerous large and beautiful butterflies. Among the most striking are the Ornithopterae or bird-winged butterflies. They exhibit remarkable differences between the sexes in size and in the colour-pattern and shape of their wings. The wing-span of the females may be as much as 9 in. The males are smaller but more striking in colour and outline; they have broad splashes of brilliant metallic green, blue and gold off-set by velvet black. The females usually have pale mottling on a dark brown velvety background with an iridescent sheen.

Of the other orders of insects which are all abundantly represented, mosquitoes are particularly troublesome. The malaria-carrying *Anopheles* is to be found in most of the lowland regions. Knowledge of the less conspicuous forms of insects of New Guinea is very limited.

BIBLIOGRAPHICAL NOTE

The most useful accounts of the vegetation and forest resources of Papua and the Mandated Territory of New Guinea are: C. E. Lane-Poole, 'The Forests of Papua and the Mandated Territory of New Guinea', *Empire Forestry Journal*, vol. IV, pp. 206–34 (London, 1925); and C. E. Lane-Poole, *The Forest Resources of the Territories of Papua and New Guinea* (Parliament of the Commonwealth of Australia, Melbourne, 1925).

Useful works on Dutch New Guinea include: L. S. Gibbs, *A Contribution to the Phytogeography and Flora of the Arfak Mountains* . . . (London, 1917); and H. J. Lam, 'Vegetationsbilder aus dem Innern von Neu-Guinea', *Vegetationsbilder*, vol. xv, Heft 6–7 (Jena, 1923–4).

Works dealing with the fauna of New Guinea include: A. S. Le Soeuf and H. Burrell, *The Wild Animals of Australasia, embracing the Mammals of New Guinea and the nearer Pacific Islands* (London, 1926); R. B. Sharpe and J. Gould, *The Birds of New Guinea and the Adjacent Papuan Islands*, 5 vols. (London, 1875–88); E. Mayr, 'A Systematic and Faunal List of the Birds of New Guinea and the Adjacent Islands', *Occasional Papers of the American Museum of Natural History* (New York, 1941); Nelly de Rooij, *The Reptiles of the Indo-Australian Archipelago*, 2 vols. (Leiden, 1915, 1917); P. N. van Kampen, *The Amphibia of the Indo-Australian Archipelago* (Leiden, 1923).

Chapter VI

HISTORY

EXPLORATION

Before the age of European exploration began, the existence of New Guinea was known to the peoples of the East Indies. In the fourteenth century it was regarded by the princes of the Moluccas as being amongst their dependencies. There is evidence—notably in the survival of a few Malay words and phrases—that traders and hunters visited the north coast roughly as far east as 142° 30′ E and, possibly, in some areas penetrated inland. Their voyages, however, were almost certainly infrequent, and regular trade does not appear to have grown up.

The first European expedition to sight New Guinea was probably that of Antonio de Abreu and Francisco Serrão, which had been despatched from Malacca in 1511 by the Portuguese conqueror Albuquerque to explore the Moluccas. But New Guinea first obtained notice after the visit—popularly chronicled as a discovery—of the Spanish governor of the Moluccas, Jorge de Menezes, in 1526–7. Menezes referred to the country as 'Ilhas dos Papuas'—a word probably derived from the Malayan *papuwa*, meaning frizzly haired, which seems already to have been in use in the Moluccas to describe the New Guinea people. During the remainder of the sixteenth century a number of Spanish voyagers visited New Guinea, mainly during attempts to find a route eastward across the Pacific to Mexico from the Spanish outposts, first, in the Moluccas and, later, in the Philippines. In 1528 and again in 1529 the north coast was visited in this way by Alvaro de Saavedra. At many points on the coast Saavedra found traces of gold and therefore named the country 'Isla del Oro' ('Island of Gold'). About eight years later the island was visited by another Spaniard, Hernando Grijalva, who spent some time on the north coast, especially in the region of Geelvink bay, where he was eventually murdered by members of his crew. In 1545 the north coast was again visited and explored with some thoroughness by

Ynigo Ortez de Retes. Retes was struck by the similarity of the country to the Guinea coast in West Africa and thus came to give it its present name of Nueva Guinea (New Guinea).

By the end of the sixteenth century Spanish maritime exploration was almost over. The last Spanish voyage, however, was potentially one of the most important. This was the voyage of Diego de Prado and Luis Vaez de Torres in 1606. Prado and Torres had been officers under Quiros on his voyage from Peru in search of the fabulous continent, *Terra Australis Incognita*. In the New Hebrides their ship had become separated from that of their commander, and they had determined to continue the search independently. From the New Hebrides they sailed south-west until the weather forced them to turn northward. Their plan was to proceed by way of the north coast of New Guinea to the Philippines; but, being so far to the west, they struck New Guinea on the previously unknown south-east coast. They were unable to weather the south-eastern tip of the island and sailed westward instead. This course brought them eventually to the maze of islands, shoals, and intricate passages now known as Torres strait. Through this they succeeded in penetrating. The insularity of New Guinea had thus been proved. But the reports of the voyage were not made known and the problem continued to puzzle geographers for another century and a half.

In the seventeenth century knowledge of New Guinea was increased mainly by the Dutch. In 1605, a year before Torres' voyage, Willem Janszoon was sent out from Bantam, in Java, by the Dutch East India Company to explore the waters stretching eastwards from the Banda sea. This brought him to the south coast of New Guinea, which he followed as far as the western entrance to Torres strait. There he was misled by the great number of islands into thinking that the coast of New Guinea was continuous with that of the Cape York peninsula of northern Australia, which he discovered to the southward. Other Dutch navigators sent out from Java—notably Abel Tasman—added much to European knowledge of the coasts, the people and the resources of New Guinea. One of the most important Dutch voyages, however, originated in Holland and was primarily concerned with the discovery of *Terra Australis Incognita*. This was the expedition of Willem Corneliszoon Schouten and Jacob Le Maire. After crossing the Pacific in a north-westerly direction from cape Horn, the expedition sighted what was thought to be the coast of New Guinea on 25 June 1616. It was in reality New Ireland. They followed the coast north-west and rounded the neighbouring island of Lavongai. Continuing west they sighted the Admiralty islands, and then turned south and followed the coast of the New Guinea mainland. A number of further discoveries were made, notably those of Manam and the Schouten islands.

By the middle of the seventeenth century the broad outlines of the New Guinea coastline were relatively well known. There were still, however, many stretches of coast which had not been closely examined, and these still guarded several important secrets. In 1700 a major discovery was made by the Englishman William Dampier. Dampier approached the Pacific from the East Indies, rounded New Ireland, and followed the coast southward. At the south-west point of New Britain he discovered a passage westward. The lands which he had passed round were thus shown not to be part of the New Guinea mainland. In 1767 a further discovery was made by another English navigator, Philip Carteret. Carteret entered the inlet on the coast of New Britain to which Dampier had given the name of St George's bay and found that it too was in reality a strait. The lands now known as New Britain and New Ireland were, thus, two islands and not one. Three years later the final major point of un-certainty regarding the outlines of New Guinea was removed. Records of the discoveries of Prado and Torres had, at this time, recently become known; the existence of a strait between New Guinea and Australia was conclusively proved by Cook's passage through it in 1770.

The geographical work which remained to be done in New Guinea was mainly that of detailed coastal surveying and of exploration of the interior. The former was begun partly by French expeditions —those of D'Entrecasteaux (1792); Duperrey (1823-4); and Dumont d'Urville (1827-8)—and partly by British expeditions. The first im-portant British survey in the area was that carried out by Captain Blackwood, in H.M.S. *Fly*, in 1842; he examined the estuary of the Fly river and the western shores of the Gulf of Papua. Seven years later Captain Owen Stanley, in H.M.S. *Rattlesnake*, surveyed the Louisiade archipelago and the south-east end of the New Guinea mainland. In 1873 Captain John Moresby charted considerable stretches of both the south-east and north-east coasts. At the present time much surveying still remains to be done. The penetration of the interior of New Guinea has proceeded slowly. The mountainous nature of the country, the dense vegetation, and the attitude of suspicion of many native communities towards intruders have made progress slow and sometimes costly in human life.

THE BEGINNING OF COMMERCIAL DEVELOPMENT

Until after 1860 Europeans possessed no significant commercial interests in New Guinea. Whalers had begun to frequent the waters between the northern Solomons and the Bismarck archipelago and also those to the north of the New Guinea mainland; but, owing to the backwardness of the region, they seem to have made little use of local harbours as places of refreshment. On the south coast, trading vessels bound to or from the Australian colonies occasionally put in for wood and water. No regular trade, however, had grown up. Between 1865 and 1870 a change came about. Settlements were formed, mainly by Sydney interests, on some of the islands of Torres strait as centres for pearl and *bêche-de-mer* fishing. Labourers were obtained during the earlier years, mainly from the New Hebrides, the Loyalty islands and the Solomons. Diving for pearls was a miserable occupation. The party would set out from the station in a whale boat which would be moored over the reef to be worked. In this area the men had to dive generally to depths of from four to six fathoms. They would remain under water for about a minute and then return to the surface only for long enough to recover. And their day's work was not short. On shore living conditions were generally very poor; and, ultimately of greatest importance, the labourers were often kept indefinitely after their agreed period of indenture had expired. The industry thus became of political as well as economic importance, for it compelled the governments of New South Wales and Queensland to take an active interest in maintaining order in the New Guinea area.

About 1870 trading vessels from the Australian colonies began to visit the south-east coast of the New Guinea mainland. Their principal object was cedar timber, in which they had built up a profitable trade before 1880. More important was the commercial development during the same years in the northern part of the New Guinea area. In 1871 the German firm of Johann Cesar Godeffroy und Sohn, which had its Pacific headquarters at Apia in Samoa, began to send its vessels to the Bismarck archipelago and the Admiralty islands for copra, trochus shell and turtle shell. A year later the first permanent trading station in New Guinea was founded by an Englishman at Port Hunter in the Duke of York islands. In 1873 the Godeffroy company took the same action and founded two shore stations in the Gazelle peninsula of New Britain. During the following years trade and settlement increased, though it remained concentrated within the same area. In 1883 the number of resident Europeans was about thirty (including several missionaries) and the annual export of copra was about 2,000 tons.

By this latter year New Guinea had begun to be drawn within the field of operations of the native labour traffic (vol. I, pp. 300–7; vol. III, pp. 530–1, 625–6). In earlier years the labour trade had often been characterized by the grossest use of force and fraud to obtain recruits, and a high proportion of labourers had failed to return after their period of indenture. By this time, however, some degree of control had been imposed. Naval vessels were on the watch for misdemeanours; and in Queensland and Fiji, to which a majority of recruits were taken, elaborate codes of regulations had been drawn up and were being enforced. In the Bismarck archipelago the opposition of both missionaries and traders to labour recruiting were further important factors. As a result the labour trade did not have the serious disruptive effect on native society which it had elsewhere. None the less the number of recruits obtained was considerable. It was estimated that by the end of 1883 2,500 men had gone abroad; and in the following year recruiting spread also to the Louisiade archipelago, from which many hundreds of labourers were obtained. The Pacific islands labour traffic as a whole, however, was well past its peak; and in New Guinea the assumption of control over parts of the region by Britain and Germany during 1884 (p. 289) soon reduced it to very minor importance.

Of greater ultimate importance was the interest taken in New Guinea as a place for European agricultural settlement and mining development. In New South Wales a company had been formed as early as 1867 to undertake exploration with this end in view; in England a syndicate was formed in 1875 for similar purposes; and in Germany the Deutsche Seehandelsgesellschaft was organized by a group of Berlin bankers in 1880 for the purpose of founding a colony in New Guinea. Many other schemes were propounded during these years. Several advanced beyond the stage of discussion. Notably at the beginning of 1872 a party of prospectors sailed from Sydney for New Guinea. Their ship, however, was lost on the Great Barrier Reef, off the Queensland coast, and a large number of the men lost their lives. When gold was discovered near Port Moresby in 1877 a large body of miners actually arrived in New Guinea. For a few months there was a considerable settlement at Port Moresby, with an agent of the Queensland government maintaining law and order. Many of the miners died of hunger or of fever and no important strike was made; but, though the search was for the time being abandoned, the island continued to be regarded as a future source of mineral wealth. Of less importance to the future of New Guinea, but even more productive of immediate human suffering, was the fraudulent colonizing scheme of Charles Bonaventure du Breul, self-styled Marquis de Rays. In 1872 De Rays announced in France the existence of the 'colonie libre de Port Breton'—at Port Praslin, in southern New Ireland. From this beginning his pretensions grew, till he had created (according to the wholly false brochures which he issued) the empire of Nouvelle-France, covering all eastern New Guinea and the Solomon islands. Between 1879 and 1882 over 1,000 emigrants were sent to the capital of the fictitious empire at Port Breton. Most refused to land, when they saw the total absence of settlement and the lack of land suitable for settlement at Port Breton; but a considerable number went ashore, and of them many died there.

THE FOUNDATION OF CHRISTIAN MISSIONS

The earliest attempts to undertake missionary work in the New Guinea area were made by Roman Catholics, who settled on Murua in 1847, on Rooke island in Dampier strait in 1852, and at Geelvink bay in Dutch New Guinea three years later. At none of these places, however, were the missionaries able to overcome the hostility of the natives, and the attempt was therefore given up. The first successful work in eastern New Guinea was that of the London Missionary Society. During 1871 the society landed eight native teachers from the Loyalty islands on islands in the Torres strait region. In the following year a second party of teachers, made up of men from the Loyalties and the Cook islands, was brought to New Guinea. On this occasion several stations were established on the mainland—at Tureture and Katau, between the mouths of the Fly and Baxter rivers, and near Redscar bay. Then in 1874 W. G. Lawes, the first European missionary of the L.M.S. to be stationed in New Guinea, settled with his family at Port Moresby. From this time progress was steadily maintained. Other Europeans and a growing number of native teachers from various parts of the Pacific were stationed in New Guinea; in 1884 the first New Guinea native accepted for the ministry was ordained. By this latter date the society's field of work stretched from west of the Fly delta to Samarai, in the east, and from there northward to Milne bay. The practice of the mission was for its European members to travel during much of their time round the coastal villages, gaining the confidence of the people and learning something of their languages. It was recognized that this was only preliminary work—that the people welcomed their visits mainly for the gifts they received and that only the dimmest understanding of the aims of the mission could in this way be inculcated. The next stage was the permanent stationing of native teachers in the villages and the gaining of recruits for the missionary training institutions at Port Moresby and elsewhere. After 1888 the British administration (p. 132) became a valuable ally in the work.

Meanwhile, a Methodist mission had also begun work, taking as its field the Bismarck archipelago. As in the L.M.S. mission, Europeans occupied only the controlling positions. The first settlement was made in 1875 at Port Hunter, in the Duke of York group, by the Rev. George Brown and nine Samoan and Fijian teachers. The first converts were baptized three years later. At that time the mission had recently suffered the loss of one of its Fijian ministers and three of his helpers, all of whom had been killed by natives of the interior of New Britain. Gradually, however, the presence of missionaries began to be more generally accepted; and by the end of the century a large proportion of the people in many areas—including both the main islands of New Britain and New Ireland—were actively interested in the work of the mission.

Before this the Methodist Church of Australasia had extended its field of work to the southward into what is now eastern Papua. In 1889 it had been invited by the British administration to enter that area. A conference was duly held of representatives of the L.M.S. and of the Methodist and Anglican churches, at which it was agreed that the Methodists should work at the eastern tip of the New Guinea mainland and in the D'Entrecasteaux, Trobriand, Murua and Louisiade groups. The first station founded under this agreement was established on the island of Dobu in 1891. In the same year the Anglican body, the Australian Board of Missions, began work on the north-east coast of New Guinea.

Also on the north coast, but further to the west, two German Lutheran missions were by this time at work; the Neuendettelsau missionary society had entered the Finschhafen district in 1886 and the Rhenish missionary society had begun in the Astrolabe bay area a year later.

The Roman Catholics made a renewed attempt to begin work in 1885, but again they were unsuccessful. In 1889, however, a more elaborately organized venture was undertaken. A Vicariate Apostolic of British New Guinea was formed and entrusted to the French missionaries of the Sacred Heart of Jesus (of Issoudun). Seven years later north-east New Guinea and the Bismarck archipelago were similarly entrusted to the Society of the Divine Word.

POLITICAL INTERVENTION

Although it was widely believed that New Guinea was rich in gold and other minerals and that it would eventually be important agriculturally, the development of political interest in the country was not greatly influenced by economic factors. The Dutch East India Company, which had succeeded to the claims of the Moluccan rulers over the coasts of western New Guinea, seriously contemplated action to assert its rights on only one occasion. In the years following the close of the American War of Independence the Dutch thought they saw signs of projected British expansion in south-east Asia. To protect one exposed flank of their own sphere in the Indies, they determined to occupy New Guinea; but the resources of the company at the time were insufficient to allow the plan to be carried out. A similar fear of either British or French action was responsible for the eventual assumption of possession over western New Guinea in 1828. At that time a settlement was established at Triton bay, on the south coast. This was abandoned in 1836, owing to its unhealthiness for Europeans and its exposure to attack by pirates; but the Dutch continued to demonstrate their sovereignty by occasional visits by men-of-war.

British intervention similarly developed as a result of strategic considerations. The growth of trade, the foundation of mission stations, and still more the opening up of a steamship route from Australia to India by way of Torres strait, directed increasing attention to the position of New Guinea after about 1870. It was widely felt—by naval officers on the Australia Station and by Australian politicians, journalists and others—that the security of Australia depended to a perceptible extent on the future political status of eastern New Guinea. In 1875 the government of New South Wales urged that New Guinea, the Bismarck archipelago, and various other islands be annexed by Britain without delay. At that time, however, conditions made it seem unlikely that any other Power was contemplating action in the area. On strategic grounds, the New South Wales demand appeared premature. The only factor which could have produced a more active British policy at that time was the need for maintaining order among Europeans. This, however, was

provided for by the appointment of a British High Commissioner for
the Western Pacific in 1877 (vol. I, p. 319) and by the extension
of the boundaries of Queensland, so as to include a number of the
islands in Torres strait, in 1878. Within a few years, however, the
situation had changed. The United States, France, and, most notably,
Germany were taking an increasing interest in Pacific affairs. Even
Italy and Russia were suspected by some of having expansionist aims
in the south Pacific. During 1882 public discussion in Australia took
more definitely the form of a demand for immediate annexation. In
February 1883 the Premier of Queensland cabled to London for
permission to annex New Guinea. He asked that authority to act
should be communicated to him through the same channel. When it
did not come, the Queensland government decided to proceed with
its plans, even without authority. The support of the other Australian
governments had been promised, and it was believed that the British
government was unlikely to refuse to validate what had already been
done. Colonial opinion was right in part. An early British decision
became inevitable, but acceptance of the Queensland action was not
the only form it could take. In the event, a protectorate over the
coastal areas was proposed on condition that the Australian colonies
met the expenses involved. An Inter-Colonial Convention, attended
by representatives of all the Australian colonies and of New Zealand
and by the Governor of Fiji, met at Sydney later in the year and
discussed the proposal. It reiterated the original Australian demand
—that immediate steps be taken to acquire the whole of non-Dutch
New Guinea.

Meanwhile, the Australian agitation had made more real that which
was most feared: early German action in New Guinea had become
almost certain. Hitherto, the view that colonial expansion was a
necessary accompaniment to the protection of German trade had been
held only by a minority. At this time it was obtaining much wider
acceptance, and the situation in the Pacific was one of the factors
bringing the change about. It was urged upon the German government that a policy of annexation in the Pacific would greatly increase
the already extensive German trade, whereas failure to act would lead
to the gradual loss of the markets and sources of raw materials and
labour already possessed by German firms. In August 1884 the
German government informed the British Foreign Office that it
wished to protect German interests in New Guinea and the islands.

No attempt was made to define British and German spheres of
interest in New Guinea in exact terms, but it was understood that

Britain was mainly concerned with the areas closest to Australia and Germany with the Bismarck archipelago and the north coast. During the last quarter of the year representatives of both Powers were active in the area, proclaiming British protection and German sovereignty respectively. Disputes arose regarding the extent of claims, but they were fairly quickly disposed of. A boundary settlement was published in June 1885.

ECONOMIC DEVELOPMENT AFTER 1884

The establishment of British and German control in New Guinea was not followed by any sudden economic change. Most of the trades which had grown up during the preceding fifteen years continued in existence. The export of timber declined for some years, until sandal-wood-cutting along the coast of what is now the Central Division of Papua was undertaken after about 1891. The collection of *bêche-de-mer* in the Torres strait area was carried on on much the same scale as before. By contrast, pearling did expand to some extent. Within a year or two of 1884 pearl-diving was being undertaken in the Louisiade archipelago, as well as among the Torres strait islands, to which it had previously been confined.

More spectacular was the development of gold-mining. In 1888 gold was discovered on the island of Tagula, in the Louisiade archipelago. As soon as the news reached Australia, there was a rush to the new goldfield. For about a year several hundred miners worked on Tagula, but by the end of that time production was declining. Meanwhile, however, other islands of the archipelago had been explored, not without success, for on Misima a discovery was made which was eventually to prove of considerably greater importance. The inevitable migration soon took place, and for roughly a year some hundreds of prospectors found employment on Misima. At the end of that time production did not fall to negligible proportions, however, as it had done on Tagula, but continued for many years on a diminishing scale. (Eventually it increased again; and during the years immediately before the present war Misima was producing gold to a greater value than ever before.) Prospectors were also active in other parts of British New Guinea. Eventually they met with some success. In 1895 discoveries were made on the Mambare river, in the south-east of the New Guinea mainland, and also on the island of Murua. Both these finds led to the development of productive goldfields. From the Mambare, miners moved to the Gira and the Yodda, from both of which rivers payable quantities of gold continued to be obtained over many years. The discovery on Murua attracted even more interest. So rich did it appear that during 1897 steamers ran to the island at fortnightly intervals from Queensland, bringing crowds of hopeful prospectors and supplies to maintain the growing settlement. In 1902, when alluvial mining on Murua was declining, several quartz-crushing plants were installed there, and production rose again. From about 1899 till 1906 gold production in British New Guinea is believed to have reached an annual value of between about £75,000 and £90,000. In comparison with production in other areas, this is a very small figure; but, in relation to the undeveloped state of New Guinea, it is quite a large one. It made gold-mining easily the most important industry in British New Guinea; and, since it brought considerable numbers of Europeans into contact with the native inhabitants, its significance was more than merely economic. After 1906 the industry declined. The discovery of gold on the Lakekamu river, inland from the south coast, in 1909 arrested the decline but did not restore production to its former level. Mining was not again of primary importance in New Guinea till after the discovery of the Morobe goldfield in former German New Guinea in the 1920's (pp. 205–7).

In the intervening period New Guinea depended primarily on the export of copra. It has already been noticed that in the Bismarck archipelago trade with the natives for copra was already well developed before 1884. After that time the German Neu-Guinea Kompagnie established many coconut plantations, both in the archipelago and on the coast of north-eastern New Guinea. Before 1914 a large area of planted land was in full bearing. In British New Guinea (or Papua, as it became in 1906) plantation agriculture was slower in developing. It did not really establish itself until after the passing of the Land Ordinance of 1906. In the next few years, however, large areas were leased. During the four years 1910–14 30,000 acres were planted. These lands mainly came into bearing after the war of 1914–18. Coconuts have remained the principal crop grown, though experiments have been made with many others and significant areas have been planted with rubber, cocoa, coffee and sisal (pp. 218–20).

THE ESTABLISHMENT OF ADMINISTRATIVE CONTROL

It was some years after the formal establishment of political control before effective governments were functioning in either British or

German New Guinea. In the British sphere intervention had been limited to the proclamation of a protectorate over the south coast and the country immediately adjacent to it and to the appointment of a special commissioner to New Guinea, with very limited and incompletely defined powers. The commissioner, Major-General Sir Peter Scratchley, arrived in New Guinea in August 1885. Like Sir Arthur Gordon, who had lately retired from the office of High Commissioner for the Western Pacific, Scratchley believed that the primary aim of British colonial policy must be the protection of native interests. 'New Guinea,' he wrote, 'must be governed for the natives and by the natives.' To make such a policy practicable, it was first of all necessary to bring some sort of order into relations between Europeans and natives. Scratchley, therefore, prepared regulations to control coastal shipping and to abolish some of the most undesirable practices of traders; he tried to prevent exploring parties penetrating into the interior, unless they were properly organized and equipped; and he urged Protestant and Catholic missionaries not to encroach on one another's fields of work.

In carrying out his policy he was handicapped not only by his limited legal powers but by lack of adequate physical resources. He arrived in New Guinea with only four officers to assist him in administration; there was no proper police force; and, while preparations were being made to establish an administrative centre at Port Moresby, his headquarters had to remain on board a ship. The most strenuous work awaiting him was the investigation of outrages committed by natives on Europeans or by Europeans on natives. He soon formed the opinion that in nearly every case Europeans were, ultimately, in a large degree responsible; he found that the traders were all too often 'reckless, unscrupulous, brutal, and piratical'. Yet the natives were often immediately responsible for the acts which he was called on to investigate, and had to be taught not to kill white men. But what were the means at his disposal? It was extremely difficult to apprehend a European, in most cases, by the time news of his actions had been obtained, and even more difficult to bring a charge against him successfully in a court of law. So far as natives were concerned, it was generally impossible to discover the individuals responsible. The only punishment which could be inflicted was to order a man-of-war to open fire on the village to which the guilty individuals were believed to belong, and this merely created antagonism without engendering respect for British law or authority. Scratchley died in December 1885; but, short as his period of office had been, it had been long enough for him to prove that the nebulous system of protectorate administration must be replaced by some form of Crown Colony government. The change was not made at once. But in 1888 Dr William MacGregor arrived in New Guinea to proclaim British sovereignty and to become the first Governor of the Colony of British New Guinea.

MacGregor remained in New Guinea for ten years, during which time the foundations were laid of the system of government which remained in existence till the Japanese invasion of 1942. MacGregor's ideas were similar to those of Scratchley: his aims were the protection and development of the native peoples. As the colleague of Sir Arthur Gordon in Fiji, he had watched developments in New Guinea for the past thirteen years. He was, therefore, ready to put his policy into effect as quickly as material circumstances allowed. He brought into force codes of regulations governing the alienation of native land and the recruitment of native labour. But the most striking part of his work was the series of long journeys which he made into the interior, discovering the character of the land and its inhabitants as a preliminary to the extension of political control. Another aspect of the same policy was the creation of a force of Armed Constabulary in 1890. At first this was composed of Solomon islanders, under the charge of Fijian non-commissioned officers; but MacGregor introduced native Papuans into it as rapidly as possible. Within a comparatively few years, it had become an instrument of major importance in the establishment of the rule of law and in the spreading of Western ideas through a large part of the colony. During the whole of his period of office, MacGregor was severely handicapped by lack of adequate financial resources. It had been arranged in 1888 that the administration in New Guinea should be maintained by an annual grant from the Australian colonies of £15,000, and that Great Britain should provide the running costs of a steamer for use round the coasts. At the time of his retirement in 1898 this agreement expired, and in the following years considerable expansion along the broad lines already laid down became possible. With the transfer of responsibility for the control of New Guinea from Great Britain to the Commonwealth of Australia in 1902, the territory was able to expand its services still further.

In German New Guinea an almost equally inauspicious start had been made in the years immediately following annexation. In May 1885 administrative control was placed in the hands of the Neu-Guinea Kompagnie. Like most chartered companies possessing administrative powers, the Neu-Guinea Kompagnie was slow in developing any active native policy. Not only was its primary interest commercial, but it never achieved sufficient commercial success to be able to afford to extend its sphere of political influence much further than its economic interests dictated. In general, it left the native peoples alone so long as its own affairs suffered no interference. The company, however, was relieved of its administrative responsibilities temporarily in 1889; and, when it received them back in 1893, it did so only in a limited form. One result was that in 1896 the Imperial Judge at the capital, Herbertshöhe (Kokopo), in New Britain, inaugurated locally a simple form of native administration (the *luluai* system, p. 190). After the final transfer of control from the company to the government in 1899 the *luluai* system was extended to other areas. It remained, however, the most striking characteristic of German administration, until it came to an end in 1914, that very little effort was made to bring the native peoples of the interior into contact with the central government.

MODERN NEW GUINEA

The economic and political history of New Guinea during the past thirty years is described in some detail elsewhere in this volume (Chapters IX, X). Here, it is necessary only to add that recent development has mainly followed the lines laid down in the earlier years of European activity in New Guinea. Economically, the area remains primarily dependent on gold-mining and copra production, though, of course, the value of gold production has risen enormously since the discovery and development of the Morobe field. Politically, British methods of government, and particularly of native administration, were in some considerable degree extended to former German New Guinea when it came under Australian control during the war of 1914–18. The administration of the mandated territory, unlike its German predecessor, has made a vigorous effort to extend its control into the interior of the New Guinea mainland. But, in doing so, it has retained and developed the *luluai* system, which it inherited. Despite some recommendations to the contrary, the political systems of Papua and the Mandated Territory of New Guinea remained completely separate up to the time of the Japanese invasion at the beginning of 1942. The events of the time which followed, when New Guinea was the scene of large-scale warfare, destroyed many landmarks, amongst them the political. One result has been that in March 1945 it was announced in the Australian Commonwealth Parliament that a single provisional administration for the two territories was to be set up.

BIBLIOGRAPHICAL NOTE

There is no history of New Guinea as a whole. An outline of the history of Papua is given by Lewis Lett, *The Papuan Achievement* (Melbourne, 1942). The best short account of the history of the Mandated Territory of New Guinea is in S. W. Reed, *The Making of Modern New Guinea* (Philadelphia, 1943); this contains a good bibliography. Material on Dutch New Guinea is mainly to be found in historical works on the Netherlands East Indies; there are a number of references in B. H. M. Vlekke, *Nusantara: A History of the East Indian Archipelago* (Cambridge, Mass., 1943).

Descriptive works on New Guinea are very numerous. Among the more important books by those who have known the country at different periods are: J. B. Jukes, *Narrative of the Surveying Voyage of H.M.S. Fly . . . in Torres Strait, New Guinea, and other islands . . . during the years, 1842–1846*, 2 vols. (London, 1847); J. MacGillivray, *Narrative of the Voyage of H.M.S. Rattlesnake, commanded by the late Captain Owen Stanley, R.N., F.R.S., etc., during the years 1846–1850*, 2 vols. (London, 1853); John Moresby, *Discoveries and Surveys in New Guinea and the D'Entrecasteaux Islands. A Cruise in Polynesia and Visits to the Pearl-shelling Stations in Torres Straits . . .* (London, 1876); Wilfred Powell, *Wanderings in a Wild Country; or, Three Years amongst the Cannibals of New Britain* (London, 1883); C. Kinloch Cooke (editor), *Australian Defences and New Guinea. Compiled from the Papers of the Late Major-General Sir Peter Scratchley* (London, 1887); H. H. Romilly, *The Western Pacific and New Guinea . . .* (London, 1887); George Brown, *An Autobiography* (London, 1908); J. H. P. Murray, *Papua or British New Guinea* (London, 1912); (J.) Hubert (P.) Murray, *Papua of To-Day* (London, 1925).

More specialized works include: J. H. Niau, *The Phantom Paradise: The Story of the Expedition of the Marquis de Rays* (Sydney, 1936); A. C. V. Melbourne, 'The Relations between Australia and New Guinea, up to the establishment of British rule in 1888', *Royal Australian Historical Society, Journal and Proceedings*, vol. XII, pp. 288–314; vol. XIII, pp. 145–72 (Sydney, 1926–7, 1927–8); Lewis Lett, *Knights Errant of Papua* (Edinburgh and London, 1935) (a history of administrative patrols); F. W. Eggleston (editor), *The Australian Mandate for New Guinea* (Melbourne, 1928).

Chapter VII

POPULATION

In British New Guinea and the Bismarck archipelago the native population is sparsely distributed in small, and for the most part, widely spaced villages. Large tracts of country are uninhabited and a negligible percentage is under cultivation. Native settlements which house more than 2,000 villagers are uncommon. In 1940 the enumerated native population of the mandated territory was 668,871 (including 49,067 natives of the Kieta District and excluding 39,344 indentured labourers). In 1936–7 the native population of Papua was 230,962, excluding 7,965 indentured labourers. In both areas the number of natives recorded by census officers was increasing yearly, but parts of the interior of both New Guinea and New Britain remained outside their patrols. It is thus impossible to estimate accurately the numbers still to be added to the enumerated population of approximately 1,000,000; but these are probably not more than a few hundred thousand. Similarly, average figures of the growth or decrease of population are not known, and in the following account such details will be given only for those islands which were completely controlled in 1920, and for native settlements subject to continuous investigations such as the villages around Port Moresby.

The New Guinea peoples live by subsistence agriculture and, in some cases, by fishing. Accumulation of surplus food is rarely possible; and displacements from their gardens brought about by modern warfare, the disruption of relief measures normally undertaken in times of famine and lack of medical supervision must have decreased the population during the Japanese occupation of part of the area. This account is based on conditions prior to 1942, when in the majority of districts, after a long decline, the population was either stable or even showed a slight increase. Wartime conditions have upset these adjustments and in some areas have ruined for a time the work of the administrations of Papua and the mandated territory, leaving a great range of new problems to be met.

DISTRIBUTION OF NATIVE POPULATION

No general review of the distribution of native peoples is feasible in the New Guinea area. Nor is it possible to say more of average density in an area as yet so incompletely surveyed and mapped than that it is approximately 3 per sq. mile in Papua and between 5 and 6 in the mandated territory. The region presents an immense variety of habitat, and there are many characteristic forms of utilization of the environment. Some peoples are reef dwellers and fishermen; others have their villages within sheltered harbours and give part of the year to trade; other groups are cultivators of taro and coconuts and live on atolls; some cultivate the rich volcanic soils of mountain slopes where the rain forest begins to thin out; and, high on the central plateau, other peoples congregate on the alluvial terraces of the head-streams of the great rivers which flow from this water-parting. These and many other groups, with their distinctive cultures, are found as pockets of population. High mountains, seas with treacherous tide races, or many miles of dense forest may cut them off from other groups. Outside contacts, the stimuli of trade and exchange characteristic, for example, of Java for many centuries, have only recently operated on a large scale in and around New Guinea.

The major part of the population of New Guinea and New Britain lives away from the coast. Reef dwellers are found mainly in the off-lying islands of New Guinea, in the atolls west of Manus (the Ninigo and Hermit groups) and in Manus and the islands which adjoin it, such as Rambutyo (Fig. 24). In Manus three-quarters of the people are coastal and only six interior villages are without contact with the coastal peoples. Of coast dwellers who trade by sea those of Manam and adjoining islands of the northern volcanic arc (Fig. 7), who trade with the mainland, are one of many examples. There is much sea-borne trade between the coastal villages of the Gulf of Papua. In some island groups, a fair proportion live well inland and utilize volcanic soils at considerable elevations. This is true of relatively small islands like Goodenough (Fig. 62) and Fergusson, which rise steeply from the sea and have heavy forest on the lower mountain slopes. Occupation of high-level upper basins of rivers is common throughout the fringes of the main cordillera of the New Guinea mainland. Fig. 33A shows this characteristic feature on the middle slopes of the mountains of the Huon peninsula and along the upper Markham river and its tributaries in the Morobe District. Densities here are greater than along the Huon peninsula coast (much of the northern coast is rocky

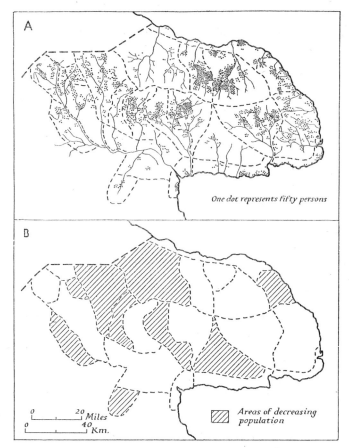

Fig. 33. The population of the Huon peninsula
A, distribution of population; B, areas of decreasing population. Based on L. G. Vial, 'Some Statistical Aspects of Population in the Morobe District, New Guinea', *Oceania*, vol. VIII, p. 385 and statistics on p. 390 (Sydney, 1937–8).

and of barren limestone). The population thins out up-slope, leaving each river basin as a largely self-contained unit.

The lower basins of the three great rivers Sepik, Ramu and Fly have a slight population, apart from the natives of Kiwai and other islands of the Fly delta who belong rather to the coastal peoples. These lower basins are ill-drained swamp lands and wide fringes of nipa, pit-pit and sago swamps stretch inland from the river banks. Patrols have frequently noticed the scarcity of riverine settlements, and it is obvious that the larger rivers of New Guinea were not arteries of native trade and lines of communication. The upper basins, especially that of the upper Sepik, support fair numbers of people, notably those on the alluvial terraces which bound the Sepik headstreams west of the Victor Emanuel range. These interior peoples are still little affected by white influences, though prior to 1940 some were showing the decline which follows initial contacts. For example, in the Morobe District, though the decline was already arrested around the coastal settlements established by whites, it was noticeable in the interior where their influence had more recently spread (Fig. 33B).

REGIONAL VARIATIONS IN POPULATION TRENDS

It is difficult to draw very definite conclusions regarding general population trends because of the inadequacy of early census material. In this part of the Pacific estimates by European navigators and traders of native populations date only from the late nineteenth century. Like all such cursory examinations, they are not reliable. Nevertheless, in some parts of New Guinea and the mandated territory the facts are clearly established, and even for the area as a whole it is possible to make a few generalizations.

The distribution of the major cultural groups is outlined on pp. 152–3. Nearly two-thirds of the 668,871 enumerated people in the mandated territory are Melanesian. Their decline is less acute than that of the small numbers of relatively pure Micronesians and Polynesians, of whom there are remnants in the western isles of the Bismarck archipelago (Micronesian) and in the islands east of New Ireland (Polynesian) where, in each case, only a few hundreds survive. Manus, with its mixed Polynesian-Melanesian strains, has now a stationary population. As a general rule, Papuans are found throughout the New Guinea mainland (except on the coastal plains), and in the interior of New Britain. The decline of the Papuans varies with the length of their contacts with whites. The first stages may be seen in those areas of the Western Division of Papua which have recently come under control. In other districts there was an initial decline, but now, after about thirty years, the population is showing a slight increase.

Samples of Stable or Increasing Populations

The population of the more settled districts of Papua, especially of the Central Division, was increasing before 1940. An annual count was taken of the villages of Elevala, Tanobada and Hanuabada on

the outskirts of Port Moresby. The Table on p. 140 is a representative
sample of the record over the period 1916–28. By 1936–7 the increase
was continuing: there were 110 births as against 67 deaths. The total
increase in the period 1916–28 was 188. Better living conditions are
partly responsible, together with more assured food supplies, thanks
to the availability of garden land on the Laloki river which was
previously inaccessible because of inter-tribal warfare.

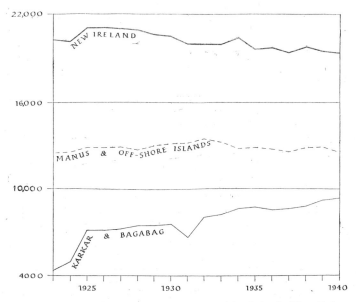

Fig. 34. Samples of native population trends from islands in the New Guinea area,
1923–40 (I)

Compiled from statistics in the Commonwealth of Australia *Report to the Council
of the League of Nations on the Administration of the Territory of New Guinea*
(Melbourne, to 1927; Canberra, from 1928).

The population of the islands off Aitape, and of Kairiru, the
Schouten group, Manam, Bagabag, and Karkar, which are all of
volcanic formation, has shown an increase during the period of the
mandate administration. Figs. 34–5 show this, as well as slight
population increases in Manus and its off-lying islands and more
marked upward trends in the totals for the Duke of York and Siassi
groups, off the north-east and west of New Britain. All these islands
were completely controlled by 1923 although the sharp upward trends
in some of the census figures for the period 1923–5 suggest that some

Growth of Population in the Port Moresby Villages

Year	Births		Deaths		Total births	Total deaths	Natural increase	Total population
	Male	Female	Male	Female				
1916	54	46	40	38	100	78	22	1,648
1917	47	43	29	32	90	61	29	1,677
1918	55	39	46	49	94	95	— 1	1,676
1919	51	47	31	30	98	61	37	1,713
1920	40	47	32	24	87	56	31	1,744
1921	50	37	30	26	87	56	31	1,775
1922	36	35	28	39	71	67	4	1,779
1923	44	48	41	35	92	76	16	1,795
1924	43	36	41	41	79	82	— 3	1,792
1925	29	34	20	35	63	55	8	1,800
1926	40	44	35	44	84	79	5	1,805
1927	34	35	25	33	69	58	11	1,816
1928	39	28	26	21	67	47	20	1,836

Based on Territory of Papua *Annual Report* for 1926–7, p. 39; for 1927–8, p. 26 (Canberra, 1928, 1929).

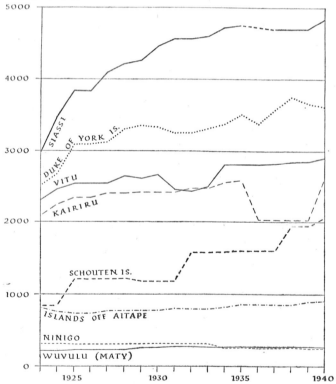

Fig. 35. Samples of native population trends from islands in the New Guinea area, 1923–40 (II)

Based on the same source as Fig. 34.

natives were omitted from the early counts. The misleading level
trends of parts of the Kairiru and Schouten islands curves result
either from absence of parts of the male population as indentured
labourers, or from incomplete census returns. Fig. 34 shows the
population of New Ireland proper as having declined slightly since
1923. Most of the islands which surround it have shown slight
increases in the same period (Fig. 36).

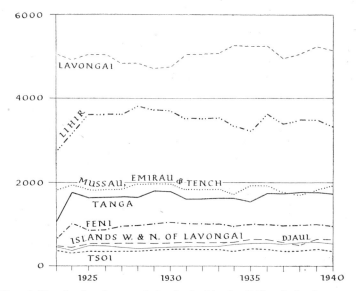

Fig. 36. Trends of native population in the islands off New Ireland, 1923–40
Based on the same source as Fig. 34.

In New Ireland especially there had previously been a decline
during the last years of German administration; in 1914 considerable loss of life occurred during a famine, and the influenza epidemics
of 1918–19 took toll of the population. It will be seen from the
following figures that only the Lihir, Tanga and Anir groups had
passed their 1914 totals in 1940. The 1914 figures do not include
German estimates of additional natives not enumerated. (See Table
on p. 142.)

In New Britain the enumerated population in 1923 was 48,300,
and it was then estimated that 13,000 natives lived outside the areas
covered by the count. The figure of 77,766 for 1940 represents an
increase in the census area rather than in the total population. In
certain regions, notably those longest under European control around

Population of New Ireland and its Off-lying Islands
(excluding indentured labourers)

Island or Group	1914	1923	1925	1930	1935	1940
New Ireland	26,488	20,235	21,067	20,516	19,644	19,417
Islands between New Ireland and Lavongai	811	591	685	698	698	698
Lavongai	6,539	5,066	5,045	4,733	5,234	5,188
Mussau, Emirau and Tench	2,160	1,821	1,843	1,978	1,958	1,910
Tabar Is.	3,483	2,287	2,555	2,489	2,135	1,952
Lihir Is.	2,828	2,764	3,625	3,718	3,250	3,394
Tanga Is.	1,241	1,008	1,663	1,800	1,571	1,778
Feni (Anir) Is.	633	650	864	1,039	879	913
Tsoi Is.	—	384	370	403	406	379
Tingwon	—	48	42	44	70	68
Djaul	—	455	498	460	547	562
Islands W and N of Lavongai	—	467	515	538	640	632
Total	44,173	35,776	38,772	38,416	37,032	36,891

Based on Commonwealth of Australia *Report to the Council of the League of Nations on the Administration of the Territory of New Guinea* for 1922–40 (Melbourne, to 1927; Canberra, from 1928).

Blanche bay, the population has increased even though tuberculosis infections rose in the early years of mandate administration. The natives of Matupi island, who are the petty traders of Rabaul, thrive and increase, though they have lost their former culture. Malaria is virtually absent on Matupi island. Decreases in population were a feature of parts of the interior of New Britain, not so much on account of low birth rates but because of high mortality rates among children between the ages of 1 and 3 years. Faulty feeding and decreased resistance to endemic diseases were largely responsible.

Between the census of 1934–5 and that of 1936–7, parts of the Morobe District with a total population of 81,000 showed increases of population. These sub-districts lay around the coast and in the eastern half of the Huon peninsula, where mission influence is of long standing (Fig. 33), in the thinly peopled Markham valley, in a belt from the middle and upper Watut river to the coast at Salamaua, and throughout the whole southern portion of the division. This position was attained in spite of an increase of 181% in recruiting of indentured labour in the district between 1924–5 and 1934–5. Recruiting is not necessarily a factor in depopulation, especially in Papua. Here labourers are generally absent from their villages for shorter periods than are those of the mandated territory. Indentured labourers—e.g., those of the goldfields of the Morobe District—live under increasingly strict and effective medical supervision. An epidemic of dysentery in the Lakekamu goldfield caused 255 deaths among 443 natives in 1909; but that of 1926–7 in the Bulowat goldfield, whilst it produced 522 cases in 5 months among a native labour force of 2,000 to 3,000, caused only 29 deaths.

The initial fall of population after the establishment of white supervision, and the gradually accelerated rise after a stationary period during adjustment, seem to have been common features of most coastal districts during the period of administration by Europeans. The following figures for 22 villages in the Central Division of Papua are typical: 1900, 10,423; 1910, 10,023; 1915, 11,490.

In some cases the tendency of the population to return to an equilibrium again, or to increase, has been long delayed. For example, in the formerly prosperous Trobriand islands a low birth rate (rather than a high death rate), infanticide, influenza and whooping-cough epidemics, and the system of *kawogala* made for a decline which became noticeable during 1920–30. *Kawogala* involves abstinence from all foods except fruits grouped as *kawailua* (which lack nutriment) during the two-year mourning period of a widow and results in the death of an infant which she may be suckling. The Papuan census returns for the period 1931–5 showed the population of the Trobriand group to be 9,664. This was a greatly improved position as compared with the early 'twenties, when there were decreases of 100 in some years, and with 1926–7, when there was a decrease of 55 and the enumerated population was 8,571. The stabilizing of the population is due to increased medical supervision, the reduction of the percentage of those natives suffering from venereal diseases (from 10% in 1918 to 1% in 1928), and the introduction of nutritious foods into the *kawailua* group.

Samples of Decreasing Populations

Persistent decline in population has occurred in many parts of the New Guinea area. The magnitude of this has varied regionally as will be seen in the following details for some sample areas.

In Papua major decreases have been recorded before and since the war of 1914–18. These occurred in the Morehead district of the Western Division, in the Suau district of the Eastern Division, in Rossel island and in the Trobriand islands. No reliable census has been made in the Morehead district and deserted villages do not necessarily imply depopulation. During an investigation made in 1930 it was found that the middle Bensbach villages were temporarily deserted because the population was attending festivals across the Dutch border in the country of the 'Europeanized' Marind-Anim. Nevertheless, there has been a progressive decrease in the area; this was accelerated by heavy mortality during an epidemic of pneumonic influenza in 1919. Over most parts of the Morehead district the average density of population is one native to 2 sq. miles of country. The Suau district of the Eastern Division lies south of the Cloudy mountains of the southern tip of Papua. It includes the coast and off-lying islands between Samarai and Mullens harbour. Between 1918–19 and 1924–5 there were 369 births and 1,007 deaths, which reduced the population under review from 6,211 to 5,573. The average annual death rate may well have been higher than 27 per thousand, as the figure for deaths probably includes few of the children who died at birth. A smallpox epidemic in 1870 and further epidemics, droughts and famines prior to 1920, seem to have started the decline which has been variously attributed to abortion, birth restriction, infanticide, primitive midwifery and official disapproval of native feasts which were formerly a means of ensuring adequate output from the native gardens. Suggested remedies for the apathetic state of the population have been to widen the social interests of the people, to teach them to improve their agriculture, and, by training and supervision, to stop the waste of child life.

Rossel is a relatively remote island surrounded by seas which are treacherous to native craft. In 1908 the population was 1,500 and had already been much reduced by blackbirding. In that year a recruiting ship returned with only half the islanders whom it had previously taken to Queensland. In 1913 there were many deaths from dysentery; by 1920 the population was 1,415, and it afterwards continued to decrease. The figures in 1920 for the 145 villages of Rossel included 406 male adults, 436 female adults, 312 male children and 261 female children under 16 years. Only 36 men had each more than three children. In 1927 deaths were almost equal to births in Rossel.

In 1929–30 the east coast of New Ireland was examined from Kavieng to Karu, which is approximately centrally placed on the east coast. This is an area where there has been much alienation of coastal land for plantations, so that gardens are now further up-slope from settlements. The natives are responsible for the upkeep of those sections of the coast road which adjoin their villages, and 27% of the able-bodied male population may be recruited in any year to remote centres. In 1929 the population of sub-districts between Kavieng and Karu was 8,645, comprising 4,846 males and 3,799 females. The

average issue per union was two children, the average surviving until
the age of two was 1·6, and the average surviving to higher ages was
1·3. There were, in all, 3,845 surviving children and 1,419 men and
women above reproductive age. Sterility was fairly common among
the younger women, a feature which was already noticeable in 1913.
On this coast epidemics, especially in 1918–19, and high infant
mortality, especially around Karu, took greatest toll of the population.
Between 1929 and 1931 the population of 35 villages visited by medical
patrols from Kavieng decreased from 4,280 to 4,122 (417 deaths
and 259 births). A remedy was sought in improved methods of infant
welfare, more intensive medical supervision (as mortality was fairly
evenly spread over all age groups) and improvements in native diet.

The Western islands of the Bismarck archipelago showed in 1940
various stages in the extinction of the native population. One native
was left on the Anchorite islands, 25 remained in the Hermit group,
225 in Aua, 248 in Wuvulu (Maty), and 263 in the Ninigo group.
Population trends for Wuvulu and the Ninigo islands are shown on
Fig 35 and those for Aua on Fig. 37. Apart from the Hermit islands
(of which Luf rises to 750 ft. and Maron to 300 ft.), these are atolls,
and the Anchorite islands in particular are liable to be overwhelmed
by high seas. The Anchorite islanders were expert fishermen and in
the nineteenth century large numbers were taken to the Carolines
for *bêche-de-mer* fishing. The few who returned brought back
epidemic broncho-pneumonia. In 1907 the population was 60, in
1927 it was 6 aged men and 3 aged women, and in 1940 there was one
male survivor.

In 1883 a German punitive expedition brought bacillary dysentery
to the Hermit islands. This became endemic for a time but has now
disappeared. By 1907, disease, enforced movement to other groups,
and alienation of land had reduced the population to about 70. In
1923, 26 natives survived, in 1930 there were 18, many of whom were
diseased, and after some improvement in their conditions (such as the
extension of medical services, which previously benefited only introduced labourers) the total was 26 in 1939. Fig. 37 shows some of the
epidemics which have contributed to the decline of population in
Aua. Malaria was introduced in 1901 from Maty, and until 1904 it
caused a great proportion of deaths. In 1904 between 500 and 700
natives of Aua were drowned when returning from Manu to the east
of Aua. By 1928 the eastern half of the island was alienated, and the
people were largely dependent on the plantation owners for their
livelihood. In 1923 the population was 272; in 1940 it was 225.

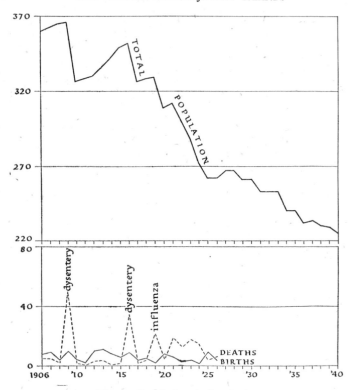

Fig. 37. Population decline in Aua

The island lies to the west of the Ninigo group. Major epidemics are noted on the curve for deaths against the relevant years. No data are available for births and deaths after 1926. The 'steps' in the graph of total population are due to the absence of a census in some years. Based on R. W. Cilento, *The Causes of Depopulation of the Western Islands of the Territory of New Guinea* (Canberra, 1928), for figures up to 1926, and on the same source as Fig. 34 for later years.

Wuvulu has been a trading station since 1900, when it supported about 2,200 natives. Malaria had previously been introduced and 30% of the adult population had died by 1901. Malaria remains dangerous in Wuvulu and Aua because the staple food is swamp taro, and the taro gardens are ideal breeding grounds for mosquitoes. By 1908 the remaining population of Wuvulu was crowded into the swampy centre of the island. The number of inhabited villages decreased until 28 were deserted in 1926. In that year the population was 325 (172 male and 153 female); and, though it stood at 318 in 1933, it had fallen to 248 by 1940.

Introduced malaria and alienation of land have reduced the Ninigo islanders from between 1,500 and 2,000 at the arrival of Europeans to about 400 in 1907 and to 209 in 1923. An increase then occurred to 270 in 1931–2, followed by a fall to 263 in 1940. As in the other islands which lie west of Manus the causes are alienation of land and low food supplies from the remaining easily exhaustible lands, a monotonous non-nutritious diet of swamp taro (or, if the land is under coconuts, of polished rice), and abortion and infanticide among an ill-nourished devitalized stock. Garove in the Vitu group, north of New Britain, is another island where alienation is a major factor in decline. In nearby Unea the diseases common to both islands are found, but far less land has been alienated and there are adequate and more varied food supplies.

COMPOSITION BY AGE AND SEX

It is not possible to obtain as yet even an approximate classification of the native population by age groups. The most that can be done, as a rule, is to distinguish adults and children. The sex classification is probably fairly accurate, though a margin of error must be allowed for owing to the difficulty of obtaining accurately the sex of very young children. Information on this point is normally acquired by census officers only by inquiry.

The Papuan administration takes the view that if the proportion of children (under 16 years) is over 33% this will satisfactorily maintain the population. To attain and pass this percentage, bonuses are paid to mothers with four or more living children under the age of 16 years. The total enumerated population of Papua, its composition by sex, and the percentage of children are shown in the first Table on p. 148.

By Papuan standards the position is satisfactory except in the Delta and North-east Divisions, and in the Samarai district of the Eastern Division. These areas have, as has been noted above, several centres of declining population. The above percentages of children are mainly higher than the average for Britain and for Australia, where the proportions of children under 15 years in 1921 were 37·0% and 35·5% respectively. These white populations have a greater longevity.

On 30 June 1940 the figures for mandated New Guinea, exclusive of indentured labourers, were as shown in the second Table on p. 148.

Sex Ratio and Proportion of Children in Papua
(*shown by administrative divisions*)

Division	1934–5			1936–7
	Total count	Percentage males	Percentage children	Percentage children
Western	13,731	48·0	39·0	39·3
Delta	17,348	53·0	25·9	17·6
Gulf	62,853	52·7	46·9	45·8
Central (W)	21,967	52·6	44·5	42·2
Central (E)	31,466	53·0	41·2	41·2
Eastern (Abau)	10,681	50·5	49·5	47·4
Eastern (Samarai)	17,359	51·0	34·0	31·4
South-eastern	11,733	50·8	38·9	36·6
North-eastern	5,614	52·0	31·1	33·3
Northern	32,156	56·7	39·2	40·4
Territory	224,908	52·0	40·9	38·7

Based on Territory of Papua *Annual Report* for 1934–5, p. 19; for 1936–7, p. 20 (Canberra, 1935, 1937).

Population of the Mandated Territory by Administrative Districts : 1940

District	Children	Male total	Female total	Total count
Morobe	56,075	60,538	67,141	127,679
Madang	57,599	76,258	72,573	148,831
Sepik	64,394	79,873	77,091	156,964
New Britain	40,862	45,271	45,078	90,349
New Ireland	14,455	18,498	18,462	36,960
Manus	4,936	6,561	6,889	13,450

Based on Commonwealth of Australia *Report to the Council of the League of Nations on the Administration of the Territory of New Guinea* for 1940, pp. 134–5 (Canberra, 1941).

From the same source the following figures have been selected as applying to some sample areas of increasing or decreasing population which have been discussed above:

Sub-district	Children	Male total	Female total	Total count
Waria	3,234	3,820	4,048	7,868
Karkar and Bagabag	4,737	4,588	4,731	9,319
Islands off Aitape	310	488	405	893
Kairiru	1,133	1,256	1,337	2,593
Duke of York Is.	1,827	1,849	1,770	3,619
Lolobau	80	77	94	171
Siassi Is.	1,902	2,413	2,368	4,781
Aua	63	139	86	225
Ninigo Is.	102	150	113	263

It has been suggested that progressive masculinity is an important factor in an index to declining population. Evidence is very incomplete as yet in the area. The above Table (for Papua), in conjunction with earlier figures, would seem to suggest that a higher degree of masculinity is not always the main factor in population decline. The population of the Northern Division (56·7% males in 1934–5) is stationary. There is no evidence that the greater percentage of males is the result of conditions since the establishment of European control, or that it is caused by female infanticide.

The average figures for 1,422 villages selected by patrols in the mandated territory for their census of 1939–40 were 51·8% males, and 38·5% children. Of the children 46% were infants less than one year old. In the preceding Table, Waria, Karkar and Bagabag, Kairiru and the Siassi islands, all centres of increasing population, show the anticipated excess of females, but the islands off Aitape and the Duke of York group, with similar population trends, have an excess of males. The population of Lolobau has declined from 208 in 1924 to 171 in 1940, but females exceed males. Excessive recruiting for the adjacent island of New Britain may be a factor here. The decline of the population of Aua has been noticed as one of the most acute in the area. Its male population far exceeds the female total. Comparable conditions exist in the nearby Ninigo islands, though here there has recently been a slight increase of population and the percentage of children is higher than in Aua. There is little evidence that the areas of increasing populations have markedly higher proportions of female births. In most years the figures for the Port Moresby villages show an excess of male births (p. 140). Manam provides a sample of a slowly increasing population in which males predominated until recently. In 1940 the total population of Manam and its adjoining island Aris (Boisa) was 3,724 (1,727 male, 1,997 female; 1,597 children). Of the 3,490 counted in 1933 on Manam alone (Aris totalled 170), 1,865 were males and 1,625 females. There was a high proportion of surviving children, owing to greater cleanliness and to more reasonable feeding of babies than is common in many areas.

Higher mortality among male children is probably a feature in most districts, as it is among European populations. In the 1,422 villages discussed above with a sample population of 167,631, 46% of the children between one and twelve years were female and 54% male, but the percentages among adults were 49·3% female and 50·7% male.

NON-NATIVE POPULATION

The following Table shows increases in the main non-indigenous population elements of the mandated territory from 1921 to 1940:

Non-native Population of the Mandated Territory

Year	European		Asiatic		Total non-indigenous population
	British	German	Chinese	'Dutch'*	
1921	715	579	1,402	215	3,173
1922	765	325	1,365	215	2,927
1923	828	312	1,347	221	2,979
1924	824	316	1,330	213	2,944
1925	944	310	1,303	210	3,045
1926	1,086	299	1,279	215	3,132
1927	1,341	293	1,259	220	3,399
1928	1,659	332	1,259	224	3,751
1929	1,808	328	1,253	213	3,928
1930	1,992	348	1,238	209	4,155
1931	1,992	370	1,179	213	4,142
1932	2,104	402	1,215	211	4,366
1933	2,842	379	1,299	251	5,215
1934	3,026	404	2,424	249	5,453
1935	3,288	442	1,448	155	5,688
1936	3,332	477	1,523	153	5,882
1937	3,329	469	1,525	155	5,897
1938	3,472	473	1,737	154	6,283
1939	3,547	473	1,890	157	6,538
1940	3,345	439	2,061	159	6,498

* This classification includes a small number of non-Asiatics.

Based on Commonwealth of Australia *Report to the Council of the League of Nations on the Administration of the Territory of New Guinea* for 1922–40 (Melbourne, 1922–7; Canberra, 1928–41).

Of those classed as 'Dutch' a small proportion were Netherlanders and the remainder Indonesians. The non-native population of Kieta District is included in the figures; in 1933 this was composed of 22 Europeans and 35 Asiatics. The 6,498 non-natives listed above for 1940 provided the equivalent of rather less than 1% of the enumerated native population which, with increases in the size of the controlled area, was 668,871 in 1940 (including Kieta) as against 187,517 in 1921. Numbers of both Asiatics and Europeans were smaller in Papua. In 1921 the total European population of Papua was 1,104; in 1940 it was 1,822. There were no sharp rises in population, such as that of the period 1926–30 in the mandated territory; the rise in those years marks the opening up of the Morobe goldfields. In both Papua and the mandated territory upward trends were primarily due to immigration and not to natural increase. The entry of Asiatics into Papua has been restricted since 1908 by immigration laws similar to those of Australia, and the small numbers of Chinese are mainly tailors and petty traders in Port Moresby and Samarai. The European population was about 400 in Port Moresby. There were approximately 150 Europeans in Samarai. The remainder were widely scattered at government stations, missions and on plantations.

The Chinese of the mandated territory were former indentured labourers who had remained since the German occupation. They showed a slow natural increase and their children were classed as Australian citizens. The Chinese lived mainly in separate quarters in Rabaul, Kavieng, Salamaua, Wau and Madang. About 1,500 lived in Rabaul, while the majority of the Chinese planters lived on the west coast of New Ireland, south of the Namatanai isthmus. The white population included about 2,000 in the Morobe goldfield region, about 1,000 in the Rabaul area, 150 round Kavieng, about 150 around Lae, about 150 in the Salamaua area and about 90 in Madang.

Many of the Germans in the mandated territory were missionaries. Those believed to sympathize with the Axis Powers, together with the few Japanese in the territory, were removed to Australia in December 1941. Before the attack on Rabaul in January 1942 most civilian Europeans and Chinese were evacuated though many missionaries chose to remain in the interior.

BIBLIOGRAPHICAL NOTE

Statistics of population are published annually in the Territory of Papua *Annual Report* (Melbourne, to 1927; Canberra, from 1928); and the Commonwealth of Australia *Report to the Council of the League of Nations on the Administration of the Territory of New Guinea* (Melbourne, to 1927; Canberra, from 1928). These reports also contain reviews of the state of the population in areas which have been selected for special investigation. Some estimates of population for islands in the Bismarck archipelago are contained in R. Parkinson, *Dreissig Jahre in der Südsee* (Stuttgart, 1907). Reviews of population problems in the area include: Hubert Murray, 'Depopulation in Papua', *Oceania*, vol. III, pp. 207–13 (Sydney, 1932–3): E. W. P. Chinnery, 'Census and Population', *Oceania*, vol. III, pp. 214–17 (Sydney, 1932–3): F. E. Williams, 'Depopulation and Administration', *Oceania*, vol. III, pp. 218–26 (Sydney, 1932–3): and L. G. Vial, 'Some Statistical Aspects of Population in the Morobe District', *Oceania*, vol. VIII, pp. 383–97 (Sydney, 1937–8). Monographs which discuss the causes and some remedies of depopulation in particular areas include: R. W. Cilento, *The Causes of Depopulation of the Western Islands of the Territory of New Guinea* (Canberra, 1928); E. W. P. Chinnery, 'Studies of the Native Population of the East Coast of New Ireland', *Territory of New Guinea Anthropological Report*, no. 6 (Canberra, 1931); and F. E. Williams, 'Depopulation of the Suau District', *Territory of Papua, Anthropology, Report*, no. 13 (Port Moresby, 1933).

Chapter VIII

THE NATIVE PEOPLES

Physical Type: Language: Culture: Bibliographical Note

PHYSICAL TYPE

The peoples of the New Guinea area are all of Negroid stock, but show great diversity of type. Broadly speaking, they may be divided into three groups: the Negrito of the central mountainous regions; the Papuans, who constitute the great majority of the population of the mainland (Plates 25–7); and, finally, the Melanesians of the south-east coastal areas, the Bismarck archipelago and most of the outlying islands (Plate 24). This classification is not a rigid one and, in the marginal areas where there has been trade, inter-marriage and probably migration, there are tribes who possess both Melanesian and Papuan characteristics. These mixed types have been called the Western Papuo-Melanesians and the Massim (or Eastern Papuo-Melanesians). The former include such tribes as the Hanuabada, Roro, Mekeo, Koita and Motu, and they live in the region between cape Possession and Orangerie bay; the territory of the latter covers the south-eastern extremity of New Guinea east of Orangerie bay and north to cape Nelson, as well as the Louisiade archipelago, the D'Entrecasteaux, the Trobriands, the Murua (Woodlark) and Tubetube (Engineer) islands. These classifications are only approximate and Melanesian types may be found in the Sepik District and as far west as Geelvink bay.

Negrito peoples (sometimes of pygmy stature), such as the Nogullo, Tapiro and Pesechem of Dutch New Guinea, are strong and muscular. The average height of the men is about 4 ft. 9 in., while the women are slightly shorter. They are round-headed (brachycephalic); faces and noses are broad; and prognathism is somewhat marked. The skin is a dark sooty brown and the hair is frizzly and almost black. Other tribes, such as the Mafulu of the upper St Joseph river in Papua and the peoples of the headwaters of the Fly and Sepik rivers, are slightly taller (5 ft. 1 in.) but possess some of the Negrito characteristics.

In contrast to the pygmies, the Papuans are dolichocephalic (the cephalic index ranges between 69 and 77); they are mostly from

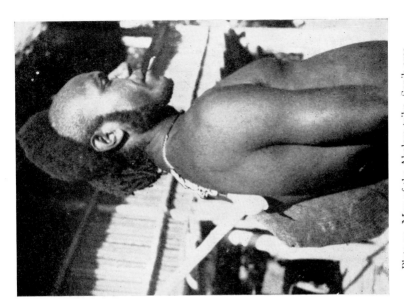

Plate 24. Melanesian woman from Emirau

This photograph shows the dark skin, frizzly hair, slightly prognathous face and thick lips. Below the necklace is a pattern made with keloids (scars from roughly healed incisions).

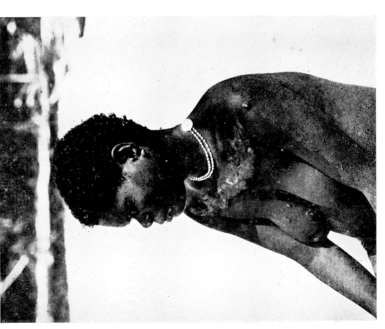

Plate 25. Man of the Abelam tribe, Sepik area

The profile shows more Papuan than Melanesian characteristics. The head shaved in front indicates that he is a married man.

Plate 27. Man from Orokolo bay, Papua
A typical Papuan profile with high receding forehead and hooked nose.

Plate 26. Girl from the mount Hagen area
She is wearing light-coloured ornaments on the head, around the neck and arms, and on the skirt.

5 ft. 4 in. to 5 ft. 6 in. high, though stature varies as between the
mountain peoples, who are of a rather stocky build, and the leaner,
taller coastal tribes, such as the Elema of the Gulf of Papua. Individuals differ considerably, however, in the modelling of face and
heads, in the fineness or coarseness of their features. There is the type
with small eyes, rather protruding brows, thick, fleshy, convex nose,
and somewhat shapeless mouth. But others, possessing a good
physique, are found among both the coastal and mountain peoples,
of whom the Abelam of the Torricelli foothills may be taken as
representative. Limbs are well proportioned; there is little body hair,
though most of the men wear a beard which fringes the jaw bones.
The profile is often striking: the nose is long and curved, and the
practice of shaving the hair off the front of the head and allowing it
to rise in a fan at the back emphasizes the line of the high receding
forehead. The skin is usually dark brown, though sometimes it is a
light copper, possibly as a result of intermarriage with Melanesians.

When decked out for a ceremony, the Abelam man, even more
than the woman, is a brilliant figure. The white necklaces and shell
armlets set off the colouring of the skin; across the black frizzly hair
there may be a beaded band or a tiara of red hibiscus, with perhaps
the plumes of a hornbill or a bird of paradise placed in the pencil
curls at the back. Sometimes the cheeks are carmined with ochre so
that the narrowness of the face and rather high cheek bones are
accentuated. The men and women, in common with most Papuan
tribes, pierce the septum of the nose and the lobes of the ears and
insert bones, leaves and shells as ornaments. At a girl's puberty
cicatrices are made on the abdomen, but the custom is rarely followed
by the men of the tribe.

The Melanesians and Massim present greater difficulties of
description, except in the Bismarck archipelago where, generally
speaking, their chief characteristics are their lighter skin colouring,
their shorter stature (as compared with the Papuans), their round,
broad faces and slightly brachycephalic heads. Among the Western
Papuo-Melanesians and southern Massim, there is a tendency to
dolichocephaly; eyes may be oblique; and the hair is sometimes wavy
or straight. More atypical of the eastern areas are some of the Buka
tribes whose skin is almost coal-black, while individuals among the
Orokaiva (near Oro bay) and in the Trobriands are tall and have
aquiline features.

A few tribes of the interior, such as the Abelam, go about completely naked; in the other tribes, dress, if it can be called such, is of

the scantiest, except where *laplap* (lengths of cloth worn as a skirt) have been introduced by traders, missionaries, and returned indentured labourers. The men of the coastal regions frequently wear a T-band of bark cloth; elsewhere, a gourd, a shell or the skin of a flying fox may be used as a penis cover. The women favour either short bark aprons—one in front and the other at the back—or brilliantly dyed grass skirts of somewhat abbreviated proportions which often leave the hips and flanks exposed. Children are usually completely naked, except for tiny shell ear-rings or a cowrie attached to the wrist. An elaborate coiffure is, in general, the prerogative of the men; women and young children are closely shaved as a rule, though on the Sepik they may flaunt a cocks-comb or a small topknot. Hair styles vary considerably; some of the men on the north coast draw the hair through a cylindrical basket; others, again, as in parts of southern Papua, let it grow in a rather unruly mop. In the Morehead district to the west, both men and women may plait the hair with grass or palm leaf.

The practice of making elaborate designs on the body by tattooing or the raising of keloids has a very uneven distribution, but the piercing of the nasal septum and the lobes of the ears occurs in the majority of tribes. Men, women and children frequently wear plaited or woven arm-bands, shell necklaces and ear-rings, but as a rule the women don ornaments mainly for feasts and ceremonies, and it is the men and young boys who go about the village during the day with a hibiscus flower or a cockatoo feather tucked in the hair or with a bunch of croton leaves in the arm-band.

LANGUAGE

The languages spoken by the peoples of the New Guinea area may be divided roughly into two groups, Melanesian and the so-called 'Papuan' or non-Melanesian. Those falling within the first category are found in the Schouten islands, north of Wewak, among the Massim and the Western Papuo-Melanesians, and in some of the villages dotted along the coast of the mandated territory, more particularly those in the vicinity of the Huon gulf, Finschhafen, Astrolabe bay, and to the west of Aitape and Vanimo.

The term 'Melanesian' applies to a group of languages which show similarities with those of the Indonesian archipelago and Polynesia. The term 'Papuan', on the other hand, refers to those languages which differ from the Melanesian in vocabulary and grammar, but it does not imply any relationship between two or more of them. In fact, Papuan types are many, and as yet the number of linguistic stocks is unknown. For these reasons they have recently been distinguished as non-Melanesian, a term which has an advantage in describing some of the aberrant types found among tribes which in other respects—cultural and geographical—are Melanesian: namely, the Baining and Sulka of the east of New Britain, and the Siwai and Nasioi of south Bougainville.

So great is the diversity of linguistic structure on the mainland of New Guinea that sometimes members of villages 5 miles apart cannot understand one another without the aid of an interpreter. It might be expected, however, that those languages which are more complex and possess multiple genders would fall within the same area. Such is rarely the case. For example, Arapesh and Tschambuli, which belong to this category, are widely separated, and their neighbouring languages, Abelam and Iatmul, are much simpler in form and have only two genders. When contact is necessary for purposes of trade, the Tschambuli employ a species of 'basic' Iatmul; elsewhere, a practice of inter-tribal adoption is sometimes followed in order to overcome the barrier to intercourse. Boys are exchanged so that they can learn the other language and later act as interpreters.

There is also a considerable variation in the size of the group which possesses a common language. For instance, the Tschambuli tribe of lake Aibom has only 500 members; the Iatmul of the middle Sepik and the Abelam of the plains to the north, who speak related languages (subdivided into many dialects), number many thousands. Again, it should be noted that linguistic and cultural boundaries are not always co-terminous. A good illustration of this is provided by the case of the tribes mentioned above. The Plains Arapesh follow customs which are similar in many respects to those of the Abelam; while the Abelam themselves, though they speak a language broadly similar to the Iatmul, have a culture markedly different from them.

Missionaries have reduced a few of the Melanesian languages to writing, namely the Kuanua dialect of Blanche bay, the Jâbem of the Huon gulf and the Ragetta of Astrolabe bay, but the distribution of any language is usually so limited that most Europeans employ Melanesian-Pidgin. This has become a *lingua franca* for the whole of the mandated territory and for parts of Papua. In its syntax it corresponds closely to Melanesian, but its vocabulary includes a large number of words of English derivation, some Melanesian terms from the Blanche bay region, and a few German, Malay and Polynesian terms. In Papua, a Melanesian language which is spoken by the Motu of Port Moresby has been widely adopted as a medium of intercourse between Europeans and natives.

Phonetically, both Melanesian and non-Melanesian languages are somewhat similar to English, but there are a few fundamental differences in the vowels and consonants. Thus, some of the non-Melanesian dialects contain the sounds *é*, *u*, and *o*, as in the French words *été*, *lune*, and *notre* respectively, and *ö*, as in the German *Götter*. There is also a *u* which is pronounced without lip-rounding. Among the consonants, the plosives *p*, *b*, *t*, *d*, *g*, and *k* are not followed by breathing as they are in English, and the *d* and *t* are frequently pure dentals. There are also two nasals which are not found in English: the palatal *n* as the *ñ* in the Spanish *señor*, and the *n* (or *ng*) pronounced like *ng* in *sing*, but often serving as the initial consonant in a word.

In the mandated territory alone some 53 Melanesian languages are known to exist. The number of non-Melanesian languages is probably much greater, for as yet large areas, more particularly in the centre and west, have not been studied from the linguistic point of view. Little research has been done on the languages spoken by the Negritos, but what results are available would indicate that they are not radically different from those used by the Papuan tribes. In the non-Melanesian groups, some 32 have been enumerated in the mandated territory (including 6 from south Bougainville), though it is possible that a few of these are similar in structure. In the Western Division of Papua, 14 groups have been distinguished, but except in two cases they bear little or no relation to one another. The best known of the non-Melanesian languages are Kiwai (near the mouth of the Fly river); Kâte near Finschhafen; Bongu in the southern part of Astrolabe bay; Monumbo to the north-west of Madang; and Valman and Arapesh, just inland from the coast in the Sepik District.

The chief characteristics of the non-Melanesian languages have been summarized as follows:

1. Multiple gender or the division of nouns into classes as in Baining, Monumbo, Arapesh and Tschambuli. This sometimes involves agreements (sentence concord) of adjectives, pronouns, or even verbs, as in the case of Monumbo.

2. Extreme complication of the tense and mode scheme of the verb. It should be noted, however, that neither Melanesian nor non-Melanesian has a passive voice.

3. Frequent occurrence of incorporation, that is the incorporation

of the pronoun subject and pronoun object in a transitive verb by means of a prefix and a suffix.

4. Power of agglutination, i.e., of building complex words out of a series of suffixes; this occurs in Kiwai.

5. Special systems of enumeration, some defective and some complicated. Many Papuan tribes reckon in fives, 5 being one hand, 10 two hands, 15 two hands and a foot, and so on. In Kâte, the numerals stop at 2, 3 being two and one. The Melanesian languages have numerals up to five which conform to the Melanesian root form, but for the other numerals they tend to follow the non-Melanesian pattern, and nowhere on the northern coast of New Guinea does the decimal system appear.

Among the Melanesian languages, those in the islands conform more closely to the 'pure' Melanesian type than those on the mainland, in that word-order does not differ greatly from English, while in the non-Melanesian the verb is placed last. Nouns are not classified, and, as a rule, there is no plural for them. The verb is not so complicated as in the non-Melanesian languages, but two characteristics may be singled out: firstly, the practice of prefixing it with a particle in order to indicate person in the subject; and, secondly, the existence of a series of suffixes which can be used to make a verb transitive.

CULTURE

GENERAL CHARACTERISTICS OF THE CULTURE

New Guinea is rich in the diversity and complexity of its cultural patterns and there is little doubt that this has been intensified by the difficult nature of the terrain, differences in topography, the multiplicity of languages and inter-village hostilities. Nevertheless, when full allowance is made for an almost infinite variation in custom, certain similarities in the broader aspects of economy, ritual and social organization can be detected. Trade, extra-village marriage, and migration have all facilitated diffusion, and nowadays where peaceful conditions have been established, natives make distant journeys. In the government-controlled areas, head-hunting, cannibalism and other unpleasant customs have been suppressed, together with some of the more unhygienic mortuary rites. Where there has been a long period of European contact, as in some parts of the Bismarck archipelago, social organization has been disrupted and many of the more elaborate ceremonies have fallen into desuetude. But on much of the mainland

and in the more inaccessible districts of the smaller islands the natives still pursue many of their traditional activities.

The Negritos are few in number and their culture resembles that of the simpler Papuan types, although they do not practise head-hunting and cannibalism. The main distinction to be drawn between the Melanesian and Papuan cultures of the area is the existence of matrilineal clans in the former (and among the Massim), while in the latter there are patrilineal clans. The Western Papuo-Melanesians, though in many ways similar to the Massim, follow the principle of patrilineal descent. Some of the Melanesians of the smaller islands also possess a more highly developed system of chieftainship; they have secret societies; and they engage in long over-seas voyages for trade and ceremonial exchange. In this they must be distinguished not only from the Papuans but also from some of the tribes living in the interior of New Britain and New Ireland. There are therefore two points which should be taken into account in any description of the customs of the New Guinea area: firstly, that both simple and complex types of social organization may be found on even a small island; secondly, that comparable types of village organization, handicrafts, economic pursuits and kinship co-operation occur in widely separated districts. Hence similar environments (such as the coasts, rivers, plains and mountains) often serve as a more valid basis for generalization than the rigid division into Melanesian and Papuan physical types or language-speaking groups.

Village Organization (Plates 28–32, 34)

New Guinea is sparsely populated and settlements are generally small and scattered. Sometimes communities numbering 1,000 members are found, as in the Sepik district; but the average size is from 50 to 200 inhabitants. The village is the most important local and political unit, for although several villages may speak the same language and share a common culture they are not bound by political ties. In the past they were frequently at war with one another and even to-day something of the traditional hostility lingers, though its expression may be limited to verbal forays, charges of sorcery and perhaps competitive exchanges. The village was never, however, a completely self-sufficient unit. It had one or two allies in the district with whom it traded and co-operated in fighting and head-hunting expeditions.

The position of the village is determined by such factors as fertility of soil, proximity to water-supplies and, in the old days, by suitability for defence. The actual layout varies considerably even on the smaller

Plate 28. The main street of Mailu village, south-eastern Papua

A good example of the clean, orderly layout of coastal villages in this area. The floors of the houses are raised on piles several feet off the ground.

Plate 29. A village on the Marifutiga river, mount Hagen area

The village has both rectangular and circular houses. There is a palisade along the street.

Plate 30. A village above the lower Wahgi gorge

Houses are of the same types as those in Plate 29. The village is sited for defensive purposes on a small hilltop. It has the added protection of a strong palisade.

Plate 31. A village near Port Moresby

The houses are built on piles over the sea, a common practice on this part of the coast. Canoe landing-stages and paths linking the houses with the shore are of wood raised on piles,

islands. Sometimes the houses cluster in a compact settlement; sometimes a long house, partitioned into family cubicles, constitutes the whole community; or, again, the village may be divided into anything from 3 to 30 hamlets, probably about ¼ mile apart. Among many of the coastal peoples houses are rectangular and built on piles, either a little back from the beach or else straddling the lagoon. The Roro of the St Joseph river area, the Banaro and Iatmul of the Sepik area, and some other tribes erect their houses on each side of a street or ceremonial ground, and in some cases this formal arrangement is closely connected with the clan organization. In the Trobriands the dwelling houses rest on the earth and encircle a cleared space, at the centre of which are yam houses and the home of the chief. But on the Gazelle peninsula, on St Matthias island, among the southern Massim and throughout much of the mainland interior, villages consist of small hamlets connected by narrow paths that wind through the tropical undergrowth. In the mountains, the houses almost seem to perch on the ridges, and gardens are made on the steep slopes near by. For purposes of defence the natives sometimes erect palisades; on the Papuan border and in the Arfak peninsula they have taken to the trees for greater security and construct their houses on top of the hacked-off branches.

Many of the houses are extremely attractive in design, workmanship and materials. Among the Abelam the hamlet is usually a pleasant place with its small plantation of bananas and papaya, and its peaked silver-grey houses overshadowed by areca and coconut palms. The ceremonial ground is kept scrupulously free of weeds and on the outskirts grow crotons, cordyline and other brilliantly coloured shrubs. Dominating everything is the men's house, rising to a height of 50 or 70 ft., with its elaborate carvings and painting. In its shade the men sit and chat, the women forming a group a little distance away, or else passing by laden with their pots and garden produce, while in the rear small daughters carry a few sticks of firewood or carefully balance a shell filled with water.

Dwelling houses usually receive less care than those reserved for ceremonies or storing food, and at the end of about three years they are apt to fall into decay. In Aua and Wuvulu in the Western islands, timber is scarce and more solid structures are erected, with high walls made of planks mortised into heavy corner posts. The principal materials used throughout the region are sago-palm leaves for thatch; areca palm for slat-flooring; bamboos, saplings and bark for walls; while various types of cane and vine serve for lashing. As mentioned previously, rectangular houses built on piles are commonly found along the coasts and rivers, but in some cases this style has penetrated to the mountainous regions. Moreover, government has encouraged its adoption as being more hygienic. The oval-shaped or round dwelling is much more rare and obtains principally in parts of the Admiralty islands and in the eastern Nassau mountains, in Dutch New Guinea. In the plains and foothills north of the Sepik, houses are triangular in longitudinal section, the ridge-pole sloping down to a few feet above the ground at the back. They may be 20 ft. long and about 12 ft. wide, and are divided into two sections: the rear portion is used for the storing of food and valuables; the front, which is partitioned off, serves as a living-room where the woman cooks, eats with her family, and keeps her pots, digging stick, netbags and other articles in daily use. The houses are built by the men and boys, and consist of sago-palm leaves split in half and lashed to a light timber framework. For the ceremonial house, individual sago leaves are bent over narrow strips of bamboo, about 3 ft. long, and then fastened with another lattice.

Many tribes have special houses for storing yams and these are carefully constructed and often decorated. In the Trobriands yam houses are built on piles, the walls consisting of round logs laid crosswise, one on top of the other, so that the harvest can be seen through the intervening chinks. Those belonging to the chief have ornamental boards and gables.

Especially typical of the mainland of New Guinea is the men's ceremonial house, known as the *haus tamberan* in pidgin-English. It is taboo to the women and frequently contains ritual objects which are seen only by those men who have been initiated. Occasionally it is a temporary structure erected specifically for a ceremony; but in general it is solidly built and may be anything from 100 to 300 ft. long, though among the Western Papuo-Melanesians it is much smaller. Those of the Abelam are particularly fine aesthetically; they are sometimes 70 ft. high in front, and the upper part, made from sago spathes stitched to a bamboo frame, is painted with red, yellow, black and white designs, which represent supernatural beings associated with the clans. Here, as in many other Papuan tribes, certain sections or even posts belong to the clans in the village who have been responsible for their construction.

SOCIAL AND POLITICAL ORGANIZATION

Among both the Papuan and Melanesian peoples co-operation in

Plate 33. Native suspension bridge over the Gauil river, New Guinea

The bridge is constructed of lianas with a solid plank as footway.

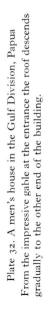

Plate 32. A men's house in the Gulf Division, Papua

From the impressive gable at the entrance the roof descends gradually to the other end of the building.

Plate 34. A house on Mandok island, Siassi group

The building is raised on piles and has walls of plaited palm leaf to which a 'panelled' effect is given by the patterns used.

Plate 35. Building a pile of yams after the harvest, Trobriand islands

A temporary ceremonial display before the yams are finally stored in the yam houses.

social, economic and ceremonial matters is largely regulated by kin-ship ties. Everywhere the family is the basic social and economic unit, possessing its own dwelling where members eat and sleep, though boys after they reach puberty go for the night to a bachelors' house.

Infant betrothal occurs in most tribes, but the adolescent boy and girl exercise considerable freedom in the choice of spouse, and among the Massim and Western Papuo-Melanesians pre-nuptial intercourse is condoned. In other areas, where the girl marries soon after puberty, greater emphasis is placed on chastity, and in Manus even casual physical contact between the sexes is hedged about with rules and taboos. The Tschambuli of the Sepik, the Keraki of the Morehead district, and the people of Emirau island favour marriage with a classificatory mother's brother's daughter. More common is the pro-cedure by which two men exchange sisters, and, among the Banaro, this is associated with the functioning of a somewhat complex social organization. Clans are divided into two sections (a right and a left), which assist each other. A man has his own particular friend (*mundu*) in the opposite section and the ideal marriage is for two *mundu* to exchange sisters with two *mundu* of another clan. In general, however, prescribed marriages or those so elaborately arranged are rare, and, excluding the clan or the group of close blood relatives, a man may select a wife either from within or from outside the village. Except where missionaries have interfered, polygyny is practised in most tribes, though generally it is limited to a small group of men of rank or wealth.

To formalize the marriage the groom, assisted by contributions from his relatives, hands over the 'bride-price' to the bride's people. This consists of shell ornaments, shell rings, shell 'currency', cere-monial adzes, dogs' or pigs' teeth—in short, of those articles which are objects of value in the tribe. Sometimes a return gift is made but it is nearly always smaller. The bride generally goes to live in her husband's village (that is, residence is patrilocal); but in some instances, as in Dobu in the D'Entrecasteaux group, the husband spends part of the year in her village. Though the women play little part in the public life of the community and the formal direction of its affairs, they have important social and economic duties, and in some cases they are responsible for providing most of the food.

Children during their first years are cared for and disciplined by the mother, but by our standards they are spoilt. Nevertheless, there is a marked tendency to treat them as responsible individuals, and at an early age they are taught their obligations to their relatives. Boys form small groups for play but also carry out minor tasks in the garden, fish, and hunt the bush for berries and small game, while the girls assist in the household tasks. The tie between brother and sister is a most important one, and associated with this is the strong bond of affection between a man and his sister's children. Where clans are patrilineal, the mother's brother fills the role of protector and friend and also performs certain ceremonial duties. Where descent is matrilineal a man at marriage, if not before, goes to live with his mother's brother, who often wields more authority than the father.

The individual generally has many opportunities to meet his relatives on his mother's and father's side during his daily activities, and this small kinship group is, in fact, one of the most important in the social organization, though it lacks the formal structure of the clan. At marriage, the individual is brought into contact with another group, his affinal relatives, and with these he associates on terms of ease, friendliness, and mutual assistance. The strict rules of avoidance between those related by marriage, which occur in so many parts of Oceania, are rare in this area, though in a few tribes such as the Banaro, the Iatmul, the Keraki and Emirau, there is a taboo on the use of personal names. Among the Mundugumor of the Sepik brothers-in-law are apt to be hostile to one another, and in Dobu the husband is treated as something of an outsider in his wife's village.

The clan has been stressed by many writers as the most important social unit in the New Guinea cultures but, as mentioned above, in every-day activities the family and close blood relatives have good grounds for claiming that position. The clan, however, is clearly defined in its structure and in its activities, which are often of a public and ceremonial character. Among most of the peoples of the Bismarck archipelago and in the Massim area descent is matrilineal, while on the mainland and in the Schouten islands it is patrilineal. In a few atypical cases, such as the Madang district, the Admiralty islands, and at Möwe harbour in New Britain, descent is bilateral—that is, it is traced through either the father or the mother, or both.

The clan has generally only one totem, a bird, but among the Massim it is associated with a series of linked totems, consisting of a bird, a plant, a fish and a snake. Frequently it has an exclusive right to the use of certain plant emblems, personal names, ornaments and designs employed in carving. One of the factors contributing to clan solidarity as a unit is the common custom by which members may live on adjoining house-sites: sometimes they occupy a whole village, sometimes only one section. Ownership of land is most generally vested in the clan but, as will be shown later, individuals and even persons belonging to other clans may enjoy rights of usufruct over certain areas for certain periods.

According to customary law clansmen are bound to co-operate, but in practice it is unusual for a man to call on the services of all; often, indeed, it is more convenient for him to ask the help of his blood and affinal relatives. There is also the convention that clansmen do not quarrel, but the dogmatism with which this principle is sometimes expressed by the natives is, in itself, a clue to the fact that fissions often occur, leading to the establishment of new branches who take up residence in another area.

On St Matthias island, clans are grouped into four sections or phratries, but this type of social organization is rare and, in the Bismarck archipelago, it is more common to find a division into matrilineal totemic moieties. In theory they are exogamous, but the rule is sometimes broken and even condoned, and their chief importance would seem to be the part they play in regulating ceremonial activities. This kind of social grouping does not obtain to any great extent on the mainland, but in many tribes, especially in the Sepik district, there is a form of dual organization in which the village is divided into two groups for purposes of initiation and ceremonial exchanges.

Distinctions of rank occur only in a few tribes, more particularly among the northern Massim, the Western Papuo-Melanesians, the Buin of south-east Bougainville, and on Manam island. Outside these areas political organization is almost everywhere democratic, in that status is not hereditary but depends on qualities of personality, skill in gardening, ambition in trade, a knowledge of ritual and, in the old days, prowess in head-hunting and warfare. In such communities, the headman is *primus inter pares* in a group of elders and he exercises authority only over his own clan or perhaps a branch of it. The Abelam provide a typical example of this type of political organization. There, the headman looks after the affairs of the younger clansmen living in his hamlet, and he confers, when necessary, with the headman of the other branches and may even play a decisive role in the proceedings. He is one who excels in gardening and who is willing and morally fitted to assume the responsibility of performing the yam magic and of observing the stringent taboos that are required. He may also have acquired a reputation for his carving and painting, and surrounding villages may call on him to assist in the decoration of a new ceremonial house. His judicial functions are not clearly defined, but he endeavours, often with success, to keep the peace, and he lends the weight of his opinion to the settlement of disputes. He decides on the division of clan land, mobilizes the labour for the clearing of bush, and takes the initiative in arranging and directing ceremonies. His position, in the last analysis, rests on his own achievements and the respect which he wins from others. The headman has no special insignia, apart from the special shell ornament worn by all the older men, nor is he treated with any marked etiquette. But at a feast he is given food before all others; he is the first to take the floor to chant clan songs and to praise the achievements of his host—also to boast of his own, for, on the whole, modesty is not considered a virtue among the middle-aged !

On such islands as Manam, Wogeo and the Trobriands, and among the Roro, Mekeo, Mafulu, and Koita of the Papuan mainland, political authority is more centralized and is wielded over a much larger group than is customary in Papuan tribes. Among the Western Papuo-Melanesians, the chief of a village may be assisted by a sub-chief and a war chief, or, if his clan occupies a number of villages, then he takes precedence over the village headmen. In the Trobriands there are also village headmen who assume leadership in a council of elders, but they are subordinate to the chief of the highest ranking sub-clan, who has considerable power. He has the right to call on his tributary villages in the island for labour, and in the old days claimed their assistance in war. He obtains much of his wealth in food from the relatives of his wives, who are generally the sisters of headmen, and formerly he received by these means 30% or more of the garden produce of the island. This wealth, however, he is bound to distribute at festivals, in payment for services, and to those dependents who are in need. He is treated with much respect and only those of his own rank may remain erect in his presence. Finally, he has at his command the services of the best sorcerers and thus maintains order and inflicts punishment.

Besides these political authorities, whose functions are not formally recognized by the government, there are the headmen (*luluai*) and interpreters (*tultul*) nominated by the administration of the mandated territory. Where possible, leaders in the village are chosen, but even where this is the case friction may arise because traditionally their influence may be limited to a kinship group such as the clan or to a small hamlet. In Papua, native constables occupy a similar position in the administration, and they are responsible for reporting cases of disorder and for transmitting the instructions of the government to the village.

ECONOMIC ACTIVITIES

The tribes of New Guinea engage primarily in agriculture, with fishing and hunting as subsidiary activities. In a few areas, such as that bordering on the mid-Fly where soil is too poor for intensive cultivation, hunting assumes more importance in the economy. On some of the islands—for example, Tubetube, Manus and Sio—the people must obtain their vegetables by bartering their fish.

Fishing (Plates 36–7)

Fishing is usually done by the men. It involves the co-operation of a large group when nets, perhaps 300 ft. long, have to be handled, or when weirs are built across the streams and nets placed over the sluices. Wickerwork traps, the hook and line and stupefacients are also used extensively, and the men sometimes fish with multiple-pronged spears on the reefs at night by torchlight. The role of the women is limited to hunting along the rocks for shell-fish and small fry. But among the Tschambuli of the mid-Sepik a somewhat unique situation occurs, in which the women are responsible for most of the fishing, while it is the men who tend the gardens.

Hunting

As compared with the importance of fishing in the economy of the small islands and coastal regions, hunting is a distinctly minor and somewhat unskilled activity in the life of the people of the interior. The products of the chase are used rather for the fulfilment of ceremonial obligations than as an addition to the family larder. The main types of game are wild pigs, kangaroos, wallabies, bandicoots and cassowaries, and several methods may be employed for their capture. When the tracks of a wild pig are seen in the vicinity of a village the men, if they feel energetic and have nothing better to do, organize a drive. A pit may be dug or a net set in the undergrowth and on this the men converge armed with their flat-bladed spears. On the Sepik plains or in the savannah country of the Morehead the grass is sometimes burnt off; or beaters may drive the game towards a spot where the hunters lie in ambush. Cassowaries are usually killed with the spear, but smaller birds are shot with bow and arrow. On the whole, however, birds are valued for the ornaments they provide rather than for their flesh. Parrots, cockatoos, hornbills, cassowaries and birds of paradise are particularly prized, and the plumes are used as ornaments for the hair, as tassels for carvings and lime spatulas, or are woven into head-dresses, some of intricate and extremely beautiful design.

In general, the diet of the mainland peoples is deficient in protein, and meat, when available, merely serves as a garnish for the meal. The domesticated pigs are usually reared by the women and later given away at a ceremony for a marriage, initiation or death. Grubs, gathered from rotting sago trunks, are considered a delicacy and a lizard sometimes makes a welcome addition to the meal. Children catch beetles and grasshoppers which they grill on the fire for a snack. Fowls are kept mainly for their feathers and are rarely eaten. Rather scrawny dogs are used occasionally for hunting, and, in some tribes, their teeth are made into ornaments and bartered for other articles.

Land Tenure

Most New Guinea natives take great pride in their gardens, and often a man or woman will pause on the path to look with pleasure at ground freshly cleared for planting or, later in the year, at a plot with its great heart-shaped taro leaves and its tall yam vines already turning yellow as the root nears maturity. He may point out his own garden with pride and, indeed, it has been said that in some tribes a man belongs to the land rather than the land to him. The tie is more than one of economic dependence; it is one of strong sentiment, for the land has been cultivated by the clan ancestors who still dwell there as spirits, guard it against trespassers, and watch over the crops.

The system of tenure is extremely complex, and statements that land is owned communally or individually may be regarded with suspicion unless an intensive study has been made of the subject. Usually the right to inherit land is dependent on membership of a clan—whether matrilineal or patrilineal—but the position is complicated by the right of the individual to use certain areas for certain periods, and to extend this privilege to persons of different kinship groups.

This is so, for example, among the Abelam, who are typical of many tribes both on the mainland and in the islands. The area of bush is vested in a clan, sometimes a sub-clan; all members may hunt there, and draw on it for their timber and water supply. The headman, in consultation with the other elders, decides what portion is to be cultivated and organizes the clearing. He then divides the ground

Plate 36. Fishing with hand nets, Emirau
A number of men surround a shoal of fish and then rush into the shoal with nets
held under water.

Plate 37. A fisherman on his way to set his fish-traps, New Guinea
These wickerwork traps are based on the same principle as the European lobster-pot.

Plate 38. Native gardens in the Wahgi area, New Guinea
The recently discovered tribes of this area are expert gardeners.

Plate 39. Yam mounds in a native garden, mount Hagen area
The stumps of trees left when the ground was cleared are visible.

into gardens about 150 ft. by 50 ft. and distributes these among his brothers and some of his sons. The new owner subdivides his plot into five or six strips, retaining perhaps three for himself and his family and lending the remainder to relatives such as his sister, his sister's son, or perhaps his mother's brother's son. In return he is generally given a plot by these persons on their land either at the same time or the following year. During tenure, the temporary owner is responsible for the upkeep and enjoys exclusive rights over the crops which he grows.

It is thus important to distinguish clearly between the right to inherit and the rights of usufruct which may be exercised by a group of blood and affinal relatives. A similar system obtains also among the Morehead district tribes, where the clan head is the titular owner and may grant cultivation rights to those who ask permission; among the Koita he receives, however, a portion of the first crop in payment.

Sometimes, a clan dies out and then any man of the village may stake a claim to the clan land providing he uses it. The ground passes into the possession of his descendants so long as they too continue to clear it for their gardens. Thus, in the last resort, ownership is contingent on use, and this is brought out clearly in those tribes where descent is bilateral. In the south-west of New Britain, for example, a woman may inherit land but, if she fails to cultivate it, she loses her title.

Elsewhere, as in Lesu on the east coast of New Ireland, certain parts of the bush, believed to be inhabited by clan animals and the spirits of the dead, belong to the clan. But ownership of land devoted to cultivation is vested in the village and each individual has rights only over the products of his labour and not over the soil. A similar system of tenure occurs in the northern Solomon islands where the headman apportions plots among the members of the village.

Gardening (Plates 38–41)

The natives produce a great variety of crops—root vegetables, legumes, sugar cane and tobacco. Coconuts, which are usually individually owned, grow along the coasts, rivers, plains and low foothills, and are an especially important item of diet in the Bismarck archipelago. Bananas are found throughout practically the whole region and, in some tribes, constitute one of the staples. Environmental conditions determine of course the distribution of certain types of food and three areas may, broadly speaking, be distinguished: firstly, rivers, swampy coastal belts and fens where the people depend on sago, eked out by yams; secondly, the plains, coasts and low hills where either taro or yams are the staple: and, finally, the high mountains where sweet potatoes, sugar cane and bananas constitute the chief articles of diet. Food preferences, however, are apt to be arbitrary, and though taro, yams, manioc, bananas and sago may all be available, one of these is usually esteemed above the others. Thus in most of the Bismarck archipelago, in Manam, and at the head-waters of the Fly and Sepik rivers, taro is regarded as the staple; while, to cite another example, among the Abelam, the Keraki of the Morehead district, and the southern section of the Orokaiva people, yams are considered the greater delicacy.

Besides the foods mentioned, the natives also eat breadfruit, the shoots of a type of sugar cane, canarium nuts and wild fruits which are available for short periods only. European plants such as maize, potatoes, pumpkins, cucumbers, tomatoes, peas and pineapples have been introduced in some areas, but in general they are not regarded as satisfactory substitutes for the traditional foods. Tobacco is grown throughout most of the mainland and is frequently smoked by the young and old of both sexes. The chief narcotic is areca nut rolled in a pepper leaf (*Piper betle*) and mixed with lime, but the Megei tribe of mount Hagen chew a wild ginger.

The natives practise a system of shifting cultivation and a garden is rarely used for more than two years in succession. Though the method is a wasteful one, the natives are, on the whole, good gardeners and possess a considerable body of empirical knowledge about plants and the suitability of different types of soil. Irrigation has been reported to exist in the Bartle bay area. In the foothills of the Torricelli range, where yam gardens are made on the slopes, a trellis of bamboo is constructed at the base of the mounds to prevent the soil washing away. Magical rites form an integral part of the agricul-tural activities and may be carried out by one man for the whole village (as in the Trobriands), by the clan head, or sometimes by a man and his wife for their own plot. Magic, however, is never regarded as a substitute for industry and for the application of the empirical knowledge which the natives possess.

Taro can be planted all through the year, but generally new gardens are made in August or September. The men perform the heavier manual labour, while the women clear away the undergrowth, burn off the rubbish and sometimes help with the fencing. The women are also responsible for much of the planting of taro, the weeding and harvesting; the men may assist in these tasks, but usually devote

Plate 40. Abelam men planting yams
The palisade in the background is built to keep out pigs.

Plate 41. Yam harvest, Abelam tribe
The yams are heaped on a layer of banana leaves.

Plate 42. Man from the mount Hagen area

The man carries a thin-bladed greenstone axe and wears a profusion of ornaments. On his forehead is a band of small cowry shells.

Plate 43. Pig prepared for a feast, Abelam tribe

most of their time to the cultivation of yams. The main gardening tools are the axe, bush knife and digging stick. Taro is planted from tops and corms; bananas from suckers; sugar cane from slips; greens from seeds; and yams from the tuber when this has sprouted.

Usually the harvest of yams is an occasion for rejoicing, display and feasts, for food is regarded as a source of prestige and a form of wealth which can be used for the fulfilment of ceremonial obligations. Yams and certain varieties of taro can be stored for several months and hence are eaten throughout most of the year. But since quantities must be set aside for seed and feasts there is often a lean period between November and February, when people subsist mainly on sago and greens. Sago palms are often individually owned but worked by a small kinship group. Sometimes the whole process is carried out by the men, as on the Tabar islands; sometimes the men cut down the palm and strip away the bark, leaving the women to remove the pith, pound it and wash it through a sieve in a trough.

Division of Labour and Specialization (Plates 42, 44–7)

While there is little specialization of occupation as we understand it in our own society, there is, nevertheless, a marked division of labour between the sexes which shows much the same pattern throughout the New Guinea area. Since reference has already been made to this, more especially in connection with economic activities, it is unnecessary to discuss it in detail here. Briefly, the women carry out most of the tasks connected with the household: the sweeping, gathering of firewood, the filling of bamboos and pots with water, the cooking and the care and rearing of the children. It should be remembered that houses are small, furniture is usually limited to sleeping mats and stools, and meals are simple. During the day the women spend most of their time in the garden, where they plant, weed and harvest the taro. Their responsibility for this crop, together with greens, tobacco and bananas, is apt to vary according to whether the men devote much time to fishing, hunting and the cultivation of yams. The women rarely fashion their ornaments, but they make skirts and the tools and utensils connected with their work. String bags are netted from the prepared bast of certain saplings, and sometimes dyed. Women in most tribes are the potters; they usually employ the coil method, rolling the clay into long thin 'sausages' and then twisting them into the desired shape. Their pots, on the whole, lack finish and decoration, but in a few areas the men make them for ceremonial purposes and incise and paint them with elaborate patterns. Women also do most of the marketing, but the ceremonial exchange of valuables and those forms of barter which necessitate sea voyages or extensive journeys on land are undertaken by the men.

Cooking generally falls within the province of the women, except for the butchering and roasting of pigs. Much of the food is boiled in pots or made into thick soups garnished with grated coconut. Yams, taro and plantains may be roasted or steamed; and sago is either boiled or baked in the form of pancakes.

The men hunt, fish and perform the heavy manual labour, such as the clearing away of big timber, the building of houses and canoes. They, rather than the women, are the skilled craftsmen and artists. Nowadays steel axes, knives and plane irons for adzes have been introduced; the use of matches has in most areas supplanted fire-making by either the plough or strap method; and razor blades are used for a multitude of purposes. But there are still many tribes who rely on the old implements—the adze with its knee-shaped haft and blade of polished stone; knives made from quartz, or from a splinter of stone, a boar's tusk, a piece of serrated shell or sharpened bamboo; and needles of flying-fox bone for the plaiting of armbands. When the relative crudeness and limited range of such tools are taken into account one is amazed at the high degree of workmanship displayed by native artefacts.

For the construction of a men's ceremonial house, a canoe or a large slit-gong, the co-operation of a team of men is, of course, essential for the handling of the timber. The work is carried out as a rule under the direction of one of the more important men, or else an expert is chosen by the entrepreneur and paid for his services in food and valuables. Reference has already been made to the elaborate architecture of some of the houses, but the achievements of some of the coastal tribes in canoe-building are also outstanding. On the Sepik and Fly rivers mere dugouts are used, but in the Massim area various types are found; the Motu, for instance, lash several hulls together, build a platform over the top and propel the craft (*lakatoi*) with crab-claw sails made from matting (vol. I, Fig. 110). In the Trobri-ands the canoe has built-up sides, intricately carved prow-boards and an outrigger (vol. I, Plate 118).

Besides the ornamentation of the larger artefacts, the men also decorate their weapons (spears, clubs, shields and bone daggers), lime gourds and lime spatulas (vol. I, Plate 141). They work shell into armlets and rings; string small shells into necklaces and head-bands;

Plate 44. Women weaving on simple looms, Emirau

The thread used is fibre from the banana stalk; tension on the warp threads is maintained by pressure of the feet on one beam against tension on the other by a band round the waist.

Plate 45. Making pots on Tumbeo island

The woman is shaping and smoothing the pot by hand.

Plate 46. Thread-making, mount Hagen area
The woman is rolling vegetable fibres on her thigh.

Plate 47. Carving a wooden spear, mount Hagen area

and weave arm-bands, wickerwork masks, fish traps, sleeping mats and bags. Designs are traditional and highly stylized and there is little scope for a display of originality on the part of the artist. Nevertheless the natives have a keen eye for fineness of carving and painting, and while most men acquire some skill in every craft, generous recognition is given to those who are outstanding as artists. Their services may be requisitioned not only within the village but throughout the district, as happens for instance in the Abelam tribe where such men play an important part in the organization of the men's ceremonial activities.

Art (Plates 48–56)

It is impossible here to do full justice to the richness and beauty of New Guinea art. A few tribes like the Mountain Arapesh import many of their artefacts or else imitate in a crude fashion the styles of the surrounding region, but this is rare and a tribe, if it is not master of all the crafts, generally achieves pre-eminence in some. Mention may be made here of the mount Hagen battle axes with their finely polished blades of greenstone; the dancing shields and prow-boards of the Trobriands; the delicately wrought lime spatulæ of the southern Massim; the smooth, regular shell rings of the Plains Arapesh; the anthropomorphic carvings of the Iatmul; the Buka pendants with their superimposed tortoise-shell filigree; and the finely incised bone daggers, the wood and wickerwork masks, and the feather head-dresses of the Abelam. (For some further details see vol. I, Chapter XIII.)

Barter and Ceremonial Exchange

There are, broadly speaking, three types of exchange in the New Guinea area: firstly, that between kin; secondly, barter; and thirdly, ceremonial exchange between trade partners. Reference has already been made to the first in discussing social organization (p. 161), and it is sufficient here to say that it obtains throughout the whole region and is based on traditionally defined obligations to give assistance to kin in time of need and to make certain gifts in connection with birth, initiation, marriage and death.

Barter. The scale on which barter takes place is, of course, determined by the resources of a village and the skill of its members in the practice of certain crafts. Thus, among the Abelam who live in fertile country and who have a rich material culture, barter is undertaken generally by individuals and involves little organization in the way of markets. Some villages have a reputation for making better netbags than others and visitors present for a ceremony will seize the opportunity to acquire some in return for lengths of shell discs (Pidgin-English, *tambu*); or, again, a skilled potter will exchange her products for sago, which may not be plentiful in her village at the time.

As distinct from this irregular barter between individuals, there is what may be called the symbiotic relationship between villages in which each lacks an essential commodity possessed by the other. Thus the mountain Kurema trade their sago for the fish of the Sepik tribes; the Mundugumdi export their tobacco, coconuts and areca nuts for the pots, baskets and sleeping bags of their neighbours; or the people of Karkar island obtain vegetables from the mainland in return for fish. Perhaps one of the best examples of organized barter is that engaged in by the Motu and Koita, who every year about September or October sail west in a fleet of about 20 *lakatoi* along the Gulf of Papua. The journey takes about three months and they exchange thousands of pots for sago. On some of the less fertile islands where there is little timber and ground for cultivation, the inhabitants must import most of their food, tools, utensils and raw materials. But they acquire not only sufficient for their own needs, but a surplus for re-export, and hence act as middlemen between various islands and the mainland. Typical of these are the people of Tubetube, Manus and the Siassi islands.

Ceremonial Exchange. Finally, there is a type of exchange which may be called ceremonial in that the element of material benefit is absent or else purely ancillary to the main purpose which is the enhancement of the prestige of those taking part. It occurs in a few tribes on the mainland, such as the Abelam where the village is divided into two groups, the men of one being ceremonial trading partners to the men of the other. Yams are exchanged and the donor endeavours to excel his partner in the quality and number he hands over. This type of ceremonial activity, however, appears in its most complex form in the institution of the *kula* of the Massim area. This links in a network of exchange the Trobriands, Amphletts, Dobu, East cape, Panayati, Misima, Murua and the Marshall Bennett islands. The valuables comprise on the one hand, necklaces of red *spondylus* shell which are handed on from one *kula* community to another in a clockwise direction; and, on the other, white shell bracelets which are given in exchange and which travel in an anti-clockwise direction. As distinct from ordinary barter, there is no haggling, and

Plate 48. Man with winged head-dress, mount Hagen area
Note also the bone through the nose septum and the cowry-shell necklaces.

Plate 49. Ceremonial mask, Abelam tribe

Plate 50. Carved and painted wooden figures, Abelam tribe
These figures, in the men's house, represent clan ancestors.

Plate 51. Masked men dancing, Mindimbit village on
the Sepik river.

prestige accrues to a man not only in the temporary possession of the ornament but also in his ability to present his partner with a return gift which is equal if not superior in quality. The acquisition of these valuables entails the organization of a long overseas expedition in which the men of a number of *kula* villages participate. Canoes are built especially for the occasion under the direction of the entrepreneurs, and during the journey many halts are made at different islands, and the opportunity taken to engage in a certain amount of barter of objects other than the ceremonial valuables.

RELIGION AND MAGIC

Cannibalism, which was indulged in largely for ritual purposes, and head-hunting, which was connected with initiation or the acquisition of prestige, have been suppressed in most parts of the New Guinea area. Again, some of the old dances, mortuary and initiation rites have fallen into desuetude in districts where European contact has been intense, as in parts of the Bismarck archipelago, or where missionaries have been established for a long period. Nevertheless it would be true to say that in nearly all tribes, certain beliefs and practices relating to the supernatural still exist, and while there is considerable variation of custom, it is possible to indicate some of the broader similarities.

Firstly, there is a widely held belief in spirits (Pidgin-English, *marsalai*) who in the remote past instituted customs and created certain natural phenomena. These sometimes assume a grotesque human form or appear in the guise of snakes, lizards or crocodiles, and are usually associated with certain parts of the river or bush. On the whole they are avoided if possible by human beings, and in the Sepik district they are regarded as especially inimical to women.

There is also a belief in the spirits of the dead who are feared in some tribes but are more often treated with respect and affection since they watch over the living. Mortuary ceremonies are elaborate and involve wailing, singing and the observance of taboos by close kin. Frequently the bones such as the skull and radius are exhumed later and kept in the house as a means of tethering the spirit, as it were, to a spot where it can safeguard the interests of the descendants. Often the names of the ancestors are invoked in the gardening and fishing magic, and in the Trobriands offerings are made to them once a year at a feast. This belief in the influence of the spirits of the dead is perhaps held nowhere more strongly than in Manus, where the male ancestors act as guardians of the men of the house, prosper their fishing and trade and protect them against malefactors, but also punish them severely for any laxity in sexual and economic matters or for infractions of the rules governing kinship behaviour. In parts of the Bismarck archipelago and the mainland the dead are also associated with the initiation ceremonies. Thus in Lesu elaborately carved boards are fashioned in honour of the ancestors and shown to the initiated; and in Buka and among the Orokaiva of Papua masked dancers impersonate the spirits of the dead.

In nearly every tribe there is some form of initiation of boys, either in childhood or at puberty, into the ritual life of the men, from which the women in nearly every case are rigidly excluded. After circumcision or incision has been performed, masked dancers, supposed to be the tutelary spirits of the men's cult, appear before the neophytes, who are then shown certain 'sacred' objects such as flutes, bull-roarers and anthropomorphic carvings.

Following on this, the boys are secluded away from the village for three months or longer under the guardianship of an older man. They must observe various food taboos, but the period is regarded as one of growth, and there is the fiction that when they emerge finally, decorated with brilliant feather head-dresses, shells, necklaces and flowers, their own mothers do not recognize them. This occasion of their return is one for rejoicing, and visitors come decked in their ornaments to watch and perhaps take part in the dances by torchlight which last from dusk to dawn.

These initiation ceremonies entail considerable preparation beforehand. Extra gardens must be planted and pigs reared or purchased for the feast. In some tribes the relatives of the boy hand over food and valuables to the initiators, as among the Abelam; or sometimes members of the two moieties may exchange shell 'currency', as in Lesu. On the Gazelle peninsula there were at one time strongly organized secret societies (*dukduk*), to which entrance could be obtained only by the giving of a feast. The members exacted tribute from the uninitiated and appeared before them as masked figures.

Girls' puberty ceremonies are generally less spectacular than those for the boys and are largely organized by the women. The girl at her first menses is secluded in a hut for a period and observes food taboos. When she emerges, she is ritually washed by her female relatives, and a feast may be held in which the women of the village take part.

Of all the ceremonies connected with the individual, initiation and mortuary rites are usually the most elaborate and involve the partici-

Plate 52. Canoe prow-board, Trobriand islands

The carving includes two human figures and the 'frigate bird' motif. It is executed in low relief on a light-coloured wood; parts are picked out in pale red. Length 28 in.

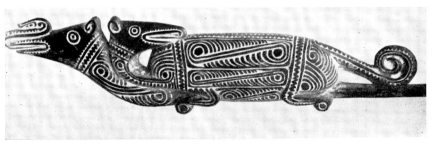

Plates 53 and 54. Two handles of wooden lime spatulae, Trobriand islands

The animal represented in these carvings is probably a dog; in Plate 54 it has two heads. Lengths of the portions shown, $14\frac{1}{4}$ in. and 13 in.

Plate 55. Painted masks, Abelam tribe, Sepik area

Plate 56. Painted design on the gable end of a men's house, Abelam tribe
The stylized human faces are linked, each with the mythical ancestor of a particular clan.

pation of many people. Birth is largely a matter for rejoicing within a small kinship group, and the ritual element lies mainly in the observance of taboos on food and sexual intercourse by husband and wife during gestation and also for a period afterwards, until it is certain that the child will live.

Reference must also be made to two other types of belief and practice centring around the supernatural, namely, beneficient magic (white magic) and sorcery (black magic). In all those tribes which have not been subjected to intensive missionary influence, magic is performed to further success in economic activities (hunting, fishing, trading and gardening), in love-making, the curing of the sick and, in the old days, in warfare. Nearly always special types of herbs are used over which spells are uttered by the magician. A knowledge of these is handed down from mother to daughter, and from father to son, or, in matrilineal tribes, from mother's brother to sister's son.

So far, the efforts of missionaries and the administration have met with little success in the attempt to eradicate the belief in black magic, and one may say that most forms of illness and death are still attributed to the machinations of the sorcerer. In some areas, such as the Sepik district and the Schouten islands, the sorcerer is supposed to seize his victim, remove his entrails by magic, sew him up again and send him back to the village to die after a specified time. Much more prevalent, however, is the form of black magic in which exuviae, nail parings or hair of the victim are sent, together with a payment, to a man in another village who is reputed to be a sorcerer. He then burns, boils or hides these personal leavings, uttering a spell, and later the victim falls ill and dies, unless effective counter-magic can be performed.

BIBLIOGRAPHICAL NOTE

There are no general works of any importance on the anthropology of the whole of the New Guinea area, and therefore the following bibliography is a list of books and articles which deal only with certain aspects of culture or with certain regions. Besides these, the reader is also referred to articles in *Oceania*, a quarterly journal published in Sydney and devoted to the study of the native peoples of New Guinea and the other Pacific islands.

General works on physical anthropology are few; the most important is A. C. Haddon, *The Races of Man and Their Distribution* (Cambridge, 1924). The art of New Guinea has received relatively little attention, apart from brief references to it in discussions of material culture. The best works on the subject are: A. C Haddon, 'The Decorative Art of British New Guinea', *Royal Irish Academy, Cunningham Memoirs*, no. 10 (Dublin, 1894); and Raymond Firth, *Art and Life in New Guinea* (London and New York, 1936). The main sources on language are articles in various periodicals. The most important of these are: S. H. Ray, 'The

Languages of Northern Papua', *Journal of the Royal Anthropological Institute*, vol. XLIX, pp. 317–41 (London, 1919); S. H. Ray, 'The Languages of the Western Division of Papua', *Journal of the Royal Anthropological Institute*, vol. LII, pp. 332–60, (London, 1923); and A. Capell, 'Language Study for New Guinea Students', *Oceania*, vol. XI, no. 1, pp. 40–74 (Sydney, 1940–1).

The literature on the social anthropology of individual tribes or groups of tribes in certain areas is a rich and extensive one. One of the earliest and most valuable publications was C. G. Seligmann, *The Melanesians of British New Guinea* (Cambridge, 1910), a survey of the physical anthropology and customs of the Western Papuo-Melanesians and the Massim. Other outstanding, and more recent, monographs on the Massim are: B. Malinowski, *Argonauts of the Western Pacific* (London, 1922); B. Malinowski, *Crime and Custom in Savage Society* (London, 1926); B. Malinowski, *The Sexual Life of Savages* (London, 1929); B. Malinowski, *Coral Gardens and Their Magic*, 2 vols. (London, 1935); D. Jenness and A. Ballantyne, *The Northern D'Entrecasteaux* (Oxford, 1920); F. E. Williams, *Orokaiva Magic* (London, 1928); F. E. Williams, *Orokaiva Society* (London, 1930); W. E. Armstrong, *Rossel Island* (Cambridge, 1928); and R. F. Fortune, *Sorcerers of Dobu* (London, 1932).

The Western Papuo-Melanesians and Papuans of central Papua have been described by R. W. Williamson, *The Mafulu: A Mountain People of British New Guinea* (London, 1912); B. Malinowski, 'The Natives of Mailu', *Transactions of the Royal Society of South Australia for 1915*, pp. 494–706 (Adelaide, 1915); F. E. Williams, *Drama of Orokolo: The Social and Ceremonial Life of the Elema* (Oxford, 1940); and F. E. Williams, 'Natives of Lake Kutubu', *Oceania Monographs*, no. 6 (Sydney, 1941).

The most important monographs on the tribes of the Western Division of Papua, in the region of the Fly river, are: G. Landtman, *The Kiwai Papuans of British New Guinea* (London, 1927); and F. E. Williams, *Papuans of the Trans-Fly* (Oxford, 1936).

The tribes of the Sepik District in the Mandated Territory of New Guinea have been the subject of a number of monographs and articles which embody the results of research carried out, for the most part, since 1930. Those of main interest are: R. Thurnwald, 'Banaro Society: social organization and kinship system of a tribe in the interior of New Guinea', *Memoirs of the American Anthropological Association*, vol. III, no. 4 (Lancaster, Pa., 1916); G. Bateson, 'Social Structure of the Iatmul People', *Oceania*, vol. II, pp. 245–92, 401–53 (Sydney, 1931–2); G. Bateson, *Naven: A Survey of the Problems suggested by a Composite Picture of the Culture of a New Guinea Society drawn from Three Points of View* (Cambridge, 1936); M. Mead, *Sex and Temperament in Three Primitive Societies* (London, 1935); M. Mead, 'The Mountain Arapesh: I. An Importing Culture', *Anthropological Papers of the American Museum of Natural History*, vol. XXXVII, part 3 (New York, 1938); R. F. Fortune, 'Arapesh Warfare', *American Anthropologist*, vol. XLI, pp. 22–41 (Wisconsin, 1939); J. W. M. Whiting and S. W. Reed, 'Kwoma Culture: Report on Field Work in the Mandated Territory of New Guinea', *Oceania*, vol. XI, pp. 170–216 (Sydney, 1938–9); J. W. M. Whiting, *Becoming a Kwoma* (New Haven, 1941); P. M. Kaberry, 'The Abelam Tribe, Sepik District, New Guinea—A Preliminary Report', *Oceania*, vol. XI, pp. 233–58, 345–67 (Sydney, 1940–1); P. M. Kaberry, Law and Political Organization in the Abelam Tribe, New Guinea', *Oceania*, vol. XII, pp. 79–95, 209–25, 331–63 (Sydney, 1941–2). There are no books on the social anthropology of the outlying islands, but a number of valuable and comprehensive articles have been published, of which the most important are: C. H. Wedgwood, 'Girls' Puberty Rites in Manam Island, New Guinea', *Oceania*, vol. IV, pp. 132–55 (Sydney, 1933–4); C. H. Wedgwood, 'Report on Research in Manam Island, Mandated Territory of New Guinea', *Oceania*, vol. IV, pp. 373–403 (Sydney, 1933–4); C. H. Wedgwood, 'Sickness and its Treatment in Manam Island, New

Guinea', *Oceania*, vol. v, pp. 64–79, 280–307 (Sydney, 1934–5); H. I. Hogbin, 'Native Culture of Wogeo—Report of Field Work in New Guinea', *Oceania*, vol. v, pp. 308–33 (Sydney, 1934–5); H. I. Hogbin, ' Trading Expeditions in Northern New Guinea', *Oceania*, vol. v, pp. 375–407 (Sydney, 1934–5); H. I. Hogbin, 'Native Land Tenure in New Guinea', *Oceania*, vol. x, pp. 113–65 (Sydney, 1939–40); and H. I. Hogbin, 'A New Guinea Infancy: From Conception to Weaning in Wogeo', *Oceania*, vol. XIII, pp. 285–309 (Sydney, 1942–3).

There is very little literature on the tribes of the mainland east of the Ramu river in the mandated territory. Some of the reports of general interest are: E. W. P. Chinnery, 'Mountain Tribes of the Mandated Territory of New Guinea from Mount Chapman to Mount Hagen', *Man*, no. 140 (London, 1934); E. W. P. Chinnery, 'Natives of the Waria, Williams and Bulolo Watersheds', *Mandated Territory of New Guinea, Anthropological Report*, no. 4 (Canberra, n.d.); E. W. P. Chinnery, 'Notes on the Natives of Certain Villages of the Mandated Territory of New Guinea', *Mandated Territory of New Guinea, Anthropological Report*, no. 1 (Melbourne, n.d.); T. G. Aitchison, 'Peace Ceremony as Performed by the Natives of the Ramu Headwaters', *Oceania*, vol. VI, pp. 478–80 (Sydney, 1935–6); S. Lehner, 'The Balum Cult of the Bukaua of Huon Gulf, New Guinea', *Oceania*, vol. v, pp. 338–45 (Sydney, 1934–5); and W. Ross, 'Ethnological Notes on Mt. Hagen Tribes (Mandated Territory of New Guinea) with Special Reference to the Tribe called Mogei', *Anthropos*, vol. XXXI, pp. 341–63 (Vienna, 1936).

The main sources on the social anthropology of the Bismarck archipelago are articles in periodicals, but a few monographs have been published. The following should be consulted: G. H. Pitt-Rivers, 'Aua Island: ethnological and sociological features of a South Sea pagan society', *Journal of the Royal Anthropological Institute*, vol. LV, pp. 425–38 (London, 1925); M. Mead, *Growing Up in New Guinea* (London 1931); M. Mead, 'Kinship in the Admiralty Islands', *Anthropological Papers of the American Museum of Natural History*, vol. XXXIV, part 2 (New York, 1934); R. F. Fortune, *Manus Religion: an ethnological study of the Manus natives of the Admiralty Islands* (*Memoirs of the American Philosophical Society*, vol. III, Philadelphia, 1935); E. W. P. Chinnery, 'Notes on the Natives of Emira and St. Matthias', *Mandated Territory of New Guinea, Anthropological Report*, no. 2 (Melbourne, n.d.); E. W. P. Chinnery, 'Notes on the Natives of South Bougainville and Mortlocks (Taku)', *Mandated Territory of New Guinea, Anthropological Report*, no. 5 (Canberra, n.d.); E. W. P. Chinnery, 'Studies of the Native Population of the East Coast of New Ireland', *Mandated Territory of New Guinea, Anthropological Report*, no. 6 (Canberra, n.d.); H. Powdermaker, 'Mortuary Rites in New Ireland', *Oceania*, vol. II, pp. 26–43 (Sydney, 1931–2); H. Powdermaker, *Life in Lesu: The Study of a Melanesian Society in New Ireland* (London, 1933); W. C. Groves, 'Report on Field Work in New Ireland', *Oceania*, vol. III, pp. 325–61 (Sydney, 1932–3); W. C. Groves, 'Tabar Today', *Oceania*, vol. v, pp. 224–40; vol. VI, pp. 147–57 (Sydney, 1934–5, 1935–6); F. L. S. Bell, 'Report on Field Work in Tanga', *Oceania*, vol. IV, pp. 290–309 (Sydney, 1933–4); F. L. S. Bell, 'The Avoidance Situation in Tanga', *Oceania*, vol. VI, pp. 175–98, 306–22 (Sydney, 1935–6); E. W. P. Chinnery, 'Certain Natives in South New Britain and Dampier Strait', *Mandated Territory of New Guinea, Anthropological Report*, no. 3 (Melbourne, n.d.); J. A. Todd, 'Report on Research Work in South-West New Britain, Territory of New Guinea', *Oceania*, vol. v, pp. 80–101, 192–213 (Sydney, 1934–5); J. A. Todd, 'Native Offences and European Law in South Western New Britain', *Oceania*, vol. v, pp. 437–60 (Sydney, 1934–5); J. A. Todd, 'Redress of Wrongs in South-West New Britain', *Oceania*, vol. VI, pp. 401–40 (Sydney, 1935–6); W. C. Groves, 'The Natives of Sio Island, South-Eastern New Guinea: a study in culture-contact', *Oceania*, vol. v, pp. 43–63 (Sydney, 1934–5); B. Blackwood, *Both Sides of Buka Passage: An Ethnographic Study of Social, Sexual, and Economic Questions in the Northwestern Solomon Islands* (London, 1935); B. Blackwood, 'Report on Field Work in Buka and Bougainville', *Oceania*, vol. II, pp. 199–219 (Sydney, 1931–2); and R. Parkinson, *Dreissig Jahre in der Südsee* (Stuttgart, 1907).

Most of the books and articles cited above deal with the traditional social structure and customs of New Guinea tribes. For studies of culture contact and change, the following should be consulted: S. W. Reed, *The Making of Modern New Guinea; with special reference to Culture Contact in the Mandated Territory* (*Memoirs of the American Philosophical Society*, vol. XVIII, 1942, Philadelphia, 1943); F. E. Williams, 'The Blending of Cultures: an essay on the aims of native education', *Territory of Papua, Anthropology, Report*, no. 16 (Port Moresby, 1935); and W. C. Groves, *Native Education and Culture Contact in New Guinea; a Scientific Approach* (*Australian Council for Educational Research, Educational Series*, no. 46, Melbourne, 1936).

There are also a number of interesting and informative books of a popular kind on New Guinea, the most outstanding of which are: J. H. Holmes, *Way Back in Papua* (London, 1926); J. V. Saville, *In Unknown New Guinea* (London, 1926); J. G. Hides, *Through Wildest Papua* (London, 1935); M. Leahy and M. Crain, *The Land That Time Forgot; Adventures and Discoveries in New Guinea* (New York and London, 1937); Lewis Lett, *Papua, Its People and Its Promise* (Melbourne, 1944).

Chapter IX

GOVERNMENT AND SOCIAL SERVICES

The structure of government and of social services in the Territory of Papua and the Mandated Territory of New Guinea is, in general, very similar. In part, this results from the fact that both are controlled by the Commonwealth of Australia. When the commonwealth government accepted a mandate over former German New Guinea, it possessed already a fund of relevant experience gained in Papua. The policies adopted by the Lieutenant-Governor of Papua, Mr. (later Sir) Hubert Murray, had indeed not passed unchallenged in Australia, but they had rather gained in prestige as a result of attacks; and, in their liberal spirit, they were in full accord with the principles imposed upon Australia by acceptance of the mandate. More fundamentally, however, the similarity is a consequence of similar local conditions. In Papua, penetration of the interior by government patrols was completed only a few years before the Japanese invasion, and considerable areas have never been under government control. In the mandated territory, parts of the interior still remain unexplored, and in 1940 only two-thirds of the total land area was either under control or in contact with government patrols. Similarly, both territories are relatively undeveloped economically, so that sources of public revenue are few and the functions of government necessarily limited. There is, in particular, little money available for social services. Missions, and to some extent other non-official bodies, thus take an important part in the provision of medical services and education.

Despite these similarities, there are a number of significant differences in structure and function between the governments of the two territories. To some extent they are due to the conditions existing in the mandated territory at the end of the period of German rule. The German administration, for example, had not pushed forward with the penetration of the interior, as the administration of Papua had done; on the contrary, it had concentrated on the development of the coastal zones, and had introduced Asiatic labour in order to do so. In the following account, the governments of the two territories are thus treated separately; but social services—where divisions of control do not generally correspond with territorial boundaries—are covered in a joint account.

GOVERNMENT OF THE TERRITORY OF PAPUA

CENTRAL ADMINISTRATION

Papua is administered, under the Papua Act, 1905, by an Administrator (until 1941 entitled 'Lieutenant-Governor'), appointed by the Governor-General of Australia and responsible to the Department of External Territories of the commonwealth government. The seat of government is at Port Moresby. The Administrator is assisted by Executive and Legislative Councils. The Executive Council is composed of eight senior government officers, as official members, and one non-official member. The Legislative Council is empowered to make ordinances for the peace, order and good government of the territory. Such ordinances require the assent of the Administrator to become operative; and for six months after assent has been given they are subject to disallowance by the Governor-General. Ordinances dealing with a number of major subjects, including divorce, the disposal of land, native labour, and the supply of explosives, intoxicants or drugs to natives, require the assent of the Governor-General before becoming operative.

Under the Administrator, government is carried on through five main departments—those of the Government Secretary, the Treasurer, and the Commissioner for Lands, and the Medical and Public Works Departments. The Department of the Government Secretary is responsible for native affairs, the constabulary, prisons, native taxation and education. The Department of the Treasurer is concerned with finance and customs, and also with posts and telegraphs, shipping and the government printing office.

DIVISIONAL AND NATIVE ADMINISTRATION

For general administration the territory is divided into eight magis-

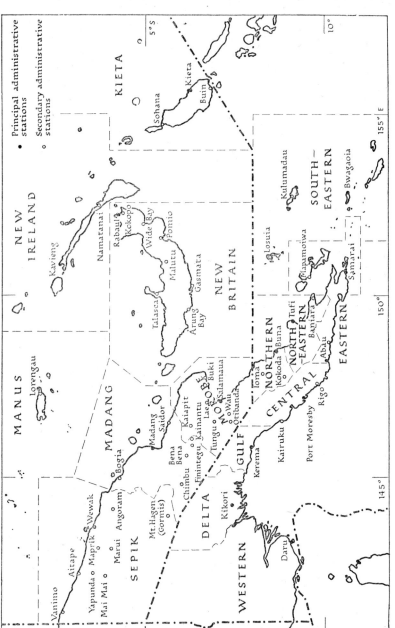

Fig. 38. New Guinea: administrative divisions
Compiled from official sources.

terial divisions (Fig. 38), each with an administrative headquarters at which is stationed a Resident Magistrate. This officer has executive authority to deal in the first instance with all administrative problems that may arise. He also has extensive judicial functions (p. 186). In some of the more populous divisions there are also Assistant Resident Magistrates, stationed at sub-centres. The duties of magistrates include the visiting of native communities; the inspection of houses, villages and roads; and the collection of taxes.

Each government station covers most aspects of native administration and also serves as a centre for the diffusion of European ideas and practices in agriculture, hygiene and other practical matters. It has, therefore, a staff of European and native specialists in many activities. These include Patrol Officers, medical and agricultural workers, a radio operator and various clerical assistants, besides a detachment of native police. There is a growing tendency to train natives to fill many of the specialist posts.

Since large areas in Papua are still under only partial government control, the work of the European Patrol Officer is of great importance. At the head of a patrol of native police and accompanied by medical assistants (frequently natives also) he accomplishes routine patrols from the government stations to the more distant parts of the district. Exploration and the establishment of contact between the government and the remoter native peoples are the main aims of these expeditions. Census work is also carried out. Simple but effective medical treatment has been found a sure means of winning the confidence of native people visited on the patrols. Other patrols are carried out specifically to maintain order and arrest criminals (p. 186).

Attempts to bring the practices of the administration into conformity with native ideas and institutions have had only a very limited success, owing mainly to the general absence of well-developed native political systems. Only in a few areas, such as the Trobriands, is there, for example, any form of hereditary chieftainship. Indirect rule, as it has been developed in other parts of the Pacific (such as Fiji) and in Africa, is not possible.

In the main, the government has relied for village administration on a system of village constables. These are picked men, chosen by the Resident Magistrates as official representatives in the main native settlements. They are unarmed and their main function is to see that Native Regulations on such matters as village sanitation and road-making are carried out. In the more developed areas, native councils have also been established. The councillors are generally the older and more experienced men. They have no executive powers but serve in an advisory capacity, advising the magistrate on measures for village government and, in particular, on the important issue of the preservation or abandonment of native customs.

FINANCE

The Papuan administration has always been severely handicapped by the small size of the annual revenue. To meet the administrative needs of the territory, the Australian government has from the first granted an annual subsidy. Its value, originally £30,000, was increased to £50,000 after the war of 1914–18, but reduced again to about £40,000 in 1932. Smaller sums have also been lent by the commonwealth for specific purposes, generally the undertaking of public works, such as harbour developments at Port Moresby.

The main local sources of revenue, as in most Pacific islands territories, have always been import and, to a lesser extent, export duties. Revenue has therefore fluctuated with the vagaries of world trade. But despite the development of the country's resources over the past forty years, the commonwealth grant even now comprises almost a quarter of the total. The post office supplies the only other large source of revenue. There is no form of direct taxation of the European population.

In 1938–9 total revenue was £167,000, giving a *per capita* figure of about 10s. With this small revenue it is clear that expenditure on public works and social services can only be on a very modest scale. Salaries of indispensable officials and the pay of the native constabulary between them account for about a third of the total expenditure. The government departments with heaviest expenditure are the key departments of the Government Secretary and the Treasurer.

A striking feature of Papuan finance and administration is the existence of a special balance sheet for purely native affairs. The expenses of native administration derive from a native tax instituted in 1918. It is imposed only in the more developed areas and is levied on all males between the ages of 16 and 36, with certain exceptions. The exceptions comprise policemen, natives who are unfit to work, the fathers of four or more children, and mission teachers and students. The amount of tax is varied to suit local economic conditions and ranges from 5s. to £1 a head per year. The proceeds from this tax form a special Native Taxation Fund which is divided for expenditure between the Native Education Fund (p. 197) and the

Native Benefits Fund, from which the medical services of the missions are subsidized and family bonuses are paid. Of recent years, the amount raised annually has been about £15,000.

LAND POLICY

Land policy from the early days of the British protectorate over Papua has aimed at securing the native peoples in the tenure of their land. No native lands have been compulsorily resumed and no private dealings in land between natives and Europeans have been allowed. It has been government policy to buy land only from natives who are willing to sell it. In every case the Administrator must satisfy himself that the land is not required or likely to be required by the owners. Using these methods, the government has bought up large tracts of land, partly for its own use, but mainly for leasing to individual planters and miners. At any particular time the government has generally had sufficient land on its hands to meet the needs of intending planters, but the initiative frequently comes from individual planters who ask the government to buy particular areas which they desire to lease. Since 1906, under the Papua Act, no freeholds have been granted.

The 1937 statistics of land tenure (the latest available) are as follows:

Land held by natives	56,828,751	acres
Crown land	845,967	,,
Freehold land	24,018	,,
Leasehold land	246,864	,,

Lands leased are classified under one of four heads—agricultural; pastoral; mission; or residential and business. Leases may be granted for any period up to 99 years. Leases and rents are subject to the performance of improvement conditions. Thus, on an agricultural lease for a term of over 30 years, rent is not payable for the first ten years and may not exceed 6d. per acre per annum for the next ten years. Rents are based on the unimproved value of the land, which is re-assessed every ten years. Up to the present, European and native interests in the land have generally not been in serious conflict. The most important instance of conflicting interests has been in regard to some of the small coral islets of the Louisiade archipelago. These islets are not permanently inhabited, but they are important to the natives of the neighbouring larger islands as gardens and as bases for fishing. At the same time, they are ideally suited for coconut plantations. Europeans have, thus, not readily acquiesced in their exclusion.

Labour Policy

The furnishing of adequate labour for plantations has always presented difficulties in Papua. The native population, with sufficient land to produce its essential needs, has shown no strong inclination to work for wages. Considerations of native welfare have precluded the adoption of any system of forced labour, and the 'White Australia' policy has prevented the importation of Asiatics or other non-Europeans.

The government has sought a temporary solution to these problems in a system of indentured native labour. Recruiting is carried on by persons licensed by the government. The maximum term of indenture is three years; the average term is said to be about eighteen months. Women are indentured for service only under a European woman. Wages, hours and conditions of work, and food and housing standards are controlled by the government. A magistrate must be present at all enlistments to ensure that the recruit understands the nature of the contract he is accepting and that he is not accepting under duress. Government officers are required to remain completely impartial in respect of recruiting, taking no action to persuade natives to accept contracts.

This system of employment is conceived as a safeguard for the natives, as well as for their employers. It is believed that in this way the natives will gain experience of steady work and of the methods of Europeans and that eventually private agreements between the individual labourer and the employer will be the normal method of engagement. Recently it appears as if the abandonment of the indenture system may have been hastened by the war.

Law, Justice and Police

Under the Papua Act, 1905, the law and law courts previously existing in British New Guinea were continued under the new administration. The main body of law consists of the principles and rules of common law and equity, so far as they are applicable to conditions in the territory. The Australian Commonwealth Parliament possesses plenary powers of legislation for the territory. In fact, it has legislated for Papua mainly on constitutional matters. It has provided that general statutes are in force in the territory only when specially extended to it. Such an extension has been made in a few instances, e.g., in respect of the Patents Act and the Trade Marks Act. The main work of legislation has been delegated to the Legislative Council, which has the power to make ordinances. The body of local law so built up covers such subjects as land tenure and sale, the employment of labour, and native affairs. One of the most important of local laws is the Native Regulations Ordinance. This provided for the establishment of Courts for Native Affairs and gave power for the making of a code of special native regulations. This code has become one of the principal instruments of the liberal, paternalistic native policy of the administration. It deals with subjects as diverse as sorcery, drunkenness, the planting of coconut palms and school attendance. Each regulation is couched in simple language and has a preamble explaining the reason for its existence.

The highest judicial tribunal in the territory is the Supreme Court (formerly known as the Central Court). It is presided over by the Administrator (as Chief Magistrate). It has jurisdiction similar to that of the Supreme Court of an Australian state. Appeal lies from its decisions to the High Court of Australia. The Supreme Court is unlike the subordinate courts in that its proceedings, even in cases involving natives, are entirely in English. Beneath the Supreme Court come the Courts of Petty Sessions and the Wardens' Courts. In addition, there are the Native Magistrates' Courts, which are held by Resident Magistrates. The magistrates are advised by native assessors, and the procedure of the courts is usually informal and adapted to local custom.

An efficient armed police force has been an essential instrument in the pacification and development of Papua. It is a necessity to-day, since there are still large uncontrolled areas where native feuds are liable to occur.

The Armed Constabulary was originally organized in 1890 by Sir William MacGregor, who had had experience of a similar body in Fiji. It was formed at first of twelve Solomon islanders and two Fijians. Almost immediately, however, the training of Papuans was begun, and they soon formed the bulk of the force. The Royal Papuan Constabulary by 1940 had a strength of 420, including about 15 European officers. These men are trained at Port Moresby and stationed in small detachments at the various government stations throughout the territory. Police patrols are employed in tracking down and arresting criminals in the remote and uncontrolled areas; temporary police camps are set up in the course of such duties. Police also accompany all government patrols and expeditions.

GOVERNMENT OF THE MANDATED TERRITORY OF NEW GUINEA

CENTRAL ADMINISTRATION

In December 1920 a mandate was conferred on 'His Britannic Majesty for and on behalf of the Government of the Commonwealth of Australia' for the government of the former German New Guinea. The mandate was one of class 'C', which gave to the Australian government virtually unrestricted powers. The actual decision that Australia should be entrusted with the government of New Guinea had been made some time before the formal issue of the mandate, so that all preparations had been made for the replacement by a civil administration of the military administration then in being (p. 133). The legal framework of the new government was incorporated in the New Guinea Act, 1920. It provided for the appointment of an Administrator, as chief executive officer, responsible to the Governor-General of the commonwealth; legislative power was vested in the Governor-General in Council. This system was modified in 1926, when an Advisory Council was created in the territory; and a substantial change was made under the New Guinea Act, 1932. This act provided for the institution of Executive and Legislative Councils, with powers similar to those of the corresponding bodies in Papua (p. 180). These two bodies were actually brought into being in the following year. The Executive Council is composed of eight official members, who are normally the heads of the administrative departments, and one non-official member chosen by the non-official members of the Legislative Council from among their own number. The Legislative Council is composed of the Administrator (as President), the official members of the executive council, and seven non-official members nominated by the Administrator. The non-official members are chosen from the European residents of the territory, so as to represent the planting, mining and commercial interests. Extraordinary members may also be appointed by the Administrator for the discussion of any particular topic; they do not possess the right to vote.

The administration is organized in eight departments—those of the Government Secretary; the Treasury; District Services and Native Affairs; Customs; Lands, Surveys, Mines and Forests; Public Health; and Public Works.

The administrative centre of the territory was at Rabaul in New Britain, until December 1941. But the liability of the town to damage in volcanic eruptions and the increasing development, administrative and economic, of the New Guinea mainland led to consideration of alternative sites. Lae, in the Morobe District, was eventually chosen. The Administrator took up residence there at the end of 1941, but most of the departments were still awaiting transfer when normal administration was brought to an end by the Japanese invasion.

DISTRICT AND NATIVE ADMINISTRATION

For purposes of local administration, the territory is divided into seven districts. Three—Morobe, Madang and Sepik—are on the mainland of New Guinea and four—Manus, New Britain, New Ireland and Kieta—cover the islands to the north and east. Some account has already been given of administration in the Kieta District (vol. III, pp. 650–1). Each district is in charge of a District Officer who administers it from a headquarters station. He is responsible to the Director of District Services and Native Affairs. His main duties are the care and welfare of the native population, the extension of exploration and government influence by means of patrols, and the enforcement of law. He has both criminal and civil jurisdiction in a limited capacity (p. 193). He is assisted in his duties by Assistant District Officers and Patrol Officers who are stationed at other government centres in the district. The larger of these are staffed by Assistant District Officers and Patrol Officers and the smaller and more numerous sub-stations by Patrol Officers only.

As in Papua, the government stations serve a wide range of functions, not all of which are strictly administrative. Law and order are maintained by means of the police stationed there; and they are the places where District Courts are held. Administrative processes such as the collection of census returns and of native taxation are also centred on the government stations. In addition, most are provided with experimental and demonstration plantations to test the suitability of new crops and to give practical agricultural advice and assistance to the natives. Above all, they are the headquarters from which patrols penetrate each district. The system of patrols serves the same functions in the mandated territory as in Papua. Fig. 39 gives an indication of the extent of government control in the territory.

There are only the rudiments of strictly local government or of

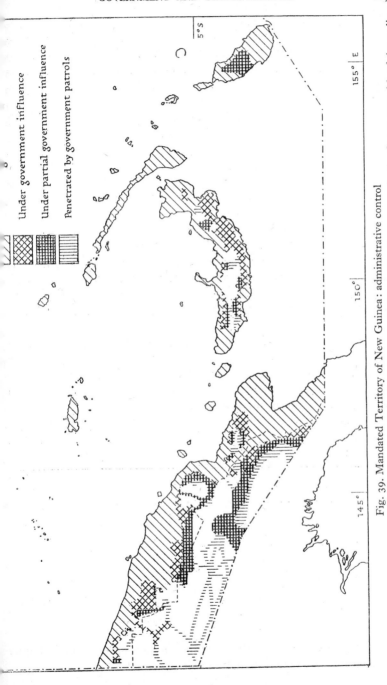

Fig. 39. Mandated Territory of New Guinea: administrative control

The pecked line on the mainland shows the general limit of the controlled area. Based on a map in the Commonwealth of Australia *Report to the Council of the League of Nations on the Administration of the Territory of New Guinea* for 1938–9 (Canberra, 1940).

Under government influence

Under partial government influence

Penetrated by government patrols

self-government by the natives. As in Papua, there is a lack of well-defined native political institutions. The present system of native administration is a development of that established by the German authorities. The Germans appointed native officials known as *luluai* and *tultul*. The office of *luluai* (or local leader) existed in pre-European days in the Blanche bay district of New Britain; it was non-hereditary and was filled by an outstanding warrior and man of wealth. The Germans accepted this system and extended it to other areas and peoples where the office had not existed. The *luluai* was selected by a government officer from among the village elders. If there were no recognized leader in a village, the choice fell on any man of outstanding personality. He had a few specific duties—the furnishing of 'boys' for labour recruiters; the supervision of road-making and village sanitation; and the collection of the annual head-tax. He was allowed to retain 10% of the taxes collected. Each *luluai* was assisted by another government nominee known as a *tultul*. His main duty was to act as interpreter between officials and the *luluai*. Another native official, the medical *tultul*, had no administrative powers but was given elementary training in first-aid and sanitary matters.

The system of *luluai* and *tultul* was taken over by the Australian administration and greatly extended as new areas were brought under control. One of the major objects of government patrols is to select and appoint new *luluai* and *tultul*. In areas under full control a development has been the promotion of certain of the more capable *luluai* as 'paramount' *luluai*, with control over the *luluai* of neighbouring villages. By June 1939 the following native officials were in office:

District	Paramount *luluai*	*Luluai*	*Tultul*	Medical *tultul*	Total
Kieta	18	482	465	464	1,429
Madang	5	580	648	775	2,008
Manus	4	124	126	129	383
Morobe	11	668	561	466	1,706
New Britain	13	697	749	580	2,039
New Ireland	14	323	314	446	1,097
Sepik	1	831	1,002	720	2,554
Total	66	3,705	3,865	3,580	11,216

Based on *Report to the Council of the League of Nations on the Administration of the Territory of New Guinea* for 1938-9, p. 28 (Canberra, 1940).

In 1936–7 village councils with functions similar to those in Papua were established experimentally in some areas.

FINANCE

The history of the public finances in the mandated territory has been different in many respects from that in Papua. When the civil administration was established in 1921, the commonwealth government determined that the territory should be made immediately self-supporting. A situation of extreme stringency resulted and lasted for some years. Funds were insufficient to permit even the adequate maintenance of works constructed by the Germans, and little new development could be undertaken. But a rapid increase in copra production and, later, the development of the Morobe goldfield greatly changed the situation. Customs revenue much increased, and a royalty of 2s. an ounce on gold exported provided an important new source of revenue.

As in Papua, the largest single source of revenue has always been import duties. These have flucutated in amount with trade conditions, but not to the same extent as export duties. To assist planters, export duties on copra have been imposed on a sliding scale dependent on the market price of copra. With the very low prices of the last decade, much copra has gone out duty-free or at very low rates of duty. Gold has suffered no such fall in value so the royalty has been a dependable as well as a large source of revenue. Native head tax has been a steady, though relatively minor source of revenue since the beginning of the mandate administration. In 1922–3 it provided about one-twelfth of the total. In 1938–9 it was still about £20,000, but then constituted only a twenty-fifth of the total revenue. This tax and the native labour tax are the main forms of direct taxation. The head tax amounts to 10s. a head per annum and is administered similarly to that in Papua. An important difference, however, is that native labourers are exempted. Instead a native labour tax is paid by the employers of native labour and amounts to 1s. per head per month. There is no income tax, but death duties are levied.

Though the commonwealth has never given the territory a regular subsidy, small grants have been made from time to time and loans provided for special purposes. The revenue per head of enumerated population in 1938–9 was approximately 15s.—50% greater than the corresponding figure for Papua. The departments of Public Works and Public Health between them accounted for nearly two-fifths of the public expenditure. As in Papua, salaries of officials make up a high proportion of expenditure.

Land Policy

In the early days of German settlement, the Neu-Guinea Kompagnie was given a monopoly in the acquisition of land, whether claimed or not by the native peoples. But in later German land legislation clauses were introduced to safeguard the rights of natives selling their lands. Settlers were not allowed to purchase land directly, but had to buy or lease it from the administration which acted as buyer. In general, freehold rather than leasehold tenure was the rule.

The Australian administration, in conformity with the principles of the mandate, preferred to grant leasehold tenure, and it has replaced the German system of land registration by one modelled on the Torrens system. Several types of leases are provided for—agricultural, pastoral and for other purposes. As in the later years of German administration, all applications for land are made to the government, which, if the native owners are agreeable, purchases the land and leases it to the applicant. Agricultural leases are granted for periods up to 99 years. Rent is charged at 5% of the unimproved value, which is re-assessed every 20 years. Areas which appear to be ownerless or waste land may by official proclamation become administration land, subject to the settlement of claims by any alleged owner. Land, native-owned or not, may be resumed by the government if it is needed for public utilities or other specified purposes, subject to the payment of compensation.

The German legacy of freehold tenure and the reparations clauses of the Treaty of Versailles have provided the mandate administration with special land problems. The treaty provided that the German plantations were to be expropriated and liquidated in favour of Australia, so in 1920 an Expropriations Board was set up to manage the ex-German interests and eventually to dispose of them by tender. By 1923 nearly all such plantations had been taken over and were being run by Australian officials. In 1926 the process of disposal of the plantations by tender began. Many were taken up by returned-soldier settlers, but the collapse of copra prices during the years 1932–5 ruined many of these small planters, whose lands were then bought up by the large plantation and trading interests.

Labour Policy

The labour policy of the mandated territory is in general similar to that of Papua. While the administration looks forward to a system of free native labour as the goal, indentured labour is still (in 1944) the rule. The Asiatics (mostly Chinese), whom the Germans imported, form an additional element in the labour supply.

Justified on the same grounds as that of Papua, the Native Labour Ordinance of 1935–6 regulates terms of employment and of recruiting and has established a system of inspections. It is administered by the Department of District Services and Native Affairs. Recruiters of native labour are all licensed by the administration. Contracts between labourers and their future employers must be signed in the presence of a District Officer who tries to ensure that the natives fully understand the proceedings and that they enter employment willingly. All are medically examined and must be passed fit for employment.

Where natives can be employed within easy reach of their homes, free labour is sometimes possible. Thus, in some of the islands of the Manus district the 'job contract' system is in vogue; local natives not under indenture tend the plantations and prepare copra. Everywhere, too, local natives may be employed as house servants without indenture.

LAW, JUSTICE AND POLICE

By the Laws Repeal and Adoption Ordinance, 1921, German law, which had previously been in force in the territory, was declared no longer to apply. In its place, English law, as in force at that time in Queensland, was adopted, and certain specified Queensland acts and Papuan ordinances were also declared to be in force. Power was reserved to the courts to construe all parts of this body of law with such verbal alterations as were necessary. Later additions to this body of law have been made mainly by ordinance, and most ordinances have been based on those of the Territory of Papua. As in Papua, a code of Native Administration Regulations has been formed. Native custom is recognized in the courts so far as it is not repugnant to European conceptions of justice and morality.

The highest judicial authority in the territory is the Supreme Court (known till 1934 as the Central Court). It is modelled on the Supreme Court of Queensland. It has original civil and criminal jurisdiction and hears appeals from the inferior courts. Appeal from decisions of the court lies to the High Court of Australia. Below the Supreme Court are District Courts, which are presided over by a District Officer or Assistant District Officer. Almost half the cases tried before these courts are ones involving breaches of the terms of indenture by native labourers. The lowest judicial tribunals are the Courts for

Native Affairs, held by a District Officer, Assistant District Officer, or Patrol Officer. Their jurisdiction is limited to matters concerning natives. Procedure is largely informal. A high proportion of minor disputes between natives, however, does not come before the regularly constituted courts. They tend to be referred either to traditional authorities—mainly village elders—or to the newer native officials, the *luluai* and *tultul*.

Even more than in Papua, an armed police force is essential to the maintenance of law and order, since the uncontrolled areas of the territory are still large. The New Guinea Police Force is an armed native force commanded by European commissioned and warrant officers. Its strength, native and European, was 1,115 in June 1940. Control is vested in the Administrator and the force is commanded by a Superintendent. About one-third of the total force, including most of the new recruits, is maintained at headquarters at Rabaul (Plate 69). The rest of the force is allotted to the various police districts into which the territory is divided. These correspond to the administrative districts with the addition of the town of Rabaul. The latter is policed by a special section of European police—an inspector and warrant officers, with a detachment of native constabulary. In each of the administrative districts the District Officer is responsible for the policing of his area. He and the Assistant District Officers and Patrol Officers are, *ex officio*, officers in the force. A detachment is attached to each government station and police accompany all government patrols. There is a small prison at each government station.

SOCIAL SERVICES

MEDICAL AND PUBLIC HEALTH SERVICES

The health of the native populations of Papua and the mandated territory is not good. Climate, living conditions and the presence of various endemic tropical diseases all contribute to a high morbidity rate. To these must be added the introduced chest ailments of pneumonia and tuberculosis. Except in the upland regions of the interior, malaria is the largest single cause of death, particularly in infancy and childhood. Malaria appears to be present in about one-third of the population; there is some evidence of partial immunity at the age of puberty. Pneumonia and tuberculosis are the principal immediate causes of death, particularly in the interior of the mainland

and among plantation labourers. Yaws is probably the most universal of native diseases in New Guinea. Its cure by novarsenobillon injections is the first consideration of the medical services. Injections given in the course of medical patrols take effect so quickly and thoroughly as to be of great assistance in winning the confidence of natives in uncontrolled areas.

The maintenance of medical and health services in each territory is shared by the administration, the missions and European employers of native labour. There are very few private medical practitioners. In each territory the responsible government department (known in Papua as the Medical Department and in the mandated territory as the Public Health Department) exercises general control and provides most of the finance needed for medical services. In Papua, money for health services for natives and Europeans come from two sources: about three-quarters of the total is derived from ordinary revenue —i.e., largely from Europeans—while the remainder is found from the Native Benefits Fund and used exclusively for native welfare. In the mandated territory all the services are financed wholly from general revenue. The proportions of medical expenditure to total government expenditure in 1938–9 were about 13% in Papua and 18% in the mandated territory.

Medical services are controlled from the administrative centres of Port Moresby and Rabaul, where the main hospitals and centres of medical research are situated. But the general organization of services is regional, based on the administrative divisions of Papua and the districts of the mandate. At each local administrative headquarters is stationed a European medical officer with assistants. He has in his charge a small native hospital. From this centre are organized routine medical patrols.

The various mission bodies (pp. 199–202) have from the first done pioneer medical work for the native population. Their trained doctors and nurses still play an important part in the medical services of the two territories. They are helped by government subsidies in the form of direct monetary grants and the free issue of various medical supplies. Papua, owing to its small financial resources, relies to a great extent on the medical personnel and hospitals of the missions. In the mandated territory a larger proportion of the medical services is provided by the administration. But the missions still maintain several fully qualified medical practitioners and nurses. Thus, for example, the Malabunga Native Hospital and Infant Welfare Centre is owned by the administration but is staffed by nurses of the

Methodist mission, for whose maintenance the administration pays an annual sum.

Employers of indentured native labour are obliged to provide hospitals and medical care for their employees. Some, as for instance the mining companies on the Morobe goldfields, maintain their own trained medical staff for this purpose; smaller concerns send their sick employees to the district hospitals. All labourers are inspected annually by government medical officers on patrol.

The main hospitals, whether run by the administration or by missions, are staffed by European doctors and medical assistants. Many of these men devote part of their time to work in hospital and part to medical patrolling. In addition to these Europeans, selected natives have been given some medical training. Parties of natives from Papua have been trained in the elements of medicine at the School of Public Health and Tropical Hygiene in the University of Sydney. On their return they are employed as travelling native medical assistants. In the mandated territory the appointment of medical *tultul* has formed part of the system of native administration. Medical officers on patrol select suitable natives for this office; after an elementary training in first-aid and hygiene these men are placed in charge of health matters in their own villages.

There are separate hospitals for Europeans and natives in each territory. European hospitals in Papua are situated at Port Moresby and Samarai; and in the mandated territory at Rabaul, Kavieng, Madang, Salamaua, Wau, Kieta and Manus. Hospitals to serve the native population (and, in the mandated territory, Asiatics) are maintained by the governments at all the main administrative centres. Some of the missions have large and well-equipped hospitals at their main stations. In Papua, major mission hospitals are maintained at Gona by the Anglicans; near Port Moresby by the London Missionary Society; and at Salamo, Fergusson island, by the Methodists. There are also numerous small hospitals and dressing-stations at mission outposts. Many members of the mission staffs have had some medical training.

There are special hospitals for infectious diseases. On Gemo island, near Port Moresby, is a hospital for natives suffering from tuberculosis and leprosy; though maintained by the government it is staffed by the London Missionary Society. In the mandated territory a leper asylum was established by the government in 1933 on Anelaua island, near Kavieng. It remains under the control of the Medical Officer at Kavieng, but staff has been provided by the Roman

Catholic mission of the Sacred Heart of Jesus. Associated with this settlement is an observation colony situated at Taskul. Suspected cases are kept under observation, and patients from Anelaua, when apparently cured, are transferred there pending their discharge. An attempt is made to segregate all lepers in these stations.

EDUCATION

Central Control

In New Guinea, as elsewhere in the Pacific, the first steps towards education of the native peoples were taken by missionary bodies. Only during the last thirty years has the administration of either territory assumed any educational responsibility. Official educational policy in both territories has been influenced by the prior existence of mission schools and by a general scarcity of funds. Government action in Papua was postponed until 1918, partly through shortage of funds and partly because the establishment of law and order and the exploration of the country were given priority over educational projects. Since the missions were already in the educational field and had set up numerous schools, both for the immediate purposes of evangelism and for the training of native teachers, it was felt that government funds would bring in a better return if used to subsidize these schools than if employed in starting government schools. From 1918 funds were made available for education from the Native Education Fund. The only government school in Papua is one for Europeans at Port Moresby.

In the mandated territory the Australian administration began with a fairly ambitious educational programme and established central training institutions at Rabaul for training outstanding natives. Funds were to be raised by an education tax levied on natives and from a tax on employers of indentured labour; the native tax has not been collected since 1922–3. Expenditure on native education fell from £18,000 in 1923 to £5,000 in 1937. Results obtained from these government schools have not been encouraging, and the administration has been content to leave most of the education of natives in the hands of the missions. It has subsidized some of the mission schools.

Primary and Secondary Education

In both territories primary and secondary education is provided on a communal (or 'racial') basis; there are separate schools for natives, Asiatics and Europeans.

Native Education. All elementary schools for natives in Papua and nearly all in the mandated territory are run by the missions. Wherever the missions have penetrated they have established schools, so that there are now several thousand village schools. In consequence, about one-quarter of the children in the controlled areas now attend school. In Papua attendance is compulsory. Most schools, especially in the more remote areas, are in charge of native teachers, who use the vernacular. In Papua, only schools using English as the medium of teaching receive government assistance. Simple examinations are held annually for the pupils from assisted schools. The size of the grant awarded by the administration is dependent on the number of successful candidates. Mission schools in the mandated territory are not under government supervision.

More advanced education for natives is almost exclusively in the hands of the missions. Promising pupils from the elementary schools are sent to intermediate boarding schools at the larger mission stations. There they are taught by European teachers assisted by native tutors. Most of the pupils from these schools become village school teachers and native preachers. In the mandated territory, in addition to these mission schools there were in 1939 four day-schools run by the government, which provided a more secular type of training. Courses in practical subjects such as native arts and crafts are included in the curriculum. One of their main functions is to provide a supply of educated natives for posts in the police force, as medical orderlies and as clerks and store-keepers in government departments.

European and Asiatic Education. Several schools for European children are maintained by the governments of both territories. There are European schools in Papua at Port Moresby and Samarai and in the mandated territory at Rabaul, Kavieng and Wau. Education for the children of the Asiatic immigrants in the mandated territory is provided by two schools at Rabaul, one maintained by the Roman Catholic mission and the other by the Methodist mission.

Vocational Education

Both governments and the missionaries have attempted to provide technical and vocational training for the natives, partly from utilitarian motives and partly on psychological grounds. They have tried to replace the former colourful and exciting occupations of warfare and head-hunting with an equally active interest in useful crafts and occupations. To this end, the administration of the mandated territory has established a well-equipped technical school at Rabaul where many branches of woodwork, metalwork, painting, plumbing, sail-making and other crafts are taught. The technical schools at mission headquarters cover a similar syllabus. An outstanding example is provided by the technical side of the teaching at the Kwato Extension Association's headquarters (p. 201). Many of the material needs of the missions, such as whaleboats, are made in these schools.

Another type of technical education is provided by the agricultural demonstration stations (p. 220) attached to the government stations and by the native plantations (p. 214) maintained in Papua.

MISSIONS (Plate 70)

The early history of mission activity in New Guinea has already been given (pp. 125–7). Fig. 40 shows the distribution on a sectarian basis of the main mission stations just before the Japanese invasion. It does not differentiate between the subdivisions of each sect. The relatively slight degree of overlapping of the spheres of operation of the sects is due to official policy, which has for long maintained a system of zoning, in order to minimize the possibility of clashes between the adherents of different sects.

Roman Catholic missionary work in the area is in charge of two different bodies. The French Missionaries of the Sacred Heart of Jesus (of Issoudun) have been at work since 1889. To them have been entrusted the Vicariate Apostolic of Papua, covering the Mekeo district and the eastern tip of New Guinea, and the Vicariate Apostolic of Rabaul, which includes the administrative districts of New Britain, New Ireland and Manus. Headquarters are at Yule island and Kokopo respectively. The mainland area of the mandated territory has been divided into two vicariates apostolic, those of Eastern New Guinea (with headquarters at Alexishafen) and Central New Guinea (with headquarters at Kairiru). Both have been entrusted to the Society of the Divine Word.

The Anglican church is represented in New Guinea by two mission organizations. The New Guinea Mission, maintained by the Australian Board of Missions, works on the northern coast of Papua. Its headquarters are at Dogura. The Melanesian Mission in 1929 established an Archdeaconry of Northern Melanesia, covering New Britain. In 1933 it extended its activities to the Morobe District on the mainland and established a station at Wau.

One of the largest Protestant missions in New Guinea is that of

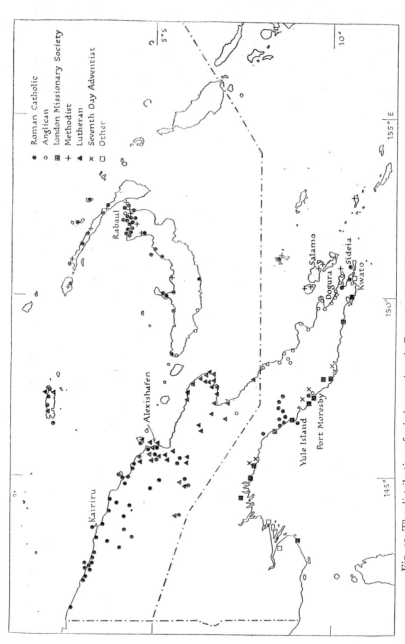

Fig. 40. The distribution of mission stations in Papua and the Mandated Territory of New Guinea

Only the major stations (i.e., in nearly every case stations with European staff) are shown. Data for the Kieta District have been omitted. Based on official sources.

the London Missionary Society (L.M.S.), which has a chain of stations on the south coast of Papua. The L.M.S. is formally undenominational, but it is supported very largely by Congregationalists. The society's headquarters are in London. Considerable administrative powers have been delegated, however, to an Australia and New Zealand Committee, which has an office in Sydney. Headquarters in New Guinea are at Poreporena, near Port Moresby. An off-shoot of the L.M.S. mission is the Kwato Extension Association, which was founded in 1891 to combine evangelism with industrial and agricultural work for its native adherents.

The Methodist church does extensive mission work in both territories. In Papua, the Methodist Missionary Society of Australasia, covers the Louisiade and D'Entrecasteaux archipelagos and has headquarters at Salamo, on Fergusson island. In the mandated territory, the same organization, centred on Vunairima in the Duke of York group, covers the administrative districts of New Britain and New Ireland.

The largest Protestant organizations in the mandated territory are Lutheran—the Lutheran Mission, Finschhafen, and the Lutheran Mission, Madang. Both were founded in German days. The former has been maintained since the war of 1914–18 by the United Evangelical Lutheran Church in Australia, and the latter by the American Lutheran church. A third small Lutheran body, the Liebenzell Mission, operates in the Manus District. It is under American control.

The Seventh Day Adventists about 1924 established a few mission stations at various points in southern Papua; and a small interdenominational body, known as the Unevangelized Mission, has been working during recent years among the unconverted peoples in the region of the Fly, Bamu and Awarra rivers.

In addition to their strictly evangelical work, all these missionary bodies actively pursue native welfare by means of education and medical services (pp. 195, 198). At their principal stations they often maintain schools for the training of pastors, school teachers, and skilled craftsmen. A typical example is the London Missionary Society station at Fife bay, where there is Lawes College, a large training school. A similar institution is the George Brown College for native teachers run by the Methodists at Ulu, in the Duke of York islands.

In addition to these main centres, most of the missionary bodies have a number of intermediate stations (Fig. 40), each staffed by a European missionary, who maintains an intermediate school and administers the simpler forms of medical aid. Far more numerous than these are the small village stations in charge of native preachers who have been trained at the training centres. The education they give to the villagers is in general very sketchy.

Despite these general resemblances there are differences in organization and policy. The Roman Catholics and, to a less extent, the Anglican and Lutheran missions, concentrate a relatively large proportion of their work at the major stations, where they rely on European staffs. The London Missionary Society and others rely to a greater extent on natives and on other Pacific islanders as teachers. Another distinguishing feature is the extent to which missions attempt to be self-supporting by engaging in trade and agriculture. The main bodies to do this are the Roman Catholic and Lutheran organizations in the mandated territory. They maintain copra and coffee plantations, desiccated coconut factories and sawmills and even stores to supply the natives with trade goods.

The development of knowledge of the native languages of New Guinea is largely an achievement of missionaries. Prayer books and sections of the Scriptures have been translated into many local languages and grammars and dictionaries have been compiled. Missionaries, too, have made important contributions to the anthropology and natural history of the area. The effect of missionary activity in New Guinea is already widespread. In the mandate it has been estimated that, before the Japanese invasion, the four main mission bodies had a total of 380,000 adherents, or more than half the natives under government control.

BIBLIOGRAPHICAL NOTE

Government and social services in Papua and the Mandated Territory of New Guinea are described in outline in R. W. Robson (editor), *The Pacific Islands Year Book* (Sydney, 1939; wartime edition, 1942). A fuller account for the mandated territory is given in the *Official Handbook of the Territory of New Guinea* (Canberra, 1937). Much detailed information, including statistical material, is given, for the two territories respectively, in: the Territory of Papua *Annual Report* (Melbourne, to 1927; Canberra, from 1928); and the Commonwealth of Australia *Report to the Council of the League of Nations on the Administration of the Territory of New Guinea* (Melbourne, to 1927; Canberra, from 1928). (Since 1941 the publication of both reports has been suspended.) Official notices, etc., are published in the *Territory of Papua Government Gazette* and the *New Guinea Gazette*.

The problems of government in Papua have been described in two books by the late Lieutenant-Governor, Sir Hubert Murray: *Papua, or British New Guinea* (London, 1912); and *Papua of To-Day, or an Australian Colony in the Making* (London, 1925). Useful accounts of problems in the mandated territory are contained in: F. W. Eggleston (editor), *The Australian Mandate for New Guinea* (Melbourne, 1928); G. W. L. Townsend, 'The Administration of the Mandated

Territory of New Guinea', *Geographical Journal*, vol. LXXXII, pp. 424–34 (London, 1933); and S. W. Reed, *The Making of Modern New Guinea* . . . (*Memoirs of the American Philosophical Society*, vol. XVIII, Philadelphia, 1943). An analysis of the law in force in both territories is contained in R. R. Garran, 'The Law of the Territories of the Commonwealth', *Australian Law Journal*, vol. IX, supp. pp. 28–42 (Sydney, etc., 1935–6). A general account of the work of administrative patrols in Papua is given in Lewis Lett, *Knights Errant of Papua* (Edinburgh and London, 1935). There are a number of books and articles by administrative officers describing their own experiences; some of these are listed in the Bibliographical Notes to Chapters II and VI. Education in the mandated territory is described in W. C. Groves, *Native Education and Culture Contact in New Guinea : A Scientific Approach* (*Australian Council for Educational Research Publications*, no. 46, Melbourne, 1936).

Chapter X

ECONOMICS

Minerals: Agriculture: Forestry: Marine Products: Labour: Trade: Bibliographical Note

Modern commercial development in New Guinea has depended principally upon the production of copra and gold. The exploitation of other natural resources, and the production of other crops, has been on a relatively small scale. The varied geological formations of the country are known to contain a wide range of minerals of economic importance, and the diverse types of soils and of climatic conditions in different areas make possible the cultivation of many kinds of crops. But the lack of good communications, the trying climate of the lowlands, and the smallness of the European population have hindered the realization of these potentialities. Plantation agriculture is still almost entirely confined to coastal regions; and mining—in a few restricted areas—is the only important form of European economic activity carried on in the interior. Over most of the country the small-scale agriculture of the native peoples (pp. 167–9) is the major form of production.

MINERALS

Since the voyages of Portuguese and Spanish explorers in the sixteenth century, New Guinea has been thought to contain great mineral wealth. The first fully authenticated discovery of gold was made in 1852 during the surveying voyage of H.M.S. *Rattlesnake*, under the command of Captain Owen Stanley. On this occasion a piece of native pottery was found containing a few grains of the metal. The development of gold-mining in south-east New Guinea and its adjacent islands during the last quarter of the nineteenth century has already been described (pp. 129–30). The growth of mining on a large scale followed the discoveries in the Morobe District of the mandated territory after 1920. Through the search for gold many other economic minerals have been found. These include ores of osmiridium, platinum, tin, copper, iron, manganese, lead and zinc. And recent discoveries of petroleum in the Netherlands East Indies have stimulated prospecting for oil on a considerable scale, so far with rather inconclusive results.

GOLD

In Papua gold production has never been very great. From small beginnings in the period 1887–9 the value of production rose to about £90,000 a year by 1900. It then declined more or less steadily till 1927–8, when only 2,173 oz. of gold (valued at £6,304) was produced. The rise in the value of gold after 1931 led to a rapid rise in production. In 1938–9 the quantity produced was 64,622 oz.

Production from the goldfields of Papua up to the middle of 1932 has been estimated, as follows:

Papua: Total Gold Production (to 1932)

Goldfield	Date of proclamation	Production (oz.)	Value (£)
Louisiade	1889	159,288	321,275
Murua	1895	207,850	717,999
Gira	1898	67,871	255,893
Yodda	1900	76,832	287,128
Milne bay	1899	14,230	49,987
Keveri	1904	4,770	17,737
Astrolabe	1906	4,263	17,547
Lakekamu	1909	37,910	142,309
Totals		573,014	1,809,875

Total exports of gold for the period 1915–39 are shown in Fig. 41.

As a result of early discoveries in Papua some prospecting was carried out in German New Guinea by both Germans and Australians. After the territory came under the control of Australia this activity increased; and in 1921 a very rich alluvial field was discovered on the Bulolo river, at Koranga creek, by W. Park. This led to the development of what is now known as the Morobe goldfield (part of this field is shown on Fig. 12). At first, Park and the other miners who joined him employed a few local natives and washed out the gold by primitive methods. The next important discovery on the field was made in 1926 when rich auriferous gravels were found on the Edie creek, another tributary of the Bulolo. A miniature gold-rush developed and by the middle of that year a hundred miners with their native labour gangs were operating on the creek.

Many difficulties and hardships were experienced in these early days of the goldfield. The journey from the coast at Salamaua,

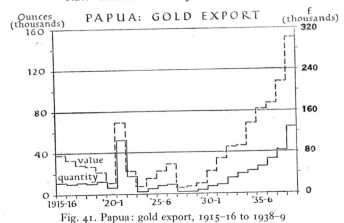

Fig. 41. Papua: gold export, 1915–16 to 1938–9

Based on the Territory of Papua *Annual Report* for 1922–3 to 1938–9 (Melbourne, to 1927; Canberra, from 1928).

32 miles away, was over mountains covered with dense rain forest and inhabited by hostile natives; it occupied from 8 to 10 days. Native carriers provided the only means of transport. The miners lived under almost constant danger of attack from natives and they and their labourers suffered severely from dysentery and malaria.

Under these circumstances, claims had to be very profitable to be considered worth working. In fact, it was estimated that production rates of under 10 ounces per day on a claim were unprofitable. Mining was rescued from this pioneer stage by Cecil J. Levien, a retired District Officer who entered the field in 1923. He saw the need for large-scale capital investment and mechanization in the mines and for better transport facilities to the coast. With some Australian associates, he formed New Guinea Gold, which bought up a large number of miners' leases on the Bulolo. The construction of a road from the coast was ruled out as too costly and difficult in a mountainous terrain subject to landslides. In 1927, therefore, Levien, with the help of E. A. Mustar, an airman, started an air transport service linking Wau, in the goldfield, with Salamaua, on the coast. Capital flowed in from London, South Africa and Canada as well as from Australia, and several large companies were formed.

Within five years, Guinea Airways, Ltd., the company founded by Levien, had become the largest aerial freight-carrying organization in the world. Other air transport companies were formed and the 'planes carried personnel and large quantities of mining machinery and stores to the field. Between 1933 and 1941, over 10,000 passen-

Plate 58. A sluice-box, Morobe goldfield

A view of the silt-laden water flowing down the box.

Plate 57. Gold-mining dredge under construction, Morobe goldfield

One of the large machines assembled from parts which were flown to the site.

Plate 59. A sluice-box, Morobe goldfield
The outlet of the sluice-box seen from below.

Plate 60. Hydraulic sluicing on the middle course of the Bulolo river
Separation of the unwanted boulders from the gold-bearing silt.

gers and 6,000 to 8,000 tons of freight were being carried annually. Large dredges (Plates 57, 62) and hydro-electric power plants were flown in piecemeal. The former, electrically driven, were set to work on the lower reaches of the Bulolo. Gold-bearing quartz veins were discovered on the upper reaches of the river and cyanide treatment of the ores was begun in 1932.

The growth of the Morobe goldfield is shown by the following Table:

Territory of New Guinea: Gold Production (to 1941)

Year or period	Production (oz.)	Value (£)
To 31 Dec. 1926	—	50,000
1 Jan. 1927 to 30 June 1928	—	426,552
1929	—	188,176
1930	—	128,580
1931	—	154,046
1932	—	434,352
1933	—	933,940
1934	257,510	1,367,616
1935	299,757	1,897,244
1936	302,619	1,704,498
1937	373,197	2,020,667
1938	403,652	—
1939	229,212	2,116,117
1940	271,575	2,878,352
1941	256,035	2,733,881

By 1939 eight large companies with a total capital of over £2,000,000 were in operation. The future prospects of the goldfield are uncertain, but it is estimated that there is certainly enough paying gold to maintain production at a high level for another twelve years.

Gold has also been discovered in other parts of the mandated territory. It has been found over a wide area in the basin of the Sepik river. No gold-bearing reefs have been discovered but alluvial claims have been worked by individual miners over a considerable area. Over 6,500 fine oz. were obtained there in 1939–40. There are other small centres of gold production in the Madang District; in New Britain; and on Tabar island, New Ireland. Total gold exports for the territory are shown in Fig. 42.

PETROLEUM

Some indications of the presence of gas and natural oil occur in several localities in the Gulf region of Papua. Oil seepages were discovered as far back as 1911, and prospecting was begun by the

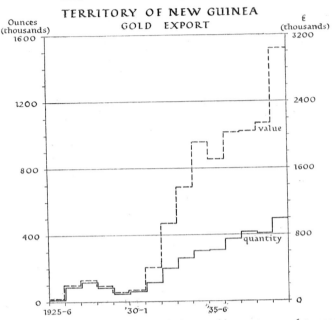

Fig. 42. Mandated Territory of New Guinea: gold export, 1925–6 to 1939–40
Based on the Commonwealth of Australia *Report to the Council of the League of
Nations on the Administration of the Territory of New Guinea* for 1925–6 to 1939–40
(Melbourne, to 1927; Canberra, from 1928).

Australian commonwealth government in 1917. The Anglo-Persian
Oil Company, Ltd. (now Anglo-Iranian), in 1919 took over the work
on behalf of the Australian and British governments. In 1921 the
British government withdrew from the venture which was continued
on behalf of the commonwealth government until 1929 without any
concrete results. Meanwhile, the exclusiveness of the government's
right to search for oil had been abandoned in 1923, and private
companies and individuals began prospecting for oil; but their
work was also abandoned in 1929. It was then clear that further
exploration would require very large financial and technical resources.
Up to this time no active exploration had been carried out in the
mandated territory, except by a geological party of the Anglo-Persian
company, which examined certain parts of the territory in 1921 or
behalf of the commonwealth government. It was not until 1936 that
as a result of new legislation, large-scale exploration was undertaken
in Papua. Royal Dutch Shell interests started work in the same year
and were followed some time later by the Island Exploration Company, Pty., Ltd., a subsidiary of the Vacuum Oil Company, Pty., Ltd.

The Papuan Oil Development Company—the Royal Dutch Shell subsidiary—carried out a great deal of exploratory work on their Papuan concession, including aerial mapping and a geophysical survey which together represented a large financial investment. The area, however, did not reveal any encouraging features and the work was eventually abandoned in 1939.

In 1938 a new petroleum code was adopted and the Island Exploration Company Ltd. and the D'Arcy Exploration Company, Ltd., joined with local interests, which had already carried out some exploratory work in Papua and the mandated territory, to form the Australasian Petroleum Company, Pty., Ltd.

Both the Island Exploration Company and the Australasian Petroleum Company have carried out extensive exploratory work. So far no discovery of oil has been announced, but the area of greatest

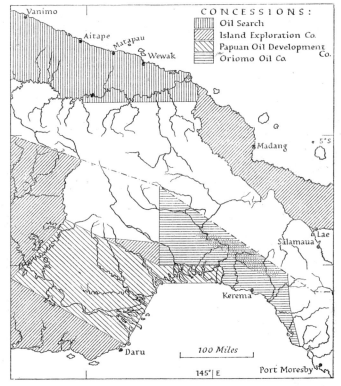

Fig. 43. Papua and Mandated Territory of New Guinea: oil concessions
The dotted area shows the locality with the best prospects for oil drilling. Based on official sources.

interest is understood to be in Papua, in the interior to the north of Kerema.

By the end of 1938 the following companies had been actively engaged in the British territories of New Guinea: the Anglo-Persian Oil Company, Ltd.; the Island Exploration Company, Ltd. (Vacuum Oil Company); the Papuan Oil Development Company, Ltd. (Royal Dutch Shell group); Oriomo Oil, Ltd.; Oil Search, Ltd.; and the Papuan Apinaipi Petroleum Company, Ltd. The spheres of activity of some of these companies are shown approximately on Fig. 43.

The last-named company is operating in the Oiapu district, some 75–80 miles to the north-west of Port Moresby, in much the same area as that examined by the Anglo-Persian. In this district is a tract containing oil-bearing mudstone. Just prior to hostilities, four holes had been drilled there to enable the best site to be selected for a deep test well.

In Netherlands New Guinea, intensive oil prospecting has been carried out by the N.V. Nederlandsch Nieuw Guinea Petroleum Maatschappij. Results in the Vogelkop (Fig. 44) have been encouraging; oil has been obtained from both shallow and deep wells.

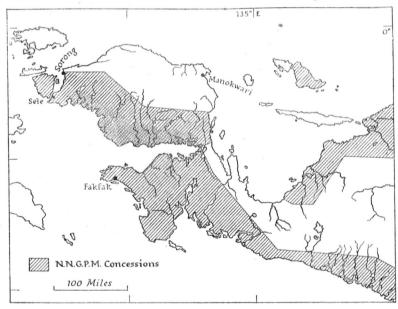

Fig. 44. Dutch New Guinea: oil concessions

The shaded area represents the concessions granted to N.V. Nederlandsch Nieuw Guinea Petroleum Maatschappij. The dotted area represents the locality with the best prospects for oil drilling. Based on various sources.

Other Minerals

Many minerals other than gold and petroleum have been found in New Guinea, but few have been exploited except on a small scale. Several types frequently occur in association in the same deposits—particularly in igneous and metamorphic rocks. Thus, in Papua, there are two mineral fields—the Sideia mineral field, which covers the island of that name, in the Eastern Division; and the Astrolabe mineral field, inland from Port Moresby. Both have been worked mainly for copper, but many rarer minerals have been found in small quantities. Copper has been mined, mainly on the Astrolabe field, since 1906. By 1913 the annual export of ore had risen to over 1,000 tons. After the war of 1914–18, when prices rose sharply, production increased rapidly and the ore was smelted locally before being exported. The peak figure was reached in 1926 when the quantity of smelted copper exported was valued at £124,262. Prices fell in 1927 and production practically ceased. In 1937 a second company began mining and smelting copper and the export in 1937–8 and 1938–9 was in each case a little over 40 tons.

Silver and osmiridium—a natural alloy of osmium and iridium—have been recovered in small quantities on some of the goldfields. Osmiridium occurs in both Papua and the mandated territory, but it was for long neglected by the gold miners, though its value per ounce was as much as fifteen times that of gold. The peak export from Papua was 208 oz. valued at £6,245 in 1920–1. Some manganese was mined in the Rigo district, near Port Moresby, in 1938–9 and 54 tons were exported. Platinum has been found near Madang and near Wide bay in New Britain. Lead in the form of galena (lead sulphide) occurs in small quantities in Murua and Misima and in most parts of Papua where gold has been found. Zinc ores are frequently associated with those of lead. Iron ores of various types, but mainly magnetite and haematite, are widely distributed, but so far have not been exploited on a large scale. The haematite ores which occur on the surface frequently contain a high percentage of copper which gives the mineral a morocco-red colour; it has been exported in small quantitites for use as a pigment.

Coal is widely distributed through Papua and the mandated territory but has never been mined commercially. Much is in the form of lignite, of which extensive deposits occur between the Vailala and the Kikori rivers, in the Gazelle peninsula of New Britain, and in New Ireland. Hard, bright coal, apparently anthracitic, has been found on the upper reaches of the Kikori river. Deposits of sulphur occur in all the volcanic areas.

Rock phosphate is found on several small coral islands off the coast of New Guinea. They comprise two groups: one at the north-western extremity of the mandated territory, including Wuvulu, Aua and Manu islands; and the other, the Purdy islands, to the south-west of Manus. It has been estimated that Aua island contains 80,000 tons and the four Purdy islands between them about 27,000 tons. Analysis of samples of Purdy island phosphate shows that it is of rather low grade with an average tri-calcium phosphate content of 23.7% (compared with 85% in Nauru phosphate). These deposits and others of bat guano in several limestone caves have recently aroused interest in the mandated territory, since plantation soils there are lacking in phosphoric acid and the costs of importation of fertilizer from Australia are almost prohibitive. Exploitation of the phosphate had not begun when the Japanese invaded the area.

AGRICULTURE

Until the discovery of the Morobe goldfield, agriculture was the main economic activity of both Papua and the mandated territory. In the latter it was almost the only form of such activity, for mineral production before 1926 was negligible. Formerly the native communities of New Guinea had mostly relied for subsistence on simple forms of shifting cultivation. Agricultural production for export began in the closing decades of the nineteenth century when European settlers began to establish coconut plantations. This copra production continued for many years as the only type of agriculture for export. In the early years of the present century, the respective governments began to experiment with the introduction of other crops. Rubber, cacao, sisal hemp, kapok and various others were tried on official experimental plantations. But none of these except rubber was adopted on any scale by private planters, and then only in Papua. Official policy in both territories has for long aimed at encouraging the native peoples to grow crops for export and has assisted them in marketing their produce. But so far, relatively few natives have been induced to grow such crops and the quantities they have produced have been small. Until the Japanese invasion in 1942, export agriculture in both territories comprised predominantly copra production on European-owned plantations employing native labour; the production of rubber both on government and privately owned plantations in Papua; and of cocoa on small privately owned plantations in

Plate 61. Transporting machinery by air to the Morobe goldfield
A large shaft being loaded into an aeroplane.

Plate 62. A dredge working on the middle course of the Bulolo river
In the background aeroplanes can be seen on one of the landing grounds.

Plate 63. Rakada plantation, Duke of York islands

These islands lie between Blanche bay and New Ireland and have been developed for a longer period than most parts of mandated New Guinea.

Plate 64. Coconut plantation at Kokopo

Behind the labourers a pile of coconuts awaits husking.

the mandated territory. Small amounts of copra, coffee and ground-nuts were produced by natives for export and in the vicinity of the main settlements some natives and Chinese grew vegetables for sale to Europeans.

COCONUTS (Plates 63–4)

In the middle of the nineteenth century the trade in coconut oil was flourishing in many Pacific islands, but New Guinea was too little known and its native people too hostile for such a trade to prosper. European interest in the coconuts of New Guinea was only aroused towards the end of last century when British and German trading stations were established on the coast of the mainland and in the Bismarck archipelago. These traded with the natives in copra and other goods. In 1883 the first German copra plantation was laid out at Ralun on Blanche bay, New Britain. Two years later, one was established on the mainland at Finschhafen. Extension of plantations both in Papua and the mandated territory proceeded slowly prior to 1914, owing to difficulties of transport and of clearing land. But during the war of 1914–18, after the Australian occupation, rapid expansion took place in the ex-German territory. The German planters were allowed to remain on their plantations; and, as prices of copra were high, they made considerable profits. Since these profits could not be remitted to Germany, they were invested in large extensions to the existing plantations. The total planted area of coconuts in the terri-tory thus rose from about 74,000 acres in 1914 to nearly 170,000 acres in 1921–2. Since 1921, plantations in the mandated territory have been transferred to British ownership by the Expropriations Board (p. 192) and, despite low prices, have (with the exception of a slight set-back in 1926–7) steadily increased in area. The total planted area of coconut plantations in the territory in 1938 was 243,000 acres. Individual plantations had an average area of 400 to 500 acres. Their total capital value has been estimated at between £4,750,000 and £5,000,000, about three-fifths of which represents the value of the expropriated German plantations. Unaffected by these special circumstances, the coconut plantations of Papua grew at a steadier rate, to a maximum planted area of 50,500 acres in 1925. Since then the copra industry has tended to stagnate. The area in cultivation fell to under 45,000 acres by 1938. During the years 1913–35 in the mandated territory the proportion of the total in bearing has varied between less than 50% and over 80%.

The area of coconut lands held by natives is difficult to assess as reliable recent figures are scarce. In Papua, native coconut plantations 'laid out, however imperfectly, on plantation lines' had a total area of over 6,700 acres in 1927. This figure ignores the considerable area of neglected native groves. For the mandated territory, no official statistics of areas of native coconut lands have been published; but in 1918 the total area in bearing was said to be about 50,000 acres.

The location of plantations (Fig. 45) has been determined partly by the needs of the coconut palm but mainly by relative ease of access. The most suitable soil and climatic conditions for the palm are generally found near the coast. The high proportion of plantations on the islands to the north and east of the mainland is made clear in Fig. 45. In the mandated territory only 17% of the area planted with coconuts is situated on the mainland.

Cultivation methods on plantations follow modern practice. Trees are generally spaced out on the quincunx system, which gives a total of 50 trees to the acre. *Alang-alang* grass, known locally as kunai, has proved a troublesome weed in the past. It is now kept in check by cattle which graze it down, or is prevented from obtaining any foothold by the growing of leguminous cover-crops. Insect pests are numerous and do considerable damage both to the palms and to the young nuts. The most serious pest is the long-horned tree-hopper (*Sexava* spp.), which feeds on the palm fronds. Other destructive insect pests include the beetle *Promecotheca antigua*, whose larvae burrow into the fronds; the elephant beetle, *Xylotrupes gideon;* and the rhinoceros beetle, *Scapanes grossepunctatus*, both of which attack the upper end of the stem of the palm.

The climate is in general too wet to allow sun-drying of the copra, and so kilns burning coconut shells are employed to dry the copra with hot air. Badly constructed kilns used by natives or by the less-efficiently managed plantations produce an inferior smoke-dried product.

Of recent years, plantations have been able to survive continued low prices only by adopting the most rigorous economy in production methods. In 1937 production costs, which naturally vary with the distance of plantations from shipment points, and with the efficiency of management, were estimated to vary between £5 and £10 per ton in the mandated territory. When average prices fall below £10 per ton (as they did from 1933 to 1935) there is consequently little or no margin of profit. A major economy has been effected by reducing the number of labourers employed in proportion to the area cultivated. Over the period 1922–35 the planted area in

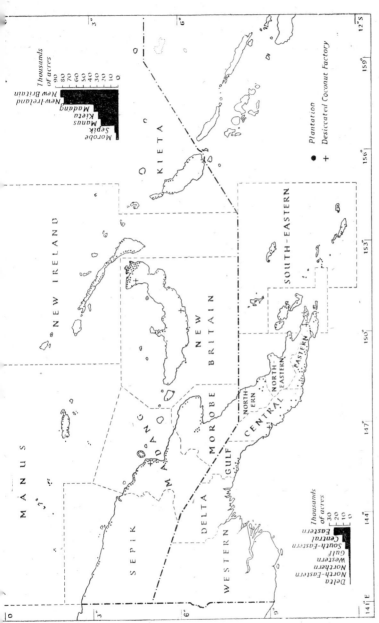

Fig. 45. Papua and Mandated Territory of New Guinea: coconut plantations

The black columns show the total area of plantations in thousands of acres in each District and Division. These totals are for plantations of all crops, but as coconuts predominate everywhere this gives an approximately true picture of coconut areas. Based on: R. E. P. Dwyer, 'A Survey of the Coconut Industry in the Mandated Territory of New Guinea', *New Guinea Agricultural Gazette*, vol. II, p. 10 (Rabaul, 1936).

the mandated territory increased by about 55%, while the number
of indentured labourers employed fell by about 15%. This reduction
has largely been made possible by the use of cattle to graze down the
undergrowth.

The quality of copra produced varies considerably. Some first-class
copra has been produced in the Duke of York group, between New
Britain and New Ireland, but most is of medium quality. In the
mandated territory there has been a tendency for the quality to
improve since the establishment of a system of government inspection

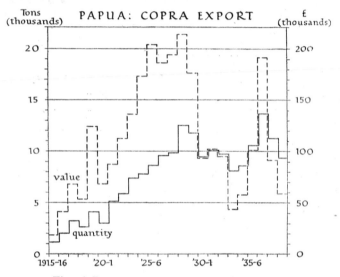

Fig. 46. Papua: copra export, 1915-16 to 1938-9

Based on the Territory of Papua *Annual Report* for 1922-3 to 1938-9 (Melbourne,
to 1927; Canberra, from 1928).

in 1929; inspectors were stationed at ports of entry and on overseas
ships while loading copra. As a result of this measure, Rabaul copra
has fetched prices on the London market above those of 'South
Seas' copra.

The quantity of copra exported (Figs. 46, 47) rose steadily till about
1929. Though prices were fluctuating, they were always high enough
to yield a working profit. From 1929, when the world depression
began to set in, prices fell with increasing rapidity till 1933-4, when
they were so low that production was continued at a considerable loss.
Nevertheless, economies in production methods were adopted and
the reduction in quantity exported was relatively slight. The

sensitivity of the industry to increased prices was clearly indicated by the considerably increased export in 1937. The copra export of the mandated territory alone in 1936 represented about 40% of the total exported from all the British Pacific islands and about 5% of the world's exportable production of copra.

During the last fifteen years a further development of the coconut industry has taken place. Encouraged by the protected market

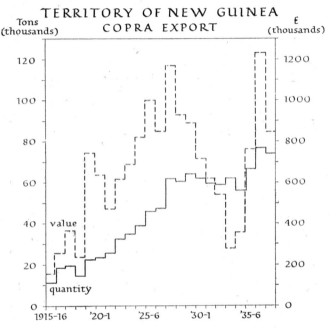

Fig. 47. Mandated Territory of New Guinea: copra export, 1915–16 to 1937–8

Based on S. W. Reed, *The Making of Modern New Guinea*, p. 193 (Philadelphia, 1943).

offered in Australia, some planters have turned to the manufacture of shredded and desiccated coconut. Six small factories have been established, three in Papua and three in the mandated territory. The export began from Papua (Fig. 48) in 1926 and from the mandated territory in 1929. Production rose steadily until by 1939 about 1,500 tons were being exported from each territory annually. It then constituted the fourth largest item by value in the export trade of Papua.

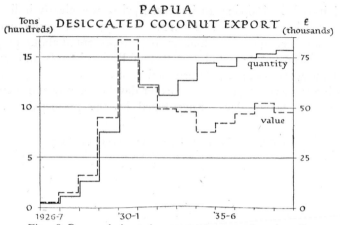

Fig. 48. Papua: desiccated coconut export, 1926–7 to 1938–9

Based on Territory of Papua *Annual Report* for 1926–7 to 1938–9 (Melbourne, to 1927; Canberra, from 1928).

RUBBER

Soil and climatic conditions in Papua and the mandated territory are very suitable for rubber cultivation, but the industry has developed only in the former. The rubber exported from Papua over the period 1885–1908 was derived from the indigenous tree, *Ficus rigo* and from indigenous vines. Para rubber (*Hevea brasiliensis*) was introduced in 1903. Government nurseries of rubber trees were established in 1907, and three government rubber plantations were begun about three years later. One of these, the Kemp Welch plantation of nearly 300 acres, has thrived and proved a considerable source of profit. Several private plantations of Para rubber have been established. The total area of all rubber plantations in the territory was 12,809 acres in 1938. Nearly all of these are situated in the Central Division, mostly a little way inland.

Indentured native labour is employed; the Papuans make skilled rubber tappers. Production and marketing costs are relatively high on these small plantations; they were said to average 4½d. per lb. of rubber in 1938. But yields per acre are also high; in general they average between 300 and 400 lb. per annum on plantations near the coast and over 500 lb. per annum in the Sogeri district of the Western Division. These figures compare well with Malayan yields. Exports (Fig. 49) reached 43½ tons by 1915–16, and, with minor fluctuations, have steadily increased to a figure of 1,290 tons in 1938–9.

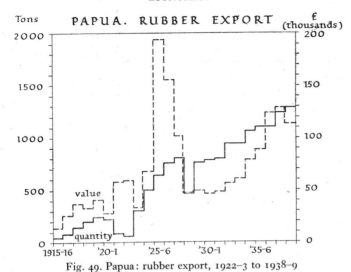

Fig. 49. Papua: rubber export, 1922-3 to 1938-9
Based on Territory of Papua *Annual Report* for 1922-3 to 1938-9 (Melbourne, to 1927; Canberra, from 1928).

Rubber production in the mandated territory has never recovered from an early handicap. In the opening years of the present century, when German planters wished to obtain Para rubber seed, British and Dutch planters required all available seed for their own plantations. Germans in New Guinea were therefore compelled to experiment with other species, notably *Ficus indica* and *Ficus elastica*. Since these produce an inferior type of rubber, tapping has been suspended. A few small areas which had been planted with Para rubber began to be tapped in 1940 when prices were high.

MINOR CROPS

No other single crop has been so important as coconuts or rubber in the economy of New Guinea. Nevertheless, at various times a variety of minor crops has been cultivated, in some instances as catch crops and in others merely experimentally. One or two, such as sisal hemp, have been persevered with in an attempt to build up new exporting industries. Some of these crops are grown in part by natives and marketed under government supervision (p. 221). Most of these products, including cocoa, coffee, sisal hemp, sago and kapok enjoy the benefit of a protected market with added bounties in Australia, but this protection has been insufficient to make their production a major or permanent part of New Guinea agriculture.

Cocoa was grown in some quantity in the mandated territory about 1920, but since that date production has fallen off. It was showing signs of recovering when the present war interrupted operations. Cultivation has been mainly limited to the rich volcanic soil of Vitu, the Bainings and the Talasea area of New Britain. The only variety grown on a plantation scale is Forastero, which yields a heavy crop. The export rose from 132 tons in 1936-7 to 315 in 1939-40.

Coffee has been grown in small quantities in the mandated territory for many years; it did not figure in the exports of Papua until 1928-9. The total area planted with coffee in 1938 was 248 acres. There were three major plantations in the mandated territory and several smaller ones. Three varieties were grown: *Coffea arabica, C. robusta* and *C. liberica*. The first thrives at a considerable altitude and has been grown near Wau on the mainland; *C. robusta* is better adapted to the lower ground and was grown on two of the three large plantations; *C. liberica* was grown for local consumption by the Lutheran mission at Finschhafen. In Papua there is a coffee plantation at Sogeri and small quantities are grown by natives.

Sisal hemp is well suited to the climatic and soil conditions of the dry belt around Port Moresby. During the war of 1914-18 considerable quantities were exported and the peak export of 536 tons, valued at £12,284, was reached in 1919-20. Since then, however, the industry has declined and hardly any has been exported since 1926. This failure has been attributed to a variety of causes, including bad selection of land, extravagant expenditure during the years of development, and the cultivation of areas so small as to be uneconomic. Despite a commonwealth bounty of £6 per ton and the very large demand for binder twine in Australia, the industry has not revived. Kapok and oil palm are both suited to local conditions, but only the first has been tried commercially. The sugar cane is indigenous to the country; no attempt has been made to cultivate it locally, but there have been various proposals to do so.

NATIVE AGRICULTURE

The traditional native subsistence agriculture has already been described (pp. 167-9). Government policy in both Papua and the mandated territory has attempted to foster native production for export. Markets have been found and agricultural demonstration stations have been established, with native instructors to teach the use of new methods and new crops. Besides these measures, an energetic policy has been pursued in Papua of enforcing the cultivation of village plantations in the more settled and developed areas. Government intervention in native agriculture began when Sir William MacGregor introduced an ordinance compelling the planting of coconut palms in suitable areas. But as no parallel steps were taken to help in marketing the crop, the measure resulted in nothing more than an unwanted surplus of coconuts. The next serious attempt to encourage native agriculture was made in 1918 when the native tax (p. 183) was introduced. Village plantations of coconuts, coffee and rice were established. Certain lands were declared plantation areas and the local villagers have been obliged to work on them for a specified number of days, under government supervision. The Native Taxation Fund provides tools and seed. The crops are marketed officially and the proceeds divided; half is returned to the workers and half is paid into the Taxation Fund to be spent on further extension of native agriculture and other native benefits.

As a result of this policy, there were nearly 7,000 acres of native plantations of coconuts in the territory by 1927. Rice, coffee, cocoa and kapok are also grown under this system. The swampy delta areas bordering the Gulf of Papua were thought to be very suitable for rice growing and several hundred acres were planted; but by 1928 operations were suspended, as the climate had proved unfavourable. Rice growing was later established in the Mekeo district. Coffee growing has been taken up on a small scale. In 1935–6 there were 18 native coffee plantations in Papua, with a total area of 242 acres. Ground nuts are another export crop which has recently been introduced in the dry belt of Papua.

In the mandated territory there have been no such comprehensive measures to foster native agriculture. But the government has introduced a system of licensed buyers of native copra and coconuts. Most of the native copra exported from the territory is first sold as coconuts to the dealers (frequently European owners of plantations), who prepare the copra themselves. Export statistics do not differentiate between copra produced from nuts grown by natives or on plantations.

Difficulties have been experienced in sustaining native interest in export crops. Fluctuations in market prices are the main obstacle. Natives do not comprehend the reasons for them and tend to feel that they are being cheated of their dues in times of trade depression. In consequence, they lose interest when prices fall and neglect their plantations.

LIVESTOCK

There is little natural pasture, either in Papua or in the mandated territory, and climatic conditions are unsuited to the keeping of some kinds of stock. Nevertheless, owing to the lack of roads fit for motor traffic, horses and a few mules have been introduced for transport purposes; large numbers of cattle are kept to graze down the undergrowth on coconut plantations. Attempts which have been made to introduce sheep have mostly failed, owing to the unsuitable climate. Goats, which are hardier under tropical conditions, have taken their place as a source of meat. Some pigs, too, are kept on plantations; many are also kept by natives throughout New Guinea.

As meat forms an essential part of the diet of native labourers, many of the plantation owners consider their cattle, goats and pigs as a major source of food for their labourers; the fresh meat is cheaper and more nutritious than the canned meat on which they formerly relied.

Dairy cattle were first introduced into the mandated territory nearly fifty years ago. Many died soon after their arrival, but their progeny, numbering over 20,000, are now widely distributed in coastal districts. They have degenerated as milk producers, but have adapted themselves to their environment and are in good health. Their feed is the natural pasture on plantations. The German government formerly maintained a breeding station at Kieta in Bougainville for the breeding and distribution of better types. These have now inter-bred with the plantation herds. A herd of Friesians recently imported to Rabaul gave the very low milk yield of $\frac{1}{2}$ gallon per cow (the average in temperate climates is 3·2 gallons per cow). There are only three commercial dairies in the mandated territory, one near Rabaul and two at Wau.

FORESTRY

Commercial exploitation of the forest products of New Guinea is only in its infancy (pp. 112–13). Difficulties of communication and the great variety of species of trees in any one locality have made lumbering difficult and unprofitable. The only widespread and sustained exploitation is carried on by the native peoples who collect the wild fruits and nuts and use many of the timbers, creepers and fibres in their daily life. The main export of forest products for many years consisted of minor forest produce collected for sale by natives. Thus, mangrove bark, dammar gum, sandalwood oil, rattan and bamboo have been exported from Papua and small quantities of sandalwood have been shipped to China.

The local demand for timber has been met partly by setting up a few sawmills locally and partly by importing timber from overseas. Several sawmills have been operated by ordinary commercial interests and by mission stations. In New Britain, small areas of forests of *kamarere* (*Eucalyptus deglupta*) have been exploited profitably to supply timber for Rabaul and outlying stations. The small townships in the Morobe goldfield have been built of local timber, chiefly red cedar and two species of *Araucaria* which grow at that altitude. Timber for use in mining has been imported into Papua from Oregon and into the mandated territory from the Philippines and elsewhere. Very little timber was exported until about 1937 when Australian sawmillers became interested in the possibilities of developing New Guinea timber. The value of exports of timber from the mandated territory rose from £180 in 1933–4 to £6,510 in 1937–8. Most is exported in the form of logs which in the latter year amounted to 3,103,996 superficial ft. Several cabinet woods, including *Draconto-melum mangiferum*, the 'New Guinea walnut', known locally as *laup*, are comprised in the total.

By the end of 1938 there were, in the mandated territory, about 58,000 acres of government land held under forest permits to cut and remove timber, while a considerable amount of felling was also taking place on leasehold property. With improved communications in the future, this industry is likely to expand considerably. A further possibility is the tapping of the nipa palm (*Nipa fruticans*) to yield power alcohol. This palm abounds in swampy coastal districts.

MARINE PRODUCTS

The seas of New Guinea and the adjacent archipelagos abound in fish and other marine products. But most of this potential wealth is unexploited. The coastal natives catch fish for their own requirements and to trade with the inland peoples, but the methods used are primitive and the quantities involved are small. Some marine products, notably pearls, pearl shell, trochus shell and *bêche-de-mer*, however, are collected on a fairly substantial scale for export. In Papua, in some years, they have aggregated some £40,000 to £50,000 in value (Fig. 50). Most of this type of fishing is in the hands of Chinese who employ native divers.

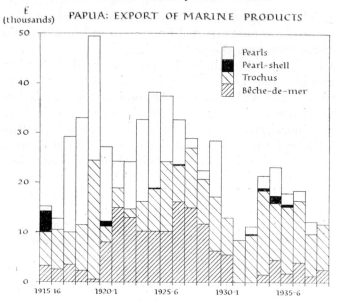

Fig. 50. Papua: export of marine products, 1915–16 to 1938–9

Based on Territory of Papua *Annual Report* for 1922–3 to 1938–9 (Melbourne, to 1927; Canberra, from 1928).

The Torres strait area is one of the most famous pearling grounds in the world, but it is within the territorial waters of Australia, so its pearls are not included in the export figures for Papua, despite the fact that many pearling luggers are registered at Daru. A high proportion of the Papuan pearls come from the Trobriand and other island groups south-east of the mainland. From 1915 to 1939 the export has averaged about 13,000 carats. Though, with few exceptions, the average quantity has not fluctuated greatly, the price has varied from about £1 per carat in 1922–5 to 3s. per carat in 1938, a fall due to the development elsewhere of the cultured pearl industry.

Pearl shell of various types is fished for both in Papua and the mandated territory. Small quantities of pearl oyster are exported, but the bulk consists of trochus shell and green snail. Papua, over the period 1918–38, exported an average annual amount of 168 tons, valued at about £10,000. Although several species of marine turtles abound in New Guinea waters, only small amounts of turtle shell are exported. *Bêche-de-mer* is plentiful and was exported in some quantity to China up to 1937; in the years prior to that date, Papua exported on an average 60 tons and the mandated territory 98 tons per annum. Only small quantities have been exported since 1937.

LABOUR

Economic development in Papua and the mandated territory has always been dependent on an adequate supply of labour for European controlled plantations and mines. The Germans, though they relied in the main on indentured native labour, formerly imported a few thousand Chinese into what is now the mandated territory. But both there and in Papua, Australia has consistently followed the policy of employing native labour. The Chinese whom the Germans introduced have been allowed to remain, but no further influx of Asiatic labour has been tolerated.

Most of the native labour employed in the two territories is indentured, though in each there is a minority of casual labourers and labourers under free contract. The number of contract labourers in both territories has grown steadily. In Papua there were about 2,000 in 1906; while in 1940 there were 17,351. In the mandated territory there were 8,300 in 1909 and 41,675 in 1939. The latest figures are of interest when compared with the total native population. They approximate fairly closely to the proportion of one-fifteenth of the total in each territory. This fraction has been held to be the maximum compatible with native welfare. Further economic development is dependent on a more extensive employment of local free labour and on greater economy in the use of indentured labour.

Indentured labourers are nearly all young men. The mandate administration and many employers encourage them to bring their wives with them to their place of employment, but so far few of them have cared to do this; some of the women who do follow their husbands into service are indentured for light work. Conditions of recruitment, employment and repatriation of indentured labour are under government supervision in both territories (pp. 185, 192). Natives are signed on for periods of two or three years. Wages vary with the type of work. On plantations in the mandated territory in 1939, 5s. per month was the standard minimum rate; 10s. was paid for particularly heavy work. In the gold mines, to compensate for the heavy work and trying climatic conditions, 10s. per month was the standard rate. In Papua the standard minimum wage is 10s. per month. In the mandated territory the maximum total cost per head of native labour to an employer has been estimated at £17 per annum.

Indentured native labour is used in spheres other than agriculture and mining. The 39,344 labourers employed in the mandated territory in 1939 were classified under the following occupations:

Plantation	20,477
Mining	7,105
Government service	1,956
Domestic service	3,385
Shipping, commerce and industry	6,238
Miscellaneous	183

Similar details are not available for Papua.

The types of work on which natives are engaged vary considerably. On plantations they mostly do the relatively unskilled work of rubber tapping, collecting, preparing and drying copra, and of keeping down weeds and undergrowth. Mining offers a wider range, from underground working to surface operations in dredging and sluicing alluvial gold, the maintenance of roads and aerodromes, and the loading and unloading of aircraft. In the ports many are employed as stevedores and warehouse hands. A growing number have been trained for technical posts including those of telephone operator, truck driver, carpenter and hospital orderly.

Since European activities are concentrated in relatively small areas and labour recruiters range over a large part of each territory, few natives are employed in the vicinity of their own villages. Where this does occur, as in some of the smaller islands, men who are employed near enough to visit their own families, or even to live at home, spend many years with the same employer, often without the bond of indenture.

During the war with Japan the labour situation in New Guinea has been greatly modified by military needs (Appendix III, p. 494).

TRADE

Before the war of 1914–18 Australia was the largest supplier of imports to German New Guinea, as well as to Papua. Both territories obtained a large proportion of their imported foodstuffs from Australia, and many imports which were ultimately of European or American origin reached New Guinea by way of Australia. The bulk of exports from Papua went to Australia; the bulk of those from German New Guinea were shipped direct to Germany. The war of 1914–18 which transferred German New Guinea to Australian control also affected trade by bringing about a shipping shortage and by closing many European markets. Australia, too, at this period applied her Navigation Act to both New Guinea territories. This act discriminated against foreign shipping by requiring foreign vessels to obtain licences to trade with New Guinea. As a consequence, exports of New Guinea produce to European and American ports were severely curtailed; but Australia found herself unable to absorb more than a small proportion of the staple export of copra. In 1925 Papua and the mandated territory were freed from these restrictions and trade with Europe and America revived. Thus, in 1927–8 half the rubber exported by Papua went to the United Kingdom; and in the following year 85% of the copra exported found markets in Europe and America. To encourage the production of export crops which could find a market in Australia, the commonwealth government in 1926 instituted a preferential tariff and a system of bounties on various minor crops.

This wider trade with Europe and America continued up to the outbreak of war in 1939, though on a restricted scale after the 1931 depression. Low prices and high freight charges have diverted the export of such commodities as rubber to Australia instead of to the United Kingdom. The United States and Mexico, however, continued to take some copra and Japan to take the bulk of the pearl shell.

Australia retains the largest share of the import trade of both Papua and the mandated territory. In recent years her share has in both cases been about half the total value of goods imported. Foodstuffs are the largest single class of goods. The United Kingdom and the United States supply a high proportion of the machinery and metal goods imported. Germany had recovered a little of her former trade with New Guinea; by 1939 about 5% of the imports of the mandated territory came from Germany.

The trends of imports and exports over the period 1918–40 in the two territories is shown in the Table on p.228. Over that period Papuan exports have almost trebled in value, while exports from the mandated territory have increased about ten-fold. Fig. 51 indicates the divergent lines on which the export trade of the two territories has developed. By 1913 the more rapid development policy of the German administration had established a larger total trade. From that period the two territories trended in opposite directions. The mandated territory from about 1925 developed gold mining so rapidly that, despite a concurrent growth in copra production, the gold export soon eclipsed in value the agricultural and other products exported. Papuan production developed far more slowly and the emphasis shifted from minerals (gold and copper) in 1913 to agricultural produce (copra, desiccated coconut and rubber), despite a decline in the value of the copra exported. As Fig. 51 is based on

Trade of Papua and the Territory of New Guinea, 1918–19 to 1940–1
(prior to 1932 in £ sterling ; after 1932 in £A)

Year	Papua		Territory of New Guinea	
	Imports	Exports	Imports	Exports
1918–19	258,112	176,247	271,861	269,666
1919–20	422,741	270,481	506,767	849,422
1920–21	484,770	172,672	661,441	673,992
1921–22	305,705	220,236	468,711	499,197
1922–23	315,423	179,452	516,455	630,892
1923–24	354,965	239,498	485,634	718,535
1924–25	459,080	367,629	537,940	858,990
1925–26	470,774	649,573	568,339	1,105,158
1926–27	455,904	454,462	660,753	1,079,855
1927–28	403,561	350,363	811,832	1,471,026
1928–29	361,271	337,365	871,441	1,146,112
1929–30	373,918	324,775	882,016	997,335
1930–31	240,074	274,354	782,765	919,431
1931–32	221,843	269,254	779,397	1,108,619
1932–33	218,016	275,866	912,365	1,581,272
1933–34	220,605	249,135	924,316	1,766,198
1934–35	269,299	294,743	948,404	2,340,624
1935–36	317,815	355,157	1,290,788	2,573,251
1936–37	452,056	524,001	1,311,623	3,389,072
1937–38	631,497	435,593	1,610,967	2,980,360
1938–39	514,808	490,158	1,340,835	2,960,753
1939–40	826,412	510,672	1,268,097	3,673,635
1940–41	539,152	492,775	962,129	3,247,585

Based on: (1) Territory of Papua *Annual Report* for 1918–41 (Melbourne, to 1927; Canberra, from 1928); (2) Commonwealth of Australia *Report to the Council of the League of Nations on the Administration of the Territory of New Guinea* for 1921–41 (Melbourne, to 1927; Canberra, from 1928).

value of exports it gives little indication of quantities. Over the period covered (and especially between 1926 and 1939) agricultural prices fell sharply (see Figs. 46–9). With the abandonment by Britain of the gold standard in 1931, and the depreciation of Australian currency in relation to sterling not long afterwards, the price of gold rose sharply. The contrast between the prosperity of the gold mines and the depressed state of agriculture was thus heightened.

The contrast between the trends of imports in the two territories is less marked. Except for a temporary decline during the 1931–3 depression, annual import figures have shown a steady rise in both territories over the period 1917–40. In Papua the average for the five-year period 1936–41 was about 80% above that for the period 1917–22; in the mandated territory the increase has been between 200% and 300%. In Papua, except during the depth of the depression, the annual imports have nearly always exceeded the exports in value.

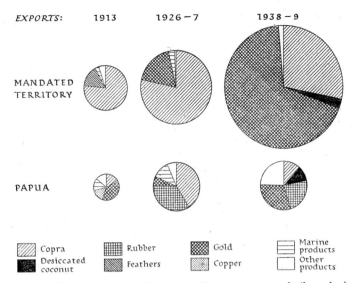

Fig. 51. Territory of New Guinea and Papua: export trade (by value)

Based on: (1) Commonwealth of Australia *Report to the Council of the League of Nations on the Administration of the Territory of New Guinea* for 1921–2, 1926–7 and 1938–9 (Melbourne, 1922, 1927; Canberra, 1939); (2) Territory of Papua *Annual Report* for 1921–2, 1926–7 and 1938–9 (Melbourne, 1922, 1927; Canberra, 1939).

Of recent years they have been swollen by considerable quantities of oil-prospecting machinery from the United States. In the mandated territory exports have been consistently greater in value than imports—of recent years more than twice their value.

In terms of trade between the two territories, Papua by reason of its intermediate geographical position served to some extent as an entrepot between Australia and the mandated territory. This is particularly noteworthy in regard to air transport.

Most of the internal trade is in the hands of large companies. The largest of these, the Burns, Philp company and W. R. Carpenter and Company, Ltd., combine trading with their shipping and plantation-owning interests. They each maintain general stores in the main settlements. Bulolo Gold Dredging, Ltd., also maintains stores in the goldfield. Some small companies and numerous individuals also run stores in the main settlements. A high proportion of the traders in Rabaul and Kokopo are Chinese. The larger plantations, such as those of the Gazelle peninsula shown on Fig. 52, have their own stores to cater for the needs of the plantation labourers.

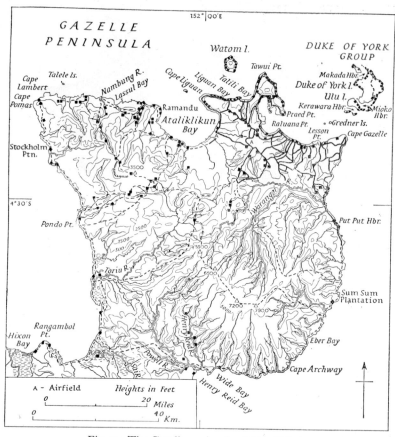

Fig. 52. The Gazelle peninsula of New Britain

The thick lines show motor roads and the pecked lines native tracks. Form lines are approximate. Native villages are indicated by squares. The symbol west of the spot height 3,500 ft. represents a precipitous mountain side. Based on official sources.

BIBLIOGRAPHICAL NOTE

Some information on the economics of Papua and the Mandated Territory of New Guinea is to be found in most of the general works dealing with the area. Among the most useful of these, for economic matters, are: Sir Hubert Murray, *Papua of To-day, or an Australian Colony in the Making* (London, 1925); and S. W. Reed, *The Making of Modern New Guinea* . . . (*Memoirs of the American Philosophical Society*, vol. XVIII, Philadelphia, 1943). More detailed information is contained in the most recent editions of the official handbooks of the two territories: *The Official Handbook of Papua* (Port Moresby, 1938); and the *Official Handbook of the Territory of New Guinea* (Canberra, 1937). Economic statistics are given in: the Territory of Papua *Annual Report* (Melbourne, to 1927; Canberra, from 1928); and the

Commonwealth of Australia *Report to the Council of the League of Nations on the Administration of the Territory of New Guinea* (Melbourne, to 1927; Canberra, from 1928).

The mineral resources of the two territories are covered in two works by E. R. Stanley: *The Geology of Papua* (Melbourne, 1924); and 'Report on the Salient Geological Features and Natural Resources of the New Guinea Territory . . .', *Report to the League of Nations on the Administration of the Territory of New Guinea* for 1921–2, Appendix B (Melbourne, 1923). A vivid description of the early years of the Morobe goldfield is given in D. R. Booth, *Mountains, Gold and Cannibals* (Sydney, 1929). A more recent work on the same subject is Ion L. Idriess, *Gold-dust and Ashes: the Romantic Story of the New Guinea Goldfields* (Sydney, 1936). Agriculture in the mandated territory is dealt with in *The New Guinea Agricultural Gazette* (Rabaul, quarterly); this contains articles on copra, coffee and rubber production and on forestry.

Chapter XI

PORTS, SETTLEMENTS AND COMMUNICATIONS

Ports and Settlements—Port Moresby: Samarai: Daru: Rabaul: Kavieng: Lae:
Salamaua: Madang: Wau and Bulolo

Communications—Shipping: Air Services: Tramways: Roads and Trails: Signal
Communications

Bibliographical Note

PORTS AND SETTLEMENTS

As New Guinea is still in the pioneering stage of economic development, there are no large towns. In terms of population the major
settlements can scarcely be considered more than villages. Except for
the goldfield settlements in the mandated territory, all the principal
settlements are coastal, and their development has resulted primarily
from their suitability as ports. Rabaul and Kavieng, which were
founded by the Germans, were carefully laid out; and considerable
thought had been given to the planning of Lae, which was in process
of becoming the capital of the mandated territory at the time of the
Japanese invasion of 1942. But, with these exceptions, the ports and
other settlements of New Guinea are typical colonial townships,
which have expanded haphazardly or in accordance with only the
most sketchy of plans. Despite the tropical climate, corrugated iron
has been the building material most frequently used. Even Port
Moresby, the capital of the Territory of Papua, had few buildings
of permanence or dignity till recent years.

Apart from these major settlements and from native villages (which
are discussed elsewhere, pp. 158–60), there are in both territories
many government stations, mission stations and plantation centres.
At government stations there are usually bungalows for the European
staff, barracks for a detachment of native constabulary, and a gaol.
At many stations a hospital is attached, and there is often a trade-
store. Mission stations vary greatly in size. At some there is quite
a large European staff. Apart from a church, nearly all have one or
more schools and many have workshops. Before the Japanese invasion
brought normal work to an end, the Roman Catholic mission at
Alexishafen, for example, had a sawmill and boat-building yard and
the Methodist mission at Salamo had a technical school. Plantation

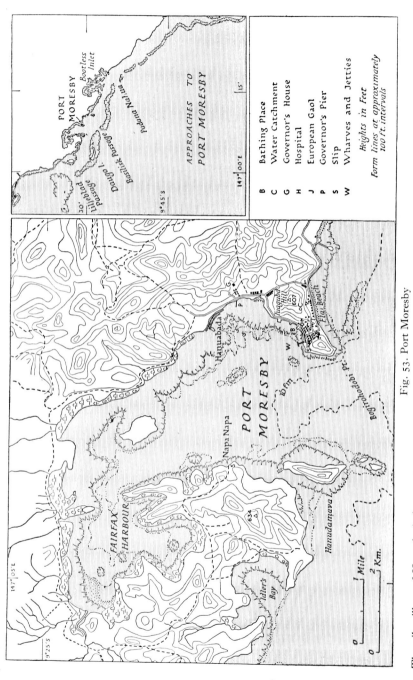

Fig. 53. Port Moresby

The pile village of Hanuabada is one of the group of three known officially as the 'Port Moresby villages'. Based on official sources and on Admiralty chart no. 2126.

establishments usually consist of the planters' bungalows, buildings for native labour, possibly a trader's store, drying kilns and copra sheds. Most of these settlements are on the coast or along the main rivers and usually have a small jetty for loading copra (Plate 68). Before the war the only reasonably well-equipped ports were Rabaul and Kavieng, in the mandated territory, and Port Moresby, in Papua. At a number of other smaller ports some facilities existed. These included Samarai, Daru, Lae, Salamaua, Madang and Aitape. There are many good anchorages. The most important of these are mentioned in Chapters III, XII, XIII and XIV. The following description of the principal ports relates, in the main, to conditions in 1941. Since that time many changes have taken place. Many of the ports have suffered from bombing, and at some—e.g., Port Moresby and Lae—further constructional work has been undertaken. In addition, some anchorages formerly little used have been extensively developed for military purposes. This development, related as it is in some instances to improvement in land communications, may have an important effect on the peacetime organization of New Guinea. The important military port at Milne bay, for example, may replace Samarai as the administrative and commercial centre of eastern Papua.

PORT MORESBY (Fig. 53; Plate 65)

Port Moresby (lat. 9° 29′ s, long. 147° 08′ E) is the capital and chief port of entry of the Territory of Papua. It had a peacetime European population of about 400. The harbour was discovered by Captain John Moresby, in H.M.S. *Basilisk*, in 1873. As a result of Moresby's report upon it, the London Missionary Society established one of its principal stations there four years later; and after the proclamation of a British protectorate over south-east New Guinea in 1884 it became the administrative centre of the territory.

The Port

The harbour is protected by a chain of barrier reefs lying about 5 miles off-shore. There are three channels through this: Liljeblad passage, about 8 miles west of the harbour entrance; Basilisk passage, nearly opposite the harbour; and Padana Nahua, about 9 miles eastward of Basilisk passage. Basilisk passage, with a least depth of 11 fathoms, is the best entrance for large vessels, but, once inside, ships have to steer north-west (along the line of two leading lights) to clear Lark patch before making for the harbour entrance. The eastern approach through Padana Nahua is 1½ miles wide and very deep, but two banks with depths of 2½ fathoms and 1½ fathoms respectively lie in the way of ships turning westward for the course inside the reef. Apart from this, navigation inside the reef is straightforward. The approach from the west, through Liljeblad passage, is partly obstructed by foul ground and only suitable for vessels with local knowledge. The entrance to the harbour, between Hanudamava island and Bogirohodobi point is rather over a mile wide, with depths of from 8 to 12 fathoms.

The bay, which forms Port Moresby harbour, is about 3 miles long, with depths of from 7 to 12 fathoms. It provides excellent anchorage and is protected from the wind by high ground all round. A smaller westward extension, known as Fairfax harbour (Nugu Nugu), with depths of from 3½ to 5 fathoms, provides smooth sheltered water in even the heaviest gales. Large parts of the shore are fronted by fringing reefs, mud and mangroves. The extreme range of the tides is 6 ft. 6 in.

Up to 1941, except for the Government House jetty, all the piers and jetties were opposite the commercial part of the town, which was built on the peninsula running out to Bogirohodobi point in the south-east corner of the harbour. The main, or Government, jetty was T-shaped and projected about 500 ft., with a length of about 240 ft. to the face of the T and a depth of about 26 ft. at low water springs. About 50 yd. to the east was the customs jetty, about 100 ft. long, and suitable only for small craft. A short distance east of the customs jetty was a small jetty with a length of 160 ft. owned by the Steamship Trading Company. Roughly 150 yd. further east of the customs pier, was the No. 2 wharf, 123 ft. long with a width of about 20 ft. at the end, and a depth alongside of about 6 ft. A new jetty, built partly of stone and situated eastward of No. 2 wharf, had a length of 300 ft. and a depth alongside of about 12 ft. The Government House jetty was suitable only for small boats.

Some of the jetties were equipped with electric light and tracks for hand-propelled trucks and on the Government jetty there was a water-supply pipe. There was a 3-ton crane on the end of the Steamship Trading Company's jetty.

Subsequent additions include a pontoon landing connected to the shore by bridge and an oil jetty. The former, situated north of the main wharf, has a length of 300 ft. and a depth alongside of about 30 ft. The latter is about ½ mile long and is situated between the main wharf and the pontoon landing. The head is about 100 ft. wide and dolphins about 400 ft. apart serve as extensions for berthing. The minimum depth alongside is 36 ft.

Water can be obtained from the pipe on the Government jetty but the supply is limited. There is barely enough water for the town in the dry season. Minor repairs can be undertaken at the Public Works Department engineering shops, at the Steamship Trading Company's works, which are situated west of the Government jetty, and at Stewart's shipyard, on the west side of the harbour at Napa Napa. At the latter two, there are slipways which can accommodate small vessels.

Sea communications are maintained by a Burns, Philp steamer every three weeks; other local and overseas vessels call (p. 246). Road surfaces round the port and for short distances inland are fair. Before 1941 few roads extended more than about 20 miles from the port, and further communications were maintained by government trails or native tracks. An airfield had been built east of the town.

The Town

The nucleus of the town, including business premises, warehouses and a few bungalows, was grouped into an area roughly 600 yd. square on comparatively flat ground between Pago hill and Tuaguba hill at the south-east corner of the harbour. Some bungalows fronted Ela beach, on the south side of the peninsula on which the town stands. The bungalows are of typical colonial timber construction, but most other buildings are of galvanized iron.

The principal buildings in the town included the government offices, the courthouse, the government hospital and the local head-quarters of various commercial firms. A small electric power station was situated on the foreshore of the harbour. The Administrator's residence was about a mile northward of the town, on the hills, over-looking the harbour. The Steamship Trading Company's works were west of the Government jetty and Stewart's works were at Napa Napa, on the west side of the bay. The European gaol was situated on an island joined to the mainland by a causeway east of Ela beach. On the eastern side of the harbour was the large native village of Hanuabada, built on piles and projecting over the sea.

Trade

The principal industry in the immediate neighbourhood of Port Moresby was stock-raising. It was, however, as a port of entry and an exporting point that Port Moresby was chiefly important. In the year ending in June 1940 exports from Port Moresby accounted for about 73% of the total exports of the Territory of Papua, and imports represented roughly 85% of all imports. The principal exports in that year were copra and timber, with small quantities of desiccated coconut, coffee and rubber. The largest single import was agricultural produce. Other large items were textiles, machinery, oils, paints and varnishes, wines, spirits, beer and tobacco. Other commodities included drugs, chemicals, wood, jewellery, leather, paper and government stores.

SAMARAI

Samarai (lat. 10° 36′ s, long. 150° 40′ e), the second port of Papua and the second most important settlement, is a small island, about 54 acres in extent, off the south-east tip of New Guinea, between Rogeia island and Sariba island. The harbour is an open roadstead off the north-west side of the island, between it and Eboma island. Approaches are through West channel, East channel and China strait. A bank extending from the north-western side of the island offers anchorage in 6 fathoms, but the bottom is uneven and difficulties are sometimes experienced in weighing anchor. Tidal streams between Samarai and Eboma island to the north-west of it often reach a speed of over 6 knots and are said to be irregular. In 1940 the wharfage space consisted of the Government wharf, Bunting's jetty and Whitten's wharf, on the west side of the island, and another jetty on the south-west corner. But all wharves and facilities are said to have been destroyed by bombing early in 1942. The Government wharf, of timber construction, had a face 240 ft. long, with a depth alongside of 24 ft. at low water springs. The other jetties were suitable only for small craft. There was electricity on the Government wharf, and tramway tracks had been laid from the wharf to warehouses on the waterfront. A small quantity of oil and 27,000 gal. of water were kept.

The Burns, Philp company's steamers provided regular communication with Australian ports, and a number of smaller vessels connected Samarai with the plantation centres, etc., of eastern Papua. There was a W/T station.

The European population of Samarai was about 150. The main street of the town was The Parade, which ran along the western side of the island. Here were situated most of the commercial premises. Apart from dwelling houses, the settlement also possessed a European and a native hospital, two mission stations and churches, two desiccated coconut factories, and various government buildings. In spite of its small size, Samarai was of considerable importance as a port and trading centre for plantations in south-east Papua and the neighbouring islands. Copra was brought to Samarai in the many small craft which touched at the various plantations and mission settlements. Desiccated coconut, copra and rubber have been the only exports of moment. In the year ending in June 1940 more copra was exported from Samarai than from Port Moresby. Imports are generally similar to those of Port Moresby though much smaller in bulk.

DARU

Daru (lat. 9° 05′ S, long. 143° 10′ E), a small island lying between the mainland of Papua and Bristow island, immediately south of the mouth of the Fly river, is a port of entry for the Territory of Papua and is the administrative centre of the Western Division. The entry into the roadstead between Daru island and the mainland has a depth of 6 fathoms but is inadequately surveyed. Sheltered anchorage can be obtained in 5 fathoms. There was one T-shaped jetty, with a length of about 1,250 ft. At low water springs the end of the jetty was dry, but at high water there was a depth of about 11 ft.

The settlement consisted only of the government station, the buildings of the London Missionary Society, a prison, one or two stores, and a police barracks. Most of the island was surrounded by mangroves.

The chief function of the port was as a recruiting centre for native labourers, most of whom were employed in the Thursday island pearling industry. Imports amounted to £2,214 in the year ending 30 June 1940. Exports for the same period totalled only £53. Most of the water-borne communication was by launches or other small craft. There was a tele-radio set in the settlement.

RABAUL (Fig. 54)

Rabaul (lat. 4° 12′ S, long. 152° 10′ E) was, before the Japanese invasion, the largest European settlement in the New Guinea area. Till 1942 it was the administrative centre of the mandated territory. The town became important when the German government in 1910 gave a subsidy to the Norddeutscher Lloyd line to make it a port of call on their service from Hong Kong to Australia. Since that time Rabaul has been the chief port of entry of the territory and its commercial centre. In 1937, however, Vulcan island crater, in Rabaul harbour, erupted, and the town was covered with a deep layer of volcanic ash. Native plantations in the neighbourhood were destroyed and about 300 natives were killed. After the eruption had ended, the people of the town, who had been evacuated, returned. But investigation showed the possibility of further volcanic activity, and it was decided to move the administrative centre of the territory to some other site. This move—to Lae, on the mainland (p. 188)—was in progress when the Japanese occupied Rabaul early in 1942.

The Port

The entrance to Blanche bay, between Praed point and Raluana point, is about 4,400 yd. wide, with deep water except for a 3-fathom patch about 400 yd. south of Praed point. Inside the entrance Blanche bay divides into three separate areas: Karavia bay, on the south, between Raluana point and Vulcan crater; and Simpson and Matupi (Greet) harbours, both on the north side. The entrance to Matupi harbour, between Matupi island and Sulphur point, is partly obscured on the west by a shoal off Matupi island, but there is a clear channel about 400 yd. wide between 10-fathom lines. The entrance to Simpson harbour is between Vulcan crater and Matupi island, with a width of about 1,800 yd. between 10-fathom lines. Inside the harbour are two obstructions—Dawapia (Beehive) rocks and a shallow bank immediately east of them. There are, however, wide channels on each side of them.

Round the shores of Blanche bay, hills rise steeply to heights of 800 to 2,000 ft., behind a narrow fringe of coastal flat covered with coconuts. There is thus ample protection from high winds. The main anchorage is in Simpson harbour, which is sack-shaped and about 3 miles long by 2 miles wide, with depths varying from about 40 fathoms at the southern end to about 2 fathoms near the head of the bay. Greet harbour, rather over 1 sq. mile in extent, has depths up to 30 fathoms in the centre. Karavia bay, with very deep water close to the shore, is unsuitable for anchorage.

Wharves, jetties and landing stages were grouped round the head of Simpson harbour. Before the Japanese captured the port, the most important were (from west to east): (i) the Toboi wharf, with a length of 270 ft. (berthing space increased by dolphins to 400 ft.), a width of 21 ft. and a depth alongside of 26 ft.; (ii) the Burns, Philp copra wharf, with a length of 240 ft., a width of 27 ft. and a depth alongside of 27 ft.; (iii) the coal and oil wharf, with a length of 65 ft.; (iv) the Government (customs) wharf, with a length of 192 ft., and a depth

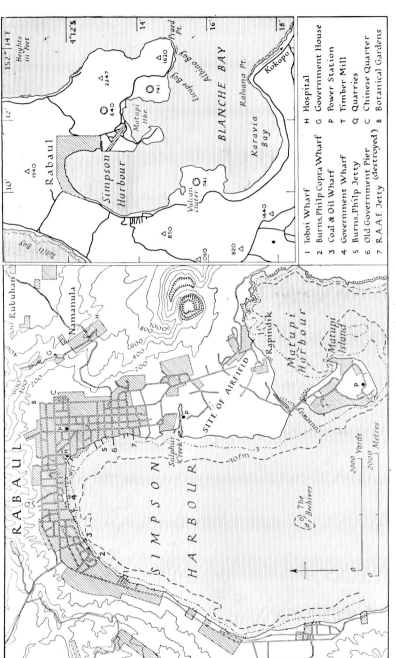

Fig. 54. Rabaul

The site of the airfield is cross-hatched on the small-scale map. This figure may be compared with the physical map of the area (Fig. 22). Based on official sources and on Admiralty chart no. 524.

alongside of 28½ ft.; (v) the Burns, Philp jetty, with a length of 370 ft., a width of 10 ft. and a depth alongside of 8 ft.; (vi) the ruins of the old Government pier (formerly the Norddeutscher Lloyd pier) which was damaged by fire in 1922; (vii) the R.A.A.F. jetty, with a length of 180 ft., a width of 6 ft. and a depth alongside of 4 ft. All were of timber or timber and concrete construction. The Government wharf, the Toboi wharf, and the Burns, Philp wharf were equipped with electric light and piped water supplies. In addition, there were several small landing stages. New wharves have been constructed during the Japanese occupation. In 1940 there were also three small jetties on Matupi island.

Warehouses, chiefly for the storage of copra, had been built round the water front, mainly near the Toboi wharf, the Burns, Philp wharf and the customs shed.

Repair facilities were limited. There were four small slipways suitable for small wooden vessels situated at Nosaki, east of the Government wharf. Minor repairs to machinery could be undertaken at the P.W.D. workshops or at one or two small engineering works in the town.

The Town

The normal population of Rabaul before the war was about 2,000, of whom rather over 1,000 were Europeans and the rest Asiatics. The settled area occupies most of the flat land on the north and east sides of the harbour. It is shut in to north and east by steep hills. The town is ambitiously laid out, with streets about 60 ft. wide running from north to south and from east to west, with blocks roughly 100 yd. square. Buildings consist for the most part of small single-storey bungalows built on piles and standing in large gardens. The principal business premises and government offices were in the main street, Mango Avenue. The north-east part of the town had become a Chinese quarter. Government House, the European hospital, and the bungalows of administrative officials were situated at Namanula, on the high ground overlooking the harbour. On the west side of Simpson harbour were native dwellings, a few bungalows and a mission station.

Communications

Rabaul had shipping communications not only with Australia and the Solomon islands but also with the Far East. Burns, Philp maintained a 3-weekly service to Australia, *via* Papua and a 6-weekly service to Australia, *via* the Solomons. A 3-weekly service between Sydney and Hong Kong and a 3-monthly service to Europe were operated by W. R. Carpenter and Company. The Norddeutscher Lloyd line ran a monthly service from Hong Kong, and the Dutch K.P.M. line ran a 2-monthly service between Saigon and Sydney, which called at Rabaul on the southbound run only.

There is an airfield south of the town. Before the war Mandated Airways ran a service to Australia, *via* Port Moresby. A few of the roads in Rabaul had been tar-sealed. Most, however, had not been surfaced in any way; but the hard volcanic rock in which they are cut stands up fairly well to traffic. The whole coastal area of the Gazelle peninsula is highly developed, as a plantation area, and it has a good network of roads (Fig. 52). These link up with the roads in the immediate vicinity of Rabaul. Before the invasion there was a local telephone system and a W/T station, which communicated daily with Australia.

KAVIENG (Fig. 55)

Kavieng is the administrative centre of New Ireland, as it was in German times. It is the largest settlement and the only port of importance in the island. It is situated at the north-west tip of New Ireland, protected by the off-lying islands of Nusa, Nusalik and Nago.

There are three entrances to the harbour: Nusa channel, in the south; Nissel pass, in the west; and North channel. Nusa channel, which is the principal entrance, is about 650 yd. wide between 5-fathom lines, with depths of from 11 to 15 fathoms in the fairway. A 3-fathom patch is said to lie in the fairway just east of Nago island. Otherwise there are no dangers. Nissel pass, between the reefs extending from Nago and Nusalik islands, is about 400 yd. wide between 3-fathom lines, with $6\frac{1}{2}$ fathoms in the fairway. But there is an awkward turn round a patch of coral inside, and the entrance is not recommended except for small vessels with local knowledge. North channel is partly obstructed by bars and rocks and is not often used, though vessels of over 2,000 tons have used it.

The harbour has a length of rather more than 2 miles and a width of less than $\frac{1}{2}$ mile. East rock, east of Nissel pass, is an obstruction. Depths in the north vary from 6 to 10 fathoms. The southern end is deeper, with average depths of 11 fathoms. The eastern shore is fringed with coral reefs and the western shore, off the three islands, is also coral-fringed, with shallow water off it. Swinging room is restricted.

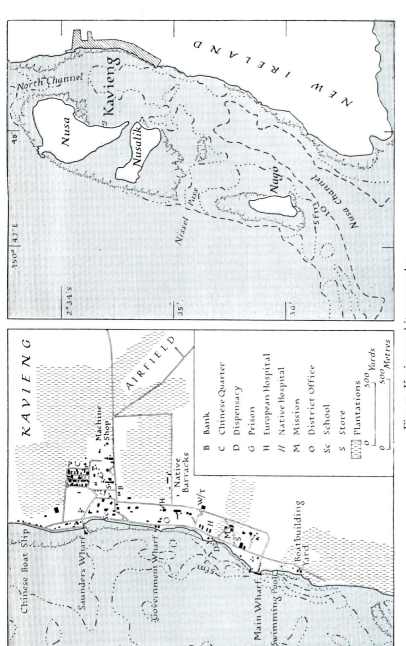

Fig. 55. Kavieng and its approaches

Based on: (1) Admiralty chart no. 2015; (2) other official sources.

In 1941 Kavieng had one wharf and two jetties. The wharf (known as the Main wharf—Plate 67) at the south end of the town had a length of about 160 ft., a width of 20 ft., and a depth alongside of 20 ft. The two jetties were known as Saunders wharf and the Government wharf respectively. The former, at the north end of the town, was 600 ft. long, with a depth of 6 ft. alongside; it was suitable only for lighters. The Government wharf had a length of 32 ft. and a depth alongside of 12 ft. There was a boat slip north of the town. The town had a population of about 30 Europeans and 250 Chinese. The principal buildings were the government station, two hospitals (one for Europeans and the other for natives), a bank and a post office. There were also a number of stores and warehouses, a gaol and bungalows. The Chinese quarter was a compact block of buildings to the north-east of the settlement, which straggled along the foreshore, with plantations occupying the flat land behind it. The principal export from the town is copra, and imports consist of stores and supplies for most of New Ireland. Regular communications by sea were maintained by Burns, Philp steamers, calling roughly every three weeks. A good road ran north-eastward from Kavieng, along the east coast to Samo, a distance of about 250 miles. Round Kavieng there are also good roads serving the plantations in the immediate neighbourhood. Signal communications consisted of a commercial W/T station communicating with Rabaul, and a tele-radio station operated by the government.

LAE (Fig. 56)

Lae (lat. 6° 43′ s, long. 147° 01′ E) is a small town on the north-west of Huon gulf and about 3 miles from the mouth of the Markham river. It came into being only in 1927, when Guinea Airways, Ltd., opened up their service to the goldfields of the Morobe district. It then became a trans-shipping point for supplies and machinery. After the volcanic eruption in 1937 which damaged Rabaul, it was decided to move the capital of the mandated territory there. The move was just beginning when the Japanese invasion of New Guinea caused both towns to be evacuated.

The anchorage, which is an open roadstead, offers little protection, but there is some shelter in an indentation of the coast to the east of the airfield. Depths vary from 10 to 20 fathoms. In 1941 jetties were grouped round the shores of a small cove east of the settlement. The most important, known as the cargo wharf, had a length of about 50 ft.

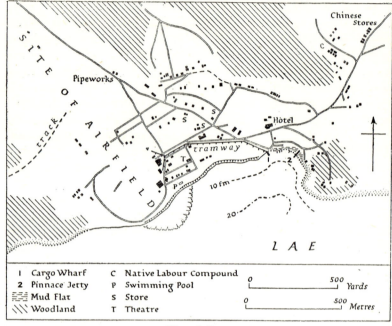

Fig. 56. Lae

This port lies behind a bank which runs along the shore. To west and east there is much silt from the Markham river which flows into the Huon gulf west of the port. The settlement has recently expanded across the Butibum river which flows south-ward off the eastern margin of the map. Based on official sources.

and a depth alongside of 4 ft. A short tramway joined this jetty with the airfield. Motive power was provided by a small petrol-driven locomotive, and there were also two steam-driven travelling cranes capable of lifting 7 tons. On the other side of the cove was a concrete jetty with a pontoon at the end. This was suitable only for small craft and was known as the Pinnace jetty. During the Japanese occupation three new jetties were built.

The town had a population in 1941 of about 150 Europeans and 80 Chinese. It consisted primarily of the hangars, administrative build-ings and workshops of the airways companies. Other industrial establishments consisted of a pipe-works, about 800 yd. west-north-west of the cargo wharf, and the Vacuum Oil Company's offices to the north-east of the Pinnace jetty. Most of the bungalows of the white residents, a few stores and a hotel, were situated on the flat ground between the cove and the airfield. There were also the Dis-trict Officer's headquarters and a small hospital. To the north-east

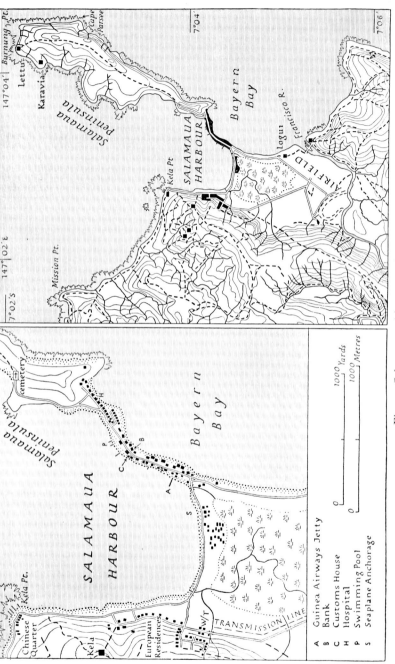

Fig. 57. Salamaua and its approaches

Form lines, at intervals of 100 ft, are approximate. Based on official sources.

of the town were a number of Chinese stores and a native labour compound.

Trade was largely limited to the import of stores and machinery for the goldfields and to the export of local produce. Shipping services are described below (p. 245). Air services are the principal means of transport (p. 247). Roads in the town have reasonably good surfaces. There was a road running parallel to the Markham river as far as Nadzab and then on to Wawin. Another ran for a short distance eastward across the Butibum river. Beyond these points land communication was by trail. Amalgamated Wireless (Australasia), Ltd., had a W/T station at Lae, as also did Guinea Airways. The latter company also maintained a small telephone system between their own buildings.

SALAMAUA (Fig. 57; Plate 66)

Salamaua (lat. 7° 04′ S, long. 147° 03′ E) is a small settlement built upon the isthmus of the Salamaua peninsula, on the south side of the Huon gulf, with a sheltered harbour in the lee of the peninsula. The town became important in 1925 as the port of arrival of gold prospectors going to the Morobe district.

The approach to the harbour offers no difficulties, but ships should steer well clear of the peninsula to avoid a reef which projects about ¾ mile northward from Burnung point. The inner portion of the bay offers good protected anchorage in depths diminishing shorewards from 30 fathoms. The south-western part of the bay is shallow and suitable only for small vessels.

Jetties are situated on the east side of the bay along the isthmus on which the town stands. In 1941 the Customs jetty, with a length of 150 ft., a width of 30 ft., and a depth of 6 ft. alongside, was the principal landing. The town has a normal peacetime population of about 130 Europeans, 100 Chinese and a number of natives. It has been the administrative centre for the Morobe District since 1926. The main settlement is built on the low sandy isthmus about ¾ mile long and 150 yd. wide, joining the head of the Salamaua peninsula to the mainland. The buildings, for the most part, consist of bungalows and stores, but the northern end of the town is occupied by hospital buildings. Other buildings include the District Officer's residence, the Customs House, and a bank. Amenities included tennis courts and a cinema.

To the west of the peninsula is a native village. About ½ mile further west is a new European settlement; the W/T station is situated here. About ½ mile north of this settlement, at Kela point, there is a Chinese settlement with a few landing stages suitable for small craft only. A road leads south of the main settlement on the isthmus for a distance of about a mile to the airfield.

Sea communication before the war consisted of the Burns, Philp service from Sydney to Rabaul; a ship called every three weeks. There was also a daily launch service linking Salamaua with Lae, 18 miles to the north. There was a weekly air service between Australia, Port Moresby, Wau, Salamaua and Rabaul, as well as a daily service from Salamaua to the goldfields at Wau. There were rough roads in the immediate vicinity of the settlements, but communication outside was by a network of tracks. There was a W/T station, communicating with Rabaul and a tele-radio set at the government station. A telephone system served the town, and a line ran inland to Wau.

MADANG

Madang (lat. 5° 12′ S, long. 145° 49′ E, approx.), the administrative centre of the Madang District, is a minor settlement at the end of the Schering peninsula with a small sheltered harbour. It is chiefly important as a shipping point for copra from the many plantations of the neighbourhood, and on account of its airfield.

The harbour is approached through Dallmann passage between the Schering peninsula and Gragät (Ragetta) island, the most southerly of a chain of islands on a barrier reef which stretches about 8 miles northwards to enclose an island-strewn lagoon. Dallmann passage is about ¼ mile wide and ½ mile long; it is said to be deeper than 12 fathoms. The harbour is a stretch of water about ½ mile long and ¼ mile wide, between Madang settlement and Beliao island, with depths of from 6 to 12 fathoms. To the south of Madang harbour between the Schering peninsula and the mainland, is the estuary of the Wagol river, which is known as Binnen harbour. Information is lacking about the depths of this stretch of water, but it is probably comparatively shallow.

In 1941 there was one wharf, with a depth of 21½ ft., east of Bode point, and there were numerous jetties or landing stages round the settlement and on the mainland, including one on the west side of Binnen harbour connected with the airfield by a road.

The population of Madang in 1941 included about 90 Europeans and 125 Chinese. The settlement was built on the end of the Schering peninsula, facing north and west with a shallow creek on the east

Plate 65. Port Moresby

A view looking north-east from the high ground behind Bogirohodobi point. On the left can be seen the Government House jetty.

Plate 66. Salamaua from the west

The settlement lies largely on the low isthmus which joins Salamaua peninsula to the swampy mainland. The airfield is placed on the firmer gravels north of the river outlet.

Plate 67. The Customs House, Kavieng
Seen from the deck of a ship moored at the Main wharf.

Plate 68. Pondo plantation
This is a large coconut plantation lying in the centre of the west coast of the Gazelle peninsula of New Britain. Sandy beaches of the type shown here are uncommon along this coast. The steep interior slopes are largely undeveloped.

side. The main buildings comprised the government station, European and native hospitals, the Lutheran mission buildings, about twenty bungalows, and the buildings of the Chinese quarter. In the surrounding area there are numerous plantations, mission stations and native villages. Two islands northward on the barrier reef were used as leper colonies.

Steamers called every six weeks. Roads run northwards to Alexishafen and southwards to Bogadjim. These are supplemented by numerous tracks running into the interior. Signal communications included a W/T station and a tele-radio set, in communication with stations in the interior.

WAU AND BULOLO

The principal settlements on the goldfield in the Morobe District of the mandated territory are Wau and Bulolo. The former had a European population of about 1,000 in 1941. The settlement included several churches, two banks, two hotels and a cinema, besides government offices and commercial premises. Most of the dwelling houses are substantially built timber bungalows. The settlement is built round the airfield, which provided it with its main link with the coast. A road runs from Wau to other parts of the goldfields. There was telephone communication with other goldfield settlements and with Salamaua, on the coast. Bulolo (Fig. 12) is about 4 miles north of Wau. Before the Japanese invasion it had a population of about 300 Europeans and some Chinese.

COMMUNICATIONS

SHIPPING

The main overseas shipping connections of New Guinea were with Australia. A mail service, under government subsidy, was maintained by Burns, Philp and Company. Ships sailed from Sydney about every three weeks and proceeded to Port Moresby and Rabaul, *via* Queensland ports. Calls were also made at the smaller ports of Papua and the mandated territory. A second service, maintained by the company, ran at 6-weekly intervals from Sydney to Rabaul, *via* the Solomon islands. A number of other overseas shipping services called at New Guinea ports. The cargo liners of W. R. Carpenter and Company called at Rabaul, *en route* from European ports to Australia.

The Eastern and Australasian Steamship Company's service from Australia to the Philippines, China and Japan also included a call at Rabaul; it ran at monthly intervals. Ships of the Dutch K.P.M. line called at both Rabaul and Port Moresby every two months, *en route* from the Netherlands East Indies to Australia and New Zealand. The Norddeutscher Lloyd service from Hong Kong to the Solomon islands also called at Rabaul. A number of tramp steamers called at New Guinea ports every year—mainly to collect copra. The following Table gives statistics of shipping at New Guinea ports shortly before the Japanese invasion.

Overseas Merchant Shipping Entering and Clearing New Guinea Ports

	1938–9		1939–40		1940–1	
	Ships	Tonnage	Ships	Tonnage	Ships	Tonnage
Papua						
British	158	312,956	168	337,578	166	325,961
Foreign	57	148,243	59	152,392	51	163,508
Total	215	461,199	227	489,970	217	489,469
Territory of New Guinea						
British	85	275,369	79	274,007	67	171,669
Foreign	28	52,223	25	39,990	27	42,681
Total	113	327,592	104	313,997	94	213,350
Grand Total	328	787,791	331	803,967	311	702,819

Local shipping services were maintained by steam or motor vessels of about 300 tons ; there were also a number of auxiliary schooners and many launches. An example of such services is given by the itinerary of S.S. *Papuan Chief*, which sailed regularly between Port Moresby and Samarai, calling *en route* at Kapa Kapa, Hula, Aroma, Abau, Mogubo, Port Glasgow, Baibara, Gadaisu and Fife bay.

Some of the rivers of New Guinea are navigable for considerable distances from their mouths. On the Lakekamu steam launches and lighters have been used to take supplies for Wau as far as Bulldog, from which point they are taken overland. The three rivers of greatest potential importance from the point of view of navigation—the Fly, Sepik and Ramu—have been described in Chapter III (pp. 78–83).

AIR SERVICES

Owing to the difficult nature of the terrain, which makes road construction impracticable in many parts, aircraft are used extensively, not only for passengers but also for freight. Still further development might have taken place if there were more land suitable for aerodromes for large commercial planes. The many waterways and lakes would offer excellent facilities for seaplanes were it not for the dangerous obstruction of floating logs. The general pattern of air communications is one of a few regular routes operated by the big air transport companies, and of numerous taxi services maintained by owners of small aircraft using small clearings as airfields.

The real stimulus to the development of air transport came with the opening up of the Morobe goldfield area in 1927. As there were no roads to the area, all engineering equipment had to be flown in. Guinea Airways, Ltd., built an airfield at Lae, and opened a service to the goldfield area. Other competing companies started services from Salamaua. After a time, however, the various operating companies were absorbed either into Guinea Airways or into W. R. Carpenter and Company's service, known as Mandated Airways. Guinea Airways maintained a direct service between Lae and Wau, the principal airfield in the goldfield area, and an alternative service calling *en route* at an airfield on the Snake river, and at Zenag, the Wampit river and Wannan. Mandated Airways flew between Sydney and Rabaul, *via* various north Queensland towns, Port Moresby, Wau and Salamaua, carrying passengers and mail once a week.

TRAMWAYS

No proper railways have been built in New Guinea or the Bismarck archipelago, but at some of the ports, notably Rabaul, Port Moresby, Samarai, Lae and Daru, short lengths of narrow-gauge track have been laid down to facilitate the handling of cargo, and some of the early mining companies laid down short lengths of track. Thus there is a line of 3 ft. 6 in. gauge running from the Dubuna copper mines to Bootless inlet, near Port Moresby; it was abandoned in 1927. Similarly an overhead cable-way between Dubuna and Laloki has been abandoned. There are also short stretches of tramway track through some of the plantations.

ROADS AND TRAILS

Throughout eastern New Guinea and the Bismarck archipelago roads are very poorly developed, but there are dense networks of trails in many places suitable for bicycles or pack transport. Fig. 58 shows the general pattern of roads and trails throughout the area. It will

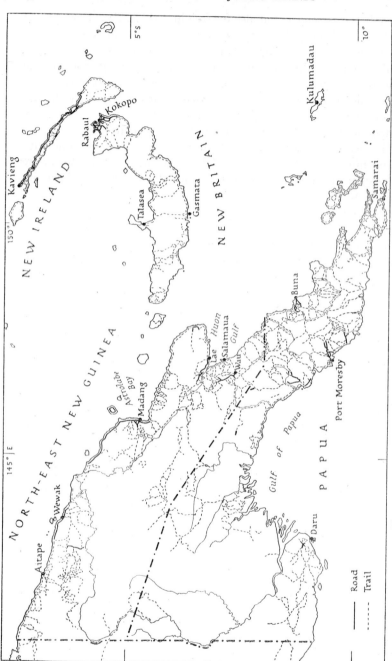

Fig. 58. Roads and foot tracks in New Guinea and the Bismarck archipelago
The main rivers, which supplement land routes are shown. Based on official sources

be noticed that the roads are nowhere continuous, but consist of isolated networks round some of the ports, or stretches along the coast and a few in the interior. Thus on the New Guinea mainland there are roads running eastward from Port Moresby; a few roads serving plantations in the Buna area; a road from Lae following the Markham valley; a long coastal stretch from Astrolabe bay to Nubia bay; and a stretch in the Wewak district as well as isolated roads in the interior, the most important of which is that from Wau to Bulolo and Edie Creek. In New Britain there is a fairly close network round Rabaul serving the plantations in the north-eastern portion of the Gazelle peninsula, and, in New Ireland, a long road from Kavieng following the east coast from Kavieng to Samo, a distance of about 220 miles.

There has been no general programme of road construction either in Papua or the mandated territory. The long stretch of road on New Ireland owes its construction primarily to the enthusiasm of a former German administrator of New Ireland. The Yule road, with a length of about 110 miles, in the Gulf Division of Papua, was built by French Roman Catholic missionaries. Other short stretches have been built by oil companies or plantation owners. The Wau-Bulolo road was built to serve the needs of the gold-mining community. The coastal road from Astrolabe bay to Nubia bay was built by the Japanese for military purposes.

Factors inhibiting the growth of roads are extensive swamps in the lowlands, the rapid growth of vegetation, damage caused by heavy rain and landslides, and in most places the lack of suitable road metal. Surfaces are usually of crushed coral, which is sometimes soft. Round Rabaul, however, volcanic rock is available, and the roads have fairly good surfaces. Bridges over the many streams are generally of timber, which is subject to rapid decay.

Trails or tracks are of considerably greater significance as means of transport than roads. In Papua there were probably well over 2,000 miles of trails in 1940. In the mandated territory, excluding New Britain and New Ireland, there were 3,930 miles of trails and in New Britain and New Ireland about 1,900 miles. There is a relatively dense network of trails in the south-eastern part of Papua. The government has constructed many of them to enable administrative officers to cover their districts adequately. The responsibility for maintaining these trails rest on the native populations in the regions concerned. There are also numerous trails made by plantation owners or by the natives themselves. The trails vary considerably in quality.

The government trails are usually well graded and carried over streams by bridges; they are suitable for bicycle traffic. In swampy patches they are often corduroyed—i.e., logs are laid transversely across the track. Many trails, especially in the lowlands, are very muddy and slippery in wet weather. Small streams are crossed by fallen tree-trunks or stepping stones; larger ones by canoes. On occasion elaborate native suspension bridges are built (Plate 33). Generally, coastal trails follow the shore, and trails in the interior follow the ridges of the mountains. Round each native settlement the trails are usually fairly well developed, and maintained in good order. The longer trails in the interior are far less frequently used, and consequently the earth surface is not so well trodden and vegetation has more opportunity to overgrow them. During the course of the fighting in New Guinea, some of the trails have been improved to take light military vehicles.

SIGNAL COMMUNICATIONS

Wireless communication in both Papua and the mandated territory and between the two territories and Australia is maintained by Amalgamated Wireless (Australasia), Ltd., on behalf of the Australian government. The principal W/T stations are at Port Moresby and Rabaul. There are less powerful stations, which communicate with these two major stations, at Samarai, Wau, Lae, Bulolo, Wewak, Madang and Kavieng. At Port Moresby a radio-telephone transmitter was also installed during 1941. Communication between the main settlements and government stations, mission stations and many plantations is maintained by 'tele-radio' sets. These are small portable radio-telephone sets, which can be operated by persons with little expert knowledge; they can also be used, if necessary, for W/T. In 1940 there were between 100 and 200 of these sets in operation.

Line-telephone systems are few in number. In Port Moresby, there is a government-owned system comprising 150 lines. Lines extend round the bay to Napa Napa, and also up the road to Rouna Falls, and on to Itakinumu. At Salamaua the government telephone system linked the business centre of the town with the airfield and the residential district of Kila, and a line is said to have been built to Lae, where there is also a small system operated by Guinea Airways. The mining companies in the Morobe District operate a line between Wau, Edie Creek, and Bulolo. In the Sepik district there is a line between the government station and the airfield at Wewak. In the Bismarck archipelago the only telephone system is that in Rabaul, which has an extension to Kokopo.

BIBLIOGRAPHICAL NOTE

The most detailed accounts of the ports, settlements and communications of New Guinea are to be found in various official reports which are not generally available. A considerable amount of information, however, is given in R. W. Robson (editor), *The Pacific Islands Year Book* (Sydney, 1939; wartime edition, 1942). Also useful are: *The Official Handbook of the Territory of Papua* (Port Moresby, 1938); and the *Official Handbook of the Territory of New Guinea* (Canberra, 1937).

Chapter XII

NEW IRELAND AND ADJACENT ISLANDS

New Ireland—Relief: Coasts and Anchorages: Social and Economic Conditions
Islands Adjacent to New Ireland—Djaul: Lavongai: St Matthias Group: Tabar
  Group: Lihir Group: Tanga Group: Feni (Anir) Group: Niguria Group
Bibliographical Note

New Ireland lies north-east of New Britain, approximately between lat. 2° 30′ and 4° 50′ s and long. 150° 40′ and 153° 10′ E. It is a long and, at certain points, extremely narrow island, trending from north-west to south-east. Djaul, Lavongai, the St Matthias group and numerous smaller islands lie off its north-west end. Four island groups lie parallel to, and on an average 30 miles from, its east coast. From north-west to south-east these are the Tabar, Lihir, Tanga, and Feni (Anir) islands.

NEW IRELAND

RELIEF

New Ireland is divided by four narrow necks of land (defined here by the names of their main coastal settlements) into five main sections (Fig. 59). The wider south-eastern section is separated from the remainder of the island by the Namatanai-Ulaputur isthmus. North-west of Namatanai, a narrow section continues to the Karu-Komalu isthmus. The next section to north-westward is occupied by the Lelet plateau and terminates at the Lamussong-Patlangat isthmus. The Schleinitz mountains run from here through the succeeding section to the Lemakot-Lemusmus isthmus. The most north-westerly section continues from this isthmus to Balgai bay and the Kavieng area.

The South-east Section. The mountains which form the spine of New Ireland reach their maximum height in this section. Behind the south-west coast of New Ireland, the Hahl mountains are about 7,000 ft. high. The highest peak overlooking St George's channel is about 7,050 ft. high. The slopes up from the west coast are steep and only slightly dissected by short streams. Except in the south-west, where there are high limestone cliffs, the hills give place abruptly

252

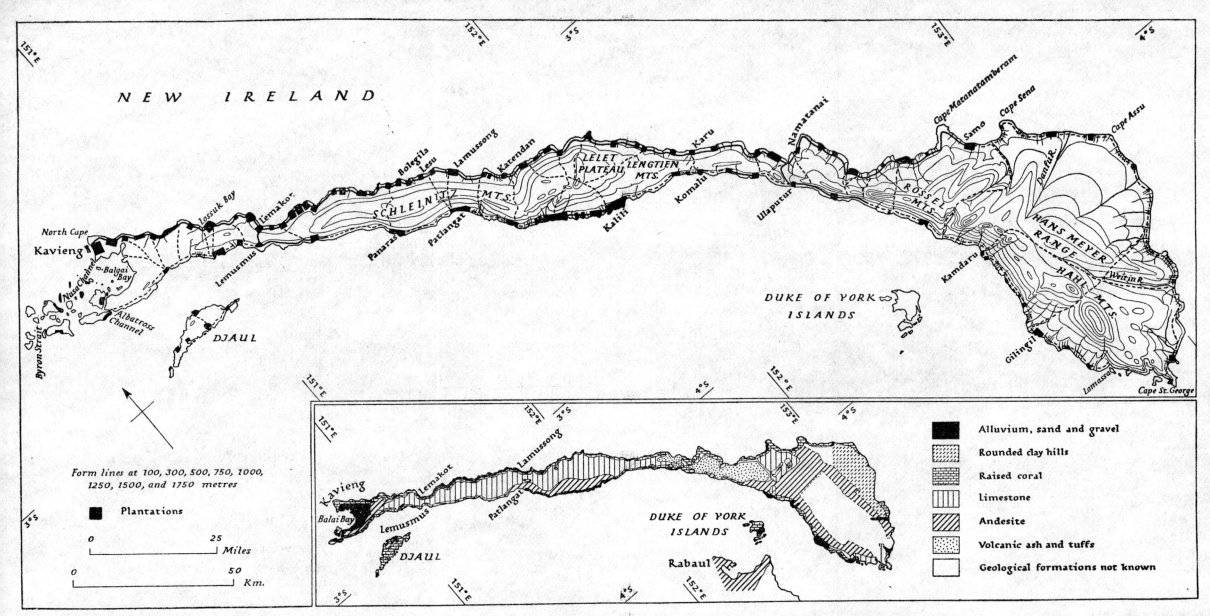

Fig. 59. New Ireland

Names of more important settlements are indicated. Based on: (1) Karl Sapper, 'Neu Mecklenburg', *Jahresberichte des Frankfurter Vereins für Geographie und Statistik*, vols. LXXIII, LXXIV (Frankfurt-am-Main, 1908–10); (2) official sources.

to a narrow coast plain. Communications in the south-west are largely by canoe, an unusual feature in New Ireland, where the natives rely largely on coast tracks. To eastward, after a sharp fall to the longitudinal trench of the Weitin river, there is a further rise to the lesser Hans Meyer mountains which are approximately 3,000 ft. high at their crest. The Hans Meyer range falls to the south-east coast in rounded hills. Both mountain masses appear to be largely of andesite and are bold and rugged. Much bare rock is exposed, especially among the stunted forests of the Hahl mountain summits. The south-eastern slopes of the Hans Meyer mountains are masked by heavy clays which support dense rain forest. The interior of south-eastern New Ireland is sparsely peopled. A discontinuous fringe of raised coral bounds the coast of both mountain masses. Reefs are best developed on the east coast. As the island narrows towards the Namatanai-Ulaputur isthmus, the Rossel mountains form the central range. The spurs projecting from their southern end are of limestone, but the main range is composed of volcanic ash and tuffs. Most of the summits are about 4,000 ft. high, but mount Konogaiang, which overlooks the Duke of York islands, is said to rise to 6,140 ft. The slopes of the Rossel mountains are cleft by deep gullies with swampy bottoms. The west coast slopes are again steeper than those of the east where the flanking hills merge into low plateaux (200 ft. high) formed of raised coral.

The Namatanai-Ulaputur to Karu-Komalu Section. Across the Namatanai-Ulaputur isthmus the forested main range descends to 300 ft. and the volcanic rocks give place to limestone, which continues as the main core of the island almost to Kavieng. The limestone ranges of New Ireland are largely rough, with many precipitous slopes and little surface drainage. Both limestone and tuff formations are largely displaced as surface deposits in the Namatanai-Ulaputur isthmus by raised coral terraces out of which rise wooded knolls. Thence to the Karu-Komalu isthmus the island is very narrow and rises to rather less than 1,000 ft. The slopes are fairly even and almost entirely forested, though across Nabuto bay from Namatanai mixed kunai and rain forest are found on the coastal raised coral and tuffs. Though undulating these are relatively low. There are many gravel spreads in the valleys of the short rivers.

The summit point on the track over the Karu-Komalu isthmus is 500 ft. high. Bands of raised coral do not extend inland here; they are narrower than the strips of raised coral along both bounding coasts, being pinched out coastwards by the limestones of the main chain.

The Lelet Plateau. The Lengtien mountains to north-westward of the Karu-Komalu isthmus are the south-eastern foothills of the so-called Lelet plateau. This is an uneven limestone mass of considerable width which has several high areas, two being over 3,200 ft. and one, in the centre, over 4,000 ft. high. The plateau is relatively well peopled, unlike other sections of the central range. There are many rough inter-village tracks. The eastern limestone slopes are steeper than the western slopes, which are of andesite. There is a band of raised coral to eastward, which forms irregular lines of terraces. Along the west coast of the plateau there is an almost continuous fringe of narrow alluvial plain on which are situated several large plantations.

The Schleinitz Mountains. Between Lamussong and Patlangat the central ridge forms the backbone of a relatively narrow but fairly high isthmus. This narrow belt of land provides a convenient division between the Lelet plateau and the Schleinitz mountains. The ridge is roughly 2,000 ft. high, while the summit of the Lamussong-Patlangat track is over 2,400 ft. above sea level. Gradients are steep on both the western and eastern slopes of the Schleinitz mountains. Large stretches of the mountain sides have little surface drainage, but deep ravines which carry streams in wet weather are common. The narrow alluvial plain appears as an outer fringe of the raised coral outcrop of the east coast in this section. The west coast is almost entirely of raised coral and cliffs are common.

The Lemakot-Lemusmus to Balgai Bay Section. The steep, forested Schleinitz mountains fall north-westward to the Lemakot-Lemusmus isthmus, where they merge into grassy hills about 500 ft. high. The mountains are heavily timbered, with many native gardens. The relatively narrow limestone outcrop which runs across the centre of the Lemakot-Lemusmus isthmus is fringed by raised coral on both west and east, and this raised reef is, in its turn, fringed by alluvial deposits on the east coast. Between the Lemakot-Lemusmus isthmus and Balgai bay the steep wooded hills rise to 900 ft. on the summit of the track between Lemakot and Lemusmus plantations and to 1,500 ft. in the hills to the north-west of the track. Slopes are steep and some small knife-edged ridges occur behind the west coast. The limestone mass of mount Kiding, the culminating point of these hills, is reported to have a cliff 500 ft. high just below its summit. The limestone core is bordered by igneous rocks in this section, and it eventually gives place to hills composed of andesite behind Balgai bay. On the north coast the series of raised coral terraces broadens north-westward, until this formation covers the greater part of the Kavieng peninsula. The lowland behind the head of Balgai bay is largely covered with recent alluvium. The only extensive swamps in New Ireland are found there. In spite of heavy rainfall totals (p. 106) swamps are generally not well developed in New Ireland, as the lack of broad coastal plains, the sharp topography of the island, the abrupt coastal slopes and the frequency of limestone and volcanic ash as surface deposits make for effective run-off. Much of the andesite outcrop around Balgai bay is at low levels. The hills which border the swamps behind the head of the bay are low and fertile. They support many villages. The alluvial soils are heavy and ill-drained and no plantations are to be found along Balgai bay. Behind the coasts of the western horn of the bay, pockets of sago swamp alternate with stretches of grass and forest on the slightly higher andesitic areas.

The Rivers

The permanent and, in the limestone areas, semi-permanent streams of New Ireland are swift and for the most part short. The longest river is the Weitin, which has carved a deep and relatively wide trench between the steep spurs of the Hahl and Hans Meyer mountains. It is less than 25 miles long. The Danfu river, which skirts the north side of the Hans Meyer mountains, has a broad bed with much gravel. It is swift and is difficult to ford in the wet season. Its valley is narrower than that of the Weitin and is about 20 miles long. In the limestone areas the rivers often gush out from subterranean courses on to the inner borders of the alluvial plains or coastal andesite zones. In some cases their courses as surface streams are only about a mile long. This is a common feature of the drainage of the east coast north of Karu. Some east-coast rivers in the neighbourhood of Namatanai and Karu are tidal for about ½ mile, but this is not a feature of the swift west-coast rivers. The Balgai river is navigable for a short distance inland, but the other rivers are useless for navigation except for a few hundred yards at their mouths.

COASTS AND ANCHORAGES

For the reasons indicated above, anchorages at river mouths are few, and sunken estuaries which might provide shelter (such as those of the cape Nelson area of Papua) are absent in New Ireland. The large development of raised reefs indicates recent elevation and not subsidence. The coasts of New Ireland are relatively straight and exposed and little shelter is afforded by the few small islands which lie close in-shore. Anchorages will not be mentioned in the following section unless they are of some importance. There are many points at which vessels may hang on to the shingle beaches or reefs, but without further development these are useless commercially.

The following description of the coasts proceeds from cape St George in an anti-clockwise direction. From this steep cape to the exposed anchorage in Lanisso bay (3 miles to the north-east), the coast is cliff-bound. Sandy beaches lie behind cape Metlik on the north side of Lanisso bay, while to the north-east of the cape a narrow sandy plain supports one of the two plantations on the south coast. The Jau river flows between gravel banks into a lagoon about a mile long lying north of the plantation. This stretch of water is succeeded by steep cliffs and uninhabited precipitous slopes which force the coast track well inland. North of the Weitin river outlet, which is bordered by sandy beaches, low cliffs of raised coral appear and the coastal track regains the shore. From this region of low cliffs backed by the spurs of the Hans Meyer range, which push southward, the coast to cape Assu (East cape) is very exposed. It has a narrow coastal flat which is partly alluvial, though behind cape Assu it is of coral masked by heavy clays and loams. At Mungai, about 7 miles south of cape Assu, on this coast section, there is a small plantation, and rather poor native villages occur every few miles. Undulating hills covered with dense forests lie behind the coast.

From cape Assu to cape Sena there are well-developed fringing reefs with a few anchorages—e.g., at Muliama plantation. This is probably the best east-coast anchorage for vessels of less than 1,000 tons. Sandy beaches alternate with marshy flats backed by coral lime-stone. North-west of Muliama two stages in the elevation of the coast are seen in terraces at heights of 30 and 100 ft. The interior hills slope uniformly to the coral platforms. The interior is un-inhabited, the dense forests being broken only by a few grass patches. Cape Sena is the north-eastern point of a blunt peninsula with an area of about 10 sq. miles, which is composed of slightly elevated coral formations with a rough and largely grassy surface. Kunai and kan-garoo grass predominate except in the wooded gullies. The surface soil is hard clay. There is a coral bench around the peninsula and very little coast flat. The indentation between cape Sena and cape Matana-tamberam is exposed and has some open beaches of coarse gravel and black sand. It is wholly fringed with raised coral, which is largely grass-covered. At the north end of the bay the coral forms five terraces, four being below the main one which runs parallel to the coast at a height of 200 ft. The east-coast road from Kavieng reaches Samo plantation, at the head of this wide indentation. It follows close to the coast for approximately 200 miles. The cape Matanatamberam peninsula is similar to that behind cape Sena in structure, area and form, though the coast is more indented. Timber strips are found only along the coast and in surface gullies.

Elizabeth bay to northward has extensive reefs off-shore which lie off mainly sandy beaches. The immediate hinterland is of limestone and is well peopled. There are signs of terracing. Alluvial flats alternate with sandy beaches and coral terraces to cape Namaredu, 3 miles east of Namatanai. Much of this stretch of coast is of volcanic ash and tuffs, and it supports several plantations. South of cape Namaredu there are several areas with cliffs between 100 and 200 ft. high, and a barrier reef lies from one to $1\frac{1}{2}$ miles off-shore. The raised coral continues along the south-east side of Nabuto bay, east of the head of which lies Halis plantation and Namatanai, the administrative centre of the southern part of New Ireland. Halis plantation is backed by a low hill on which the Methodist mission stands. Off Namatanai there is a drying reef about 100 yd. wide off a sandy shore. Small schooners may enter the anchorage through a break in the reef. By the shore there is a hotel and a Chinese store. The government offices are at the crest of the steep slope up from the shore. At the head of Nabuto bay a branch road leaves the main coast road and crosses the 300-ft. ridge across the isthmus to Ulaputur. It is said to have been built to facilitate the evacuation of part of the population of Rabaul in the event of an eruption of the Blanche bay volcanoes. Rabaul lies (in a direct line) about 50 miles south-westward.

From Namatanai to Karu the coast is backed by limestone hills which reach about 980 ft. and are flanked along the coast first by lower hills composed of volcanic ash, and, north-west of this outcrop, by raised coral terraces. Low cliffs appear at intervals and north of Ramat plantation they force the coast road on to the foreshore. Some sandy beaches appear behind the fringing reef. Streams are short and their banks are gravel strewn. The low coastal hills above the valley bottoms have loamy soil, and this undulating stretch of coast supports four plantations. The Karu-Katendan stretch of coast flanks the Lelet plateau and slopes up steeply to it. Raised coral occurs in small irregular masses, which push out of the clayey topsoil. Along the coast the raised coral forms low cliffs, which overhang several sections of the coast road. The plantations of this area are small and recently established and there are no good anchorages which might serve them.

South-east of Katendan there is over 1,100 yd. of mangrove swamp along the shore. This is backed by precipitous hills. Katendan plantation is of small acreage and is developed on a group of low hills and swampy stream valleys.

From Katendan to Lamussong there is a good deal of rough limestone land, partly covered with coralline sand, which alternates with alluvial flats. Behind Pinikindu Methodist mission, about 3 miles south of Lamussong, pandanus and kunai patches are found among the thin forests. Lamussong has a Roman Catholic mission, and a plantation with largely clay soil. The bordering hills which rise to the Schleinitz mountains are well forested and of limestone. At least half of the Lamussong-Lemakot coast strip is under plantations, and behind Bolegila there is a small cocoa plantation well up the slopes of the Schleinitz mountains. The plantations are situated behind rather poor exposed anchorages which lie off the sandy beaches of this coastal strip. Low cliffs fringe the minor headlands and around the heads of bays there may be sago swamps. The interior is broken limestone country, deeply furrowed by gorges which carry swift streams in the wet season. Depressions are common where the surface has subsided over the courses of underground rivers. Several of the plantations have many pot-holes, intermingled with undulating surfaces covered with heavy clay.

North of Lemakot the forest thins out at first and there are a number of villages on a sandy coastal flat. Northwards to Lossuk bay there are some level sandy stretches and low cliffs, but the main formation is a longitudinal band of raised coral about $\frac{1}{2}$ mile wide, which gives place inland to a belt of swamp of the same width. Lossuk bay would take several craft of 50 tons on its inner side. The 700 yd. of sandy beach at its head is the longest beach between Namatanai and Kavieng. The beach is backed by mangrove swamps.

The stretch of coast between Lossuk bay and the North cape is almost continuously reefed, and both littoral and interior are lowlying. There are several beaches of firm coralline sand and six plantations; three of these are of considerable size. Copra is sent by road to Kavieng. Large loading jetties are uncommon. Many native villages and gardens are found on the coastal margins of the forest. The low clayey hills give place towards the North cape to undulating plains, with sandy patches on their slight elevations and swamps in their minor depressions. Behind North cape there is a narrow sandy beach flanked by many native gardens.

The coast curves south-westward towards Kavieng after the North

cape is rounded. There are fringing reefs off-shore. Anchorages are
good between Nusa (a planted island), Nusalik and Bagail, and the
Kavieng shore. Details of the port and settlement of Kavieng are
given on p. 240. Behind the shore runs a coral ridge 30 ft. high. It is
usually a grassy bank 100 yd. from the shore, but parts of it are
40 ft. high and precipitous. Grass and swamps alternate with the
planted areas behind Kavieng.

Between the two peninsulas which curve round Balgai bay, and
Lavongai, there are many good anchorages in the shelter of groups
of small islands, but there are also many reefs which are awash at low
water. Navigation beyond the limits of the recognized channels may
be difficult. The head of Balgai bay has few anchorages. There is a
fringing reef broken only at the mouths of short sluggish streams and
tidal creeks. Mangroves extend inland for 3 miles in some areas.
The largest islands lie between Byron strait and the western peninsula. They include Selapui and Baudissin and, east of these
respectively, Bangatang and Mane. On each island there is a plantation. Selapui has the highest hill of the group, namely a central point
300 ft. high. The Balgai bay coasts of these islands have mangrove
swamps. Other shores are sandy and reefed. Within the area enclosed
by them lie several smaller flat islands. These include Ungan, which
has a mission station, and Lemus, east of Bangatang, which is flat,
with a hard surface of coarse sand.

Baudissin is separated from the New Ireland mainland by the
Albatross channel. The most north-westerly section of the west coast
of New Ireland runs from this channel to the narrow neck of land
behind Lemusmus. The hilly island of Djaul is visible from most
points on the coast. There are three plantations on this section of
coast. Kaut plantation, opposite the centre of the north coast of
Djaul, has a good sheltered anchorage through an entrance about
75 yd. wide. Vessels of up to 700 tons may tie up at the jetty at
Sicacui plantation, 6 miles west of Lemusmus. Much of the lowland
which lies between the plantations is fringed with mangroves.
Towards Sicacui the interior hills begin to rise steeply. The raised
coral fringe is narrow along this coast and terraces are not well
developed. The plantation at Lemusmus is Chinese-owned and lies
inland from the coast.

The Lemusmus-Patlangat coast has a continuous shore reef and
no major indentations or good anchorages. The adjoining limestone
hills have very steep faces and are almost waterless in some sections.
This area is thinly populated, except for the 12 miles between Panaras

and Patlangat plantations. Much of the shore is cliffed, and at Panaras copra is loaded down chutes from the top of the 30-ft. cliff into boats which hang on to the fringing reef. Between Patlangat and Kalili there are several large plantations of which the largest are those owned by Burns, Philp around and north-west of Kalili. These plantations are linked by the longest stretch of road along the west coast. The large Kalili plantation has sandy loam soils and is fairly flat. The remainder are more undulating, and on their alluvial strips the heavy clay soils are very soft and difficult to work in wet weather. Rolling wooded country lies for a short distance behind the plantations and passes quickly into the steep flanks of the Lelet plateau. Kalili has a well-sheltered anchorage for vessels of less than 1,000 tons. The entrance is 75 yd. wide and was marked by leading beacons.

Between Kalili and Komalu much of the raised reef surface is wet only after rain, and the topsoil is thinly spread. The fringing reef is practically continuous and low cliffs backed by irregular terraces are common. Behind Komalu, where there is a mission station, the flat coast strip runs back for 200 to 300 yd. It is sandy and well drained. The 20 miles of coast between Kokola and Ulaputur has one anchorage for a vessel of 1,000 tons. This is at Labur bay, the only inlet in a straight coast. The steeply rising hills are forested, though towards the Ulaputur-Namatanai isthmus kunai patches are common inland. At Ulaputur there is a mission station and a rough coast road which runs south-eastward for about 20 miles.

The long stretch of coast between Ulaputur and Gilingil has been only slightly developed by Europeans. The plantations are small and largely under Chinese management. Broken shore reefs, stony or rocky beaches, deep water off-shore, steep bounding mountains and short, swift streams are common features. Parts of the coast are cultivated by a widely scattered native population. At Kamdaru there is a large swamp behind the shore. From here to Gilingil patches of raised coral with terraces from 6 to 30 ft. high alternate with small pockets of swamp, which accumulate where shingle beaches dam the outlets of streams. Behind Gilingil rough raised coral surfaces extend for a mile inland. A track leaves the coast here and utilizes a col in the Hahl mountains before it descends to meet a track which follows the Weitin valley.

The coast between Gilingil and cape St George has a relatively wide coastal flat composed of limestone terraces and alluvium as far as Lamassa. Steep slopes rise to the highest mountains of New Ireland behind the coast. These are of andesite and are rugged and forested. From Lamassa to cape St George high cliffs surround both bays and headlands, and in some parts almost equally precipitous slopes continue inland. The coast is more indented than most of the west coast and there are two fair-sized islands off-shore. The ruggedness of the hills does not allow the coast track to continue beyond Lamassa. The hinterland is forbidding, being rough and forested, with many exposures of bare rock. The settlement founded by the 'Marquis de Rays' in 1880, half-way along this rocky coast at Port Breton, survived for only a short time (p. 125). The Chinese-owned plantation on the north side of cape St George lies on Lambon (Gower) harbour. This harbour is 32 to 50 fathoms deep and cannot be used as an anchorage. Steep limestone hills rise to 1,700 ft. within 3 miles of the cliffed shore. Reefs are steep-to and very narrow north of the Lambon harbour plantation.

SOCIAL AND ECONOMIC CONDITIONS

During the German occupation of what is now mandated New Guinea, northern New Ireland was developed commercially as rapidly as the Gazelle peninsula of New Britain. Extensive areas of flat or gently undulating land are of limited extent, and the coast plains are narrow. Thus European settlement and agriculture, both German and British, have been confined to the coastlands which lie along the flanks of the steep interior mountains. A considerable proportion of the narrow coastal lowlands is under coconuts and other plantation crops, but these plantations rarely extend inland for more than 2 miles. More commonly, they reach for only a mile inland. With the exception of the coasts of the Gazelle peninsula, no part of the New Guinea area is so intensively developed by Europeans as the coast of New Ireland.

The chief factor in this development has been the road along the east coast from Kavieng to Samo plantation. This road was engineered by the Germans and is the longest motor road in mandated New Guinea. Much copra is carried along the east coast by this road, an unusual feature in an archipelago which relies largely on sea transport for its trade. The natives are responsible for the upkeep of those sections of the road which adjoin their villages. Fig. 59 shows further stretches of motor road, notably the road across the narrow isthmus between Namatanai and Ulaputur, and three sections of motor road along the west coast. The longest of these runs through the group of plantations between Katanu and Kalili, which are largely owned by Burns, Philp. Other sections of the coast are served by tracks, and there are additional tracks across the narrower parts of the island. The swampy lowlands around Balgai bay are ill-developed and have no roads or trackways. The rocky and steeply cliffed hinterland of cape St George has no tracks in the area between Lamassa and the outlet of the Jau river, 3 miles north of Lanisso bay. This is one of the few areas in which the native peoples use canoes in preference to other means of transport.

In 1940 there were 164 plantations in New Ireland with an area of 121,865 acres, of which 79,569 acres were under cultivation. The main yield was 20,625 tons of copra. Small areas had been planted with cacao, coffee, kapok and rubber, and some cacao and coffee were interplanted with other crops, but the yields from all these crops were only very small when the Japanese occupied the island.

The native population of New Ireland was estimated at 19,417 in 1940. This represented a considerable decrease since 1914, when the German census officers reported the total as 26,488 (see Table on p. 142). In 1940 the total native population of New Ireland and the islands which lie off it was estimated at 36,891. Figures for the native population of each of the off-lying island groups are quoted in the section dealing with these islands (pp. 263–8). The native peoples of New Ireland are garden cultivators, and their settlements are thus governed by the same physical controls as those of the European and, on the west coast, Chinese plantation owners. Native villages are found further inland than the plantations, but relatively dense native settlement is limited to the coastal belt. The exceptional area is the Lelet plateau, in the centre of New Ireland. This is a steep-sided limestone mass with a relatively flat top, and it supports a considerable number of native settlements. Many rough tracks link these villages and run from them to the adjoining coastlands. Garden produce is carried down to the lowlands and traded. The densely forested interior highlands of New Ireland, and in particular those of the wider southern end, are otherwise very sparsely peopled. The European exploitation of the east and, to a lesser degree, of the west coast has affected the native peoples adversely. Much of their best garden land has been alienated, with the result that they have been obliged to clear the forests off hillsides well up-slope from their villages. The native women have thus to travel some distance to their daily work and may have to carry heavy loads of garden produce back to the villages. It is thought that native food supplies are of poorer quality and less plentiful under these conditions. This and other possible factors in the decline of the native population are discussed on pp. 144–5.

Apart from Kavieng, the main administrative centre and port of New Ireland (p. 240), the only non-native settlement of any size is Namatanai on the east coast, which is a district sub-station. It has relatively good communications both by sea and land. In 1940 about 180 Chinese and 25 Europeans lived there. The southern half of the island, southward from Karu, is administered from Namatanai. Europeans were otherwise scattered throughout the island and lived mainly on the plantations and at mission stations. The missions were largely Roman Catholic and Methodist. The former were most numerous.

ISLANDS OFF NEW IRELAND

The mass of small islands which lies between Byron strait and the Kavieng peninsula is shown on Fig. 59 and has been described on p. 259. The island groups described in the following pages lie at fair distances from the mainland of New Ireland. Djaul is the nearest off-lying island, being about 8 miles off-shore. The St Matthias group is most distant, lying about 100 miles north-west of Kavieng.

DJAUL

Djaul is an undulating forested island which is separated from the north-west of New Ireland by Gazelle channel. It is 16½ miles long and 4½ miles across at its widest extent. Djaul is mainly hilly, with only small isolated areas below 200 ft. in height. The culminating point is 741 ft. high. This is mount Bendemann, behind Bendemann harbour in the centre of the north coast. Raised coral outcrops are found over the entire surface, with the exceptions of small outcrops of andesite (shown on Fig. 59) and of the north-eastern plain, where the limestone is overlain by alluvium. Most of the native population (562 in 1940) lives in the north-east of the island.

From cape Kanum, the most easterly point of Djaul, the north coast runs in a north-westerly direction to Sumuna plantation. There is a reef 100 yd. wide off most of this section. The coast is bordered by a low marshy plain backed by limestone hills. Two inlets lie west of Sumuna. These are Lamatau and Bendemann harbours. Lamatau harbour is well sheltered but takes vessels of only 100 tons. There is a muddy beach at its head. Bendemann harbour is free of reef at the entrance. South-westward from Bendemann harbour the coast is reef-fringed to Kollepine harbour. Vessels of less than 700 tons can enter this harbour by day. The land behind the plantation on the west side of Kollepine harbour has a rough coral surface.

Around the west of Djaul and the off-lying island of Mait, to westward, there are reefs up to 1½ miles off-shore. Mait has a trading store and plantation. It is composed of rugged coral and is separated from Djaul by Mait channel, a dangerous stretch of water about ½ mile across which is full of reefs. The most important south-coast anchorages in Djaul are Phoenix, Palmen and Fischer harbours. The first two are fairly well sheltered anchorages with mangroves along the foreshore. They take vessels of up to 200 tons. The south-coast reef continues off their shores. There are many coral patches between Palmen and Fischer harbours. Fischer harbour is very deep, but vessels of up to 700 tons may anchor 200 yd. off-shore. The head of the harbour has a white sandy beach. The south-east coast to cape Kanum is backed by coral terraces at heights of 50 and 100 ft. These carry native gardens and secondary growth.

LAVONGAI (Fig. 60)

The centre of the east coast of Lavongai (New Hanover) lies about 24 miles due west of Kavieng. The intervening sea is filled with a mass of small islands. Lavongai is a compact land mass with one major projection, the western peninsula. The island is about 35 miles long from west to east and about 22 miles across from north to

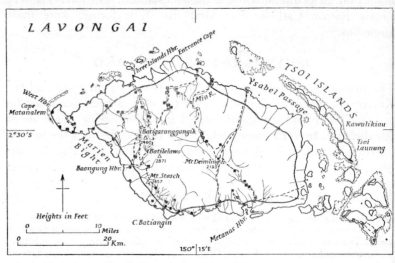

Fig. 60. Lavongai and its off-lying islands

The continuous line represents the good track which encircles the island. The broken lines show rough inter-village tracks in more broken country. Native villages are shown by squares. Based on official sources.

south. From the western peninsula barrier reefs run along the north-west and north-east coasts and enclose many small islands. Within the northern coral fringe lie lagoons bordered by further reefs on their inner shores. Fringing reefs are also practically continuous along the south-west and south-east coasts. Lavongai is largely hilly, though its mountains slope more gently to the north-west, north-east and east coasts where there are wide stretches of rather low-lying land. The mountain axis is known as the Lavongai range (Tirpitz Gebirge). It curves from north-west to south-east and has several outstanding peaks. At the north-west end lies Batigaranggangik (2,460 ft.), from which the range runs to Batilelawo (2,871 ft.). A parallel line of peaks duplicates this section of the range on its northern side. It is this northern line which rises to mount Deimling (2,133 ft.). Hills run outwards from the mount Deimling massif in all directions. Mount Stosch, or Batisuilaua (1,857 ft.), is an isolated blunt cone, which lies between Batilelawo and the south-west coast. Several lower volcanic remnants lie near the south and south-west coasts. Hawilamas (656 ft.), behind Marien bight, is another example.

Many streams drain outwards from the interior mountains. They include the Min, whose headstreams flow parallel to the north side of the central ranges for many miles, and the Mosse, which flows into the north entrance to Ysabel passage. The deeply dissected interior of Lavongai rests on a core of older rocks, but much of the northern coastal lowlands are of raised coral.

The only good harbour on the south coast is Metanas harbour where there are anchorages in depths of 16 to 23 fathoms. The reefed island of Bati Tam which rises to a low dome lies east of the harbour mouth. The remainder of the south coast has a steep-to coral reef and a hilly interior. The south-west coast is similar with the fringing reef usually less than 1,000 yd. in width. Baongung harbour is centrally placed on it. Here there are depths of 20 to 30 fathoms in an anchorage which is exposed to the south-west. Kating mission lies at the head of the harbour. The coast curves round Marien bight and turns westward along the low coral mass of the western peninsula of Lavongai. Cape Matanalem is its most westerly point. The barrier reef curves outwards off the cape and then north-eastward to run parallel to the coast. Off the north-west shore of the western peninsula it encloses West harbour. Here there are anchorages in 13 to 24 fathoms, and the bottom is of fine coral sand. The coast is fairly high from here to Entrance cape (the most northerly point of Lavongai) and has many small bays with swampy heads. The barrier reef supports many islets, including the three which lie west of Entrance cape. These are Kung, Dunung and Naitap, which lie off Three Islands harbour, a stretch of water which is mainly clear of dangers.

East of Entrance cape the coast trends south-eastwards along Ysabel passage. Between the cape and the reefs around the Entrance islands is the wide entrance to Ysabel passage. Here there are depths of 10 to 18 fathoms. The Lavongai coast of Ysabel passage is backed by relatively low-lying platforms of raised coral. Ysabel passage narrows between the Tsoi islands and Lavongai but broadens again south-wards. There are many islets and reefs in its southern section, off the fairly low coast of eastern Lavongai. Dense forests and coconut plantations cover most of this coast.

A track with a reasonably good surface runs round Lavongai, mainly at a short distance inland. Lesser tracks take off from it to run from north to south across the interior hills. These tracks link up many more native villages than does that which runs around the island. The native population of Lavongai lives mainly at some distance from the coast. It was estimated at 5,188 in 1940.

The Tsoi islands which lie on a wide barrier reef east of Ysabel passage include, from south-east to north-west, Tsoi Launung, Kawulikiau, Mirimbang, Tsoi Buka, Tsoi Buga and Tsoi Boto. Kawulikiau is 4 miles long and is the largest island of the group. All are low-lying with mainly wooded surfaces, and they have some extensive sand flats on their west coasts. Several coconut plantations are to be found in the group.

The small Tingwon islands lie on the further side of Lavongai, 15 miles west-south-west of cape Matanalem. They are small wooded islands which rise from a reef 7 miles long from west to east. Beligila lies east of the long western prolongation of the reef. Tingwon, the largest island, lies at the north-east end of the reef, and Kolenusa is centrally placed on it. Anchorages are available only for small craft in the area; most of the bounding reef dries at low water. There is a landing through a break in the reef at the north-east end of Tingwon. The reef is narrower along the east coast of each island. In 1940, 68 natives lived on the three Tingwon islands.

ST MATTHIAS GROUP

Mussau, Emirau and the islands which lie off them are separated from Lavongai by Ysabel channel. Mussau, which is about 20 miles long from north-west to south-east, is the largest island in the group. It is approximately 10 miles across and is largely hilly and wooded. The highest peak (2,130 ft.) lies behind the south-west coast, in an area where there are many limestone outcrops. This region of limestone hills is free of dense forest, having a largely grass cover which passes into pandanus scrub on the higher points. The lowest part of Mussau is in the south-east behind Thilenius point. Here, and behind the sandy beaches of the north-east coast, are the villages of a large proportion of the inhabitants of Mussau. The south-west coast has much mangrove swamp, which fronts on to a sea full of reefs and coral patches. Several small low islands lie off this coast. Emananus and Eloaue, two narrow bands of land, are the largest of them. Mussau is bounded by a narrow fringing reef. Emananus and Eloaue lie within an oval reef which is about 7 miles across in maximum extent from west to east.

Emirau (sometimes known as Storm island) was sighted by Dampier in 1699 and named by him Squally island. It lies 12½ miles south-east of Mussau and is 8 miles across from east to west. It is a deeply indented island and rises gradually northward to a group of rolling hills. The south end has a plantation and many native gardens. A fringing reef which encircles Emirau broadens off the west end to enclose several small islands. In Hamburg bay, on the north-west coast, there is an anchorage in 9 to 10 fathoms. Eulolou harbour is a small sheltered anchorage on the south-east side of Emirau.

Tench island lies 39 miles east of Emirau and 60 miles almost due north of Kavieng. It was sighted in 1790 by Lieutenant Philip Gidley King. It is a small oval island ½ mile across. The west side is densely wooded, and here a landing can be made through a break in the otherwise continuous reef. The native population of Mussau, Emirau and Tench was 1,910 in 1940.

TABAR GROUP

The Tabar islands (also known as Gardner islands) include three main islands; Tabar is the most southerly, Simberi is the northern island, and Tatau the central island. Tabar lies about 50 miles north-west of Namatanai and a roughly similar distance east-south-east of Kavieng. Its long axis runs from north-west to south-east and is about 11 miles in length. The maximum width is about 5 miles. Two higher points rise out of the central hills. They are a peak about 1,300 ft. high at the north-west and one about 1,470 ft. high behind the steeply sloping south-east end. Off Teripax plantation on the south-west side of the narrow channel between Tabar and Tatau there is an anchorage, which is sheltered from the south-east trade winds, in 5 to 10 fathoms. Within the channel the least depth is 9 fathoms and here there is a well-sheltered anchorage off Sigarrigarri (Zigarregarre) plantation.

Like Tabar, Tatau is densely wooded. Its hills rise to less than 1,000 ft. The island is roughly 8 miles from north to south and 6 miles in maximum width. The west coast is fairly indented and has five small bays. Behind them, and especially along the north coast, are many native villages. Mabau island is a small low islet which is separated from Tatau by a deep and narrow channel.

Simberi lies about 2 miles north of Tatau and is 6 miles long from north-east to south-west. A volcanic cone with steep slopes rises to about 1,000 ft. behind the east coast. Most of the coastal slopes are steep and there are reefs round most of the shore. Barrier reefs lie 6 miles off the west coast. The passage between them and Simberi is open at the south end. The reef is joined on to the north coast of the island. The small island of Marwiu lies on the barrier reef.

In 1940 the native population of the group was 1,952. The largest number of people was on Tatau.

LIHIR GROUP

This group includes Lihir (Gerrit Denys island) and three small islands lying to the north-east of it. These are, from north to south, Mahur, Masahet and Malie. Lihir lies about 30 miles north of Namatanai, and is 18 miles long from north to south. It is largely volcanic and has some outstanding peaks over 1,500 ft. in height. A few active mud craters and a hot spring behind Luise harbour on the east coast suggest that activity has not entirely ceased. The coastal slopes are steep and have deep gullies and dense forests. Mangrove swamps fringe the heads of inlets. Luise harbour on the east coast is a sheltered anchorage in 10 to 12 fathoms between two hilly peninsulas. A track crosses the central hills from this coast to Lalagot bay on the west side. The three islands to the north-east of Lihir are small and reefed. Mahur and Masahet rise to fair heights and are well wooded. Mahur has a fairly dense population. The native population of the Lihir group was 3,394 in 1940.

TANGA GROUP

The Tanga group lies some 50 miles south-east of Lihir and 27 miles north-east of cape Sena in New Ireland. The largest island is Malendok. Boang lies to the north-east of Malendok across a channel about 4 miles wide. Nekin and Tefa, which are joined by a broad reef, lie south-west of Malendok. All the islands are densely forested and are of fair heights. Lif has two main peaks and rises steeply from its bounding reefs. The highest peak of the central ridge of Malendok is 1,197 ft. high. The narrow channel between the reef which projects from Lif and Malendok is clear and apparently deep. There is an anchorage in 19 fathoms in the lee of a small peninsula which runs north-eastward from Lif into this channel. A coconut plantation covers the broader peninsula which juts out from the south-west of Malendok. Boang appears to have a greater number of villages than the other (higher) islands. In 1940 the total native population of the Tanga group was 1,778.

FENI (ANIR) GROUP

The Feni islands, comprising Ambitle, Babase and Balum, lie about 30 miles due east of East cape in southern New Ireland. (They are frequently called the Anir islands.) Ambitle and Babase are hilly and largely of volcanic rocks. A peak rises to 1,884 ft. in the centre of Ambitle and there is a hill 873 ft. high in the interior of Babase. On Ambitle there is a geyser which throws water to a height of 50 ft. The north end of Ambitle is a low peninsula which has two coconut plantations on its shores. Across Salat strait is the smaller island of Babase which is about 8 miles from west to east. The diamond-shaped island of Ambitle is 10 miles long from north to south and 8 miles wide. Between Ambitle and Babase lies a broad bay which is open to the south-east. Balanum bay on the west coast of Ambitle is a better anchorage, with shelter from both the north-west monsoon and the south-east trade winds. There is a coconut plantation (Nan-Sow) on the southern lowlands of Babase. Balum lies on the reef which curves off the north shore of Babase. It is a small island, being rather more than a mile long from west to east. There is a passage through the fringing coral to a boat jetty at the west end of Balum. Coral reefs lie as much as 1½ miles off the north-west coasts of Ambitle and Babase, but on their other coasts reefs are less well developed. The native population of the Feni islands was 913 in 1940.

NIGURIA GROUP

The Niguria group lies about 80 miles north-east of the Feni islands, and, unlike the volcanic islands off eastern New Ireland, is a group of 'low' islands. There are in the Niguria group about 50 coral islets on two atolls which cover a distance of approximately 20 miles from north-west to south-east. The south-eastern atoll is the larger, the enclosed lagoon being about 20 miles long and 5 miles wide. The western reef of this lagoon is broken by a passage which leads into an anchorage with depths of 9 to 14 fathoms. Nugarba (Goodman island) at the south-east end of the larger atoll is the largest island. Sable islet, which is surrounded by a reef, lies 18 miles south-south-west of Nugarba. The north-west atoll of the Niguria group is about 5 miles long and has a passage at the south-west end between the lagoon and the channel which separates the two atolls. This channel is free of dangers and is 3 miles wide. The sand and coral soils of the Niguria group support several coconut plantations. In 1940 there were about 80 natives and one resident white trader in the group.

BIBLIOGRAPHICAL NOTE

The best general account of the physical geography of New Ireland is Karl Sapper, 'Neu Mecklenburg', *Jahresberichte des Frankfurter Vereins für Geographie und Statistik*, vols. LXXIII, LXXIV (Frankfurt-am-Main, 1908–10). Coasts are described in the Admiralty *Pacific Islands Pilot*, vol. I (6th edition, London, 1933). There are references to the area in R. Parkinson, *Dreissig Jahre in der Südsee* (Stuttgart, 1907). The St Matthias group is described in H. Nevermann, 'St Matthias Gruppe', *Ergebnisse der Südsee-Expedition, 1908–1910*, II (Ethnographie), A (Melanesien), Band II (Hamburg, 1933). An account of social conditions in north-east New Ireland will be found in E. W. P. Chinnery, 'Studies of the Native Population of the East Coast of New Ireland', *Territory of New Guinea Anthropological Report*, no. 6 (Canberra, 1931). A detailed study of the economy of an east-coast community in New Ireland is made in Hortense Powdermaker, *Life in Lesu* (London, 1933).

For maps see Appendix I.

Chapter XIII

THE ADMIRALTY ISLANDS AND THE
WESTERN ISLANDS

ADMIRALTY ISLANDS

The Admiralty islands lie off the northern coast of New Guinea,
between lat. 1° 50′ and 3° s and long. 146° and 148° E. The main
island, Manus, is very much larger than any other island in the group.
The remaining islands are grouped south of Manus in a rough semi-
circle from east through south to west. The largest of these are
Rambutyo, Lou, Baluan, Pak, Tong and Mbuke.

MANUS

Manus is about 50 miles long from west to east and 17 miles in
greatest breadth. At the eastern end lies the crescentic island of Los
Negros, separated from Manus only by the narrow Loniu passage.
The southern half of this island is 7 miles long. Manus and Los
Negros together stretch from east to west about 60 miles. Along the
north coast of Manus there is a long fringe of islets set on a barrier
reef. They continue the curve of the northern peninsula of Los
Negros island and enclose the long Seeadler (sea eagle) harbour.
This lagoon varies in width from 2 to 7 miles (Fig. 61).

Relief

Manus belongs to the 'continental' or 'high' islands and is largely
hilly and deeply dissected. Along the coast steep slopes alternate with
swampy lowland embayments; there is no continuous coastal plain.
Manus may be divided into five physical regions: (i) the south-west
peninsula; (ii) the western uplands; (iii) the central valley; (iv) the
eastern uplands; (v) the eastern lowlands and Los Negros.

The South-west Peninsula. This unit is joined to the remainder of
Manus by the isthmus which runs between Kali and Malai bays. The

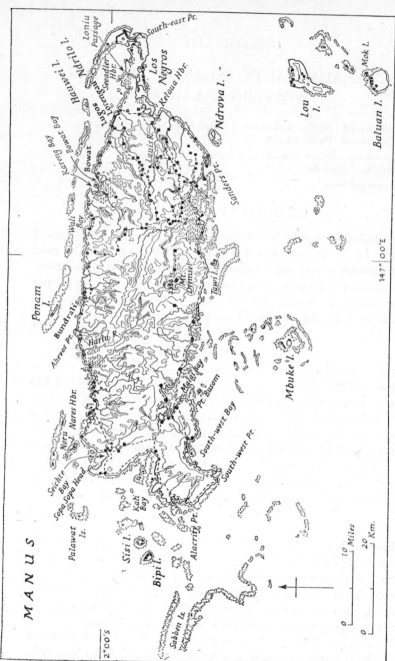

Fig. 61. Manus and its off-lying islands

Form lines, at intervals of 500 ft., are approximate. Native villages are shown by squares. Short stretches of motor road are

peninsula curves round South-west bay, which appears to be surrounded by part of a crater rim. The hills drop steeply to the bay
from heights of about 600 ft. The crest line is from ½ to ¾ mile from
the inner shores of the bay. Behind this crest the hills slope more
gently to the western shores of the peninsula and to Kali and Malai
bays. The flat-topped mount Hahie rises to over 600 ft. between
South-west bay and the head of Malai bay. The streams draining to
South-west bay are short. The remaining streams are longer and drain
radially from the rim of South-west bay. Coastal plains are only
slightly developed around the south-west peninsula. The coast track
runs at fair heights above some sectors of the shore.

The Western Uplands. These uplands extend from behind the west
coast of Manus to about 147° 05' E. They are separated from the
eastern uplands by the central valley. The main watershed of the
western uplands runs from west to east at distances varying between
3 and 6 miles from the south coast. It runs through two peaks in the
centre of the island which are 1,794 ft. and 1,500 ft. high. In the
south-east of the western uplands mount Dremsel and its southern
spurs form the watershed. Mount Dremsel (2,356 ft.) is the highest
point in Manus. A secondary watershed runs along a ridge which lies
roughly parallel to and north-east of the main water-parting. This
line of hills separates the basin of the Harlu river from those of the
shorter rivers which flow to the north coast. The higher peaks of this
ridge lie at about 1,400 ft. and 1,900 ft. The north coast of the western
upland region is overlooked by a further series of peaks. These are
more isolated hills. The best example is the conical peak which rises
to over 1,100 ft. and lies east of the mouth of the Harlu river. The
western uplands are dissected by deep gorges into a confused mass of
hills with long spurs. There are many points at heights of over 1,000 ft.
on the long ridges. The west coast is hilly, but behind it runs a
relatively low belt of land between Seichte (shallow) bay and Malai
bay. This lowland is occupied by the valleys of the Uganada river and
its tributary the Dranui river which flow to Seichte bay. The main
mass of the western uplands rises sharply east of the basins of the
Uganada and Dranui rivers. The western uplands fall sharply to the
north and south coasts of Manus. Lowlands are found only around
the lower courses of the larger rivers. The lower Harlu and Kauwa
rivers are separated by a belt of swampy lowlands 2½ miles wide, but
steep hills close in around their mouths. Behind the south coast lie the
swampy lowlands of the Watani and lesser rivers which flow into the
sea further westward, towards Malai bay.

The Central Valley. This depression is drained northwards by the short Kormoran river and southwards by the Wari river. The divide between them is occupied by a depression 2 miles long from south to north and rather more than a mile wide. Streams flow down its steep slopes and downwards through a line of sink-holes around its margins. As underground streams they probably contribute water to the head-streams of both the Kormoran and Wari rivers. In its middle course the Wari runs underground for about ½ mile. The floor of the depression is about 500 ft. high. Between it and the upper Wari river the land rises to 700 ft. The main track across Manus runs along the eastern slopes of the central lowland from the mouth of the Kormoran river to Metawarri, 3 miles upstream on the Wari river. It keeps mainly to the crest line east of the lowland, though the northern part of the track runs along the lowland and over the northern sector of the depression.

The Eastern Uplands. Only the north-western part of the eastern uplands rises to over 1,000 ft. This occurs in the group of hills which is just over 1,500 ft. high and overlooks the depression in the central lowlands. The eastern uplands drain north-eastwards and eastwards by means of the Tingau, Lauis and several shorter rivers. Their narrow valleys separate groups of low-lying hills drained by numerous tributaries. The main ridge lines of the southern hills are utilized by several inter-village tracks. A second group of tracks runs between the villages which lie on the southern slopes of the Tingau valley. Both groups of tracks have links with Lorengau, in the east, and with the central depression to the west. The chief peripheral areas of swampy lowland are those around the Maramam river on the north coast and the swamps of the lower Lukuli river to the south-west of the eastern uplands. The Lukuli swamps are continuous with those of the lower Wari river.

The Eastern Lowlands and Los Negros. The eastern highlands fall gently eastwards to the undulating lowlands of the east coast. The lowlands continue across Lonui passage into Los Negros. This is a very indented and largely swamp-covered plain, with a maximum width of 3 miles. There are several low ridges rather more than 100 ft. high, notably in the western half of Los Negros. The northern half of this island is low-lying and much of it is under plantations. Papitalai harbour and its western creek, which lie within the bend of Los Negros, have dense swamp on their shores. The two firmer areas of the coastline support the settlements of Lorengau, the administrative centre of Manus, and Momote plantation and its aerodrome. A high bank rises steeply behind Lorengau and continues inland as a low plateau.

Coasts and Anchorages

Off the north and east coasts of Manus the approach is clear, being obstructed only by the chain of barrier reefs and islands which stretch along the coast westward from Los Negros to enclose Seeadler harbour. On the south, however, there is a complicated mass of reefs and islands, which stretches from Rambutyo island in the east to Western island in the west. Navigation in these waters is intricate and very difficult without local knowledge.

The north coast may be divided into the area occupied by Seeadler harbour, on the one hand, and the remainder of the coast westwards from Bowat mission to Sopa Sopa head, on the other. The eastern end is fronted for its whole length by a fringing reef which dries in places at low water. It is possible to cross the reef in boats at high water and land on a beach near Lombrum plantation. At certain points on the eastern side of Seeadler harbour negro heads provide awkward obstructions. At the western end of this coast section, on the east side of Lorengau bay, the fringing reef is about 300 yd. wide. Outside this there is a coral shelf. Here it is covered by only 4 ft. of water at low tide, but elsewhere it is more deeply submerged and is more or less characteristic of the entire northern coast of Manus.

There are on this coast several bays which afford excellent anchorage, notably Lombrum bay, which can accommodate vessels of up to 4,000 tons in about 7 fathoms. Papitalai harbour extends inland in a series of creeks and affords anchorage in 8 fathoms. Both these bays have jetties. Protected anchorage is also found off Mokareng plantation, where Burns, Philp steamers anchor in 16 fathoms. Most of the shore of Los Negros is low and is occupied by plantations, but further west, near Loniu passage, the narrow channel which separates Los Negros from Manus, the shore is swampy. Further east, near Lorengau, there are more plantations. Most of the coast near Lorengau and around Butjoluo bay is fringed by mangroves. The islands on the barrier reef to the north, Koruniat, Ndrilo, Hauwei and Pityilu, are surrounded by reefs and planted with coconuts.

The other, longer but less developed, section of the coast, west of Bowat plantation, is protected in its eastern end by a continuation of the barrier of reefs and islands which forms Seeadler harbour. Along its western end a similar island chain protects Nares harbour. In many places the interior mountains reach almost to the coast but there are small patches of alluvial land with swamps and mangroves round the various bays. The principal inlets are Bowat bay and Kareng bay in the east (separated by Labahan island), Balscot bay, Boudeuse bay and Seichte bay. Anchorage can be found in Balscot bay, Drugul bay and in most parts of Nares harbour if care is taken to avoid coral heads. Kareng bay and Seichte bay are badly obstructed by coral patches. Most of the shores of Seichte bay are fringed by mangroves, as are also the mouths of the rivers which drain into this stretch of coast.

The west coast between Sopa Sopa head and South-west point curves round the deep indentation known as Kali bay. The whole of this coast is coral fringed and has wide reefs. In Kali bay there are numerous patches of coral. Mangroves and swamps fringe the greater part of the shore and steep wooded slopes rise behind them. Anchorage can be found near the south-west point of Kali bay, where there is a jetty which serves a small plantation. From Alacrity point to South-west point are a series of small indentations, formed by the estuaries of small streams which flow down from a series of sharply dissected hills. These hills rise from immediately behind the mangrove fringe.

The coast of the eastern or outer side of Los Negros, and the south-eastern coast of Manus as far as Sanders point, is backed by low-lying land covered with extensive marshes except in the eastern side of Los Negros, where most of the land is well drained and is under plantations. There are various bays along this coast, for example, Hyane harbour, Bird Island bay, and Kelaua harbour. These harbours are not deep and are partly obstructed by coral. Large vessels do not use them. Amo and Ndrova islands offer anchorage for schooners visiting the plantations on them. The whole coast is fringed by coral reefs which are narrow and steep-to in the east but develop into a series of off-shore reefs west of Bird Island bay. Breaks up to 50 yd. wide occur in the reefs off the mouths of various streams. From Sanders point to South-west point the coast is backed alternately by steep hills and, around the river mouths, by swamps. There are occasional patches of mangrove behind a continuous fringing reef. Complicated patches of coral extend for considerable distances off-shore, and there are several native villages built on piles off the shore. The only major indentations are Patusi bay, immediately west of Sanders point, Malai bay, and South-west bay. Coral patches are particularly frequent in Patusi bay and in Malai bay, but the water between these patches is generally deep. In these three bays there are various anchorages which are used by schooners.

Social and Economic Conditions

Manus was discovered by the Dutch navigator Schouten in 1616. Though visited by British and French ships, the islands of the Admiralty group were only slightly affected by European contact until after 1875. German sovereignty over the group was proclaimed in 1884. Between that time and 1914 European plantations and both Roman Catholic and Lutheran mission stations were established. The group was not brought under administrative control till 1912. In 1914 the islands were occupied by Australian forces. In 1942 they were occupied by the Japanese.

Prior to the Japanese occupation the European population of Manus and its off-lying islands, including the wives and families of planters, amounted to about 100. This total included 4 government officers, 15 missionaries (including 6 women) and 25 planters. Asiatics included 1 Japanese, who owned the Momote plantation and aerodrome, two Chinese and two Filipinos. The native population of the whole group amounted to about 13,000, of whom about 10,000 lived on Manus.

The native peoples can be divided into three distinct social groups: the Usiai or inland people, the Matankor or coastal agriculturists, the Manus or sea people. The Usiai live in scattered groups, usually of about 10 persons, in the interior. Their economy is based on primitive subsistence agriculture. Gardens are scattered and lie at some distance from the villages because the soil is often poor. Fresh patches are cultivated each year. The Matankor are also agriculturists, but they live on the coast or on the off-lying islands and undertake some fishing. The Manus are a truly maritime people, who never build villages inland and generally inhabit settlements built on stout piles about 8 ft. above the reefs or coastal swamps. Long communal houses (about 60 ft. by 20 ft.) are characteristic of their settlements.

The Manus form the dominant group. They have no agriculture and are dependent on fishing and on trade with the land dwellers for other supplies. They exchange fish or crustacea for sago, taro, beans, bark and lime-gourds, and exchange turtles for timber to make their canoes and houses. In addition to this highly developed barter system, they have their own elaborate system of ceremonial exchanges which comes into force on occasions such as birth, betrothal and marriage. The articles exchanged include dogs' teeth and various shells. Their religion consists largely in a belief in 'ghosts of the dead', who are believed to continue their earthly activities after death. A considerable part of native activities are devoted to the propitiation of these ghosts, who are supposed to exercise considerable influence over the daily affairs of each individual and family.

The administrative centre of the Manus group is Lorengau. The settlement had a white population of about 50 people in 1940 and included administrative buildings, a hospital, a gaol, government stores, a police barracks, customs sheds and a jetty. Other settlements where there are Europeans are the mission stations and plantations. Four missionary bodies were at work. The Roman Catholics had five stations on Manus and the neighbouring islands. These were at Bundrales, Bowat, Lessau, Susi and Papitalai. The Protestant Liebenzell (Lutheran) mission had stations at Lugos, Loniu and Nada. A Hungarian Protestant mission station was situated on Pityilu and there was a Seventh Day Adventist mission station on Lou.

Few of the native villages had a large population. Among the largest in 1942 were Loniu, on Los Negros island, and Lauis, which lies 2 miles up the river of that name. Each probably had a population of about 300 natives. In addition to the permanently inhabited villages, there were also groups of huts built at various points on the tracks across the island, which were occupied only spasmodically.

Communications

Overseas communications were normally maintained by Burns, Philp steamers, which called once a month. Round Manus and the nearby islands there was a considerable traffic by means of native canoes. These were well-built outrigger craft which navigated the waters inside the reefs and penetrated short distances up many of the rivers. Occasionally they were used for longer voyages to the more distant islands of the group.

Land communications, except for a short stretch of road suitable for motor traffic between Lorengau and Lugos and some coral roads near Momote plantation on Los Negros, consisted entirely of tracks. These were of two types, tracks built by the government to facilitate patrolling and administration, and native footpaths. The government tracks had better surfaces. One track follows the north coast from Lorengau to Kali bay; another runs in a south-westerly direction for about 14 miles, to join a track running southward from a point east of Bundralis to Patusi bay. There are various branches east of this track. A track is indicated in some recent maps as running along the south coast and around South-west point and Alacrity point to Kali bay, but the existence of a continuous track in this southern sector is uncertain. It is possible that the track consists of a series of native footpaths of varying widths.

RAMBUTYO

Rambutyo (lat. 2° 17′ s, long. 147° 48′ E) is the second largest island in the Admiralty group (Fig. 24). It is roughly triangular in shape with a base which is about 10 miles across from west to east. The centre of the island rises to a volcanic peak over 700 ft. high. The western peninsula has a low ridge rather more than 100 ft. high. Behind the north, east, and south coasts there are several flat swampy regions. The whole island is fronted by reefs. Near the western end of the north-west coast is a small bay with a sandy beach. Except for a small patch of coast east of this bay, the rest of the coast is fringed by a wide shelving reef with occasional patches of coral sand. There are many mangrove swamps. Off the north point of the island the reef continues in a north-easterly direction for about 10 miles and supports a group of islets known as the Horno islands (Fig. 25). The east coast is reefed for the whole of its length, although there is one break opposite a small boat harbour. Landings could probably be made over the east and south coast reefs. Anchorage can be found in a bay with a depth of 14 fathoms near the south-west point of Rambutyo and north of Langembulos island. Small craft can enter the lagoon and find more secure anchorage.

The total population, mostly native, is about 800. The western end of Rambutyo and three of the Horno islands are planted with coconuts. Communications are mainly by canoe. There is a short road running through the plantation on Rambutyo.

LOU AND NEIGHBOURING ISLANDS (Fig. 61)

Lou island (lat. 2° 24′ s, long. 147° 23′ E) is a small steep volcanic island with three peaks. The central peak reaches a height of 900 ft. The vegetation is generally sparse. The north-west and north-east coasts are fronted by fringing reefs which are narrow along the northern parts but widen further south. Behind the reefs there are steep cliffs. On the south-east side there are also reefs. Cliffs are again present, though they are less steep than those further north. Anchorages for schooners may be found in a small bay near the south-west point of the island. Small craft with local knowledge can use a small bay a mile west of the north-eastern point.

There is no fresh water except that obtained by catchment, but brackish water may be found on the beach. The total population was about 300 in 1940. The people live in four villages, Umerei, Umbua and Lago, on the north-east coast, and Baun on the southern slopes of the central peak. There is a mission station at Umbua.

Lying in a chain to the south-east of Lou are Baluan, Mok island, Pam Ling and Pam islands, the St Andrew group and the Fedarb islands. Of these Baluan (lat. 2° 32′ s, long. 147° 21′ E) is the most important. It consists of a densely wooded and roughly circular volcanic cone and is surrounded by reefs. There is an anchorage in 14 fathoms between Baluan and Mok island. This is entered through a pass 44 yd. wide. A passage through the reef on the north side provides access to the village of Pirilik. There is also a good landing on the island of Mok and a sandy beach behind this landing. The total population of Lou and Mok is about 800, of whom 500 live in four villages on the north side of Baluan and 300 in two villages on Mok. Pam Ling and Pam islets, which lie about 2 miles to the north-east of Mok, are uninhabited and offer no facilities for anchorage. About 3 miles north-eastward from Pam Ling island lies a complicated cluster of islets and reefs known as the St Andrew group. One of these islets is planted with coconuts, and a few labourers live on the plantation. There are no other inhabitants. Good anchorage for vessels of up to about 2,000 tons can be found among the reefs of the group.

About 4 miles north-eastward lie the Fedarb islands. This group consists of the islets of Chokua, Sisiva and the two Lolau islands. These are grouped on a semi-circular reef which is open to the west. The enclosed bay forms an anchorage with good protection from the trade winds for vessels of up to about 650 tons. A boat jetty provides facilities for landing on Sisiva which, with the Lolau islands, is planted with coconuts.

South-west of Lou lie the Johnson islands, a group of three rocky and uninhabited islets.

PAK

Lying about 12 miles eastward of Los Negros island is Pak island, which is about 5 miles long and ½ mile wide at its western end, and 1¼ miles wide at its eastern end. The whole island is of coral and only about 12 ft. high. The whole of the coast is surrounded by a reef which dries at low tide. There are sandy beaches at various points. The off-lying islet of Ulunau offers protection for schooners. Opposite Ulunau island are a boat jetty and a store. There are also breaks in the reef about a mile east of the south-west corner of the island. Here a landing could be made in boats. Most of Pak is occupied by a plantation. There are two native villages.

TONG

Tong island (lat. 2° 02′ s, long. 147° 45′ E) is a volcanic cone, with a basal diameter of about 3½ miles. Hills rise steeply from the shore; there is a central depression which contains a lake and a swamp. The whole island is surrounded by a coral reef, which is narrow except off the east coast where it curves away from the shore to form a lagoon. In this there is sufficiently deep water to form an anchorage suitable for schooners. There is a native village with a population of about 60. To the east of Tong island lie the islet of Towi and the two islets of Los Reyes. None of these provides an anchorage.

MBUKE ISLANDS (Fig. 61)

The Mbuke islands (between lat. 2° 18′ and 2° 23′ s, long. 146° 47′ and 146° 54′ E) lie about 24 miles west of Lou island. They consist of Mbuke, Vogali, Jambon, Uh and Olan. Mbuke has a height of approximately 800 ft. and its slopes are steep. Long tongues of coral reef extend north-eastward and south-westward from it. There is a population of about 250. Vogali is flat and is planted in the west. In the east hills rise to a height of about 50 ft. Uh and Olan are both planted with coconuts. Anchorage for small vessels may be found between Mbuke and Vogali.

THE PURDY ISLANDS

In the extreme south of the Admiralty islands are the Purdy islands. They lie between lat. 2° 50′ and 2° 55′ s and long. 146° 14′ and 146° 26′ E and consist of four low coral islands and two isolated masses of coral. The larger islands are known as Rat, Bat, Mole and Mouse. All are surrounded by coral reefs. Bat island in the west of the group consists of two islets on a common reef. There is said to be an anchorage on the west side of Bat island. Deposits of phosphate are known to exist on three of the islands but they have not been worked.

THE WESTERN ISLANDS

To the west of the Admiralty islands lie a number of small low-lying islands and clusters, which are often described collectively as the Western islands. They stretch from the Kaniet islands (lat. 0° 52′ S, long. 145° 31′ E) south-south-west to Wuvulu (lat. 1° 43′ S, long. 142° 50′ E). Anchorage facilities are poor except in the lagoons of the Ninigo and Hermit groups.

The native population was formerly comparatively dense, but recruiting, diseases spread by Europeans, and German punitive expeditions have reduced its number considerably (pp. 145–7). The Anchorite islands, for example, which had 60 inhabitants in 1907, had only one inhabitant in 1940. In physical type the natives were more akin to the Caroline islanders than to the natives of New Guinea. This resemblance extended to their language and to a lesser extent to their culture. They were skilled fishermen and seafarers, who built large sailing canoes (vol. I, Fig. 103) and voyaged far afield. To-day many of the islands have been planted with coconuts, and indentured labourers from the New Guinea mainland have been brought in to work them. Sea communications are generally by schooner.

KANIET ISLANDS

The Kaniet islands (lat. 0° 52′ S, long. 145° 31′ E) consist of 6 small islets which lie on a broad reef. In the south-west part of the reef there is a small lagoon, which is entered through a boat passage. Vegetation is generally sparse. The interior of Kaniet island, the largest of the group, is mainly swampy. On the south side of this island there are a number of plantation buildings, including a bungalow, a hospital and copra sheds. They are all in a poor state of repair. Tatak island was set aside as a native reserve, but the village on it is said to be deserted. In 1940 there were about 30 native labourers on the islets of the atoll; out of the former native population 5 then survived. The total planted area was about 500 acres. There is no anchorage, though schooners have anchored on the reef-edge in calm weather. Landing is made over the reef on the east side of Kaniet island.

SAE ISLANDS

The Sae islands (lat. 0° 45′ S, long. 145° 17′ E) are two low islets of which the larger has an area of only 40 acres. They are also known as the Anchorite islands. To-day they are uninhabited, though visited occasionally from the Kaniet islands. Both have a fairly dense vegetation and birds and crabs are plentiful. There is no anchorage.

HERMIT ISLANDS

The Hermit islands (between lat. 1° 26′ and 1° 36′ S, long. 144° 58′ and 145° 11′ E) lie about 90 miles in a west-north-westerly direction from the Admiralty islands. They are a cluster of steep-sided volcanic islands surrounded by an extensive reef-rim. This encloses a large lagoon about 10 miles across. Scattered round the rim are several small coral islands. There are many facilities for anchorage in the lagoon; but the north-eastern end is shallow, and the north-western end is probably too deep. The principal entrances are North-west entrance, which is 500 yd. wide but not much used, and West entrance, which is about 1¾ miles wide with depths of up to 20 fathoms. South-east entrance is narrow and intricate. Northward of South-east entrance a break in the reef opens up to form Alacrity harbour, from which a boat passage leads to the northern part of the lagoon. Alacrity harbour affords good shelter in from 8 to 10 fathoms. Other anchorages can be found inside the lagoon, notably in or near Carola bay on the south-east side of Luf island, or to the south of Maron island.

The largest of the islands within the Hermit islands lagoon is Luf, a long narrow island which runs from north-east to south-west. It is roughly 4 miles long, and steep wooded hills rise in the centre to 800 ft. The north-west side has a straight coast and is fringed with a coral reef along its whole length. The other coasts also have coral fringes. Near the north-east end of the island there is a sharp indentation which is known as Carola bay. Except around Carola bay, most of the south-east coast is bordered by mangrove swamps. The Admiralty chart shows a jetty at the head of Carola bay. To the north of Luf lies a small volcanic islet known as Tset. Maron island lies to the west of Luf. Maron is about 3 miles long and is roughly U-shaped. A small cape projects southward from the south coast. It consists of three peaks separated by two low sandy necks of land. The eastern part is known as Akib. The whole island is completely surrounded by a reef, which extends northwards from the western end to enclose the island of Jalun. At the south-west point of Maron is a jetty with a depth of 10 ft. at its head. The only settlement is near this jetty, and here the plantation manager has a house. The islets on the reef are low and sandy and are mainly covered with scrub and forest.

NINIGO GROUP

The Ninigo islands (between lat. 1° 05′ and 1° 39′ s, long. 144° 02′ and 144° 31′ E) include 7 atolls of varying size. Six of them form a chain stretching from the most north-easterly, Heina, through Pelleluhu, Ninigo and Sama, to Sumasuma in the south-west. Liot, which consists of a single small lunate island surrounded by a reef with a small lagoon on its western side, lies about 20 miles east of the southern end of Ninigo atoll.

Ninigo atoll consists of a large irregular lagoon with islands distributed at intervals around the reef-rim. Longan, Meman and Ahu, on the west side, and Mal, in the extreme south, are the largest islands. They are mainly planted with coconuts and there are plantation buildings and a jetty on Longan. There are a number of passes with deep water into the lagoon. That most frequently used is Longan entrance which runs between Longan island and Meman island. It has a depth of 4½ fathoms and a width of about 250 yd. The lagoon has not been completely surveyed and there are many coral patches, but vessels of up to 4,000 tons have anchored near Longan island. Flying boats have used the southern part of the lagoon near Mal island.

On the north side of Ninigo atoll and separated from it by a deep narrow channel is Pelleluhu atoll. This is roughly circular, and the reef-rim encloses a lagoon about 10 fm. deep and 4 miles long by 3 miles wide. Several low islands, the largest of which is Ahaltin, lie on the reef which encircles the south and east sides of the lagoon. A canoe passage on the south side gives access to the lagoon for small boats. Larger vessels can anchor outside the lagoon off the south-east of Ahaltin. Landing can be made opposite the anchorage through a gap in the reef. Elsewhere the reef dries at low water. At all times the sea breaks over the reef. Most islands on the atoll are planted with coconuts and there are various plantation buildings on Ahaltin. The only inhabitants are plantation labourers.

Lying about 3 miles east of Pelleluhu is Heina atoll. It is roughly circular with a lagoon about 2 miles in diameter. The reef-rim completely surrounds the lagoon and low islets stand on it. A boat passage with 5 ft. of water at high tide gives access to the lagoon, which is studded with coral heads. There is no anchorage. Most of the islands have coconut plantations.

Sama atoll lies about 4 miles west of Mal, the southernmost island of Ninigo atoll. Sama is a small atoll with three islets. The lagoon within the continuous reef-rim is about ¾ mile long. Sama is planted with coconuts and the plantations are run in conjunction with those on Mal island. Landing is made over the reef at high tide.

Sumasuma, about 3 miles southward from Sama, consists of a reef which encloses a lagoon about 1½ miles long. The one island of the atoll is L-shaped and encloses the lagoon on its north-east and south-east sides. There is no passage into the lagoon and landing can only be made over the reef at high tide. Even then it is difficult to land. Anchorage can be found by vessels of up to 3,000 tons in suitable weather off the northern tip of the island.

Awin atoll, about 8 miles south from Sumasuma, has a circular reef-rim surrounding a lagoon about ¾ mile in diameter. On the eastern and southern sides of the reef-rim are two small low-lying islands, Awin and Maletin. Awin has a swamp in the centre but is otherwise planted with coconuts. There is no passage into the lagoon. Landing is made over the reef at high tide. Schooners have anchored on the reef-edge in favourable weather.

Manu

Manu island (lat. 1° 18′ S, 143° 35′ E) is small and low, having a maximum height of only 4 ft. The total area is 62 acres. It is entirely planted with coconuts and has a few native houses on the south-east side. A small deposit of phosphate has been reported. The only inhabitants are labourers employed on the plantation. The island is surrounded by a sand-covered reef. On the south-east side this is narrow and landing is easy over a steep sandy beach. There is no anchorage, but schooners have anchored on the reef-edge in suitable weather.

Aua

Aua island (lat. 1° 27′ S, long. 143° 03′ E) is composed of raised coral. It is about 25 ft. high. The length of the island from west to east is about 2 miles and the width about 1 mile. About 200 acres are under coconuts. The rest is thickly wooded except for areas used by the natives as gardens. The population was 225 in 1940 (Fig. 37). Several deserted villages bear witness to a much larger population in former times. The shore of Aua is fronted by a fringing reef which is up to 400 yd. wide on the north side, but about 50 yd. wide in the south. Landing is difficult except in gaps in the reef and is usually made only in fine weather. A break about 100 yd. wide has been made in the reef by blasting. The gap thus formed occurs near the eastern end of the south coast. As the seaward coast is steep-to outside the reef-edge, anchorage is difficult to find. The normal anchorage is in 4 fathoms over a patch of coral 1,000 yd. from the east end of the south coast. There is also a possible anchorage further west along the same coast.

Wuvulu

Wuvulu (lat. 1° 43′ S, long. 142° 50′ E), also known as Maty, is a flat coral island with a total area of roughly 3,000 acres. It has a central swamp. In shape the island roughly resembles a dumb-bell, the waist being formed by a wide bay which curves into the north coast. The bay on the north side forms only a very slight concavity in the coast, but that on the south side, Maloe bay, is a wider indentation. Except for two native reserves, one in the north-west and one in the south-west of the island, the whole surface is planted with coconuts. The population consists of about 300 natives and approximately 80 indentured labourers. Comparatively fresh water can be obtained from the swamp or from shallow wells. The main plantation buildings are at Agita at the head of Agita bay. Here there are a jetty, a manager's bungalow, drying sheds, storage sheds and native labourers' quarters. Three native villages, Auna, Tumuvalli and Onne, are situated near the south-west point of the island, near the centre of its western coast, and near the north-west point respectively. They are linked with Agita by a rough road. The shore is surrounded by a shelving reef up to 100 yd. wide, except in Maloe bay, where it narrows to 60 yd. There is a narrow sand beach behind it. The jetty at the head of Maloe bay projects about 20 yd. into 6 ft. of water. Landing can also be made over the reef at a number of points. Schooners generally anchor in Maloe bay or off the village of Tumuvalli. Both anchorages are exposed.

BIBLIOGRAPHICAL NOTE

General information on the islands described in this Chapter is contained in the Admiralty *Pacific Islands Pilot*, vol. I (6th edition, London, 1933; with supplement, 1944); and in R. W. Robson (editor), *The Pacific Islands Year Book* (Sydney, 1942). A detailed account of the Admiralty islands is given in G. Thilenius, 'Admiralitäts-Inseln', *Ergebnisse der Südsee-Expedition, 1908–1910*, II (Ethnographie), A (Melanesien), Band III (Hamburg, 1934). Sociological studies of the people of Manus are: Margaret Mead, *Growing up in New Guinea* (London, 1931); and R. F. Fortune, *Manus Religion: An Ethnological Study of the Manus Natives of the Admiralty Islands* (*Memoirs of the American Philosophical Society*, vol. III, Philadelphia, 1935). The Western islands are described in R. Parkinson, *Dreissig Jahre in der Südsee* (Stuttgart, 1907). An account of Aua, primarily anthropological, but containing some historical and geographical material, is G. L.-F. Pitt-Rivers, 'Aua Island . . .', *Journal of the Royal Anthropological Institute*, vol. LV, pp. 425–38 (London, 1925). For maps see Appendix I.

Chapter XIV

THE SOUTH-EASTERN GROUPS

D'Entrecasteaux Islands: Murua: Trobriand Islands: Louisiade Archipelago:
Bibliographical Note

THE D'ENTRECASTEAUX ISLANDS

The D'Entrecasteaux islands, which are named after their discoverer, the French navigator Bruni d'Entrecasteaux, consist of the three large islands of Goodenough, Fergusson and Normanby, and many small off-lying islands. The group is situated to the north-east of East cape, on the New Guinea mainland. Geologically the group is mainly of volcanic origin, but recent elevation of the area has raised masses of coral limestone in coastal areas. The total population of the group is about 30,000. In physical type the people belong to the Massim, or Eastern Papuo-Melanesian, group. Their culture is in general similar to that of the inhabitants of the eastern tip of Papua and of the Trobriand and other groups to the east. Their main means of livelihood are the cultivation of yams, taro and other garden crops, and fishing in the coastal waters. An extensive trade is carried on between different groups in such commodities as obsidian which occur locally. The islands are administered as part of the Eastern Division of Papua and are in charge of an Assistant Resident Magistrate stationed at Mapamoiwa on Fergusson island. Mission activity in the islands is exclusively in the hands of the Methodists.

GOODENOUGH ISLAND (Fig. 62)

Physical Geography

Goodenough, the most westerly of the D'Entrecasteaux group, is separated from cape Vogel on the mainland by the Ward Hunt strait about 16 miles wide. The island is about 24 miles in diameter from north to south. Most of it is over 1,000 ft. in height. The mountains ascend to a crescent of steep-sided cones which lies across the centre of the island. The line of 6 peaks, spaced at an average distance of 1 mile apart, culminates in the two central cones of Vineuo (8,350 ft.) and Oiautukekea (8,000 ft.). Drainage is radial from this watershed and from the ridge which branches from it towards the

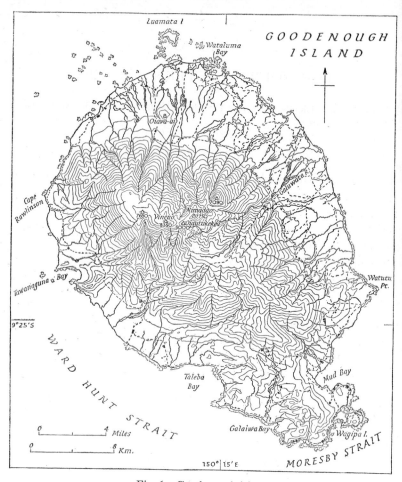

Fig. 62. Goodenough island

Native villages are shown by squares and foot tracks by dotted lines. Much of the island is forested, although the north-eastern lowlands and better populated areas have much cleared land. Mangrove swamps are not indicated. Form lines are approximate. Based on official sources.

south-east. The river valleys are deeply etched into the volcanic massif. The central mountains fall steeply on all sides to 400 ft. In the west and south this slope is continued into the sea, but on the north, north-east and south-west the gradient changes suddenly and a more gradual slope carries the rivers outwards. The rivers of these lower areas are markedly braided below the change of slope; islands and duplicated channels are common in all the main streams. On the north and east of the island lies a belt of country 3 miles wide between the foot of the mountains and the coastal mangrove swamps. A good deal of this land appears in origin to be raised coral reef. The last signs of volcanic activity are to be seen in a group of hot springs behind the mangrove swamps, 4 miles north of Watutu point.

Coasts and Anchorages. The coast of Goodenough has few marked promontories or indentations. On the north and east the coastal belt consists of alluvial spreads and mud-flats which are largely covered with mangroves. In the north this coastal belt is broken by the volcanic hill of Oiava-ai, a cone over 1,400 ft. high, and by the similar hill of Wataluma. In contrast with the east and north-east coasts, the west coast and the southern peninsula present rocky or cliff faces to the Ward Hunt and Moresby straits. Poorly developed fringing coral is present on sections of all coasts. It is best developed on the south-east, where it links Wagipa island with Goodenough.

The best anchorages on the east coast are in Mud bay; north of Watutu point; and about 1 mile further north, off Belibeli. Mud bay must be approached from the Fergusson island side of Moresby strait, owing to the reefs off Wagipa island. The bay, which is a focus of European settlement, is well sheltered. There are two jetties on the southern side. Just north of Watutu point a large vessel could anchor, sheltered from the south-east wind. Similar protection is offered further north at Belibeli. Wataluma bay, on the north coast, is of use only for small craft. On the south-west coast, Taleba bay provides sheltered anchorage in 10 fathoms, 100 yd. from the shore.

Social and Economic Conditions

The native population of Goodenough is about 8,000. The natives are a sturdy people and many of them in the past have volunteered for underground work in the gold mines of Misima and Murua. Many native villages are situated on the coast, especially in the south and west, where there is little flat land between the mountains and the sea. Others form an almost continuous belt of habitations on the more level ground between the foot of the mountains and the swamp lands on the east and north. Here are the most fertile garden lands and communication is relatively easy. The main villages are linked by native tracks.

The only Europeans on the island at the outbreak of the present war were about half a dozen planters and missionaries. At Wataluma was situated the only Methodist mission station in charge of a European missionary. There were in addition 23 stations in charge of native mission teachers. There were three small European plantations, all on or near the coast.

FERGUSSON ISLAND

Physical Geography

Fergusson lies to the east of Goodenough, from which it is separated by Moresby strait. The native name for the island is Morima, a name which is applied in a narrower sense to the district and people in the middle of the south coast. The island is of irregular shape, nearly 40 miles across from east to west and about 20 miles from north to south. It is composed of three volcanic masses separated by a long north-western and a short south-western isthmus, here referred to as the northern and the southern isthmus. The northern isthmus (Fig. 15) has lake Lavu, probably a crater lake, centrally placed. The ridges curving round the lake reach 200–300 ft., but the southern isthmus has a narrow through way which is less than 50 ft. high. Both drain mainly to the eastward. The northern mountains reach a maximum height of over 5,700 ft. and their main streams flow down their long northern slopes. There are suggestions of faulting along south-north lines on these slopes. The central mountain mass is L-shaped. Along the north-south limb, which cuts across the heart of Fergusson island, the higher sharp cones stand out at heights of over 4,600, 5,700 and 6,000 ft. The southern portion of the central mountains is made up of ridges with a roughly west-east trend. Cones are less prominent but heights of over 5,200 ft. are attained. The lower south-eastern cones lie within an indented peninsula. On the north lies Numanuma crater (1,600 ft.), with a steep slope 900 ft. down into the crater. Further conical hills lie to the south. A lesser peninsula at the south-western end projects into Dawson strait and carries mount Oiau (1,200 ft.).

Most of the island is covered with dense forest, though there are several patches of grassland. Mount Oiau is the only hill mass completely free from forest. Swamps of mangrove fringe the coast at the head of most of the bays. Inland of these are freshwater swamps of nipa and sago palms.

Coasts and Anchorages. Little is known in detail of the coasts of Fergusson as very little survey work has been done. In general, there are few sharp promontories or narrow bays. The most prominent are Seblugoma (Sebulagomwa, Ebeoa) point, the southern tip of the island, and a point north of Seymour bay. Fringing coral reefs with off-lying patches are developed locally on all coasts, but their extent is imperfectly known. On the west coast, north of Seymour bay, the hills fall steeply to the sea and there is very little coastal plain. Behind Waluwea point there is a well-sheltered and concealed anchorage. Landing can be made at a jetty or on a sandy beach at the head of the bay. Seymour bay is backed by mangrove and sago swamps. The bay itself is much encumbered with coral patches. South of Seymour bay the coast is fringed with coral and backed by low limestone hills; at Mapamoiwa, the government station, there is a small jetty with a depth of 4 fathoms alongside; it is exposed to the north-west. The south coast from cape Mourilyan to Salamo is similar in general features with a low coral cliff and a narrow fringing reef. The government track follows the shore. At Salamo is an almost land-locked bay, sheltered by a small promontory and by Nesamari and Mumunu islands. The shores of the bay are swampy and fringed with mud-flats. Landing can be made at a wharf suitable for vessels of up to 50 tons. Another jetty has been built to serve a plantation in Kemadia bay, a few miles to the eastward of Salamo. Seblugoma point is bordered by a broad reef. Much of the east coast is fringed with a narrow reef. Sebutuia bay is full of reefs and has a big swamp at its head. The north coast has few outstanding features and is very exposed to the north-west winds. Anchorage can be obtained in Hughes bay, which is thought to be free from dangers.

Social and Economic Conditions

The native population is about 10,000. The south coast is the most densely settled area and has an almost continuous belt of dwellings. Other groups of villages lie on the forest-free eastern slopes of the northern ridges at heights of between about 2,000 and 3,000 ft., and in the middle Salamo valley at about 500 ft. The European population consisted of the Assistant Resident Magistrate, about 10 missionaries, and 2 planters and traders. Mapamoiwa, the government station, and Salamo, the headquarters of the Methodist mission, are the main centres of European settlement. The natives live by cultivating gardens of yams and other crops. They generally produce a small surplus for sale to traders. There are a few European coconut plantations on the coast. The largest, of 400 acres, is at Kededia, east of Salamo.

ISLANDS OFF FERGUSSON

A chain of a dozen or more islands and islets lies off the north and east coasts of Fergusson. All appear to be of volcanic origin and rise abruptly from great depths. The most westerly of the islands are the Amphlett group. Of the 6 main islands in this group—Watota, Wawiwa, Yabwaia, Nabwageta, Urasi and Wamea—Wamea is the largest. It is about 6 miles long from north to south and rises into 3 peaks, the highest of which exceeds 1,200 ft. Yabwaia, only 2 miles across, rises to over 1,600 ft. Several of the other islands reach heights of 1,000 ft. and more. There is very little fringing reef except on Watota, which is surrounded by it. The native villages are situated on shingle beaches. Anchorage may be obtained in a small bay on the west side of Wamea in 12–14 fathoms.

The islands off the east coast are generally similar. Uama and Kawea, about 7 miles off Gilawelabana point are both less than 3 miles long. Sanaroa (Welle island) to the south of these, and about 3 miles eastward of Numanuma crater, is much larger. It is about 9 miles long from north-west to south-east, and, though relatively low, is probably of volcanic origin. The shore reef is only passable for small boats. Behind it is a low coral bank backed by higher cliffs. The island is mostly covered with forest, though there are several villages and native coconut groves and a coconut plantation of 200 acres.

About 1½ miles southward of Seblugoma point on Fergusson lies Dobu island, also of volcanic origin. An extinct crater 900 ft. high occupies the centre of the island and traces of volcanic activity are also to be seen in hot springs. The lower slopes and coastal plain are planted with coconuts and densely populated. The coast is almost completely fringed with reef. Landing is possible on a sandy spit at the north-western corner of the island, where there is a Methodist mission station. North-east of Dobu lie the smaller islands of Neumara and Oiaobe.

NORMANBY ISLAND

Physical Geography

Normanby lies to the south of Fergusson from which it is separated by the 2-mile-wide Dawson strait. The island is about 40 miles long from north-west to south-east, and is of irregular shape. From its south-west point an L-shaped foot trends eastward and a longer peninsula projects northwards. The whole island is hilly and coastal plains are but slightly developed. The axial ridges are not of even heights but are interrupted by several passes which are crossed by native tracks. The main passes are between Sewa bay and the east coast; in the northern part of the island, from Perry bay to Atuia bay;

and the Lonana gap in the south. The last gap has the north-south ranges of the eastern peninsula parallel to its course, and to the west of the gap lie the sharper scarps of a west-east range of mountains which slope steeply southwards to Goschen strait and attain a height of 3,400 ft. within 1½ miles of the coast. To the north of this range the island narrows around a central scrub-covered cone over 2,900 ft. high. Between this cone and the north-western peninsula of Normanby, the broken and less deeply dissected hills are lower, though two hill-masses attain the 2,000-ft. mark, and Solomonai, the highest point of the ridge which forms this peninsula, is about 3,000 ft. high. The island is for the most part densely forested. Mangroves are only well developed at the heads of one or two bays.

Coasts and Anchorages. On the west coast, from cape Dawson southwards to Ubuia island, the hills descend to within 20 yd. of the shore. There are sandy beaches fringed with narrow reef. Similar features mark the coast from Ubuia to Sewa bay. Sewa bay, 5 miles wide and 3 miles deep, with two shelving inner harbours, has muddy beaches, mostly fringed with mangrove. It is almost completely landlocked, being protected from seaward by Pwasiai (Vaseai) island and by hilly peninsulas projecting from the west and south shores of the bay. The main entrance, south of Pwasiai island, has a width of about 200 yd. and a least depth of 27 fathoms. The bay inside provides excellent anchorage protected by hills 500 to 2,000 ft. high. The usual landing is at a jetty on Randolph point.

The south coast has sandy beaches and broken patches of fringing reef. Hills rise steeply from the sea throughout its length. Landing is possible at most points, though there is little shelter from the south-east winds. Anchorage is possible between cape Ventenat and the small Ventenat islands. The east coast has a succession of rocky coral beaches fringed by reef, with occasional sandy coves. The hills fall steeply to the sea. The north coast has similar features, though there is a small coastal plain where the Sawatupwa river enters the sea. Sawataitai bay can be entered by large vessels for anchorage, though navigation is made difficult by many reef patches. It has a swampy shore-line backed by a wide coastal plain. A jetty on the western coast of the bay was built to serve the Sawataitai coconut plantation.

Social and Economic Conditions

The native population numbers about 10,000. The only Europeans were about 5 planters and missionaries. The native villages are mostly distributed round the coasts, particularly on the west, south and east.

Others are situated inland in the valleys and on each isthmus. There was a Methodist mission station staffed by Europeans at Bunama on the south coast.

The only land communication is provided by native tracks. A coastal track, maintained under government supervision, encircles the island. There are two or three European coconut plantations on or near the coast. The largest, of 750 acres, is at Sawataitai bay.

MURUA

Murua (Woodlark island) has its eastern end approximately in lat. 9° 15′ s, long. 153° 15′ E. It is an irregular island about 44 miles long from west to east with widths varying from about 5 miles in the west to about 18 miles across the centre (Fig. 63). The area of the whole is approximately 370 sq. miles. Although there are no port facilities the island is scheduled as a port of entry for the Territory of Papua. Gold mining has been undertaken.

Immediately west of Murua and separated from it by an extremely narrow channel, is the small hook-shaped island of Madau. From the southern extremity of this island a chain of coral reefs and islets stretches south-eastwards. Nusam island, separated from Madau by the shallow Boagis passage, is the most northerly island in this chain. From 15 to 25 miles to the west of Murua are the Marshall Bennet islands, a group of four small raised atolls. Roughly 28 miles south-west of Murua is the Egum group, a circular reef enclosing 14 islets. To southward are the two small Alcester islands, while 30 miles to the east is an atoll which supports the 7 islets known as the Laughlan group.

Physical Geography

All these islands have been elevated relatively recently and have much raised coral in their surface deposits. Murua is typical. Rough coral surfaces with sharp pinnacles are common. The intervening hollows are often filled with humus and provide good soils for native agriculture.

Three main areas of higher land stand out from the otherwise low-lying surface of Murua. The north-east is a region of active elevation which rises sharply from the sea and within ½ mile of it attains an average height of 200 ft. Coastal lowlands are almost non-existent on its seaward side. In most places this coastal ridge falls equally sharply inland to a low-lying longitudinal trough. This relatively broad west-

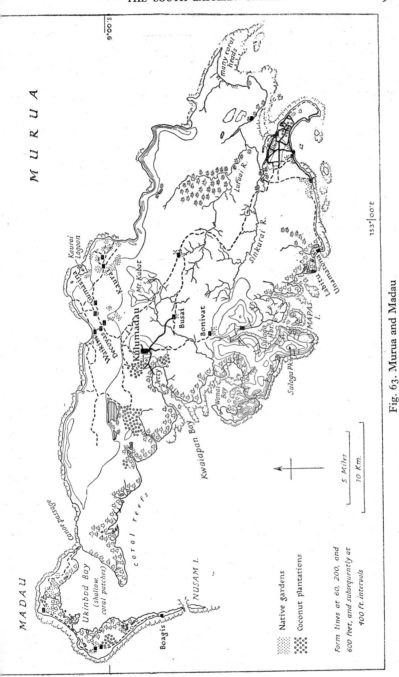

Fig. 63. Murua and Madau

Roads are indicated by solid lines and foot tracks by broken lines. The roads of the south-eastern peninsula are on a plantation. Form lines are approximate. Native villages are shown by rectangles. For *Ukinbod* read *Unkinbod*. Based on official sources.

to-east lowland is broken by two conical peaks, Kulumadau hill (approximately 300 ft. high) and, to eastward, mount Kabat (roughly 400 ft. high). The central lowland of Murua is mainly below 40 ft. in height and runs from Unkinbod bay eastward to Kumarau bay. Its western and southern coasts are heavily fringed by mangrove swamps. Two hill masses rise sharply on the southern side of the central trough. The first group of hills lies due south of Kulumadau hill and around Wonai bay and Suloga harbour and reaches its maximum height (about 1,200 ft.) in Suloga peak which stands close to the south coast. The second elevation is the isolated hill which lies south of the eastern end of the trough between Kumarau bay and Guasopa harbour. These steep-sided hills rise from the heavily forested plain in such a way as to suggest that, prior to elevation, they were islands set on a shallow shoal or the outstanding islets of an atoll.

The two longer rivers of Murua are the Sinkurai and Lufuai rivers which flow south-eastwards into Kumarau bay and drain the central trough. The Munai river flows transversely across the west of the trough from its sources on the slopes of mount Kabat to Wonai bay. The northern coral ridge has little surface drainage, though at the foot of its landward slope three large sink holes appear to have been clogged by decaying vegetation and each supports a lake with a swampy margin. Madau on the western side of Unkinbod bay is largely low-lying, like that part of western Murua which it adjoins. Its inner shores are covered by mangrove swamps. The seaward side is partly comparable to the north coast of Murua in that, behind the long fringing reef, a coral ridge rises from the shore. In Madau this is present behind the west coast and is only about 20 ft. high. It is probably a raised coral terrace representing the most recent stage in the elevation of the two islands.

Coasts, Anchorages and Landings

The approach to Murua from the west is obstructed by the chain of reefs and islands stretching southwards from Madau. A gap in the reefs can be negotiated by vessels of up to 4,000 tons. The area between the barrier and the western part of Murua is studded with coral patches. The shore west of Nelson point is marshy and difficult to cross. East of Nelson point and as far east as Kumarau bay there are numerous broken reefs and off-lying islands. The indentations and mouths of streams along this coast provide the only good anchorages in the island. The northern coast, for its whole length, is steep-to and rises sharply to a height of from 200 to 400 ft. There are beaches in

Buyuasi bay and Kaurai lagoon. Landing is difficult on the former, owing to the presence of coral ridges which front the beach, and in the latter owing to a bar at the mouth.

The best anchorages are in Kwaiapan bay, Suloga harbour and Guasopa bay. Kwaiapan bay is roughly 5 miles long and 1 mile wide. It opens out immediately east of Nelson point. The anchorage is at Bwoi Bwoi, where there is a depth of from 8 to 10 fathoms, but the inner part of the bay is shallow with depths of only 2 to 3 fathoms. Cargoes have to be taken by lighter for 3 miles to the jetty at Bunkanai. Suloga harbour, lying just east of the most southerly point of Murua, is well sheltered from all winds, but is of limited size. It is divided into three parts, namely, an outer harbour protected by Mapas island and roughly 1 mile long by $\frac{1}{2}$ mile wide with depths of 8 to 10 fathoms, an inner harbour with depths of 6 to 10 fathoms, and beyond this, a shallow inlet suitable only for launches. Guasopa harbour, 7 miles east of Suloga, is an extensive bay, with depths of 5 to 14 fathoms. There are many shallow patches at the eastern end. The bay is fronted by a section of barrier reef on which is situated Vavi islet. There are only two entrances. The main, or western, entrance has a width of about 300 yd. and depths of up to 14 fathoms. The eastern entrance is shallow, but is used by local craft. It has depths of up to 9 ft. Anchorage is also possible in Buyuasi bay and Waspimat bay.

Social and Economic Conditions

In 1847 a Marist mission was established on Murua but was abandoned soon afterwards. In 1884 the area was included in the proclamation by which Papua became a British possession. Gold was discovered in 1895 and until about 1925 considerable quantities were mined and exported. Since the opening up of the goldfields of the Morobe district, however, mining has virtually ceased; and the only economic value of the island appears to lie in its coconut plantations. In 1941, before the islands were evacuated, there were 16 Australians living in Murua. These included the Assistant Resident Magistrate, who was also the Collector of Customs, and traders and planters. The European quarters consisted of the magistrate's house, a trader's store and the police barracks and gaol at Kulumadau. There were also European houses on the plantations and at the old mining sites at Busai, Reilly's creek and Bonivat. There were two concrete buildings near the jetty which served Kulumadau.

The native population numbered 823 in 1941. About 200 of them lived at Kaurai, 100 at Decoyas, and most of the remainder along the eastern part of the south coast near Guasopa bay, Suloga harbour or Wonai bay. There were two villages on Madau island.

The people are Melanesians, with a certain amount of Papuo-Melanesian admixture. Their language is Melanesian and is common to Murua and the neighbouring islands. A high proportion of the adult males can speak English. The people live mostly by subsistence agriculture and gardening. Missionary influence has spread only very slightly.

Murua and the surrounding islands are administered as part of the South-eastern Division of Papua, for which the administrative centre is Misima. The senior official on Murua was the Assistant Resident Magistrate. He was assisted by four policemen. The native villages had native councillors who dealt with local matters and who were assisted by village policemen. Malaria is present, but owing to the relatively healthy sites of their dwellings is not serious among Europeans.

Sea communications were maintained by steamers which ran to Australian ports roughly every two months. Native villages often had large sailing canoes capable of carrying 60 men. These were used for coastal voyages. There were also many small canoes capable of carrying about 6 men, and 3 European-owned launches. The only road in the island (apart from those on plantations) runs from near the jetty in Kwaiapan bay to Busai. It has a coral surface. Two lorries operated on it. These were the only motor vehicles in the island. Various tracks branched off this road. One ran to Kulumadau and on to Decoyas, Waspimat bay and Kaurai lagoon. Another led eastwards from Busai to the plantation at Guasopa and westwards along the coast to Suloga harbour. Two tracks, one from near Kwaiapan bay, and one from Busai, led to Bonivat. In the west of the island, which is swampy and uninhabited, there were no tracks.

THE TROBRIAND ISLANDS

The Trobriand islands lie approximately 90 miles to the north of East cape in Papua (Fig. 64). They take their name from Denis de Trobriand, an officer of one of the ships of the D'Entrecasteaux expedition.

Physical Geography

The group comprises four main islands—Kiriwina, Kaileuna, Kitava, Vakuta—and several small islets. They are all formed of raised coral limestone. Kiriwina, the largest, is about 30 miles from north to south and appears in origin to be part of a raised atoll. Its north, north-west and east coasts are backed by a ridge of rugged and broken coral, which rises steeply to heights of up to 100 ft. Within this remnant

Fig. 64. The Trobriand islands

The villages shown had populations of 100 or more in 1936. The extent of the reefs south of Kaileuna is unknown. Based on: (1) Leo Austen, 'The Trobriand Islands of Papua', *Australian Geographer*, vol. III, no. 2, p. 12 (Sydney, 1936); (2) official sources.

of the former atoll rim, the land which once formed its lagoon floor is level and low-lying. Much is covered with freshwater and brackish swamps. The drier areas of level ground are very fertile and form the garden land of the native population. Vegetation is nowhere dense except in the swamps which are covered with man-groves, pandanus and swamp grasses. Secondary scrub covers the fallow areas of garden land and there are some large forest trees on the old atoll rim. The smaller islands, with the exception of Kaileuna, show no comparable central depression. The fauna is less varied than that of the mainland of New Guinea. It includes bush pigs, wallabies and bandicoots, a few crocodiles and numerous apparently non-poisonous snakes. Parrots and cockatoos are abundant.

The east and north coasts of Kiriwina are fringed with reef about ¼ mile broad which is sunken at its outer edge. Behind the narrow beach the coral cliffs of the old atoll rim rise to heights of 50–100 ft. Landing can only be made through several boat passages through the reef, but is dangerous during the south-east trade wind season. There is no good anchorage though large vessels could find some shelter towards the south of Muiau bay. The north coast is generally similar to the east, though the shore reef extends further seaward. Most of the western coast of Kiriwina fronting the Kiriwina lagoon is of very different character—low-lying and backed by swamps. The lagoon itself is rendered very shallow and dangerous by extensive reefs and coral patches. Off it lie the small islands of Bomapau (Baimapu) and Muua. The usual anchorage for small vessels is about 1 mile off Boli point in from 7 to 9 fathoms. Large vessels can anchor off Muua.

Social and Economic Conditions

The Trobriands for purposes of administration form a sub-division of the South-Eastern Division of Papua. Losuia is the government station where the Assistant Resident Magistrate lives. The European population before the present war was about 20, including 9 missionaries, 3 traders and 2 planters. The total native population was about 8,400, of whom 7,500 lived on Kiriwina and its adjacent islets.

The native people are almost unique in Papua in that they live under a system of hereditary chieftainship. Socially, they are divided into matrilineal clans and sub-clans—i.e., they trace descent through the female line (p. 162). They live by gardening and fishing. As gardeners they are probably the most skilful in Papua. They produce more than enough yams, taro, bananas and other crops to meet their own needs. Numerous pigs and poultry are kept. The inhabitants of villages fronting the Kiriwina lagoon live by fishing; they exchange a surplus of fish for vegetables with the inland gardeners. All are keen traders and take part in the *kula* (p. 172). The canoes in which these *kula* voyages are undertaken are richly ornamented, single-outrigger vessels.

Two missions maintain stations in the Trobriands: the Methodists and the Roman Catholics. Both are situated near to Losuia.

Kiriwina has a network of good, well-drained tracks averaging about 6 ft. wide. They are lined with coconut palms planted at the direction of a former administrative officer. There are few forms of production for export. Surpluses of native-grown vegetables are bought by plantation and mine owners in neighbouring islands to feed their labourers. There are also two small European-owned coconut plantations, one on Muua and one on Kitava. Pearls form the main export produce. Native divers are employed by Europeans to fish in the Kiriwina lagoon. Of recent years the fisheries have shown declining returns. Nevertheless the bulk of the Papuan export of pearls has always come from the Trobriands. Most of the pearls are not of good quality, but they find a ready market in India.

THE LOUISIADE ARCHIPELAGO

The name Louisiade archipelago is applied to the chain of islands and reefs off the eastern tip of Papua, between lat. 10° 10′ and 11° 50′ s, long. 150° 55′ and 154° 30′ E (Fig. 65). The group containing Rogeia, Sariba, Moresby and their off-lying islands is generally excluded, but is here described for convenience under the above heading.

Geologically, the archipelago is composed of metamorphic rocks, mainly slates and schists. The islands have experienced much erosion and large-scale subsidence has occurred, during which coral reefs have grown round their shores. Fringing reefs have developed round the coasts of most of the islands; but more striking than these are the very extensive barrier reefs, the largest of which surrounds Tagula and extends as a sunken barrier westwards almost to the south-east end of Papua. Some of the smaller islands are composed wholly of coral limestone.

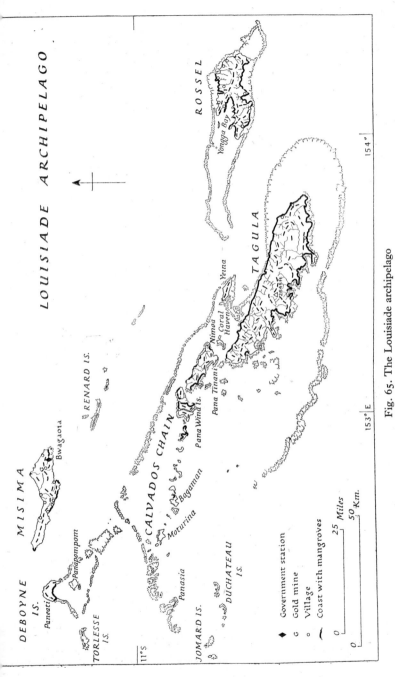

Fig. 65. The Louisiade archipelago

Based on: (1) Admiralty Chart no. 2124; (2) other official sources. The archipelago also includes Moresby and other islands to the west of Jomard island. For *Paneati* read *Panaeati*.

For administration most of the archipelago falls within the South-Eastern Division of Papua, though the Conflict and Engineer groups and the Rogeia-Moresby group are included in the Eastern Division. The native population (with the exception of the Rossel islanders) form part of the eastern Massim, or Eastern Papuo-Melanesians, a classification based partly on physical and partly on cultural distinctions.

THE ROGEIA–MORESBY GROUP

The term Rogeia–Moresby group is here applied to the islands of Rogeia, Sariba, Sideia, and Moresby with their off-lying islets. They are formed throughout of volcanic and metamorphic rocks. There is a fairly dense native population. In 1921 the total for these islands and the nearby Engineer group was 3,804.

Rogeia, the westernmost of the group, is about 4 miles long from north-west to south-east, with a maximum width of about 1½ miles. There are two peaks in the northern part of the island, the higher of which rises to 1,215 ft. Coral reef fringes parts of the north-east and south coasts. To the south of Rogeia lies a scattered group of small islands, the largest of which is Doini.

A channel nearly 3 miles wide separates Rogeia on the north-east from Sariba. In the middle of the channel lies the small island of Samarai, on which is situated the port, settlement and administrative centre of that name (p. 236). Sariba itself is an island of irregular shape about 5 miles from north-west to south-east with numerous hills rising to heights of from 500 to 900 ft. The coastline is deeply embayed with sandy beaches on the south-eastern side and mangroves fringing the three large bays on the north-east coast. Fringing reef is particularly well developed on the shores of Raburabu, the middle of the three bays.

Separated from the south-east end of Rogeia by the 200-yd. Sawa Sawaga channel lies Sideia, a rugged island which encloses on three sides the large Niuniu Ridikwa bay. The coasts of this bay have not been surveyed. Those of the south-western part of the island have sandy beaches and narrow fringing reefs. A chain of wooded hills varying from 300 to 1,320 ft. in height forms a spine to the island which is from 1 to 2 miles in width. The rocks of Sideia are rich in economic minerals, mainly copper. The whole island has been proclaimed a mineral field (p. 211). There are several villages and a mission station.

Moresby (Basilaki) island is separated by the narrow Kawana Madowa (Fortescue) strait from the eastern side of Sideia. The largest island of the group, it is about 12 miles from east to west, with a greatest width of about 7 miles. The heavily wooded Fairfax ridge which runs east and west forms the dominant feature of the relief. It contains three well-defined peaks, of which mount Fairfax, the highest, reaches 1,740 ft. The coasts are considerably indented and generally rocky, though there are mangroves on the section fronting the Kawana Madowa channel. Off the south-east coast lies a cluster of small islands, including Haines island, Katai and Katokatoa. Anchorage can be obtained on the south coast in Hara Harau bay in 13 fathoms. There is also anchorage on the east coast in James bay and in Sawateira bay in 14 fathoms.

THE ENGINEER AND CONFLICT GROUPS AND ADJACENT ISLANDS

The Engineer and Conflict groups lie to the east of Moresby island and to the south of Normanby island in an expanse of shallow sea studded with coral reefs and patches. None of their component islands is large; the largest, Naranarawai, is only about 3 miles long. The main islands of the Engineer group are of metamorphic rocks encrusted in parts with more recent coral limestone, but the smaller islands in this group and all those in the Conflict group are composed of coral limestone.

The Engineer group comprises the 3 main islands: Berriberrije; Naranarawai (Skelton island); and Kuriva (Watts island). Berriberrije (lat. 10° 35′ s, long.

151° 12′ E) is the westernmost of the group. It is about 2 miles long from north-west to south-east and about ¼ mile wide. The island is well wooded and the summit rises to 596 ft. There is anchorage off the northern coast in 15 fathoms.

Naranarawai, separated from Berriberrije by a channel 600 yd. wide, is the largest of the group. It is about 3 miles long and rises to a maximum height of about 500 ft. The western coast has a succession of sandy coves. There are two villages on the same coast.

Kuriva is the easternmost of the group. It is about 2¼ miles long from north-west to south-east, about ¼ mile wide, and rises to 400 ft. near its western end. The island is thickly wooded. The north coast is steep-to but there is a beach bordered by sunken reef on the south coast.

To the south of this group lie two small islands, Anagusa (Bentley island) and Nari (Mudge island). Anagusa, 8 miles south of Naranarawai, is an oval island 1½ miles from east to west which rises to 350 ft. The coast is surrounded by fringing reef. There is a village on the north-east coast. Nari, about 6 miles south of Anagusa, is somewhat smaller and surrounded by a narrow fringing reef. There are no inhabitants.

The Conflict group (lat. 10° 45′ S, long. 151° 43′, approx., at Panasesa island) is a large oval atoll enclosing a lagoon about 20 miles long from east to west. There are 14 islands of coral limestone on the reef, which is continuous on the east and south but broken by numerous passages on the north and west. Within the lagoon are numerous coral patches and two islands. Irai, the largest island in the group, is about 3 miles long. Other major islands on the atoll include Panasesa, also at the western end, and Auriroa and Muniara at the eastern end. Some of the passes into the lagoon are deep; that most used by vessels is Ship pass, south-east of Irai. Inside the lagoon there is anchorage in depths of 15 fathoms or less. Outside it are three small islands of coral limestone which are generally included within the Conflict group. They are: Lunn island, about 5 miles to the east; and Sarupai and Bunora, about 9 and 11 miles respectively, north-north-east of the atoll.

THE DEBOYNE AND TORLESSE ISLANDS

The Deboyne islands lie on and within a large triangular barrier reef which extends between lat. 10° 40′ and 10° 52′ S, long. 152° 17′ and 152° 32′ E. The Torlesse islands lie on a much smaller reef about 3 miles to the west of the Deboyne reef.

The Deboyne islands are formed of metamorphic rocks with superficial deposits of coral limestone in coastal regions. Panaeati, the largest, lies on the northern angle of the triangular reef. It is crescentic in outline and about 5 miles across from east to west. The interior rises in several hills, the highest of which reaches 700 ft. The north coast has coral limestone cliffs 20–100 ft. high. The inner shore fronting the lagoon is also of rugged coral but much flatter. The native population is about 600. There is an almost continuous line of native houses fronting the western coast. A small Methodist mission station is in charge of a Fijian.

On the north-east side of the reef are several small islands, including Panauya Wana and Horuga Rara. On the south and west sides of the reef are only one or two small sandy cays. In the centre of the lagoon are Panapompom and Nivani islands. Panapompom is a triangular island about 2 miles across from east to west. Lightly forested hills rise to a maximum height of 500 ft. On the west and south coasts are sloping sandy beaches; on the east is a rocky coral foreshore. There are several native villages. Coconut plantations run inland from both south and north-east coasts. Nivani is a small island about 900 yd. to the south of Panapompom. It contains two hills 310 and 257 ft. high respectively. The north-east coast has a sandy beach suitable for landing; elsewhere the coast consists of a coral shelf. A coconut plantation covers the island.

The Torlesse islands are three small flat islands of raised coral. They lie on the northern side of a reef and from east to west are named Tinolan, Bonabonawan and Bonabonakai (Pana Nui). The last is planted with coconut palms which are tended by the natives of Panaeati.

MISIMA

Misima, one of the four largest islands of the Louisiade group, lies about 8 miles north-east of Panaeati, with cape Ebola, its western extremity in lat. 10° 38′ s, long. 152° 31′ E.

Physical Geography

The island is 25 miles long from east to west with a maximum width of about 6 miles. It is composed mainly of very old igneous and metamorphic rocks. In many coastal regions these are overlaid by much more recent deposits of coral limestone which occur in terraces at about 200-ft. intervals up to nearly 1,000 ft. above sea level. A chain of well-rounded hills forms a spine to the narrow western half of the island. In the eastern half of the island two ranges, parallel to north and south coasts, contain between them a broad valley which opens on to a bay on the south coast. The highest peak, mount Oiatau (Koia tau), is in the western range; it rises to 3,400 ft. There are 5 other peaks which exceed 2,000 ft. in height in this half of the island. The streams on the island are mere mountain torrents, each only a few miles long. Most of the island is covered with forest, though the gardens of the relatively dense native population and the activities of gold miners have destroyed much of the virgin forest, especially in coastal areas. In some parts the forest has been replaced by grassy patches, in others by secondary growth. There are some savannah areas in the east. On the coast are a few narrow stretches of mangrove swamp.

The most striking feature of the coast of Misima is the great depth of water close in-shore. Although coral reef fringes much of the shore, it has either been elevated to form a slight cliff or consists of a narrow shore shelf, except at the south-east end of the island, where the shallow Managun lagoon is enclosed by reef. The lagoon is about 2 miles long by 1 mile wide. Two boat passages give access to it, one at the north-eastern end and one immediately west of Managun island (an islet which lies on the reef). Each has about 4 ft. of water at high tide. The lagoon is shallow and studded with coral heads. Immediately to the west of it is Bwagaoia harbour, a narrow strip of water between the shore reef and the reef which encloses the Managun lagoon. It is about 800 yd. long and 100 yd. wide with depths of 5–11 fathoms. These dimensions only give swinging room to a small vessel. A T-shaped wharf has been built on the west side of the harbour. It has a frontage on the end of 34 ft. with a depth alongside of 30 ft. Vessels moor by tying up to trees. There is a 2-ton crane on the wharf and a light railway 100 yd. long leads to the Burns, Philp store. There are no anchorages on the south coast westwards of Bwagaoia. For some miles the coast is sandy with rough coral projecting through the sand. Further west there is a narrow mangrove belt fronted by a narrow fringing reef. The western end of this coast as far as cape Ebola is a succession of steep cliffs rising to about 100 ft. About 1 mile south-east of the cape is a sheltered anchorage for a small vessel. Similar cliffs line the north coast for some miles eastward of cape Ebola. The central part of the north coast has sand and shingle beaches with fringing coral only at the promontories. The eastern third of the north coast has no anchorage areas; it is formed by cliffs of rough coral 50–100 ft. high.

Social and Economic Conditions

The European population at the outbreak of the present war numbered about 80. Most of this total were engaged in gold mining. The native population was then about 3,200, with the addition of about 650 indentured labourers from other parts of Papua who were employed in the mines. The natives speak the same dialect as do those of Panaeati. There was an Assistant Resident Magistrate at Bwagaoia. Misima is a major centre of gold mining. There were four companies operating at the outbreak of the present war : Cuthbert's Misima Goldmine, at Umuna ; Gold Mines of Papua, at mount Sisa ; Quartz Mountain (Papua), at Tauhik ; and a local syndicate working in the Ara creek. The first three of these companies were mining reef gold. The natives pay their £1 head-tax from the proceeds of panning for alluvial gold in the streams. Just before 1940 the total value of production from Misima averaged £100,000 per annum. The natives practise subsistence agriculture and produce no surplus of vegetables. The labourers in the gold mines are fed on imported rice and on vegetables, mainly from the Trobriand and the D'Entre-casteaux islands. Despite the many freshwater streams, Europeans depend on catchment and storage of rain water.

THE RENARD ISLANDS

The Renard islands (lat. 10° 51′ S, long. 152° 59′ E, at Kimuta island) are three small islands lying about 15 miles south-east of Misima. They are formed of raised coral limestone and are surrounded by broad fringing reefs. Kimuta and Nivabeno are linked by the reef. Oreia lies on a separate reef 3½ miles to the east of Nivabeno. To the north of Kimuta is a group of two small islets on a similar reef patch. Kimuta is about 4 miles long from east to west. It rises to 200 ft. and is covered with native gardens and light forest. The beach on the north coast is sandy, though landing is difficult except in dinghies. Nivabeno is about 1 mile long. It is flat, sandy and planted with native coconut groves. Landing can be made fairly easily over the shore reef to the north except during north-westerly storms.

THE TAGULA REEF AND THE CALVADOS CHAIN

The Calvados chain of islands with the large island of Tagula are all situated within a large barrier reef (Fig. 65). The loop of reef is about 112 miles from east to west. It is particularly massive on the south and east. On the south-west it is largely sunken to a depth of 6–9 fathoms. To the north of the Calvados chain the reef is of an unusual 'cellular' construction, consisting of a chain of small atoll reefs separated by narrow passes. Many of the small lagoons enclosed by these component atolls contain islets with heights varying from 40 to 530 ft. They appear to be composed of volcanic rocks, schists and limestones. Immediately outside the barrier reef the sea floor falls away steeply to great depths. Inside the reef, depths range from about 10 fathoms to about 40 fathoms.

The best of the numerous passes for ships entering the lagoon are at the western end, immediately to the north of the Jomard islands ; Cormorant channel, about 15 miles north-eastward of this ; and Wuri Wuri passage, in the northern side of the reef. The lagoon itself offers unlimited anchorage for vessels of all sizes.

The Calvados chain itself divides the lagoon into a northern and a southern section. It is a chain of over 20 islands and islets, stretching from Panasia in the west to Nimoa in the east. The islands appear to be composed of old igneous and metamorphic rocks with raised coral limestone cliffs on parts of their coasts. All are rugged and many rise to well-defined peaks of 500–1,000 ft. in height. Virgin forest is rare as the islands are well peopled and much of their area is occupied with garden land or disused garden land. Many patches are covered with kunai grass.

The shores of the islands are considerably indented and are, for the most part, fringed with coral. This usually takes the form of a shelf or raised reef which is high enough to form low cliffs on the south-east coasts but which is less pronounced on the north-west, where there are sandy beaches suitable for landing. On the larger islands at the eastern end of the chain long stretches of coast are fringed with mangroves. All except Panasia and Utian at the western end of the chain are easy to approach, and anchorage is possible almost anywhere off their coasts. Fresh water is difficult to obtain except on Moturina, Panawina and Panatinani. The native population of the islands is about 300. The people's gardens are poor, but they are skilful net fishermen.

The main islands of the chain from west to east are Panasia, Moturina, Bagaman, Abaga Gaheia, Panawina, Hemenahei and Panatinani. Panasia (lat. 11° 08′ s, long. 152° 20′ E) has cliffs 100 ft. high on the east coast. Landing is possible over a coral shelf midway along the north coast. Moturina is about 3 miles long from east to west. It rises in a pyramidal hill to 990 ft. There are sandy beaches on the north coast. Landing is possible over a coral shelf on the south-west side and good sheltered anchorage can be had to the north-west of the island. There are villages on the north coast. Panawina, one of the larger islands, is rectangular in shape, with promontories projecting to south and west; it is about 4½ miles from east to west. Two hilly ridges run parallel with the east and west coasts and rise to heights of 800 ft. and 945 ft. respectively. The valley between the ridges is filled with swamp. There is a sheltered sandy beach on the west coast. A reef which dries at low water, links Panawina with Hemenahei. Mangrove fringes the coast of both islands. Panatinani, the easternmost of the chain is also the largest. It is about 12 miles long from east to west and 2–3 miles wide. A ridge of hills extending nearly the whole length of the island rises abruptly from the south coast and falls gradually to the north and east. The highest point, mount Guyuba (1,110 ft.), is about 3 miles from the eastern end of the island. Panatinani is well wooded and there are numerous groves of coconut palms near the coast. The coast is mostly formed by a coral shelf; much of it has a fringe of mangroves. Good anchorage in the south-east trade winds can be obtained in 10–12 fathoms in Buvara bay on the west coast. Other anchorages are available in Hati Lawi and Hei Hutu bays at the south-eastern end of the island.

Other islands within the Tagula reef, though not included in the Calvados chain, include Yeina (Piron) island, off the north coast of Tagula, and the Duchateau islands at the western end of the lagoon enclosed by the reef. Yeina is a lozenge-shaped island about 6 miles long from east to west and 120 to 260 ft. high. Mangroves fringe the coast except at the east end where the shore is rocky with a few sandy beaches. The Duchateau islands (lat. 11° 17′ s, long. 152° 21′ E, at Pana Boboi Ana) are a group of 3 small wooded islets of raised coral situated on the sunken section of the Tagula barrier reef. Pana Boboi Ana, the westernmost and largest, is 75 ft. high. It is surrounded by a sunken reef. Landing is possible on the north-western side, where the reef is much broken. Pana Rura Wana and Kukuluba, of similar height, lie respectively on the western and northern sides of a reef ½ mile eastward of Pana Boboi Ana. Several miles to the west of the Duchateau islands lie the similar Montemont and Jomard groups.

TAGULA

Tagula, also known as Sudest, is the largest island in the Louisiade archipelago. It is about 45 miles long from east to west and extends between lat. 153° 11′ E and 153° 47′ E and between long. 11° 20′ s and 11° 39′ s. It, with the Calvados chain, is enclosed within a lagoon protected by a large barrier reef (pp. 27, 296).

Physical Geography

Tagula is composed of igneous and metamorphic rocks overlaid by coral limestone in coastal regions. A more or less continuous mountain ridge follows the length of the island. The highest point, mount Riu (Rattlesnake), is 2,645 ft. high, with a sharp rocky peak. Several other peaks reach heights of 1,000 to 2,000 ft. Many spurs buttress this ridge, particularly on its northern side. Although there are no large rivers, the ridges and spurs are intersected by numerous streams which make their way down to north and south coasts. The largest of these are the Feiori on the north, and the Iyuba (Tabamba) on the south. Most of the island is covered with tropical rain forest, though grassy ridges dip down to the western part of the north coast. Between the main ridge and the south coast is a considerable area of coniferous forest, the trees of which exude a gum of commercial value.

The north coast of Tagula has few prominent features. The south coast, by contrast, is deeply indented with several narrow bays sheltered from the south-east by promontories. Both coasts for most of their length are lined with a narrow belt of mangrove swamp. On the south coast this is for the most part backed by a low coral cliff about 20 ft. high. Most of the south coast has a well-developed wide fringing reef. In places this is as much as 2 miles wide. The north coast is mostly free from reef except for its middle section, where the Tagula barrier reef approaches the coast and becomes a fringing reef. It also forms a complicated network of reefs and small lagoons linking Yeina island with the north coast. At the eastern end of the island some shelter is provided by the reefs off cape Siri. The lagoon between the barrier reef and the north coast is so encumbered with coral that it can only be navigated by small vessels in a good light. Just north of the western end of the island is a sheltered area of water with suitable depths for anchorage. Landing is difficult on nearly all parts of the coast, owing to the fringing reef which is mostly sunken, and to the mangrove belt on the shore.

Social and Economic Conditions

The native population of Tagula numbers about 1,500. The people live in small, well-built villages, the largest of which are in the interior. Owing to the small size of the villages, each of the seven village constables has charge of a district containing several villages. The European population has never been large. No paying deposits of minerals are now worked; little land has been taken up for plantations; and missions have made no headway with the native population. In consequence, at the outbreak of the present war, the European population consisted of about 5 traders and prospectors.

Economic resources are few. Gold was discovered in some quantity in the 1880's, but since the days of the gold rush (p. 129) only small quantities have been won. Some *bêche-de-mer* and pearl shell are exported. About 600 acres of land have been planted with coconuts by Europeans and small quantities of copra exported. But of recent years the plantations have been neglected and the export has ceased. The gum from the forest on the south-east coast is collected by natives and exported. The export averaged about 70 tons per annum and fetched prices in Sydney of £15 to £25 per ton.

ROSSEL ISLAND

Rossel island (lat. 11° 22′ s, long. 153° 59′ E, at West point) is the most easterly of the Louisiade archipelago. It was discovered by Bougainville in 1768 and was later visited by D'Entrecasteaux who named the island after one of his officers.

Physical Geography

Rossel is situated in a lagoon within a very complete barrier reef. It is about 20 miles long from east to west with a greatest width of about 10 miles and an area of about 100 sq. miles. It is an irregularly-shaped island with a large bay at its western end. The main topographical feature is a chain of mountains which runs westwards from the eastern end and divides into two chains, one on each side of Yongga bay on the west coast. Mount Rossel (2,750 ft.), at the eastern end, is the highest point. It is a sharp peak with precipitous ridges on the north and west. Four miles to the west of mount Rossel, at the point where the range divides, is a broad dome-shaped hill 2,000 ft. high. Short spurs descend to north and south coasts from the main range. The valleys between them contain swift-flowing streams. Most of the island is covered with rain forest which is thickest near the coast. Inland on the slopes, where the natives cultivate their gardens, are many patches of grassland and secondary growth. Much of the coast has a narrow fringe of mangroves.

Depths outside the Rossel lagoon are very great but within it are suitable for anchorage, except in the northern and south-eastern parts where the lagoon is encumbered with coral. The reef itself is an almost continuous barrier with very few passages through it. On the north and south-west coasts of Rossel it approaches close enough to become a fringing reef. Within the reef on the south coast there are 2–7 ft. of water, according to the tide. For a few miles westward of West point the coast is cliffed. Further east the headlands are rocky, while the bays are fringed with coral flats with sand or mud and mangrove behind. Small vessels can find anchorage by entering the lagoon by Gwe passage, near the western end of the south coast, and by Gware passage, near its eastern end. The east coast is mainly a series of low cliffs and banks of raised coral with, in places, a mangrove belt. There are several passages through the barrier reef, though none is suitable for large vessels. The north coast has generally similar features. Relief opening, midway along the reef on this coast, is suitable for vessels of up to 300 tons. Small vessels can proceed inside the reef both eastward and westward of this opening. Off the west coast the big expanse of the Rossel lagoon offers extensive anchorage in 16–30 fathoms. Entrance to the lagoon is through the wide and clear Rossel passage at its western end. The western coast also has a coral shelf with a mangrove fringe, though there is a sandy beach in Yongga bay and another at the head of Mission bay, a pocket in the northern shore of Yongga bay.

Social and Economic Conditions

The natives of Rossel, unlike the Massim inhabiting the islands to the westward, speak a Papuan language and show few Melanesian cultural characteristics. They number about 850 and live in small villages with an average of about 5 houses in each. The largest village is probably Kwaidada, near West point. The only Europeans in Rossel at the outbreak of the present war were a single family living at Abelati on the south coast. There were no European missionaries, but native Methodist mission teachers were established in five villages. The natives live by subsistence agriculture and fishing. A few small coconut plantations have been established by Europeans. A herd of 300 cattle was kept at Abelati.

BIBLIOGRAPHICAL NOTE

The main source of information on the physical geography of the islands described in this Chapter is the Admiralty *Pacific Islands Pilot*, vol. I (6th edition, London, 1933; with supplement, 1944). Works dealing with the people of the area are cited in the Bibliographical Note to Chapter VIII. A general account of the Trobriand islands is given in L. Austen, 'The Trobriand Islands of Papua', *Australian Geographer*, vol. III, pp. 10–22 (Sydney, 1936). The geology of the Louisiade archipelago is described in W. M. Davis, 'Coral Reefs of the Louisiade Archipelago', *Proceedings of the National Academy of Sciences of the United States of America*, vol. VIII, pp. 7–13 (Washington, 1922).

Plate 69. Recruits for the New Guinea Police Force on parade in Rabaul
The wooden buildings with verandahs and corrugated-iron roofs are typical of most
of those to be seen in New Guinea settlements.

Plate 70. Nordup church, New Britain
Nordup lies about 5 miles north of Praed point, in the north-east of the Gazelle
peninsula. The typical village church lies below the steep northern slopes of The
Mother.

Plate 71. Jaluit atoll, Marshall islands

A 'sink' or depression in the atoll rim near the village of Jabor in the south-east of Jaluit.

Plate 72. Enybor island, Jaluit atoll

A depression in the centre of the island. Enybor is separated from Jabor island by South-east pass.

Plate 73. Rongelap, Marshall islands

The lagoon face of part of the atoll rim, showing typical scrub and coral beach.

PART TWO

THE JAPANESE MANDATED ISLANDS

Chapter XV

GENERAL REVIEW OF THE JAPANESE MANDATED ISLANDS

Physical Geography: History: Population: The Native Peoples

The territory administered by Japan under mandate from the League of Nations comprises the Caroline islands, the Marshall islands, and the Marianas (Fig. 66). Together these three groups stretch from lat. 1° to 20° N and from long. 130° to 170° E and cover a sea area of over 3,000,000 sq. miles. Though the total number of islands in the three groups is very large, the land area of even the largest of them is quite small. The Carolines number nearly 550 separate islands and islets, and stretch between the Palau group (long. 134° E) and Kusaie (long. 163° E). Their total land area is only about 600 sq. miles. There are five islands, or clusters of islands, of volcanic formation— Palau; Yap; Truk; Ponape; and Kusaie. The remainder of the group is made up of atolls, mainly with very small land areas. The Marshall islands lie east of the Carolines, roughly between long. 161° and 173° E and lat. 5° and 15° N. The western line of islands is known as the Ralik chain and the eastern as the Ratak chain. All the Marshall islands are atolls. The most important is Jaluit. The lagoons formed by these atolls generally provide excellent anchorages, but the total land area of the whole group is not more than about 65 sq. miles. The Marianas stretch northward from the central Carolines for about 450 sq. miles. The largest island in the group, and that closest to the Carolines, is Guam, which is excluded from the Japanese territory and is an American possession (Chapter XXI). The most important of the islands under Japanese jurisdiction is Saipan. All the islands of the Marianas group are of volcanic formation.

PHYSICAL GEOGRAPHY (Plates 71-9)

A submarine volcanic ridge stretches southwards from Japan through the Bonin islands, the Marianas, Yap and Palau towards the western

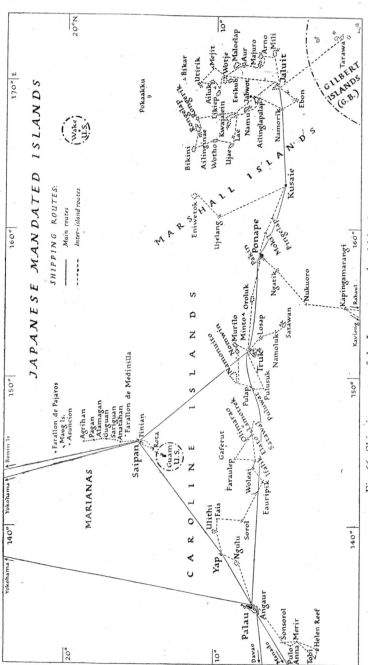

Fig. 66. Shipping routes of the Japanese mandated islands

Eniwetok and Ujelang are included in the Marshall group. Kusaie is part of the Caroline group. Based on T. Yanaihara, *Pacific Islands under Japanese Mandate*, map facing p. x (Shanghai, 1939).

end of New Guinea. Its peaks emerge from the sea in the form of island clusters. Along the east side of this ridge there are trenches, with depths of up to 5,000 fathoms. East of this ridge and its bordering trenches stretch a series of submarine elevations on which stand the greater part of the Carolines and the whole of the Marshall islands.

The northern Marianas, which lie roughly half-way along the main north-south ridge, are a series of volcanic peaks, some of which are still active. They rise more or less as a continuation of the submarine slope and are mostly tilted so that the eastern side is steeper than the west. The southern islands of the Marianas have their volcanic cores covered with limestone and show traces of frequent elevation in the form of numerous raised coral terraces, which are especially well developed on Saipan. In the Palau group the large islands of Babelthuap, Arakabesan and Koror are composed of volcanic rocks, while the islands to the south are of raised coral limestone. A correlation of the geological formations of the Carolines and Marianas has been worked out. This classifies Yap, with amphibolite rocks, as being pre-Tertiary in formation. Palau and the Marianas have tuff agglomerates, andesites and limestones, all of Tertiary age. Kusaie and Ponape are largely of basalt, which has cooled into columnar masses with a polygonal section. This structure is clearly visible in the cliff at Jokaj (vol. I, Plate 6), an island connected with Ponape by a causeway. In the other islands much erosion has taken place, producing rounded hills and rolling country with a lateritic soil. In Ponape and Kusaie erosion has not been carried so far, and deep valleys and rocky peaks are characteristic.

The raised limestone of the southern part of the Palau group and the southern Marianas produces high plateaux with few or no surface streams but with dense vegetation. The low coral formations are of two types, small single islands rarely more than 1 to 2 miles long and atolls with a coral rim, on which wooded islets are scattered at intervals. The coral rims often surround lagoons of considerable depth and extent.

COASTS AND ANCHORAGES

Whether of volcanic or limestone formation most islands in the area are surrounded by a reef. This may be a fringing reef stretching out from the shore for up to $\frac{1}{2}$ mile, sometimes awash at low tide and sometimes partly submerged. It frequently happens that a reef stands some way from the shore, with deep water inside it, and offers anchorage facilities. In many places, especially on the eastern sides of the islands exposed to the north-east trade winds, there are steep cliffs and rocky foreshores. On the flatter coasts extensive belts of mangroves occur, making access to the shore difficult except where channels have been cut to provide passages for canoes approaching native villages. The reefs of the atolls vary considerably; sometimes they are submerged to depths of about 5 fathoms. There are often gaps through which large vessels can be navigated into the lagoons. Landing on the seaward side of lagoons is frequently difficult because of the heavy surf which sets in. The shore on the east side of such islands is generally built up into a beach crest from 6 to 8 ft. high, consisting of fragments of dead coral. The shores on the lagoon sides of islands on atolls usually consist of shelving beach. This is sometimes, though not always, fringed by a shallow coral reef which can usually be crossed at high water.

The mandated islands have many good anchorages. For example, the large atolls of the Marshall islands, such as Jaluit, Kwajalein, Eniwetok and Arno, offer very fine anchorage areas, though in most cases the land area is so small that harbour facilities are lacking. Truk (p. 389), in the centre of the Carolines, has a diameter of about 30 miles. Moderate-sized volcanic islands lie within the lagoon. This is a magnificent anchorage and was developed as a Japanese naval base. Most of the remaining atolls are comparatively small, offering protection for small vessels only. The 'high' islands do not, as a rule, provide good harbours. Metalanim and Ponape harbours in Ponape, Lele harbour in Kusaie, and Tomil harbour in Yap offer excellent protection in limited space. Tanapag on Saipan has had to be improved by large harbour works to make it suitable for the requirements of the sugar industry. The island of Angaur has no good anchorage and ships have to tie up to moorings. On the other hand the stretches of water between the complicated groups of islands south of Babelthuap form magnificent anchorages, as, for example, round Malakal and Koror.

CLIMATE

Over the very large area covered by the mandated islands climatic conditions differ slightly from place to place, but except in the islands north of 15° N the climate tends to be very uniform throughout the year at any one station. The climate is oceanic in character and is predominantly under the influence of the north-east trade winds, though west of long. 140° E southerly and south-westerly winds prevail in the northern summer.

From November to April the prevailing winds over the whole area are from north-east or east. From May to October south-east winds prevail east of long. 140° E with a considerable component from the east. In the northern summer the south-east trades are dominant over the southern Carolines and east Marshalls. Regions as far north as

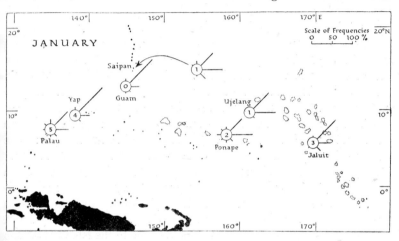

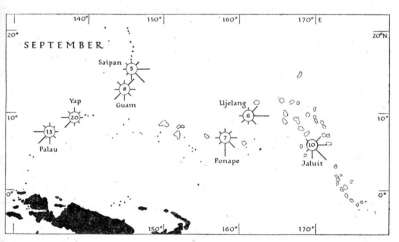

Fig. 67. Winds of the Japanese mandated islands, January and September
The figures inside the circles indicate the percentage frequency of calms. The wind force is not indicated. Based on Air Ministry Meteorological Office *Weather in the China Seas and in the Western Part of the North Pacific Ocean*, vol. II, pp. 656, 660 (London, 1937).

Saipan experience high proportions of south-easterly winds. West of 140° E, notably in Palau and Yap, south-westerly or westerly winds are experienced in the period July–October. Fig. 67 shows wind directions in the area for the months of January and September.

Typhoons normally develop in the area bounded by 5° and 20° N, and 130° and 150° E; they occasionally occur east of 150° E. The mean latitude of their origin moves progressively north from roughly 7° N in April to about 16° N in August and then in the reverse direction from September to March. They generally move at a speed of about 10 knots in a westerly or north-westerly direction, and sometimes recurve. Typhoons may be experienced in any month, though they are most frequent between July and October, and rarest between February and April. In a normal year, about fifteen typhoons may be expected to form in the rectangle outlined above, and possibly a few outside it, though by no means all pass sufficiently near any island to cause serious disturbance. As many as four typhoons in a year have been known to pass near enough to Guam to produce gales, and rather less near Yap; the majority pass between them. These islands lie in the western margins of the rectangle which, by reason of the convergence of tracks, has greater typhoon frequency than the eastern half. Severe typhoons have occurred as far east as the Gilbert islands, where a severe storm did considerable damage to the island of Makin in December 1927, and the eastern Caroline islands of Ponape and Kusaie are not immune.

Visibility is good over the whole area. Fog is very rare and mist infrequent. Cloud amount over the sea is fairly constant, with mean monthly amounts varying from 4-tenths to 6-tenths. In the extreme north-west, however, the mean amount of cloud is as high as 7-tenths in December. Over atolls somewhat similar conditions probably prevail, but over the larger mountainous islands the cloud cover is more complete. The average number of cloudy days (i.e., days with more than 8-tenths of the sky covered) and of days with clear sky (i.e., less than 2-tenths of the sky covered) at Palau, Saipan, Ponape and Ujelang during 6 to 10 years' observations are shown in the Table on p. 311. At Kusaie conditions are probably very similar to those at Ponape; conditions at Ujelang are probably fairly typical of those over most atolls in the area.

In general, rainfall is heaviest over a belt between lat. 1° 30′ and 8° 30′ N, which includes the greater part of the Carolines. The average annual rainfall within this belt, which marks the zone in which the north-east and south-east trades meet, is over 120 in. This total is

Average Number of Cloudy and of Clear Days

	J	F	M	A	M	J	J	A	S	O	N	D	Year
Palau (1924–34):													
Cloudy	16·0	14·0	15·0	3·0	19·0	18·0	23·0	21·0	19·0	19·0	14·0	16·0	207·0
Clear	0·1	0·1	0·2	0·1	0·2	0·1	0·1	0·1	0·1	0·1	0·2	0·1	0·4
Saipan (1927–34):													
Cloudy	12·0	9·0	6·0	5·0	10·0	8·0	19·0	18·0	19·0	15·0	7·0	7·0	135·0
Clear	0·5	1·6	0·5	0·5	0·4	1·0	0·4	0·4	0·3	0·1	0·5	0·6	6·8
Ponape (1928–34):													
Cloudy	20·0	16·0	18·0	19·0	19·0	18·0	15·0	14·0	15·0	15·0	16·0	18·0	203·0
Clear	0·1	0·1	0	0	0·1	0	0·4	0·3	0·1	0·7	0·3	0·1	2·4
Ujelang (1894–7, 1912–13):													
Cloudy	2·0	1·0	0·7	0·8	4·0	3·0	2·0	2·0	5·0	5·0	3·0	1·0	29·0
Clear	0·8	0·7	1·0	0·2	1·0	0·3	0·8	0·7	0·2	0·5	0·2	2·0	8·0

Source: *Weather in the China Seas and in the Western Part of the North Pacific Ocean*, vol. II, p. 671 (London, 1937).

Mean Maxima and Minima of Cloud Amounts
(tenths of sky covered)

	J	F	M	A	M	J	J	A	S	O	N	D
Palau:												
Maximum	8·3	8·1	7·8	7·8	8·6	8·5	9·4	9·0	9·0	9·0	8·1	8·6
Minimum	7·1	6·1	6·7	6·8	7·4	6·9	8·2	7·1	7·5	5·1	6·6	6·9
Saipan:												
Maximum	7·5	7·7	7·1	6·7	7·7	6·5	8·8	8·7	9·4	8·0	7·5	6·4
Minimum	6·2	5·4	5·2	4·6	5·8	5·4	5·9	6·8	6·9	5·6	4·6	5·3
Ponape:												
Maximum	9·0	9·0	8·3	8·9	9·1	8·4	8·3	8·1	8·2	8·3	8·2	8·7
Minimum	7·3	7·1	7·3	7·0	6·7	7·7	6·2	5·9	6·9	5·1	6·7	6·9

considerably augmented over the larger islands by orographic rain. The total is as much as 255 in. on the west coast of Kusaie, as against 177 in. on the east coast, 6 miles away across mountains which rise to approximately 2,000 ft. North of this belt rainfall totals are lower (80 to 100 in. in the Marianas, and 80 in. at Ujelang in the Marshall islands).

Seasonal variation too is by no means uniform throughout the area. Jaluit in the south of the Marshall group has a total annual rainfall of about 160 in., with a minimum in February of about 8 in., rising to about 16 in. a month from May to July. Ujelang in the north of the Marshall islands has its lowest monthly totals (about 2 in.) from January to March and its greatest (about 10 in.) in September and October. Regimes similar to those of Jaluit obtain in most of the atolls of the east Carolines (Fig. 68—Kusaie). In the west Carolines, which are nearer than other groups to the Asiatic low-pressure system in

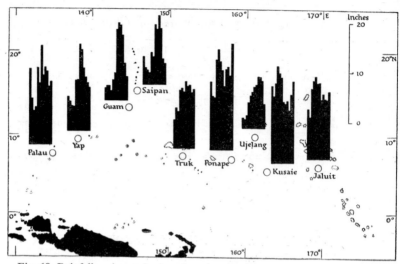

Fig. 68. Rainfall regimes of selected stations in the Japanese mandated islands
The position of selected islands are indicated by circles. Based on the same source
as Fig. 67, p. 674.

summer, the greatest rainfall is generally in July and August, but at
Palau there is a secondary maximum in December and January. In
exceptional years the July figures have been 46 in. at Yap and 32 in.
at Palau. In any month, especially on Palau, the rainfall is rarely less
than 4 in. In the Marianas the conditions are somewhat similar to
those of Yap, though totals are rather lower. Fig. 68 shows the mean
monthly rainfall in each month for the major stations in the area, but
owing to considerable variability of the rainfall from year to year,
means are of little value in estimating the probable rainfall of any
one year.

Fig. 69 shows temperatures in each month at Palau, over a period
of 9 years' observations. The temperature over the whole area is
remarkably uniform both seasonally and regionally, but there is a
noticeable seasonal variation in those islands in the Caroline and
Marshall groups which lie north of 15° N. South of this latitude the
mean monthly temperature is seldom less than 79° or more than
83° F., and the difference between the means of winter and summer
months is rarely more than 2° F. in the Carolines and Marshalls. In
the Marianas group the range increases from about 3·5° F. in the
southern islands to as much as 16° F. at Rasa (maximum, 83° F. in
July; minimum, 67° F. in January). The daily range usually amounts
to about 10° F. Day temperatures vary from 83° to 89° F. and night

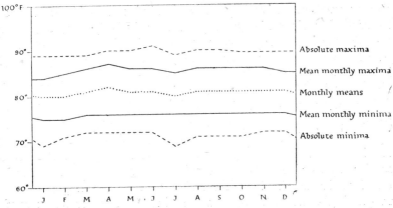

Fig. 69. Annual temperature regimes, Palau
Based on official sources.

temperatures from 74° to 77° F., to the south in the Carolines and Marshalls, but both are slightly lower to the north of 15° N in the Marianas. In winter, temperatures are lower than the average in those islands which lie nearest to Asia.

Mean relative humidity is fairly high all the year round with little seasonal variation. Monthly mean values vary from 77% to 80% in the early part of the year to 83% to 86% between July and October in the Carolines, Marianas, and northern Marshalls, but at Jaluit in the southern Marshalls, where the maximum mean humidity is 86%, the minimum is still as high as 82%.

VEGETATION

The vegetation of the Carolines, Marshalls and Marianas is very like that of many other of the smaller islands of the Western Pacific; that of Guam is dealt with separately (p. 466), though it is similar in most respects to that of the other islands of the Marianas. In all these groups the flora is mainly Indo-Malayan in character, most of the species being also found in the neighbouring islands of the Malay archipelago, though a few, notably some of the palms, are endemics, not known from elsewhere.

As everywhere in the Pacific there is a strong contrast between the vegetation of the coral islands, poor and few in species, and the more luxuriant and much more varied vegetation of the 'high' volcanic islands. Thus the Marshall islands, which are entirely coral, have a very poor flora. Species of plants are few and of these a large proportion are weeds or cultivated plants obviously introduced by man. The handful of species which are apparently truly indigenous are all of wide distribution and found on coral islands in all parts of the Pacific. The poverty of the flora is partly due to the salt-water spray, which in the season of the north-east trades sweeps right over the islands, killing much of the vegetation or turning it yellow.

Perhaps the most conspicuous of the native plants is *Scaevola frutescens*, called *kenat* by the natives, a shrub 10–15 ft. high, which forms a solid wall of vegetation on the seaward side of the islands and provides a certain amount of shelter. The other plants include a species of pandanus, the seeds of which are washed up by the sea and germinate in the drift-line; a few ferns; the mangrove *Bruguiera*; and the *gudill* (*Terminalia catappa*), a tree which is abundant on many of the atolls.

The chief cultivated plants are *Pandanus utilis*, the breadfruit and the coconut. The last flourishes on stony ground with a surface of broken coral, but when planted on sandy alluvium soon becomes sickly. The natives bake the fruits of the pandanus and crush out the sap, which sets to a thick porridge; this is made into rolls and provides a useful food for sea journeys. The pandanus leaves are used for house-building, for making mats and sails and for many other purposes. Vegetable gardens are made with the help of soil imported from other islands. About the coral islands in the Caroline and Marianas groups little need be said; the vegetation is like that of the Marshall islands, though more luxuriant. The coconut palm grows on every island of sufficient size; it is the only plant which grows luxuriantly. Other common trees are the breadfruit, which is important on these islands as a source of timber as well as of food, several kinds of pandanus, *Calophyllum inophyllum* and *Terminalia catappa*. Many of the coral islands are fringed by mangrove swamps, but the mangrove trees are smaller and of fewer species than on the 'high' islands. Apart from the few trees the vegetation consists of herbaceous plants and shrubs, all belonging to species common throughout the Pacific. The shrub *Scaevola frutescens*, here growing about 3 ft. high, covers large areas on many of these islands.

The 'high' Carolines fall, from the point of view of vegetation, into two groups: the eastern, including Kusaie, Ponape and Truk, appear to be entirely wooded when seen from the sea; the western group, including Yap and the volcanic islands of the Palau group, are mainly covered with grassland, trees being found mainly near the coast and along streams. The reason for this difference between the two groups

Plate 74. The west coast of Saipan

A view to the north-east from a low point about one mile north of Garapan. The hills are those of the northern ridge of Saipan.

Plate 75. A boulder, Kusaie beach

Large masses of volcanic rock are common off the coast,

Plate 76. Vegetation on Likiep, Marshall islands
Typical scrub vegetation of soils formed from disintegrated coral.

Plate 77. Kusaie lagoon
The mangrove fringe of the narrow southern lagoon.

is uncertain; probably it is because the eastern islands have a more evenly distributed rainfall.

On Kusaie the coast has in some places a dark green fringe of mangroves, in others white sandy beaches with a background of coconut palms, mango and breadfruit trees. The chief tree in the outer part of the mangrove belt is *Sonneratia*; further in *Heritiera* and *Barringtonia* are met with. At the mouth of streams there are patches of nipa palms. On the sandy beaches the creeping stems and deeply cleft leaves of the goat's-foot convolvulus cover the ground; with it grow the silvery-leaved tree *Tournefortia argentea*, a great many creepers, including *Derris uliginosa* and a wild jasmine, and many other common shore plants.

In the interior of the island the original forest, or most of it, has long since been destroyed, its place being taken by secondary forest 30 to 40 ft. high, which shrubs and lianas make into an impassable jungle. The taller trees which here and there raise their crowns above the rest are mostly banyan figs. Among the trees there are small scattered clearings covered with shrubs and tall grass.

The natives cultivate patches of taro, sugar cane, yams, sweet potatoes, etc., moving on to fresh ground as soon as the productivity of the old begins to fall. Besides these vegetable gardens large areas of the island are covered with mixed plantations of fruit trees and palms. Breadfruit, coconut palms, bananas, lemons and oranges grow here together with various wild species, with an undergrowth of ferns and rank weeds, the general appearance resembling a park or botanical garden which has run wild.

Both Ponape and Truk are partly cultivated and partly wooded, like Kusaie, and there are patches of grass mixed with the forest. On Truk there is some high forest which may be a remnant of the original virgin forest. On the steeper slopes the forest becomes dwarfed to a mere scrub and grasses as tall as a man are mixed with the bushes. Ponape and Truk are the home of a palm, *Coelococcus carolinensis*, the seeds of which provide a kind of vegetable ivory that has long been one of the exports of Ponape. The tree is like a sago palm, but has a trunk 20 to 30 ft. high; it is planted by the natives and also grows wild by streams.

The vegetation of Yap is representative of the western 'high' islands. There are three concentric zones: first, the mangrove and shore vegetation; then a belt of cultivated land, which is so thickly planted with trees as to look like forest; then, covering the whole of the hilly interior of the island and occupying about three-quarters of its area, there is a gently rolling grassy savannah with scattered pandanus trees (Plate 78).

The mangrove forest is 30 to 50 ft. high and consists of many separate sections, intersected by channels, which, at least at high tide, are navigable by small boats. The largest expanses are in the bays of Gagil island and on the south-east coast of Yap island. The mangroves which grow furthest out to sea are the two stilt-rooted Rhizophoras, which in places extend out on to the bare coral reef; on the landward side, where the ground is uncovered at low tide, these give place to *Sonneratia acida*, which has lighter green foliage, and several other species.

On sandy shores where there are no mangroves, and in many places on the inside of the mangrove belt, there is the usual beach vegetation of grasses and herbaceous plants, such as *Ipomoea pes-caprae*, *Euphorbia atoto* and *Vigna lutea*. A few small trees grow with these plants. A showy species found here is *Crinum macrantherum*, a lily, with a head of magnificent white flowers borne on a stem 3 ft. long. Where the land begins to rise behind the shore there is in most places a belt of thick woodland. The trees are low and bound together into an impenetrable mass by creepers, one of which, *Caesalpinia nuga*, has a stem armed with formidable backward-pointing thorns.

The native cultivation, as on Kusaie, consists of semi-wild plantations of trees and small vegetable patches, some near the villages, others scattered over the countryside. Many useful plants, among others the papaya and the citrus fruits, sow themselves and it is impossible to distinguish between what is cultivated and what is wild. In the plantations bananas, coconuts, breadfruit, Tahitian chestnuts and other trees are grown. Areca-nut palms are only less plentiful than the coconuts, the natives being great betel-chewers. *Piper betle*, the leaves of which are chewed with the areca nuts, is common everywhere, climbing up the tree trunks.

Taro, here called *nfeu*, and the similar-looking *lack* (*Cyrtosperma edule*), are grown on damp soil, either in small natural swamps by streams or in rectangular pits a few yards wide dug out by the natives. Other native vegetables include several kinds of yams, sweet potatoes, and sugar cane. In addition, hibiscus, crotons, *Cordyline terminalis* and other plants are grown for ornament.

The grassland of the interior of Yap makes a sharp contrast with the tropical luxuriance of the narrow cultivated belt. Making his way upwards on to this grassland, the traveller has in most places to pass through dense thickets of bamboos, sometimes 300 to 400 yd. wide, before emerging into the open. The grass grows to knee-height and is mixed with many herbaceous plants, including an interesting pitcher plant, *Nepenthes phyllamphora*, and scattered bushes. The whole savannah is sprinkled with trees of *Pandanus tectorius*, growing on the average 10 to 20 yd. apart, but sometimes closer and sometimes absent altogether. In wet places the grass gives place to sedges, while exceptionally dry ground—for instance, the ridge which crosses Gagil island—is like a desert, the soil being quite bare or dotted with dwarf bushes and other low-growing drought-resistant plants.

Small woods and groups of trees are found here and there in valleys. The chief tree is *Calophyllum inophyllum*, which also occasionally grows with pandanus on the open savannah. This, with *Cynometra ramiflora*, *Afzelia bijuga*, the breadfruit tree and the stems of palms, provides the chief timber supply of the island.

The vegetation of the volcanic islands of the Palau group closely resembles that of Yap. There is a narrow cultivated belt, but the greater part of the area consists of rolling grassland with scattered palms and pandanus trees. Trees grow better than on Yap, perhaps because the soil is more fertile, and some reach a considerable size. The large tree, *Serianthes grandiflora*, belonging to the pea family, is used to make the celebrated native canoes.

The vegetation of the Marianas, apart from Guam (p. 466), is little known, though in recent years the Japanese have given some attention to it. In most respects it seems to be similar to that of the Carolines. The larger islands are girdled with mangrove forests, on the landward side of which there are generally sandy beaches with herbaceous vegetation. In the tangled beach forest which forms a narrow belt behind this herbaceous zone the common trees include *Hernandia ovigera*, species of *Pandanus* and *Barringtonia*, and *Excoecaria agallocha*, a tree with a very poisonous milky juice. Behind the beach forest is the cultivated area in which the coconut palm is the chief crop; in addition the breadfruit, papaya, banana, Tahitian chestnut and other common tropical fruits are grown. Wild trees, including one of the pea family, which is largely used as a building timber, grow mixed with the cultivated species. Further into the interior of the islands the cultivated area comes to an end and gives place to secondary rain forest, and on Saipan and Tinian to grassland. The abundance of creepers makes the forest very difficult to walk through; one of the most striking trees is a fig (*Ficus*) with an enormously thick trunk. The soil is poor and most of the trees are consequently of no great height. A number of useful timbers are found in the islands, including *Calophyllum inophyllum*, *Intsia bijuga* and *Serianthes grandiflora*.

Fauna

Apart from those introduced in European times, the only mammals found in the islands are pigs, rats and bats. Pigs and rats are found almost everywhere. The pigs are principally of two kinds—the one long-snouted and lean; the other short and fat. A fruit bat, or 'flying fox', is found on Yap. Deer and cattle (including the *carabao*, or water buffalo) were introduced into the Marianas by the Spaniards. Dogs, mostly of a coppery-brown colour and often tailless, are kept by the natives both as watch dogs and for food. Cats are also found in some native communities.

Land birds are not very numerous. They include a reddish-brown parrakeet (*cherret*) which is peculiar to Ponape. There are various kinds of doves, pigeons, a kind of blackbird, a red-breasted honey-eater (*Myzomela rubrata*), which seeks its food on coconut palm spathes, and several kingfishers, a species of pigeon and an owl. Sea-birds include a sandpiper, varieties of white gull known as *kake*, three kinds of heron and some terns.

Reptiles are many and varied and include crocodiles in the rivers of Babelthuap in the Palau group, an iguana found in the Marianas and another in Yap. There is also a large black skink, variously known as *kieil*, *kuel* or *kiuen*; this lives in holes in the ground which are frequently burial places. Among many kinds of lizard are a brownish-black house lizard and a small green lizard with a bright blue tail, which is the most common reptile. A curious species of horned frog is also found. Two species of snakes are reported from Palau.

Eels are plentiful and much feared by the natives. One species, called *madro* by the natives, is amphibious, and has its habitation in the marshes behind the mangrove swamps. It is green in colour, up to 3 ft. long and 1 in. thick. Many kinds of freshwater eels abound in pools on the larger islands and grow to a considerable size.

Among insects are a house-fly (which is very common), a sand-fly, butterflies and moths, ants, fleas and beetles; there are also spiders, scorpions and centipedes. The scorpions are small and sand-coloured. Their sting, though painful, is not very dangerous. Centipedes are common in the thatch and under the floors of native houses. The marine fauna includes various species of crab, among them a large brown crab (known by the natives as *alemang*), which inhabits the edges of mangrove swamps; a digging crab (known as *paru*); and the robber crab (*Birgus latro*). Turtles are plentiful. Lobsters and crayfish are frequently caught by the natives for food. Amongst many kinds of fish, bonito are most sought after by fishing expeditions.

HISTORY

Discovery

The Marianas and most of the Caroline islands and Marshall islands were discovered early in the history of European activity in the Pacific. Guam, in the Marianas, which was discovered by Ferdinand Magellan in 1521, was the first island in the South Seas on which Europeans made a landing. The natives of Guam stole one of Magellan's boats, for which reason he named the group the Ladrones ('Robber islands'), a name by which they continued to be known till recent times. About four years later an expedition sent out by Don Jorge de Menezes, Spanish governor of the Moluccas, visited the western Carolines. This was commanded by Diogo da Rocha. A number of islands were discovered, apparently in the Palau group. Other Spanish navigators, following Magellan's path to the Moluccas, passed through the islands. In 1526 the expedition of Loyasa and Del Cano (at this stage under the command of Toribio Alonzo de Salazar) discovered an island in the northern Marshall islands or eastern Carolines and visited the southern Marianas. A year later Alvaro de Saavedra passed through the same region, making several fresh discoveries. Many more islands were seen in 1542 by Ruy Lopez de Villalobos. A new stage in the penetration of the islands was begun with the expedition of Miguel de Legaspi in 1564–5. Legaspi saw many islands in both the Carolines and Marianas, and the small packet *San Lucar*, which temporarily deserted the expedition, visited a number of others. Legaspi's object was the establishment of a Spanish settlement in the Philippines, and from this time onwards Spanish vessels passed regularly through the fringes of Micronesia on their voyages from Acapulco, in Mexico, to Manila.

In 1579 Guam was visited by Francis Drake, in the *Golden Hind*. From that time onwards there were many navigators of nationalities other than Spanish passing through the area. In 1586 another English voyager, Cavendish, called in at Guam. In 1600 the Dutch navigator Oliver van Noort was there, and sixteen years later the Dutch fleet of Joris van Speilbergen called there in the course of a voyage round the world. Voyagers crossing the Pacific before the south-east trades, bound for the East Indies, were certain to pass at some point through the Micronesian islands. Thus, long before many important island groups further to the east had been sighted, the main outlines of this part of the Pacific were known.

Spanish Colonization of the Marianas

Spanish sovereignty was proclaimed over the Marianas in 1564 by Legaspi, at Saipan. The islands became a recognized place at which the galleons passing backwards and forwards each year between the Philippines and Mexico could refresh and revictual, but for over a century there was no permanent Spanish settlement in the group. In 1668, however, the Jesuit priest Diego Luis Sanvitores founded a mission there. The missionaries were opposed at first by a Chinese settled on Guam, where he had been wrecked some twenty years before, and by the Chamorro wise men (the *makuhna*). In addition, they roused the indignation of the young unmarried men by trying to abolish the large club-houses, where the latter lived with unmarried girls, and antagonized the parents by baptizing children against their will. In 1670 one of the missionaries was killed after forcibly baptizing a child. Sanvitores himself was killed for the same reason two years later. After this there ensued a war of extermination, which lasted with some peaceful intervals for 23 years. The Spanish forces were small and their opponents many, and the ferocious massacres of the natives by the Spaniards were no doubt partly caused by fear. But the bullets of the Spaniards were more than a match for the slingstones of the natives. Peace and order appear to have been maintained in the islands without the need to station a garrison there. When Dampier visited Guam in 1686 he found that the Governor had the support of only 20 to 30 soldiers; and when Woodes Rogers was there in 1710 he was able to obtain supplies without the Spaniards being in a position to interfere with his proceedings.

The early hostility of the Chamorro to the Roman Catholic missionaries was gradually broken down. In part, the missionaries gained their popularity through supporting the natives against the aggressions of the Spanish soldiers sent to the islands. They built a school at Agaña, in Guam, and established several very successful farms on the island. In 1769, however, they were deported from the island, under the terms of a decree of the King of Spain. Their lands were confiscated to the Crown and cultivation was subsequently neglected. Their missionary work was taken over by the Augustine friars.

After the expulsion of the Jesuits little advance was made, socially or economically, until well into the nineteenth century. In 1828, however, Don Francisco Ramon de Villalobos was sent to the Marianas to study conditions there. He urged the introduction of a policy of free trade, since it was difficult to enforce customs regulations, and with the opening up of trade with China the islands were increasingly placed on the verge of an important trade route. He also proposed various measures for the encouragement of agriculture, and built a kiln for the manufacture of pottery. In 1851 a party of 65 convicts from the Philippines was landed in Guam. It was hoped that they could be employed on agricultural work to the advantage of the islands; but, owing to the difficulty of guarding against mutiny amongst them in such an isolated colony, the experiment was soon abandoned. A few years later Japanese were brought to Guam. Some failed to survive the change in environment, and the remainder returned home.

Outside the Marianas Spanish activity in the area was almost negligible up to this time. Attempts were made by Roman Catholic missionaries to land on several of the Carolines, but no success was obtained.

The Visits of Whalers and Traders

Among the best known of early visits to Palau is that of Henry Wilson, who was wrecked there in 1783, while acting as captain of one of the English East India Company's ships. He lived there for a year, building a schooner with native assistance and sailed away after hoisting the British flag. He was followed by Captain John McCluer, sent with two ships from Bombay. McCluer claimed Palau as British territory and remained there for 15 months, but he finally abandoned his plans and the group was never annexed.

By about 1840 the Carolines had begun to be visited by a considerable number of whaling vessels. On Ponape and Kusaie, in particular, there were quite large numbers of Europeans. Some had abandoned their ships to remain as beachcombers for the rest of their lives; others resided in the islands for only a few months, until a satisfactory position was offered them on another vessel. At certain seasons of the year, when the sperm whalers were working in this part of the Pacific, it was not unusual to find four or five whaling vessels at Metalanim, in Ponape, or at Lele, in Kusaie, at the same time. Most were American vessels.

One of the earliest forms of trade in the Carolines was that in *bêche-de-mer*. Many of the islands were tried—Ponape, Kusaie, Yap, and several of the islands of the Palau area. Most active in this enterprise were vessels under the British flag and under Spanish colours. Ultimately of far greater importance was the trade in coconut oil, and later in copra, built up in both the Marshall islands and the Caroline islands by the German Godeffroy company, from its Pacific islands headquarters in Samoa, and by other firms centred on Honolulu.

Missionary Activity

Contemporary with the growth of whaling and trade in the Carolines and Marshalls was the beginning of missionary work. In 1852 the American Board of Commissioners for Foreign Missions, a predominantly Congregationalist body, established mission stations in Kusaie and Ponape. During the following years the mission extended its work to many other islands in the Carolines and Marshalls. From the first Hawaiian missionaries worked beside their American colleagues, and in 1857 the Hawaiian Evangelical Association became formally connected with the work. By 1874 the mission was sufficiently well established for a considerable extension in its educational programme to be made and for much of the responsibility to be devolved upon native teachers.

Spanish-German Rivalry

Although German commercial interests were extensive in both the Marshall islands and the Carolines by about 1870, the German authorities continued for some time to be anxious to avoid any political commitments in the Pacific area. The Spanish government, however, became concerned as to its sovereignty over the Carolines. The first overt incident occurred when the Spanish consul at Hong Kong requested the Governor of that colony to levy customs dues on a German vessel about to sail for Palau. This he refused to do. The Spanish government then proclaimed Spanish sovereignty over the Carolines and issued a decree instructing all vessels proceeding to the Carolines to put in first at the Philippines. Considerable diplomatic activity between the governments of Spain, Germany and Great Britain followed this move. Finally, in 1877, all three governments exchanged notes recognizing complete freedom of trade to islands not actually occupied by any European country. In 1882, as the result of a local dispute, two British warships bombarded the village of Melekeiok in Palau. This led the Spanish government to announce their occupation of Palau and to send ships to proclaim their formal occupation of Yap in 1885. They were forestalled, however, by the Germans, whose policy had changed, and who had already hoisted their flag in Yap. The Spanish government protested and the matter was referred to the Pope, who decided in favour of Spain. The Germans withdrew and annexed the Marshall islands later in the same year.

Spanish Occupation of the Carolines

After the decision of the Pope in favour of the Spanish claims, the Spanish authorities occupied Yap. They also raised their flag on Ponape, and in 1887 established a settlement on that island—the Colonia de Santiago. From the first they found the situation on Ponape difficult. A Roman Catholic mission station at Kiti, in the south of the island, had become embroiled in a quarrel with the Congregationalist mission on the island. In 1887 the head of the latter mission, E. T. Doane, was deported to Manila. This action was later to lead to complications with the United States. At the same time a native rising broke out in Ponape fostered by the discontented native converts of the American mission. Punitive expeditions and further native risings and massacres followed in rapid succession. During this troubled period the American corvette *Alliance* arrived off the coast of Metalanim demanding compensation for the expulsion of the missionary. The Spaniards paid an indemnity and the remaining American missionaries were removed from Ponape to Kusaie. The embittered feelings of the two nations remained. The rebellion continued until the appointment of Don Jose Pidal as commander at Ponape in 1894, when a more conciliatory policy was adopted. In 1896, however, on his retirement, another rebellion broke out.

In 1898, at the end of the Spanish-American war, Guam was ceded to the United States by purchase, and in the following year the remaining Spanish possessions in Micronesia were ceded to Germany in exchange for a cash payment of about £850,000.

German Occupation of the Marshall Islands

From 1888 the government of the Marshall islands was carried out by German Imperial officials who were paid and advised by the Jaluit company, and this system continued until 1906. From 1899, however, the other German possessions, including the Carolines and Marianas, were administered directly by a Governor appointed by the Emperor, and finally in 1906 the Jaluitgesellschaft surrendered its authority. German administration continued until the outbreak of war in 1914. The islands were then occupied by Japan. In 1920 they were handed over to Japan under mandate from the League of Nations. Their later history is covered in later sections of this and the following Chapters.

POPULATION

Before their discovery by Europeans, the Carolines, Marshall islands, and Marianas were thickly populated. Subsequently, a decline set in.

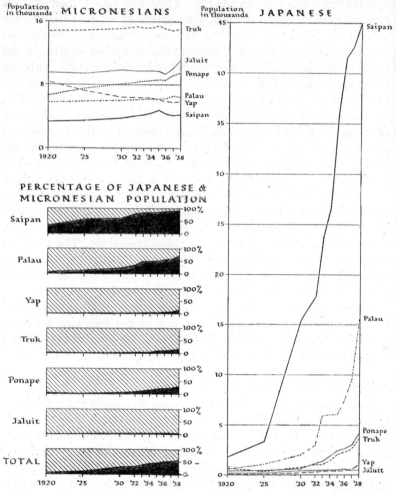

Fig. 70. Comparison of the growth of Japanese and Micronesian population in the Japanese mandated islands (percentage of Japanese and Micronesians by districts and of the total population of the mandated islands)

The Japanese element is shown in solid black. Based on statistics in the *Japan-Manchukuo Year Book* (Tokyo, 1934–40).

Tuberculosis and venereal diseases were among its major causes. In 1920 the native population of the area was 48,505 (including 2,824 Chamorro, of mixed Micronesian, Tagalog and European origin—see p. 327). At that time there were also 3,671 Japanese and 46 'foreigners' in the islands. A comparison of Japanese and Micronesian population (Fig. 70) shows that between 1920 and 1938 there was a very large increase in the number of Japanese, who increased to 70,141, and a small increase among Micronesians, who numbered 50,868 at the latter date.

The Japanese

Comparison of the growth of the Japanese population by districts shows that in Saipan, the numbers of Japanese rose from the initial figure of 1,758 in 1920 to 44,991 in 1938. In the other administrative areas the Japanese population increased more slowly, reaching the following figures: Palau, 15,669; Yap, 1,119; Truk, 3,657; Ponape, 4,201; Jaluit, 504. Large-scale increases in Palau, Ponape, and Truk occurred at a later date than in Saipan and clearly followed the economic development of the islands. Sugar planting in Saipan was followed by the development of fishing, mixed farming and bauxite mining in Palau, and starch manufacture in Ponape. A population increase which occurred in 1938 in Yap may be explained by the development of bauxite mining in that island. In the Marshall islands (Jaluit district) the only important industry, copra production, is in native hands. Lack of precise information makes it difficult to determine how far the increase is due to a natural increase and how far it is due to immigration. The comparatively small number of women in proportion to men in the early years shows that most of the original growth was by immigration and not by natural increase. Later, however, the proportion of women to men rose considerably. The following Table shows the percentages of Japanese men to women between 1920 and 1937 in the whole of the mandated islands:

Year	Men	Women	Women per 100 men
1920	3,097	574	18·5
1925	5,074	2,356	46·4
1930	12,262	7,573	61·7
1935	31,158	20,703	66·5
1936	33,313	23,183	69·5
1937	34,706	24,274	69·7

Based on T. Yanaihara, *Pacific Islands under Japanese Mandate*, p. 30 (Shanghai, 1939).

From 1930 to 1937 the natural increase was about 10,000, while in the same period the total increase was just under 40,000. Immigration, therefore, accounted for about three-quarters of the increase in this latter period, and for a considerably higher proportion before 1930. Between 1932 and 1937 the average birth rate among the Japanese population was 52 per 1,000, while the death rate over the same period was 12·8 per thousand.

Micronesians

The two following Tables show the birth and death rates of the Micronesian population (excluding Chamorro) for 1925–9 and 1935.

Average Birth and Death Rates of the Native Population, 1925–9

District	Births per 1,000	Deaths per 1,000	Increase per 1,000
Saipan	31·6	34·4	− 2·8
Yap	14·4	44·1	− 29·7
Palau	24·4	21·5	2·9
Truk	23·8	24·1	− 0·3
Ponape	25·5	21·7	3·8
Jaluit	17·0	16·7	0·3

Based on T. Yanaihara, *Pacific Islands under Japanese Mandate*, p. 46 (Shanghai, 1939).

Birth and Death Rates of the Native Population, 1935

District	Births per 1,000	Deaths per 1,000	Increase per 1,000
Saipan	36·4	26·5	9·9
Yap	12·0	28·0	− 16·0
Palau	24·3	12·8	11·5
Truk	30·1	27·8	2·3
Ponape	27·1	13·1	14·0
Jaluit	20·8	22·9	− 2·1

Based on T. Yanaihara, *Pacific Islands under Japanese Mandate*, p. 46 (Shanghai, 1939).

THE NATIVE PEOPLES

The area administered by Japan under mandate embraces all of Micronesia with the exception of the Gilbert islands. The inhabitants, though by no means homogeneous either in physical type or culture, are sufficiently similar to be regarded as of one racial and cultural group. There is, however, a broad distinction between those Micronesians originally inhabiting the Marianas and those in the Caroline and Marshall islands. The Japanese, following the Spaniards, differentiate between them, calling the former Chamorro, and the latter by the Polynesian word *kanaka*, simply meaning men. The latter term has no racial or cultural significance and will be avoided by using the term 'native' to apply to all the indigenous population except the Chamorro, who will be referred to specifically.

The Chamorro came under Spanish influence during the later seventeenth and eighteenth centuries. They intermarried with Spanish and Tagalog immigrants, so that there are probably no Chamorro to-day of pure Micronesian descent. They accepted Christianity and adopted the dress, agricultural implements and methods of house-building of their Spanish rulers (Plate 104). They retained their language, however, and many of their traditional institutions, including matrilineal descent. At the present time most of the Chamorro live on Guam, but there is also a considerable Chamorro community on Saipan. Many are employed by the Japanese as petty officials, overseers or labourers in the sugar mills on Saipan, and in the mines on Angaur. Many raise crops of maize, sweet potatoes, tobacco, etc., mostly on a subsistence basis, on their own lands or as tenant farmers. The Chamorro are discussed in detail in the Chapter dealing with the island of Guam (pp. 468–71).

The natives of the Caroline and Marshall islands are not so strongly influenced by contact with European civilization, and they are not employed to any great extent by the Japanese in skilled tasks, being employed only as labourers in the phosphate workings or in the construction of roads.

Both the Chamorro and the 'natives' are friendly and hospitable, although a native rebellion broke out in Ponape in 1911. They are said to resent the Japanese. Even the poorest natives will always offer food, and at night-time provide a sleeping mat, though they expect a gift in return. In business, chiefs will bargain hard but honestly, but it is said that commoners will attempt to take advantage of anyone who is negotiating with them.

PHYSICAL TYPE

The Micronesians are closely related to the Polynesians in physical type, but there are many traces of Melanesian and Indonesian admixture. The peoples of Micronesia are of medium height and well built. Their skin is in general a light brown, only slightly darker than that of the Samoans. Hair is generally straight or wavy, though typical Melanesian frizzly hair sometimes occurs. As a rule the Micronesians have long faces with high foreheads, broad cheek-bones, wide noses and large, though not prognathous, mouths. The epicanthic fold does not occur more frequently than among Polynesians. The cephalic index varies considerably, being as high as 80 in Palau. Heads are longer towards the east. In the Marshall islands the average cephalic index of a sample of the male population was 71·6.

LANGUAGE

The native languages throughout the area belong to the Malayo-Polynesian family. Their grammar and syntax, which are complex, have been briefly described in vol. I, p. 386; an example is given in the description of the language of the Chamorro of Guam (p. 470). There is considerable variety in the dialects spoken from island to island. Malay and Melanesian affinities are more strongly marked in the west; closer relationships with Polynesia are seen in the Marshall islands.

The Japanese in their educational system have laid great stress on the teaching of Japanese for administrative purposes and as a kind of *lingua franca*. Since native children have been attending Japanese schools for about 25 years, it is reasonable to suppose that many natives can now speak Japanese. The spread of Japanese speech among natives, and a partial decline in native dialects have probably been facilitated by the movements of labourers from outlying islands —e.g., those who come to work in the phosphate mines of Angaur and in other commercial undertakings.

Owing to missionary influence some European languages are spoken. In the Marshall islands and in Kusaie, as the result of the work of American missionaries, many of the older men speak English. Owing to the former presence of German missionaries in Palau, there are some German-speaking natives there.

CULTURE

Houses (Plates 80–1)

Throughout Micronesia, except in the Marianas, where the Chamorro build houses of wood or plaster in European style, dwellings are of wooden construction and rectangular or occasionally hexagonal in plan. The roofs are generally thatched with palm leaves, and screens of mat or wicker do duty as walls. In general a platform of stones about 3 ft. high serves to elevate the house above the ground level. Timber floors are sometimes found. In addition to the ordinary dwelling-houses there are ambitious structures used as club-houses for the young unmarried men, for the entertainment of visitors, and

Plate 78. Scrub vegetation in the interior of Yap

Much of the interior of Yap is covered with scrub. In the foreground is one of the pandanus trees which are common constituents of this type of vegetation.

Plate 79. Pandanus, Wotje atoll, Marshall islands
Typical pandanus scrub on a coral island.

Plate 80. A village in the Caroline islands

The houses are of timber-frame construction, with thatched roofs. They are typical of the houses of the more developed parts of the Caroline islands, such as the Palau group.

Plate 81. A house in the Caroline islands

The light construction is suited to the climate; the walls are of movable panels of wickerwork.

for other ceremonial occasions. These club-houses (*bai*), which are built by the combined labour of the whole community, are most common in Palau and Yap. Each village has not less than two and sometimes as many as six. They are usually some 15 ft. wide, and 50 ft. long with a lofty roof of thatch sloping steeply from a ridge-pole running the whole length of the building. The ridge-pole projects at each end, giving a characteristic pointed appearance. The ends and sides are of wood and are ornamented with elaborate carving and painted designs, both geometrical and zoomorphic. There are doors at each end and occasional doors and windows at each side. Access to the doors is gained by posts notched to serve as ladders.

The framework is of heavy timber of breadfruit or *Callophyllum* wood, lashed together with coconut sennit. In Palau the main structural members are arranged in two rows which slope upwards to meet in a line, where they support the ridge-pole. In Yap, however, three rows of vertical poles are used. The central one supports the ridge-pole, while the lower ones reach only as far as the eaves.

Dwelling houses are built on the same general principles, but are smaller and of more primitive construction, especially in the more easterly islands. Almost everywhere the pitch of the roof is lower than in the ceremonial club-houses. Dwelling houses are frequently dark, dirty and insanitary and have no windows. The Japanese have granted a subsidy towards the construction of more sanitary dwellings with corrugated-iron roofs built to a standard specification (p. 345).

Settlements (Plate 82)

In many parts of the mandated islands, notably the more remote atolls, there are no true villages. Settlements consist of series of isolated dwellings and out-buildings built in a line along the lagoon shore of an atoll with gardens surrounding the houses. Where trading posts or churches have been set up, true villages have come into being. There is no general plan for villages; the arrangement usually depends on the conformation of the ground. In the island of Yap there is usually a rough stone causeway or jetty for canoes to land, with a few huts on the beach. A road leads inland to the centre of the village, where there is a square or meeting place known as *arau*. Coconut palms, houses, and taro patches are distributed near this more or less at random. Each village is divided into two halves, each half having its own club-houses, but the *arau* is a common meeting place for both sides of the village. In some villages in Palau the dual organization of the village is carried to such lengths that there are two distinct channels through the mangroves and two quays, each used exclusively by the two moieties into which the village is divided. The stone paving on the paths of the villages usually stops short at the limits of the settlements.

Social Organization

As elsewhere, the basic social unit is the family, consisting of a man, his wife, and their children. But family ties are extended considerably, and each family is part of a well-developed clan system. Each clan is supposedly descended from a common ancestor, frequently an animal. Taboos exist against the eating of the totemic animal, but these are treated seriously only in Palau. Clans are not limited to narrow district boundaries; their members are scattered in small numbers over many parts of the Caroline and Marshall islands. Villages or island communities are made up of numerous subsections of clans with counterparts in other islands. Clan affiliation is important to the natives for many reasons. Travellers feel sure of shelter and sustenance when visiting an island where there are some of their own clan. Marriage is exogamous—i.e., it can be contracted only between people of different clans. Rank and status are obtained through membership of noble clans. Land is frequently owned on a clan basis and work is generally organized among people of a particular clan. The clans are governed by chiefs, whose relative importance is discussed below (p. 331). Except in the four south-western islands of Merir, Pulo Anna, Sonsorol and Tobi, descent is through the female line. In former times a man lived with his wife's clan, but this rule is being broken up under Japanese influence. In Yap, patrilocal residence is general. Divorce, contracted on the wish of either partner, is frequent, but a sum is usually paid in compensation if either party remarries. Strict fidelity is expected of married couples, but no great value is set upon the premarital chastity of either sex. Girls who have served for a period in the young men's houses are not regarded as less desirable wives than other women.

Clubs and Societies

In the west Carolines the men's clubs attain considerable development and are housed in large well-built ceremonial buildings. Every man belongs to a particular club according to his age and position in the village. Each club is presided over by the senior man of the highest ranking clan using that particular club. In former times they formed a sort of garrison since the young men, who always slept in them, were thus gathered ready to repel an attack in the night. With the more settled conditions resulting from the alien occupation of the islands this function has ceased, but the clubs remain the centres for the organization of village activities such as house-building, road-making, and public works generally, as well as fishing expeditions. The club-houses are the ceremonial and recreational centres of the villages. Visitors were entertained and given lodging in the *bai*. Women, usually supplied by arrangement with a neighbouring village, entertained the men and served as formal prostitutes. No social stigma attached to them if they came from socially important clans, and in Yap on returning to their own villages they were each presented with a large piece of stone money (p. 336). Women from servile clans, however, would probably remain in the club-houses for life. The institution has been prohibited by the Japanese, but how far the prohibition has proved effective is uncertain.

Rank, Chieftainship and Political Organization

The typical form of political organization in the islands in former times was that in each clan the senior man was chief and that the chief of the most important clan in an area acted as a paramount chief. Though the centralized Japanese administration has been super-imposed upon this structure, it still largely survives. There are some important variations from it in particular areas. In Palau the village, and not the clan, is the basic political unit. The heads of the more important of the seven to twenty kinship groups which go to form a village constitute a council. The senior member of the council is the headman of the village. The other councillors are graded after him in order of seniority, and each member of the council has certain specific functions. The headman deals with external political matters. The second man deals with domestic matters. The third was responsible (before the Spanish occupation of the islands) for the defence of the village. Groups of villages, in Palau, formed themselves into con-federacies, of which there were about 8 or 10. The most important were Koror and Melekeiok.

In Yap, where there were about 100 villages, each had a chief who was the senior member of the most important clan. These villages were grouped into eight rival confederacies with paramount chiefs. There was, moreover, a rigid class system. There were two noble clans from which chiefs were drawn, three clans of free people, and three of servile people. There is a distinct difference in status in native minds between villages. Whole villages would be inhabited by noble, free, or servile clans, and while each village had its headman or chief and council of elders, paramount chiefs were drawn only from the villages with noble clans. Slave villages owned no land but merely occupied it, and they were liable to provide labour for the noble villages. Marriage between the different classes was discouraged. Special deference was paid to chiefs and people of noble rank. A commoner meeting a chief would step aside and bow deeply, and would only address him when sitting. Canoes would not pass a chief's house until given permission to do so. To-day, in some parts, a man does not shake hands with a married woman, as this may be regarded as a sexual advance; very great deference is shown to wives and daughters of chiefs.

The peoples of certain of the neighbouring atolls had a different status. They were regarded as vassals (*primathau*) and paid tribute to certain dominant villages in Yap. The obligation was not, however, entirely one-sided. Visitors to Yap from the islands of *primathau* status, e.g., Mogamog, Fais and Sorol, became guests when they visited the paramount village. A modern, and certainly unexpected, result of this obligation has been brought about by the establishment of a Japanese school on Yap. Children from the outside villages go to Yap for their schooling, and during their stay the people are bound to support them. Similarly travellers on their way from islands of *primathau* status to work in the phosphate mines of Angaur (or on their return) can claim subsistence. A feudal due and its reciprocal obligation have thus virtually been reversed under modern conditions.

In the Marshall islands each clan, whatever its distribution in the group, has a chief whose primary duty is to administer the land, and each section of a clan (in a particular settlement or on a particular atoll) has its own petty chief or headman. Over all, in former times, were a number of paramount chiefs. These were clan chiefs who had gained ascendency over their fellow chiefs. Considerable deference was paid to them, and they received tribute on a more or less feudal basis.

Inheritance and Land Tenure

Generally inheritance is through the female line, but exceptions occur, as in the islands south-west of Palau. The system is being changed under the influence of the Japanese, of missionary activity, and of the growth of the conception of private property. In matrilineal societies status is transmitted through the mother and not through the father. Material possessions belonging to a man do not, as might be expected, go to his son but to his sister's son. But it frequently happens that even in a matrilineal society, especially where the concept of individual property is more highly developed, inheritance is patrilineal. Thus in Yap a man's possessions go to his eldest son, or sometimes to any child he chooses. Frequently, for example, he will leave a taro plot to his favourite daughter—an appropriate inheritance since taro-growing is women's work.

Land is usually held, by native usage, on a collective basis. In Palau land belongs not to the individual, but to the *blai* (a group larger than the simple family, which forms a sub-section of the clan). The land is administered by the head of this group, who also owns individually a small piece of land (usually a taro plot) known as 'the basis of the title', and upon this his rank and chieftainship depend. This qualification for chieftainship applies also in many other parts of the mandated islands. Such land may be sold or given away, and whatever the rank of the receiver his social status will be raised to that attached to the particular piece of land. In Truk, and also in Yap, there is a distinction between the ownership of the land, which belongs to the clan as a whole, and to the ownership of trees and produce which belong to the cultivator. In Ponape, prior to 1910, all land in the hilly regions was communal, but, where cultivated, it was divided into fields which were worked by the clan under the instructions of the chief. In principle, he arranged the collection and distribution of produce for the general benefit; but, in practice, his position of authority frequently tempted him to assume a despotic position, and the produce came to be regarded as tribute. Particular plots tended to be associated with individuals and a man's sister's son inherited the right (and the duty) of cultivating definite plots. After the Jokaj rebellion of 1911, however, the German authorities divided the land into plots owned by individuals, with the proviso that it should be inherited by a system of patrilineal primogeniture.

In the Marshall islands land is divided between numerous clans and allotted to individual members of the clan to work. Each member of the clan contributes produce to the chief, who divides it among the clan. The system was used by the Germans, who collected a poll tax in copra through the chief.

Religion

The native theological beliefs divided supernatural beings into heavenly gods, gods of nature, earthly gods and ancestors. The heavenly gods were, with the exception of the god of death, not regarded as playing a very important part in the guidance of human affairs. Nature gods, the personification of natural phenomena, such as winds and hurricanes, were very greatly feared and propitiated by sacrifices of food. By far the most important were the earthly gods. They were the tutelary deities of important families or deceased ancestors.

There was no separate priestly caste. It was believed that all persons possessed the power of invoking the good offices of the lesser spirits, and some were thought to have inherited or acquired the ability to deal successfully with the major gods. Certain particularly successful men were thought to have the power to communicate with the gods and interpret their wishes. In Palau, for example, any man who could convince his fellows that he had the necessary qualifications could become a priest and ranked with the chiefs of his village or district.

These gods had their 'canoes' in which they were supposed to visit the earth. Sometimes an altar actually took the form of an outrigger canoe, and at Truk models of double canoes, which are no longer extant, are used for religious purposes. Taboos on eating certain animals, applicable to particular clans, are attributable to the belief that the spirit of the clan ancestor inhabits the animal in question. Magic or sorcery is supposed to cause illness and various precautions are taken to guard against this. Discarded clothes, nail parings, and excreta are carefully burnt or concealed to prevent malignant sorcerers doing harm to the owner by a process of sympathetic magic, and amulets are sometimes worn. There is a belief in an after-life, and there are certain qualifications necessary to attain paradise. One is the possession of the correct pattern of tattooing, another is a record of loyalty to one's clan.

Despite the influence of Christian missionary teaching and of German and, more recently, Japanese laws and administrative practices, this system of beliefs still greatly colours the life of the native peoples.

Economic Activities

The native peoples depend mainly upon subsistence agriculture and fishing for their food supply and upon the production of copra to obtain money for the purchase of imported goods. The principal food crops grown are taro, yams, coconuts and breadfruit. Pandanus, bananas and other fruit are also grown on a smaller scale. Two varieties of taro are cultivated, one on dry ground, the other on wet.

Plate 82. Fengal village at Port Lottin

A typical lagoon-side village almost hidden in a grove of coconut palms. Note the outrigger canoes.

Plate 83. Canoes drawn up on the beach at Sonson, Tinian

The nearest canoe has a raised stem. A new concrete pier is seen in the background.

Plate 84. A piece of stone money, Yap

The 'coin' is 12 ft. in diameter; it was imported to Yap from Palau.

Plate 85. Fish weirs on the east coast of Map island, Yap

The two arrow-shaped enclosures of rock walling are fish traps. They are built to retain fish which swim in-shore at high tide.

'Dry' taro is grown only once on a piece of land which is then allowed to lie fallow, but cultivation of swamp taro is continuous; as soon as one crop is harvested (after a growing season of about eight months) another is planted. On Palau and Yap, marshy patches round the villages are used for cultivation; in the coral islands and atolls trenches are dug in depressions in the ground and sufficient moisture is thus obtained.

Coconuts are adapted to many uses, and the acreage has been increased considerably to provide copra for commercial purposes. The meat of the coconut is grated and eaten with various foods. The milk of the young coconut provides a beverage and is of particular value where water is scarce.

The unfermented sap from young coconut buds is fed to infants in lieu of milk. This is collected, as it is in Nauru, by cutting off the end of the flower bud and binding the stalk tightly. After a while the stem droops and sap runs out. If left to ferment this sap soon becomes intoxicating. If it is desired to prevent this process, the sap is boiled until it becomes a sweet thick syrup. At first the Japanese forbade the tapping of coconuts to prevent the manufacture of alcohol by the natives. In view, however, of the hardship to the natives with children this rule was waived to the extent of allowing each family to tap one tree per child with the permission of the local hospital authorities.

Pigs and poultry are kept, but animal husbandry is on the whole undeveloped. Fishing is almost as important as agriculture on the larger volcanic islands and considerably more so on the atolls. Weirs are built to catch fish between tides (Plate 85). Nets are made from pandanus or coconut fibre and hooks from shell. Bonito are caught from canoes with a spinner, and flying fish are netted by the light of torches made from candle-nut.

All the islanders are expert navigators and were formerly accustomed to make long voyages between the various atolls. In the Marshall islands elaborate charts were constructed from the midribs of palm-leaves. Islands were indicated by small shells, currents and swells by short sticks attached in appropriate positions. The canoes in this area (vol. I, p. 439) have excited more admiration than those in any other part of the Pacific. The large craft, which are now obsolete, had an over-all length of about 60 ft. and carried a large triangular sail. Built-up canoes of deep section with an asymmetric hull to counteract the outrigger characterized the Marshall islands, the Marianas and most of the Carolines. They were extremely fast and very weatherly; they were used for trading, war or racing. A regular fixture, for example, was a canoe race round the island of Babelthuap. To-day only small fishing canoes are made on native lines, but several schooners of European design have been built. Native navigation between different atolls was, however, discouraged by the Japanese; and most travel before the war was undertaken on the Japanese inter-island steamers and schooners.

In former times native commodities were traded over long distances by sea, but in recent years Japanese stores have been set up in most of the larger islands and the principal trade has been in copra. Japanese currency has been in use, but various native commodities have continued to be accepted as the proper media for many kinds of exchange. These native currencies may be subdivided into two classes. On the one hand, there are some substances which have a definite market value and which may be used in all forms of purchase. On the other— and of far greater importance—are those materials which are associated exclusively with certain forms of ceremonial exchange, such as that which takes place at marriages or on the conclusion of a treaty of peace. In the Marshall islands the natives used a form of shell ornaments made from spondylus shells. These were exchanged on many social occasions. In the Caroline islands many objects have been used by the native peoples as 'money'. At Truk cakes of *taik*, a yellow powder made from turmeric and used for painting the body, were the basic medium of exchange. They had a more or less standardized value. An axe would be worth from five to ten cakes according to size, and a string of black and white shells cost one *taik*. But payment was also made in kind on occasion. For example, a canoe builder received the first catch of fish made from the vessel. In the Palau group several commodites were important items of exchange. Certain small yellow or red stones which were shaped into triangles and circles were most valued and usually passed only between the major chiefs. Another highly prized form of 'money' in Palau was made from old opaque coloured glass. The last two, in contrast to those of Truk, have a value based on their rarity and general desirability, and they did not circulate much, being used only on political or social occasions. The best known and perhaps the most curious item in exchange is the stone 'money' of Yap (Plate 84). This consisted of perforated discs of calcite reaching a diameter of as much as 6 ft. 6 in. The stone was quarried and cut into shape in Palau and then conveyed about 250 miles by canoe or raft to Yap. The smaller stones circulate freely. A quite small one will buy a large pig. The larger ones are used only for purposes of ceremonial exchange. They are generally stored or exhibited outside the *bai* (club-house). A village short of 'money' which is required for some ceremonial occasions will make a present of food or some other commodity to a neighbouring village. They, even if they did not want the gift, will feel obliged to present a stone to the donors of the food. Large stones are not moved owing to their weight, but their ownership changes hands. One piece in particular lying in deep water, from which it cannot be salvaged, is frequently transferred from one owner to another as though it were a bank balance. The history of each piece of stone money is well known. A piece will not be accepted until its authenticity has been verified. A similar investigation takes place in the exchange of the rarer forms of native money in Palau. The Japanese have found that modern imitations of Palau currency in plain glass are rejected as forgeries. A European trader, however, once found a means of producing acceptable native currency and of profiting thereby. He made stone discs for disposal in Yap from the calcite quarry in Palau from which the original Yap discs had been obtained. These were accepted by the people as genuine.

(For Bibliographical Note see Chapter XVI.)

Chapter XVI

THE JAPANESE MANDATED ISLANDS *(cont.)*

Government: Social Services: Economics: Communications: Bibliographical Note

GOVERNMENT

The first period of Japanese administration in Micronesia from 1914 to 1922 was of necessity a military one. The officer in command of the Japanese naval forces set up a government in the Truk group, and the officers commanding the garrisons on the islands of Saipan, Palau, Yap, Ponape and Jaluit were made responsible for the general administration of the regions under their command. The arrangement was essentially of a temporary character, and instructions were issued to the effect that as far as possible the existing German laws and customs should be observed, and that the authority of the native chiefs should be maintained. A form of civil administration was set up in 1918, but affairs were still effectively under naval control. The withdrawal of Japanese naval forces was not begun till 1921. In the following year the system of government which has since been in operation was inaugurated.

CENTRAL ADMINISTRATION

The headquarters of the government, the South Seas Bureau (*Nanyo Cho*), are at Koror, in Palau. At its head is the Governor (sometimes spoken of as the Director). He has legislative and limited judicial powers, in addition to his executive powers. Until 1941 he was responsible in most matters to the Japanese Ministry of Foreign Affairs and in some matters to various other ministries. Since that time he has been made responsible to the newly organized Greater East Asia Ministry.

For administrative purposes the government is divided into a Secretariat, a Department of Domestic Affairs, and a Department of Economic Development. The Secretariat is subdivided into confidential, record and research sections. The first deals, as the name implies, with confidential matters, and also with the appointment of officials, with pensions, and with ceremonies. The second deals with official documents, proclamations, translations, records and publications. The third section, dealing with developmental plans,

338

Plate 86. Two stone pillars marking an ancient grave, Tinian
These pillars were erected before the Spanish occupation of the islands.

Plate 87. Foundations of a breakwater, Nanmatol island, Ponape
A view looking north-east along the coast.

Plate 88. Administrative buildings, Garapan
Characteristic Japanese government buildings in the main settlement of Saipan.

Plate 89. The District Governor's residence, Saipan
This building shows the undistinguished, Western-style architecture characteristic of Japanese government enterprise in the mandated islands.

was abolished in 1940 and a section in the Department of Domestic Affairs was created to carry on its work. This department is divided into five sections : those concerned with local affairs (now superseded by a planning section), financial affairs, taxation, police and public works. The police section, besides dealing with purely police matters, is also responsible for health services, quarantine and harbour administration, and fire protection. The public works section deals with town planning, in addition to normal civil engineering and repair work, and it has control of certain minor institutions such as the civil engineering station on Saipan.

In addition, a number of institutions concerned with research, cultural matters, etc., are directly controlled by the central government. These include the Marine Products Museum at Koror; the Tropical Industries Experimental Station, with headquarters at Koror and branches on Ponape (Plate 90) and Saipan; a marine products experimental station at Koror; a meteorological observatory at Koror, with out-stations at Ponape, Truk, Jaluit, Kusaie and Yap; and a 'South Seas National Shrine'.

DISTRICT ADMINISTRATION (Plates 88-9)

The mandated islands are divided for administrative purposes into districts. Up to 1943 there were six of these, with headquarters at Saipan, Koror, Yap, Truk, Ponape and Jaluit. In 1943, however, the territory was reorganized to form three districts only—a northern district, with headquarters at Saipan ; a southern district, with headquarters at Truk ; and a western district, with headquarters at Koror. The district governments are known as Branch Bureaux. Each is presided over by a District Governor, who is charged with the execution of general policy and who possesses the power to initiate policy in local matters. At least until the recent reorganization his staff usually consisted of a police officer and one or more clerks, with the part-time assistance of the staff of the local government hospital and of any other specialist officers in the area. The duties of the Branch Bureaux include the collection of taxes, the control of the police force, the maintenance of hospitals and prisons, the supervision of industries and of public works, the organization of relief measures, and the conduct of the census.

Also under the jurisdiction of the Branch Bureaux is the system of native administration. Two grades of native officials are appointed by the District Governors—village chiefs and village headmen. The former have jurisdiction over several villages, the latter over only one.

Normally the traditional leaders are chosen. Their duties include informing the people of new laws, reporting periodically on the state of the population, and generally maintaining law and order in their area.

LAW, JUSTICE AND POLICE

The basic law of the mandated islands is the law of Japan, modified to suit local conditions. One important set of modifications deals with the application of native custom in matters affecting natives. Civil cases between natives are dealt with according to native custom unless this is contrary to 'public order and good morals'. In questions of land tenure native custom prevails pending a complete survey of land tenure. Persons other than government officials may not enter into contract with natives for the acquisition of land, except with the sanction of the Governor of the territory. In criminal matters certain offences which can legally be committed only by natives (such as the consumption of intoxicating liquor) are dealt with specially.

Another important set of rules are those relating to the employment of Japanese indentured labour. In general, these are very much looser than those found in any British territory in the Pacific. No standard form of indenture is imposed. The principal restrictive rule is that requiring a detailed report from all employers of such labour, giving the number, age, sex, hours of work, and rates of pay of labourers and an account of the conditions in which they are living and doing their work. Rules relating to native labour are similarly ill-defined.

The highest judicial body in the islands is the Court of Appeal at Koror. This is composed of three judges, with a chief judge as president. Beneath this court there are three District Courts, each presided over by a single judge sitting alone. Both types of court possess criminal and civil powers. A public prosecutor's office is attached to each of the courts of justice, and its sphere coincides with that of the court to which it is attached. Litigation is not heavy, and even then most cases are between Japanese. In 1932, out of a total of 66 ordinary civil cases, only 6 were between natives and 4 between natives and Japanese. The remainder were between Japanese. In criminal cases the native offences out-numbered the Japanese by 619 to 551, but 438 of these were for breaches of the liquor laws. In respect of other criminal offences—including gambling, assault, fraud, blackmail, and illegal fishing—Japanese offenders were in the majority.

Infringements of native custom by natives are generally dealt with by village headmen, who are authorized to give sentences of hard labour. Minor infringements of Japanese law by natives—e.g., failure to register births or deaths, or to destroy insect pests—are dealt with in the same way.

The total strength of the police force in 1936 was 187 men. Of these 134 were Japanese, including 1 police inspector and 20 sergeants. At the time there were 53 native policemen. More recently there has been a tendency to increase the strength of the police force, and to reduce the number and authority of the native chiefs. The policeman is frequently a man with an agricultural training, and is expected by his example in growing his own crops to stimulate an interest in modern methods in the minds of the natives. He also serves to keep an eye on native authorities.

GOVERNMENT ECONOMIC POLICY

The Japanese government on assuming control of the territory determined to develop its resources to the full, so that they might support the maximum number of Japanese colonists. They established agricultural research stations, developed harbour facilities in Palau and on Saipan, subsidized heavily, and framed a labour policy which would encourage immigration.

The policy towards individual companies has been in practice, though not specifically, to encourage monopolies. The two small sugar companies which started production during the last war were amalgamated into the Nanyo Kohatsu Kabushiki Kaisha (South Seas Development Company), whose primary interest was in the sugar industry on the island of Saipan. The government assisted this company by clearing land till development was complete, and then charged a very low rent. The regulations did not prevent competitive organizations from being established, but all schemes had to be submitted to the Governor of the territory and in practice no competitive company has ever been given permission to start business.

Many undertakings were at one time public works run by the government. In this connection may be mentioned the phosphate working in Angaur. To-day the phosphate is mined by the South Seas Colonization Company (Nanyo Takushoku Kabushiki Kaisha). The change in practice was slight. The government officials managing the mines remained in their posts, but they were paid by the company instead of by the government, which, however, held a majority of the shares in this company. The South Seas Trading Company

(Nanyo Boeki Kaisha), which runs the inter-island steamer service, has small trading stations in some islands and holds a virtual monopoly of their trade. There is an item in the budget for 1936 of 60,000 yen for the organizing expenses of the South Seas Colonization Company established in that year. The company's interests include practically all aspects of economic activity, except for the copra and sugar industries, although their primary interest is in the mining of phosphate. Altogether this company has control of over 20 subsidiary companies. Below are listed the more important companies operating in the islands in which the South Seas Colonization Company had a large interest in 1938:

Name	Capital (yen)
South Seas Aluminium Mining Company	2,000,000
South Seas Electrical Company	500,000
South Seas Marine Products Company	2,000,000
Mantaku Pineapple Company	2,000,000
Pacific Pearl Company	1,200,000
Japan Pearl Company	1,500,000

The South Seas Colonization Company holds a majority of the shares in the Pacific Pearl Company and Mantaku Pineapple Company, and a smaller interest in the other concerns.

Government Research Stations

As a stimulus to development the Japanese government set up an agricultural and industrial research institute, subsequently known as the Tropical Industries Experimental Station, with stations at Palau, Saipan and Ponape, and a Marine Products Experimental Station at Palau. There are also experimental farms in other islands.

These stations not only conduct experiments in the growth of different varieties of plants and vegetables, and the breeding of improved stock, but also organize lectures on their activities for the enlightenment of the individual farmers and fishermen. The comparatively recent discovery of bauxite is no doubt one of the many consequences of the establishment of this research institute. While the results of this work are available to the individual farmer and fisherman they are primarily of value to the great capitalist semi-government companies. Moneys allocated in 1938 to these two research establishments amounted to 162,846 yen.

Experiments in the growth of about 230 different varieties of fruits, vegetables and grasses were conducted in 1935. Among the more successful of these was that of crossing Japanese rice with Javanese strains which produced a breed suited to the climate and soil of the islands. Further, Javanese cassava has been found suitable for cultivation in Ponape.

Subsidies and Indirect Encouragement of Industry

It has always been the policy of the South Seas government to encourage development by clearing land and leasing it to colonists or companies. No rent is charged in the initial phases of development and only a small one later. Lemon hibiscus is being planted, to rehabilitate land exhausted by the constant growing of yams. The labyrinthine roots of the hibiscus break up the hard dry soil, and in a few months there is a light soil ready for further sowing. The government is even said to have shipped soil to the coral atolls of the Marshall islands to improve their fertility; the soshyo tree from Formosa is being planted on barren rocky land. This tree is said to grow 30 ft. in 3 years, and it is anticipated that its decaying leaves and wood will in the long run provide fresh soil in those areas which are at present useless.

Any copra farmer who applies to the appropriate bureau is given a corrugated-iron roof for his drying shed. The extra heat collected by the iron roof causes copra to dry in five days instead of the normal ten. In addition to this practical help direct subsidies are paid towards various undertakings. A subsidy of 10 yen per hectare is paid on land planted with pineapples and cultivated for two years. Pig farmers receive a subsidy of 6 yen per pig and government-owned pigs are lent to farmers for breeding purposes. Subsidies are also paid on goats, cows and poultry and on water tanks.

PUBLIC FINANCE

In the early days of Japanese control a small subsidy was granted by the imperial exchequer, but as time passed and islands became more prosperous this was withdrawn, and the islands not only became self-supporting but built up a surplus. Of late years part of this surplus has been transferred to the general account of Japan.

Revenue is collected by a poll tax, port clearance dues, customs duties, a mining tax and a levy in kind on copra from the Marshall islands. This last is in lieu of the poll tax and is a survival of the German method of taxation in this region. The poll tax is collected from Japanese and natives alike, and is graded according to the wealth of the person concerned. A rich Japanese or an important native chief will pay 50 yen. The very poor pay 1 yen. Port clearance dues and the mining tax form by far the largest items of revenue.

In the year 1937–8 the total revenue was 7,188,802 yen, to which was added a surplus from the previous year of 3,551,203 yen, making a grand total of 10,740,005 yen. The principal items were: port clearance dues, 5,256,261 yen; mining tax, 23,586 yen; and customs duties, 101,786 yen. Interest on shares held by the government in industrial undertakings, sale of property, stamp duties, etc., totalled 182,832 yen.

Expenditure for the same period was divided by the Japanese into two categories, ordinary and extraordinary. The former, consisting of administrative salaries and expenses, social services and government enterprises, amounted to 3,689,520 yen. The latter, which covered public works, subsidies to industry and agriculture, as well as additional social services and development projects, amounted to 3,882,446 yen, the total expenditure being 7,571,966 yen.

An analysis of the separate items under the two headings shows that of this sum 2,111,428 yen, or about 28% of the total expenditure, was paid in salaries, wages, pensions, etc., to administrative personnel; 1,629,318 yen, or 21·5%, on communications; 1,188,146 yen, or 14·3%, on public works; 390,969 yen, or 5%, on agricultural and industrial development; 237,724 yen, or 3·1%, on education; and 1·4% on health.

The very large items for salaries, communications and public works are a measure of the intensive development policy pursued by the Japanese. The large sum devoted to communications represents subsidies to shipping lines, constructional work for airfields, aids to navigation, purchase of ships, and operating costs. Public works include sums for construction and maintenance of roads, harbour works and water works. Palau harbour works account for 892,340 yen and Palau water works for 71,815 yen. Sums for the development of industries include such items as 162,846 yen for the operating costs of the Tropical Industries Experimental Station, and the Marine Products Experimental Station. Large subsidies were paid in respect of manufactured goods, forest and marine products, and for the purchase of fishing equipment.

Currency

Throughout the mandated islands Japanese currency is used. This is based on the yen. Smaller coins are the sen, equal to one hundredth part of a yen, and the rin, a tenth part of a sen. There is a post office savings bank and a money order system.

SOCIAL SERVICES

HEALTH SERVICES

For a long period the native population of the islands was declining (p. 324). Since 1920 it has been more or less static, except in the Yap district where the decline has continued. Probably the major factor in decline has been introduced disease, and the present more hopeful position seems to be closely related to the improvement in health services brought about by the Japanese administration.

Considerable information on health conditions in the area is now available. Tuberculosis and venereal disease are the biggest problems to be tackled. A survey of Yap in 1930 showed that fully one-third of all males between 8 and 60, and of females between 8 and 50 years old, were suffering from one or other kind of venereal disease. In this connection it is interesting to notice that syphilis is extremely rare in Palau, Yap and Saipan, while gonorrhoea is almost universal. Most adults in these islands suffer from framboesia (yaws). The Japanese are treating framboesia with salvarsan. In the Marshall islands, where framboesia is rare, syphilis is prevalent. After tuberculosis and venereal diseases, the most prevalent complaint is amoebic dysentery. Among Japanese school children 23% in the area are infected with some form of intestinal parasite. The native children are far more seriously affected. The corresponding figure for them was 79% in 1931.

Other important causes of ill-health among the native population are the wearing of damp and dirty clothes—often through lack of a second set to change into—and living in dark and ill-ventilated houses. The Japanese argue that the problems of clothing and housing are primarily economic, and that when the natives have been taught to work and fit into their economic system these problems will tend to disappear. One enlightened step they have taken has been to prepare a specification for a model hut and to undertake to pay half the cost. Particulars are simply that the roof must be of corrugated iron, windows must be provided, and the floor, which is to be raised a metre from the ground, must be solid.

The government has established hospitals at Palau, Yap, Truk, Kusaie, Saipan, Jaluit and Angaur, and employs 24 doctors, 7 pharmacists and 30 nurses. In addition they maintain a group of travelling physicians, who go from island to island by motor boat. At government hospitals both Japanese and natives are treated, and in 1935 a total of 19,590 Japanese and 21,012 natives were dealt with. There are, in addition, one or two private hospitals run by the South Seas Development Company. Native girls from the schools are trained in the hospitals and then sent back to their villages. They usually settle down, marry, and act as unpaid nurses as occasion arises. Depots have been established under the charge of the village chiefs for the distribution of simple medical stores. A nominal charge is now made for treatment in hospital. Vaccination is compulsory, and a leper colony has been set up in the Palau group. Compulsory cleaning of native houses is enforced on occasion.

EDUCATION

In former times education was entirely in the hands of missionary bodies. In mission schools the curriculum generally consisted of religious instruction, plus reading and writing in the language of the country from which the missionaries had come. Thus a considerable number of the natives learnt English, German or Spanish. The German administration established only one school in the area—a school on Saipan, which provided a four-year education for selected Chamorro youths.

The Japanese authorities have pursued a much more active policy. Two kinds of government schools have been established. These are 'elementary schools', for the children of Japanese settlers, and 'public schools', for native children. The elementary schools are modelled on those of Japan itself. In 1937 there were 23 of these schools, with 131 teachers and 8,637 pupils. This gives a ratio of pupils to teachers of 66 to 1. In the same year, there were 24 public schools. They had 60 Japanese teachers, 24 native assistant teachers, and 3,097 pupils. Attendance at the schools is made compulsory in some areas; in others it has remained voluntary, but parents are strongly encouraged to send their children whenever a school is within reach. In the more isolated islands a quota is determined upon, fixing the number of children to be sent away to school, and the village headman is instructed to choose those to be sent. In 1936 56% of native children in the major islands were attending school. In the major islands of the Palau district the figure was over 95%, and in Saipan it was 83%. Instruction includes, in addition to the basic subjects, some elementary science, geography, and Japanese. In some schools agricultural instruction is also given. There are also several institutions providing vocational instruction for selected natives after they have left school. At Koror there is a Government Woodworkers'

Plate 90. Agricultural research station at Ponape

Improved varieties of many tropical agricultural crops have been produced at the government experimental stations.

Plate 91. Roman Catholic mission church at Yap

This is the church of the Spanish Capuchins at Yap town. The view shows the peninsula, with Donitsch island off the end of it.

Plate 92. Phosphate loading pier at Akalokul, Peleliu
Phosphate is being tipped through the side of a truck into a lighter.

Plate 93. Phosphate loading chute at Saipan village, Angaur

Apprentice School, providing a two-year course in carpentry, and taking some thirty pupils annually. The agricultural research station on Palau absorbs a further group of pupils; on Yap and Truk, where no such stations are established, the experimental farms set up by the government each trains about ten students every year. An elementary course in hygiene and simple medicine is given to selected students in the hospital at Jaluit.

MISSIONS (Plate 91)

While the largest part of the native population is nominally Christian, many of the native cults and practices survive. Christianity came first to the Marianas in the form of Roman Catholicism, introduced by Spanish missionaries in 1688, and the conversion of these islands, as far as it went, was more or less forcible. The American Board of Commissioners for Foreign Missions founded mission stations on Kusaie and Ponape in 1852 (p. 322). When the Spaniards set up an administration in Palau and Yap they brought missionaries with them. The Germans substituted German missionaries for Spaniards, and when the Japanese occupied the islands all missionaries except the Boston mission in Kusaie were evicted. Later, the Japanese, appreciating the value of missionary work, subsidized their own Protestant church, which organized a South Seas Mission (the *Nanyo Dendo Dan*) and sent it to the mandated islands. Spanish Capuchins and some German Protestants were allowed to return in small numbers. According to Japanese statistics of doubtful reliability, there were in 1926 13,391 Roman Catholics and 12,660 Protestants of various denominations in the islands. That is to say, slightly over 50% of the native population were nominally Christian. In 1936 the number of Catholics had risen to roughly 18,000 as against 21,500 Protestants, aggregating about 75% of the native population. The native Christians of the Marianas are all Catholics. In Palau, Truk and Ponape, the Protestants slightly outnumber the Catholics and in the Marshalls the whole native population is nominally Protestant.

ECONOMICS

The Japanese have developed very fully the rather small resources of the mandated islands. In German times the only important industries had been the making of copra (mainly in the Marshall islands) and the extraction of phosphate (on Angaur). The copra trade has been expanded by the Japanese; phosphate extraction has been developed on many additional islands; and a number of new industries have been built up. In the Marianas a flourishing sugar industry has been created, and fishing and the collection of a variety of marine products have been developed on a large scale—notably in the Palau area. The value of production in most of the major industries in 1938 was as follows: agriculture and livestock, 4,872,000 yen; forestry, 4,018,000 yen; fishing, etc., 6,622,000 yen; manufactured goods (including sugar), 28,909,000 yen. Figures for mining are not available for 1938. In 1935 the products of mining were valued at 3,500,000 yen. (In 1935 the yen was valued at 1s. 1½d.)

MINERALS

Phosphate (Plates 92–3, 101–2)

Deposits of phosphate were discovered in the island of Angaur in 1903, but it was not till 1908 that the Deutsche Südsee-Phosphat-Aktien-Gesellschaft obtained mining concessions. Mining started in the following year. A railway track was laid down and an iron loading-bridge was built to lead out to ships moored in deep water. Production increased rapidly from 8,761 tons in 1909 to 54,000 tons in 1913. After the war all the German company's property was acquired by the Japanese government and worked by them as a state undertaking. In 1936, however, the workings were handed over to the newly formed South Seas Colonization Company. Further survey work led to the discovery of phosphate deposits of varying quality in the neighbouring islands of Peleliu, Tobi, Sonsorol and Pulo Anna; on Fais, Gaferut (Grimes island) and Ponape in the Carolines; Ebon in the Marshall islands; and on Saipan, Rota, Tinian and Agrihan in the Marianas. The largest reserves are on Angaur. The deposits are not entirely in the hands of the South Seas Colonization Company. The deposits on Gaferut are owned by the South Seas Trading Company and those on the Marianas and on Peleliu by the South Seas Development Company, whose principal interest is in sugar. In 1941 the islands which were being worked for phosphate were Angaur, Saipan, Peleliu, Ebon, Sonsorol, Rota and Tobi. The production figures for 1939 were: Angaur, 143,420 tons; Peleliu, 26,303 tons; Fais, 43,821 tons; Tobi, 4,269 tons; Saipan, 20,679 tons; Rota, 43,049 tons. No information is available for phosphate production in the other islands. Some of them may not have been mined in 1939. The total production for 1939 from the available figures was 281,541 tons. Compared with the 1939 figure for Ocean island and Nauru (1,277,188 tons) this total is small, but that for Angaur alone is comparable with that of Makatea, which produced 170,627 tons. Phosphate mining is the only regular industry in the mandated islands which makes large demands on native labour. The administrative and technical posts are filled by permanent Japanese officials. In 1936 two Chinese were also employed. Overseers are usually recruited from Chamorro who have settled in Angaur with their families. Manual labourers, however, are recruited for a period usually lasting for one year from Yap, Truk and the surrounding islands and atolls.

Bauxite

Recent investigations revealed the presence of bauxite in the lateritic regions of Palau, Yap and Ponape. The Nanyo Aruminyumu Koyyo Kaisha (South Seas Aluminium Mining Company) (p. 342) was formed to undertake the working of these deposits. The initial workings were on the island of Babelthuap. It is uncertain whether the other deposits have been mined. In 1938, 30,000 tons of ore, yielding 7,500 tons of aluminium, were mined. The estimated output for 1939 was 100,000 tons of ore with a yield of 25,000 tons of aluminium. The extent of these deposits is not known accurately, but in 1939 it was stated that they were sufficient for the needs of Japanese industry for twenty years.

Other Mineral Deposits

Small quantities of iron have been found in Yap and Ponape, and deposits of low-grade coal in the south and west of Babelthuap. Manganese occurs in the north of Babelthuap and on Saipan, asbestos on Yap, and fireclay on Palau.

AGRICULTURE

There are three branches of agriculture in the mandated islands : the intensively developed sugar industry, fostered by Japanese capital; coconut growing for copra production, which is in native hands; and small-scale cultivation of cassava and many vegetables and fruits.

There are only minor seasonal variations in climatic conditions and crops bear all the year round. Dangers to crops include typhoons, which are liable to do damage to coconut and breadfruit trees; insect pests, birds and rats cause great damage also. Rice is attacked by the common rice bug *Leptocorisa varicornis*, the presence of which has hindered rice cultivation; sweet potatoes by a form of weevil, *Cylas formicarius*, and various caterpillars; and taro by the leaf-hopper, *Megamelus proserpina*, and by the larvae of various moths. Elaborate regulations have been made by the government for the control of these pests, establishing the liability of farms to report and destroy them. The government has a right to requisition labour to fight pests and to inspect crops for signs of insects. The regulations permit a rigid inspection of all crops and seeds transported from one place to another.

Minor Agricultural Crops (Plates 97–8)

The Japanese have developed the cultivation of many kinds of fruits and vegetables, mostly for local consumption. Of these minor crops the principal ones grown on a commercial scale are pineapples and other fruits. The majority are in Japanese hands. A few Japanese grow taro but it is almost entirely a native-grown crop. Small quantities of sugar cane are grown by natives. Rice and grain are grown in small quantities, as also are peas and beans. Other vegetables, which include taro, cover a larger acreage.

The native-grown crops are spread over the whole area. Taro-growing is especially developed in pockets of marshy ground round the shores of Babelthuap. Breadfruit is more important in the high islands of volcanic formation, while taro is the staple crop in the atolls. Usually a few vegetables are grown near the dwelling-houses, but the main crops are in large fields some distance away. Japanese horticulture, which is mainly of a subsistence character but includes some commercial crops, is grouped round the Japanese settlements. Thus, there are large numbers of gardeners in Palau and Saipan in particular, and considerably fewer in Ponape, Yap and Kusaie; there is virtually no commercial horticulture in the atolls.

A minor agricultural enterprise of increasing importance is the growing of cassava, which is extremely rich in starch. This has its centre in Ponape, where the uplands are particularly well suited to the crop. The industry has been developed by the South Seas Development Company. Mills were set up, and starch manufacture was begun about 1936 (Plate 96). The company has leased land for the purpose from the administration, sub-let it to Japanese cultivators, and undertaken to purchase the whole of their crop. It has been estimated that a hectare of land will yield 250 bags of cassava a year.

Sugar (Plates 94–5)

Sugar is cultivated and refined only in the Marianas. It was first grown commercially in 1916, when the cultivation of 48 acres was undertaken. By 1919 this area had increased to about 1,200 acres.

Plate 94. Sugar refinery on Rota
This view shows the large scale on which the sugar industry is carried on.

Plate 95. Sugar refinery on Tinian
In the foreground is a small steam locomotive used on the narrow-gauge railway connecting the cane-fields with the mill.

Plate 96. Tapioca works at Metalanim, Ponape
A view of the settling tanks.

Plate 97. Rice growing at the agricultural experimental station, Ponape
At such stations new strains of rice suitable for local conditions have been produced.

The two companies operating the sugar industry were not strong enough to weather the trade fluctuations which followed the war of 1914–18 and amalgamated to form the South Seas Development Company. Owing to government support and a monopoly position, this company had by 1930 under cultivation in Saipan all land which was suitable for sugar. They then extended their operations to the neighbouring islands of Rota and Tinian. Now fully one-fifth of all available land in the mandate is devoted to sugar growing. In addition to their original refinery on Saipan they built new factories on Tinian and Rota. By 1937 the amount of sugar produced had risen to 58,560 metric tons, molasses to 19,053 metric tons, and alcohol, including alcoholic drinks, to 1,026,432 gal. Compared with the great sugar-producing areas of Hawaii and Fiji, with productions of about 950,000 and 150,000 tons respectively, the figures are small; but, when the size of the area available for growing sugar cane and the comparative youth of the industry are considered, the figure is seen to be a relatively large one.

Native Micronesians are not employed in the industry. The majority of the labour is furnished by Japanese indentured labourers from the Ryukyu islands, and a few Chamorro are also employed. Apart from production on the company's estates, further supplies of sugar are obtained from tenant farmers and from independent farmers working their own land. This last source is, however, very small; only 136 families, owning as little as 1,000 acres, produced sugar for sale to the company in 1936.

The tenant farmer, under the terms of his contract, occupies land already leased by the South Seas Development Company from the government. This land must be cultivated under the instructions of the company; and the farmer is compelled to sell his whole crop at a price fixed by the Director of the South Seas Development Company. He is, however, allowed to grow small quantities of vegetables for his own consumption. About 75% of total cane production is by tenant farmers.

Copra

Copra production, the principal industry in German times, still plays an important part in the economy of the mandated islands. About 125 sq. miles, or three-fifths of the cultivated land, are planted in coconut palms for the production of copra. In the Marshall islands a tax in kind, paid in copra, was instituted and is still collected by the Japanese in lieu of a poll tax. Both German and Japanese authorities encouraged the planting of trees. Copra plantations are most numerous in the Marshall islands, but coconut palms are plentiful throughout the area in the low, sandy coastal lands. Copra production in the six administrative districts in 1938 was as follows: Jaluit, 6,389 tons; Ponape, 3,517 tons; Truk, 2,458 tons; Yap, 1,090 tons; Palau, 600 tons; Saipan, 884 tons. Total production was thus 14,938 tons.

FORESTRY

The Tropical Industries Experimental Station has carried out various experiments in afforestation. It has recommended the planting of teak, Ceylon cinnamon, casuarina, mahogany and acacia. A planting programme was begun in Palau in 1936. In the Palau district the most important timbers are sandalwood, ammui, kashimoroku, and mangrove. Mangrove timber is commonly used for charcoal.

FISHERIES

Fishing is important both in the subsistence economy of the native peoples (p. 335) and in the commerce of the islands. Commercial fisheries have been given considerable support by the Japanese authorities. They are concerned, on the one hand, with the catching of fish to be dried or canned for export and, on the other, with the collection of shells, such as trochus, white and black oyster, and with the culture of pearls.

Those engaged in fishing, either for subsistence or commercially, are required to hold a licence from the authorities. In 1939 there were eleven companies engaged in commercial fishing, and a large number of Japanese settlers worked as fishermen on their own account or, more commonly, as members of a group of from 20 to 30.

There is a system of licensing fishermen. Until 1936 native fishermen engaged in subsistence fishing were not required to hold such a licence, but from 1936 onwards the possession of a licence became obligatory. Applications for a licence for subsistence fishing had to bear the name and address of the fisherman, two maps of the area to be fished, and particulars of the fish to be taken and intended fishing seasons. Licences were issued by District Governors and were valid for three years. Commercial fishing, too, could only be undertaken in boats owned by Japanese. Considerable sums were granted in subsidies for equipment, and for the construction of ships, and canneries.

At one time the government provided launches for groups of from 20 to 30 men who wished to undertake fishing. Careful regulations have been made instituting close seasons for various kinds of fish and research has been conducted at the Marine Products Experimental Station at Palau. With this assistance, a flourishing industry has grown up. In 1939 eleven companies, with a total capital of 7,205,500 yen, were engaged in fishing, and the total fish products reached a value of 6,622,000 yen in the previous year. The number of licensed fishermen in the Palau district in 1937 was 2,046, of whom only 71 were natives. In the other districts where fishing was less well developed there were fewer Japanese fishermen. In Yap, for instance, there were only 3 Japanese licence-holders. In the Marshall islands, where native fishing is very well developed, there were only 3 licensed bonito boats in 1935. These figures indicate clearly the concentration of commercial fishing in Palau. Below is a Table listing the quantities and value of fish taken in Palau in 1937.

The Commercial Fishery, Palau, 1937

Fish	Quantity (metric tons)	Value (yen)
Bonito	13,775	1,152,125
Tuna	190	26,127
Mackerel	2	374
Horse mackerel	5	1,153
Cybium niphonium	8	1,652
Grey mullet	3	1,412
Shark	6	293
Other fish	26	4,055
Shell fish (trochus, etc.)	—	3,783,012
Bêche-de-mer	—	257
Total	14,021	4,970,460

Of the various fish taken, bonito is the most important. Bonito fishing is an all-weather industry. Sardines or lures are trailed behind motor-launches, the noise of whose engines is said to attract the fish. Formerly the fishing was carried on by native canoes, but these are rapidly being superseded. The greater part of the bonito catch is dried for export. The fish are cleaned, smoked, and then placed in damp sheds to mildew. They are then placed in the sun and allowed to mildew several times until they are a dark red colour and mildew ceases to grow. The catch is then ready for export. Roughly similar methods are used in curing bêche-de-mer.

Tuna is canned and exported to Japan, whence a portion is re-exported to the United States. A cannery has been built in Palau, but inadequate canning facilities had, up to 1937, restricted the full utilization of this catch.

Of the shell fish *hakucho* and trochus are the most common. They are collected for their shells. Pearl oysters are cultivated, apparently only in Palau. Here there are oyster beds on the south side of Koror. Pearls are harvested each year but stored until there is a profitable market.

LABOUR

The available native labour in the islands is not large, and the majority of natives were engaged in subsistence agriculture. The employment of native labour by the Japanese is normally limited to the phosphate mines, where not more than 400 were employed. A few were in government service and a small number in other industries. The usual unwillingness of the natives to apply themselves to regular and monotonous work for any length of time was overcome in the case of the mining industry by the adoption of short-term contracts, usually for a year. Recruits came largely from Truk and the neighbouring islands, though in the earlier years of the mandate administration many were drawn from Yap. Their absence was thought by the League of Nations to be a cause of the decline in the population of that island (p. 326). The Japanese have relied largely upon immigrants from the Ryukyu islands to provide them with an adequate supply of labour.

TRADE

It is estimated that in 1913, when the islands were still a German colony, the external trade of the area amounted to about 3,000,000 yen, of which 1,000,000 represented imports and the rest exports. These consisted principally of copra and phosphate. The figures in 1920 were about the same, imports being 973,000 yen and exports, 2,180,000 yen. Trade has expanded rapidly with the increase in the settlement and exploitation of the islands. Exports have risen steadily, reaching 18,424,000 yen in 1934, 25,260,000 yen in 1936, and 46,923,000 yen in 1938. Imports have risen similarly but have always been less than exports. In 1934 they stood at 12,969,000 yen; in 1936 at 19,081,000 yen; and in 1938 at 30,658,000 yen.

Under Japanese administration, the rapidly expanding sugar industry became far more important than phosphate and copra (Fig. 71), though these two commodities for many years took second and third place in the list of exports. Marine products, comparatively unimportant in the early years of the mandated administration, have grown considerably since 1934. The chief items are dried bonito and

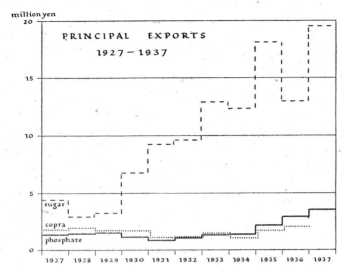

Fig. 71. Principal exports from the Japanese mandated islands, 1927–37
(in million yen)

Figures of copra export are not available for 1937. Based on statistics in the *Japan-Manchukuo Year Book* (Tokyo, 1934–40).

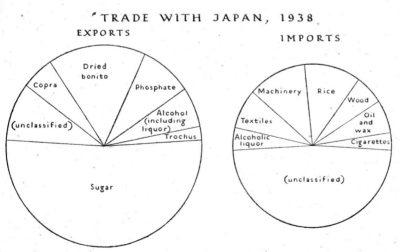

Fig. 72. The trade of the Japanese mandated islands with Japan in 1938
Based on various sources.

trochus shell. The value of dried bonito exports even exceeded the values of copra and phosphate in subsequent years.

Available statistics show that imports were divided between rice and padi, sugar, alcoholic liquor, cigarettes, oil and wax and their products, textiles, timber and machinery (Fig. 72). Import values in 1927 were: rice, 492,000 yen; sugar, 189,000 yen; cigarettes, 163,000 yen; oil, wax, etc., 179,000 yen; copra, 53,000 yen; timber, 309,000 yen. Imports of all these items, except copra, increased steadily, the rate of growth keeping fairly close to that of the Japanese immigrant population. Copra, imported in small quantities from the Gilbert islands for re-export to Japan, remained a small item and served only to augment the large supplies grown in the mandate. Machinery, not listed in available sources, became an increasingly valuable import from 1936 onwards. In 1935 it had amounted to 462,000 yen.

The proportion of trade with foreign countries is negligible, only 4·7% in respect of exports and 3·5% in respect of imports being with countries other than Japan.

COMMUNICATIONS

Sea Communications

Owing to the exclusive policy of the Japanese government, no foreign ships call regularly at the ports in the islands, and it is a rare occurrence for foreign ships to be given permission to visit them. The needs for communication are of two kinds—direct communication with Japan, and communication from east to west within the islands. Saipan, with its considerable development of sugar production, and Palau, the administrative centre, are the points for the concentration of services and the principal exporting centres (Fig. 66). The main trans-oceanic services suit this plan admirably. The Nippon Yusen Kaisha, which receives a subsidy, runs four services. The first is the Saipan line, which runs 24 times a year from Kobe *via* Moji, Yokohama and Fushimito to Saipan, Tinian, and Rota, returning *via* Fushimito, Yokohama and Osaka to Kobe. The East-Round line runs 10 times a year, following the same route to Saipan, and continuing to Truk, Ponape, Kusaie and Jaluit. The West-Round line operates 20 times a year, following the same route to Saipan, then continuing to Manado in the Celebes, *via* Yap, Palau, Angaur and Tobi, and returning *via* Davao, Angaur, Palau, Yap and Tinian to Saipan, thence by the usual route to Kobe. The East-West Connecting line runs 6 times a year, from Kobe, Moji and Yokohama direct to Palau, then to Angaur, Truk, Ponape and Kusaie. Since 1938 ships of the Nanyo Kauen Kaisha (South Seas Marine Transport Company) have called 6 times a year on their voyages between Japan and Java. Finally, a freight vessel calls at Angaur about 10 times a year to load phosphate. The ships normally used vary in size from about 2,000 tons to 6,000 tons gross.

Inter-island services are maintained principally by the Nanyo Boeki Kaisha (South Seas Trading Company), which runs local services linking up outlying islands with Yap, Truk, Ponape and Jaluit respectively. Local communication on islands or atolls before the Japanese arrived was very largely by native canoe, and, in Palau and Yap particularly, villages near the coast are almost always provided with a rough stone jetty for unloading canoes. These craft are native-built, up to about 30 ft. over-all, and are equipped with sail (vol. I, p. 435). Japanese motor fishing sampans and schooners are also available.

Tramways

There are no public railways in the mandated islands, but narrow-gauge industrial lines are found in connection with phosphate workings or on sugar plantations. Thus, on Angaur and Peleliu there are 2-ft.-gauge railways connecting the phosphate workings with the crushing plant and loading pier, and on Saipan there are narrow-gauge lines to the sugar mill.

On Peleliu the trucks are man-handled, but on Angaur and Saipan there are small steam locomotives, probably using coal fuel. Tanks fed by catchment are installed at various places along the line to provide water for the locomotives.

Roads

Formerly, there were paved causeways in the villages of some of the larger islands, such as Palau and Yap, and certain road works were undertaken during German occupation. The forced labour for road construction was one of the causes of the Jokaj rebellion in Ponape in 1911. Road construction under Japanese authority has been considerable in the larger islands. In Saipan, for example, roads ring the island and serve the sugar plantations. In Palau there is a good network of roads in Koror island, with causeways to Malakal and Arakabesan islands. On Babelthuap roads run along the south-west corner, opposite Koror, to the village of Airai and from there to the north of the island. In the atolls, roads are generally few, and on some non-existent, but the Japanese have built many roads in the more important atolls such as Jaluit.

Air Communications

Commercial air services in the mandated islands were in the hands of the Dai Nippon Koku Kaisha (Great Japan Aviation Company), which operated two air lines in 1941. These were a service from Yokohama to Palau, *via* Saipan, opened in 1939, but not operated regularly till 1941, and a line operating between Palau and Dilli in Portuguese Timor. Inter-island services between Palau, Yap, Truk, Ponape and Jaluit and between Saipan and Palau were projected in 1940, and probably operated for a short time. The route-pattern of air services thus covered the same ground as that of the main shipping services. Four-engined flying boats are said to have been used on these services.

Signal Communications

In German times, a cable station was established at Yap with lines running to Guam, Shanghai and Manado. During the war of 1914–18, these cables were cut, but the line to Shanghai was subsequently linked up with the Japanese line to the Ryukyu islands, and so provided a link with the Japanese mainland. The line to Guam was also repaired, but subsequently this line was broken by a hurricane and the Japanese made no attempt to repair it. Similarly the line to Manado was broken in two places and this too has apparently not been repaired.

The Japanese rely very largely on wireless telegraphy for signal communications. There was a powerful civil station on Palau, communicating with Japan. Subsidiary to this, were stations at Angaur, Peleliu, Yap, Truk, Ponape, Jaluit, Saipan and Tinian. Messages from these stations were for Japan, and were either relayed from Palau by W/T, or from Yap by cable. In addition, there were numerous W/T stations in the less important islands, mostly operated by the army or navy. Public telephone systems were installed at Saipan and Palau.

BIBLIOGRAPHICAL NOTE

There is considerable general information on the Japanese mandated islands in R. W. Robson (editor), *The Pacific Islands Year Book* (Sydney, 1939; wartime edition, 1942). The fullest general account of economic and political conditions is T. Yanaihara, *Pacific Islands under Japanese Mandate* (Shanghai, 1939; London and New York, 1940). Also useful is Paul M. Clyde, *Japan's Pacific Mandate* (New

York, 1935). There are two 'popular' books on the area by Willard Price: *Rip Tide in the South Seas* (Chicago, 1936); and *Japan's Islands of Mystery* (London, 1944). A descriptive work, particularly useful for its account of former conditions in Ponape, is F. W. Christian, *The Caroline Islands* (London, 1899). Other works dealing with the islands are: 'Allgemeine Auskunft über das Inselgebiet der Karolinen, Palau und Marianen', *Deutsches Kolonialblatt*, vol. xiv, pp. 683–4 (Berlin, 1903); Henry E. Crompton, 'A Journey to the Mariana Islands, Guam and Saipan', *Natural History*, vol. xxi, pp. 126–45 (New York, 1921). The *Deutsches Kolonial Lexicon*, 3 vols. (Leipzig, 1920), is a useful, though obsolete, reference work for the area. H. Seidel, 'Saipan die Hauptinsel der Deutschen Marianen', *Globus*, Band lxxxvi, pp. 279–82, is a general account of the Marianas.

There is no general work in English on the physical geography of the whole area, though many papers have been published in Japanese dealing with specific points. Brief abstracts of many of these are given in English in the *Japanese Journal of Geology and Geography*, particularly in vols. xvi and xvii (Tokyo, 1939, 1940). Several papers will be found in *Contributions of the Institution of Geology and Palaeontology of the Tohoku Imperial University*, nos. 17–28 (Senday, 1934–7). The raised reef formations are discussed in Risaburo Tayama, 'Terraces of the South Sea Islands under Japanese Mandate', *Proceedings of the Imperial Academy of Tokyo*, vol. xv, pp. 139–41 (Tokyo, 1939). Risaburo Tayama has recently published several geological studies in the *Bulletin of the Tropical Industrial Research Station*, published in Palau. W. H. Hobbs, 'Mountain Growth, a Study of the Southwestern Pacific Region', *Proceedings of the American Philosophical Society*, vol. lxxxviii, pp. 221–68 (Philadelphia, 1944), discusses the geological history of many of the islands. This paper is well illustrated by diagrams and sketches.

Information on coastal phenomena in the above account is largely derived from the Admiralty *Pacific Islands Pilot*, vol. i (London, 1933; with supplement, 1944). The climate of the area is adequately discussed in the Air Ministry Meteorological Office *Weather in the China Seas and in the Western Part of the North Pacific Ocean*, vol. ii, pp. 647–702 (London, 1937).

The most useful works on the vegetation of the area are: A. Engler, 'Notizen über die Flora der Marshallinseln', *Notizblatt der botanischen Gartens und Museums zu Berlin*, vol. i, pp. 222–6 (Berlin, 1897); G. Volkens, 'Die Vegetation der Karolinen, mit besondere Berücksichtigung der von Yap', *Englers Botanische Jahrbücher*, vol. xxxi, pp. 412–77 (Leipzig, 1902); R. Kanehira, 'The Forest Trees of Micronesia', *Tropical Woods*, vol. xxix, pp. 1–6 (New Haven, 1932); P. Kanehira, 'On the Phytogeography of Micronesia', *Proceedings of the Sixth Pacific Science Congress*, vol. iv, pp. 595–611 (Berkeley and Los Angeles, 1940). Also useful are a note by G. Volkens in *Allgemeine Botanische Zeitschrift*, vol. x, p. 61 (Karlsruhe, 1904); and F. H. von Kittlitz, *Twenty-four Views of the Vegetation of the Coasts and Islands of the Pacific* (translated by B. Seemann, London, 1861).

An account of early exploration in Micronesia will be found in W. E. Safford, 'Useful Plants of the Island of Guam', *Contributions from the United States National Herbarium*, vol. ix (Washington, 1905). More recent events are dealt with in the Foreign Office *Peace Handbooks*, vol. xxii, no. 146 (*Former German Possessions in Oceania*).

Historical and geographical material is contained in a series of works published by the Hamburg Museum. These volumes are primarily anthropological. The general title is G. Thilenius (editor), *Ergebnisse der Südsee-Expedition, 1908–10*, II (*Ethnographie*), B (*Mikronesien*). The relevant numbers are: W. Müller, *Yap*, Band II (Hamburg, 1917–18); A. Krämer, *Palau*, Band III (Hamburg, 1919–29); E. Sarfert, *Kusae*, Band IV (Hamburg, 1919–20); A. Krämer, *Truk*, Band V (Hamburg, 1932); A. Krämer, H. Damm, and E. Sarfert, *Inseln um Truk*, Band VI (Hamburg, 1935); P. Hambruch, *Ponape*, Band VII (Hamburg, 1932–6); A. Eilers, *Inseln um Ponape*, Band VIII (Hamburg, 1934); A. Eilers, *Westkarolinen*, Band IX

(Hamburg, 1936); A. Krämer, *Zentral-Karolinen*, Band X (Hamburg, 1931); and A. Krämer and H. Nevermann, *Ralik-Ratak (Marshall Inseln)*, Band XI (Hamburg, 1938).

Other ethnographical works include: A. Matsumura, 'Contributions to the Ethnography of Micronesia', *Journal of the College of Science, Tokyo Imperial University*, vol. XL, no. 7 (Tokyo, 1918); W. N. Furness, *The Island of Stone Money* (Philadelphia, 1910); J. S. Kubary, *Ethnographische Beiträge zur Kenntnis des Karolinen Archipels* (Leiden, 1895); and A. Erdland, *Die Marshall-Insulaner* (Münster, 1914).

The primary source on the administration of the Japanese mandated islands is the Japanese Imperial Government *Annual Report to the League of Nations on the Administration of the South Sea Islands under Japanese Mandate* (Tokyo, 1920–36). Useful information on administration is contained in some of the general works cited above, especially those by T. Yanaihara and Willard Price.

Statistical material of varying reliability can be found in the *Japan-Manchukuo Year Book* (Tokyo, 1934–40); the 1941 edition of this compilation appeared with the new title of *Far East Year-book*. J. Alvin Decker, *Labor Problems in the Pacific Mandates* (New York, 1940), deals with the employment of natives and the conditions of Japanese immigrants.

For maps see Appendix I.

Chapter XVII

THE CAROLINE ISLANDS

Palau Group: Islands South of Palau: Yap Area: Truk Area: Ponape Area

The Caroline islands (Figs. 73, 83, 88) are scattered over a wide area of sea. They extend from approximately lat. 3° to 10° N and from long. 131° to 163° E. They are treated here in four groups, centred upon Palau, Yap, Truk and Ponape respectively. In each section of the Chapter the islands of major importance are described first.

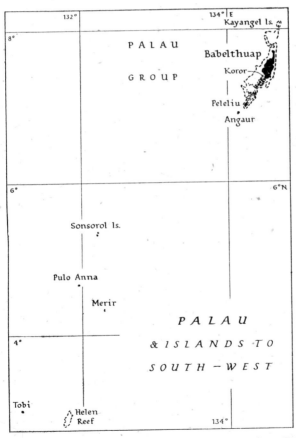

Fig. 73. The Palau group and south-west Caroline islands. Based on official sources

THE PALAU GROUP

The Palau group (Fig. 74) lies approximately betwee nlat. 6° 50' and 8° 15' N and long. 133° 50' and 134° 45' E. It consists of a compact group of about 200 islands with a total land area of about 200 sq. miles, surrounded by a reef about 70 miles long, which encloses a lagoon on the west side.

All the larger islands of the group are 'high'. Babelthuap (the largest island), Arakabesan, Koror and Malakal are volcanic. The remainder are of coral limestone, mostly elevated to considerable heights. In addition to the main group there are the Kayangel islands, a detached atoll to the north, and Angaur in the south. The latter is a small island devoted entirely to the mining of phosphate. The group contains the Japanese administrative centre for the mandated islands. The waters round Malakal harbour, Kossol passage, Shonian harbour and other places in the group offer facilities for anchoring a large fleet. The islands are described from north to south.

THE KAYANGEL ISLANDS

The Kayangel islands, lying about 18 miles north of the main island of Babelthuap, consist of four small islets on a penannular atoll about $4\frac{3}{4}$ miles long and $2\frac{1}{4}$ miles wide. The reef itself varies in width from about 400 yd. to 1,600 yd. The islands are all low and sandy and are situated on the eastern and southern part of the atoll. The largest, Kayangel (Ngajangel), is bow-shaped and about $1\frac{3}{4}$ miles long with a sandy beach on the side facing the lagoon. There is a boat passage on the west side of the lagoon, which is shallow and probably studded with coral. It has also been stated that there is a boat passage into the lagoon to the west of Gorak on the southern part of the reef, from which a boat channel was cut to the beach. A recent map does not show any signs of this passage. It may have been blocked by a hurricane which struck the Palau group in 1913. The three smaller islands were then completely overwhelmed and Kayangel suffered a great deal of damage. Before the hurricane, palms were growing on all the islands and the native population of about 100 people lived in two villages in Kayangel, which were joined by a stone causeway. The lagoon has since been used by the Japanese as a base for seaplanes.

BABELTHUAP

Physical Geography

Babelthuap (Figs. 75–6) is a roughly pear-shaped island about

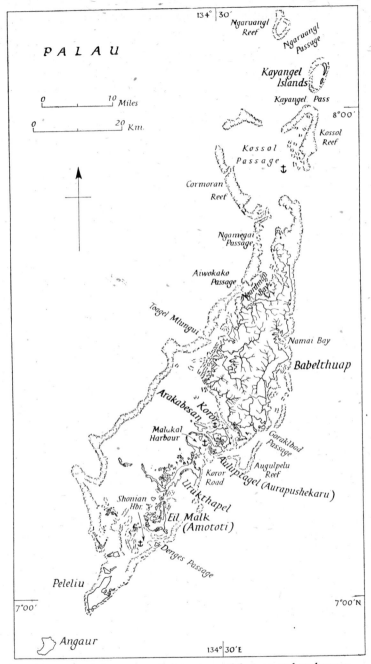

Fig. 74. The Palau group: drainage, coastal features and anchorages
The eastern coastlands of Babelthuap are largely occupied by raised reefs. The phosphate deposits of Angaur and Peleliu lie on the same formation. The larger number of volcanoes lie on the west sides of the larger islands. The east coasts front on to an oceanic deep; barrier reefs are best developed off the west coasts in the lee of the eastern, rising, coasts. Based on official sources.

27½ miles long with a maximum width of about 10¾ miles; the north part consists of a peninsula about 8 miles long. The whole of the central part is rounded, rolling, steeply-sloped country with the highest points formed by a line of hills which run from mount Tuns (Ked-ra Tund) in the south to the extinct crater of mount Agade in the extreme north. Spurs of higher ground run westwards from the main ridge to mount Katteluel and enclose an area of low-lying land surrounding Ndarengueivig bay, part of which is swampy and fringed with mangroves.

The line of hills along the northern peninsula varies in height from about 100 ft. to 400 ft. It is interrupted at various points and falls to as low as 40 ft. at three gaps where the peninsula is narrow. Except for a few islets in the south which are joined to the main island by mangrove swamps, the whole area is of volcanic rock. Most of the soils of Babelthuap are lateritic clays which are derived from volcanic debris. These soils are generally friable and well-drained; but certain areas near the coast, which are alluvial, are swampy. Most of the interior is wooded. Parts are grassy savannah-like country with scattered palms and pandanus, but some of the higher ground is completely barren. Vegetation is thicker in the valleys and round the coast. The off-lying islets are of coral limestone and are thickly wooded. Rivers are numerous and nearly all reach the sea through mangrove swamps. They are mostly small and easily forded. The most important are the Ngardorok, which has the small Ngardok lake on its upper reaches, and three streams which flow into Ngatpang (Uleull) bay on the west coast. The Ngardorok is navigable in its lower course by ships' boats.

Coasts. The whole island is surrounded by a fringing coral reef which in many places is so shallow that even native canoes avoid crossing it; they land at built-up causeways which extend to the reef edge, rather than on the beach. On the east coast there are a few detached reefs which form a chain running southwards. On the west side there is a barrier reef, which is broken by some passages, and runs from the north of Babelthuap to Peleliu. This reef encloses a lagoon roughly 40 miles long and 8 miles wide at its widest point. Some parts of the lagoon are obstructed by coral but others would provide suitable seaplane anchorages.

Large stretches of the coast, particularly the bays, are occupied by mangrove swamps, but elsewhere stretches of sandy beach occur, particularly on the east coast. Immediately behind the beaches are groves of palm trees and various types of scrub. On the east coast

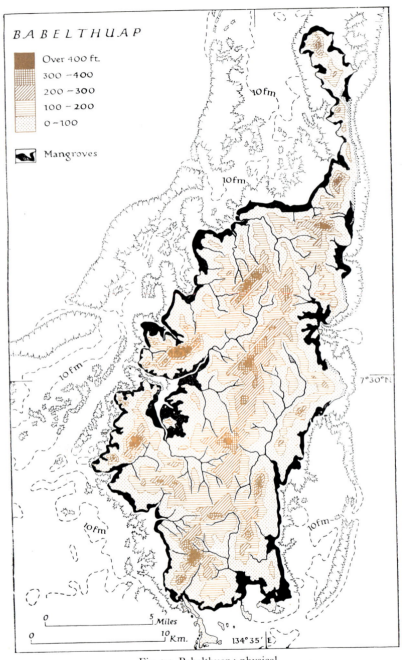

Fig. 75. Babelthuap: physical

Dotted areas along the coast indicate sandy beaches. The highest peaks are volcanoes. Much of the area below 200 ft. consists of raised coral reefs. Based on
official sources.

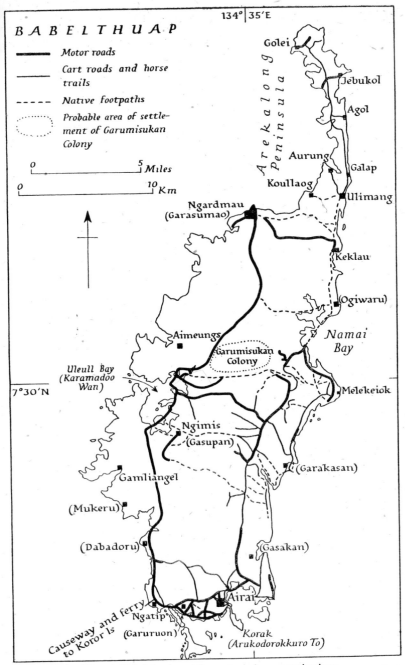

Fig. 76. Babelthuap: settlements and communications
Japanese place-names are given in brackets. Based on official sources.

365

there is a beach at Agol which stretches about 5 miles south to
Ulimang (Uliman), with a causeway leading to the reef edge at Galap;
here the ground rises to about 150 ft. to a spur upon which the village
is situated. The whole of this stretch is fronted by a reef, but for the
most part this is submerged to depths of 6 to 30 ft. Behind the Galap
spur are low-lying fields, in which swamp taro is grown. The next
beach is just north of cape Pkulatap-rival (Ogiwaru point), which
marks the northern edge of Ngamai (Namai) bay. The only passage
in the reef which is suitable for boats is opposite a particularly dense
belt of mangroves. There are three boat passages (described in one
account as blind re-entrants and not true passages) into Ngamai bay,
but the whole of the shore is fringed with mangroves. In the north
of the bay is a small stream about 30 ft. wide and 6 ft. deep at its
mouth. It can be navigated by ships' boats at high water. There is a
wide sandy beach backed by steep cliffs and fronted by a reef between
Ngamai bay and Melekeiok. At Melekeiok (Fig. 77) there is a causeway leading to the reef edge, and also a pass through the reef.

South of Melekeiok a spur of reef runs parallel to the coast up to
3 miles off-shore. There is a lagoon between it and the fringing reef.
Various passages lead into this lagoon from both east and south. Off
the south coast the reef continues far enough to seaward to enclose
several off-lying islands. There is a break with a channel 5 ft. deep
near Arikumu point. Mangroves grow very richly along the shore.
The off-lying islands are of coral limestone and are well wooded and
fairly high. The larger ones are Nardueis, Arukodorokkuro (Korak),
and Garreru (Pkulapnei). Arukodorokkuro has a landing near
Arikuma point at its southern end, and is joined to the mainland near
Airai village by a native-built causeway.

The whole of the west coast has wide stretches of shallow fringing
reef, behind which are dense belts of mangroves, except for some
less swampy patches off the western end of the northern peninsula.

Anchorages. There are few opportunities for anchorage round
Babelthuap. Airai lagoon is probably too exposed and too full of coral
to be satisfactory for anything other than small craft, although
H.M.S. *Espiègle* entered the lagoon from the south of Melekeiok in
1883. Ngardmau bay on the northern part of the west coast is protected from all but west winds and provides anchorage in from 8 to
10 fathoms. North of Babelthuap the large area known as Kossol
passage has been used as an anchorage. At various points around the
coast there are native-built causeways and a few jetties or piers have
been made by the Japanese. The largest of the latter is that at

Fig. 77. Native causeway, Melekeiok

This causeway, at Melekeiok, on the west coast of Babelthuap, leads to the edge of the reef. Based on A. Krämer, *Ergebnisse der Südsee Expedition, II; Ethnographie, B: Mikronesien*, Band III, Teilband II, p. 88 (Hamburg, 1919).

Ngardmau which is of concrete with an extension which forms a basin for small craft.

Social and Economic Conditions

There are few Japanese settlers in Babelthuap in comparison with the numbers on Koror immediately to the south and on other large islands in the mandate. A few are administrative officials, others are engaged in mining bauxite which is loaded at Ngardmau in the north of the island. Deposits of manganese have been found in the north; fireclay is present; low-grade coal occurs at Airai in the south. Mining of coal is undertaken, but there is no information concerning the working of the other deposits.

Native villages are almost all on or near the coast. The largest are Airai, with a native population of about 700 and a Japanese military barracks, and Melekeiok with about 100 natives. Villages are thickly grouped along the northern peninsula and down the east coast of the island, but are more sparsely spaced in the west. Native life is still based primarily on a subsistence economy of taro-growing and fishing, but many people have been employed by the Japanese either in road-making or as labourers in the phosphate workings on Angaur. It is possible that they are also employed in bauxite mining.

Land communications (Fig. 76) consist of one or two motor roads, supplemented by cart and packhorse tracks and by native trails. The motor roads are usually about 12 ft. wide and are paved with stone in some places. Other sections are soft and difficult to negotiate in wet weather. The small bridges vary in width; some are as narrow as 6 ft. They are usually of wood and incapable of carrying a heavy load. Cart and pack-horse tracks are narrow and usually in bad condition. Native tracks are rarely more than 2 ft. wide.

Two motor roads follow the south coast. A single motor road runs along the west side of the island and, after following the valley of the Garumisukan river, terminates about $1\frac{1}{2}$ miles south of Ngardmau point. Branches from this road cross the island to Melekeiok and Keklau on the east coast. Up the east side of the island communication is possible between Airai and the north of the Arekalong peninsula, but much of this through route is over cart tracks and part of it is made up of native trails.

Ferry services link Babelthuap with Koror. A large W/T station has been erected at Airai.

Koror and Adjacent Islands (Figs. 78–80)

The central part of the Palau group, including Koror, Arakabesan, Auluptagel, Ngargol, Malakal, and numerous smaller islands, is the administrative and commercial centre of the Japanese mandated islands. It obtains its importance largely through the excellent anchorage facilities available. The area is often spoken of, as a whole, as Palau (or Koror) harbour. The largest island, where the principal settlement is situated, is Koror. Arakabesan, which lies to westward, was a service reserve from which all civilians were excluded. Malakal island is the nucleus of the commercial port. The other islands are apparently uninhabited and serve mainly to enclose large stretches of water suitable for anchorages (Plate 99).

Physical Geography

Arakabesan, Malakal and the west of Koror are of volcanic rock. They are mainly covered with savannah and the hills are wooded. The eastern side of Koror, as well as the whole of Auluptagel, Ngargol and Urukthapel are composed of raised coral limestone. They are thickly wooded and rise steeply from the sea, mainly to a

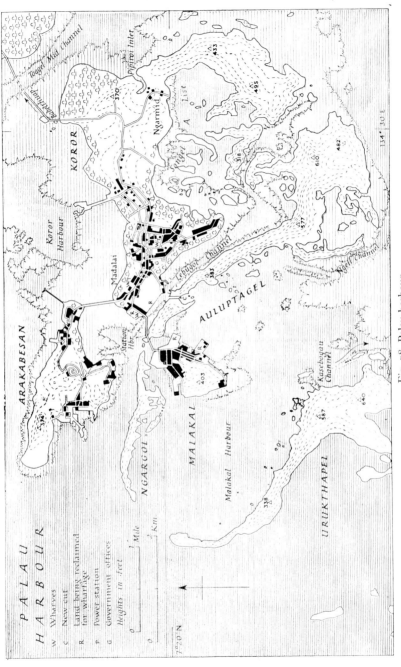

Fig. 78. Palau harbour

The more widely spaced horizontal shading indicates coral reefs which are dry or awash at low water. Form lines, at intervals of 120 ft, are approximate. Based on official sources.

height of about 70 ft., although at certain points they reach as much
as 600 ft. Almost all the coasts are fringed with reef, and, especially
around the volcanic islands, are fringed with mangrove swamps. On
the limestone islands, the rocks which occur along the coasts have
been undercut by wave action for a height of about 6 ft. The volcanic
islands have soils which are generally similar to those of Babelthuap,
while those which are of limestone are covered with clay derived from
the raised coral. Masses of coral rock project from the clay cover.

Channels, Anchorages and Port Facilities

The whole area provides numerous anchorages, protected by reefs
and islands and connected with each other by deep channels. Koror
road, off the south-east edge of the fringing reef which encloses all
the islands, is a large anchorage with depths of between 12 and 20
fathoms. Hardly any shelter is provided to the east by Augulpelu
reef, a large detached mass of coral. Between it and the mainland lies
the deep Arangel channel.

From Koror road the Toagel Mid (Ogurutaageru) passage leads
between Koror and Babelthuap to the lagoon enclosed by the barrier
reef on the west side of the group. A passage, which is encumbered
with coral, leads from Koror roads to Songel A Lise, a stretch of
water mainly enclosed by Koror island, filled with steep islets and
bounded on the south-west by Auluptagel. It has too many coral
patches for use by any vessels other than small craft. The Ngell
channel (closed to shipping in normal times) and the Kasebogau
(Malakal) channel, which is intricate but has depths of not less than
4 fathoms, lead into Malakal harbour proper.

Malakal harbour, the principal shipping point in the area, is some
3 miles long by 2 miles wide, with ample anchorage for several ships
in from 12 to 23 fathoms. In the northern part of the harbour is
Malakal island, where several wharves have been built and other
facilities provided. To the north the islands of Ngargol and Auluptagel (Aurapushekaru) lie in an arc resembling a breakwater. To the
south is a similar natural breakwater formed by a projecting spur of
Urukthapel. A channel about $\frac{1}{2}$ mile wide between Ngargol and
Urukthapel provides an outlet to the lagoon to the west; the gap
between Ngargol and Auluptagel, improved by removing a small islet,
and by a separate artificial passage not less than 6 ft. deep and 90 ft.
wide cut in Auluptagel, leads into the Lebugol channel (its north-
western end is sometimes known as Station harbour) on the west of
Koror. This channel provides a passage from Songel A Lise to the

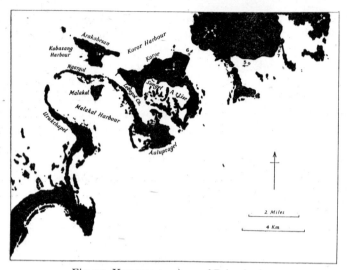

Fig. 79. Key map to views of Palau harbour

Mangrove swamps have been treated as land to conform with the appearance created by the views. The numbers indicate the positions from which the views were sketched or photographed. The arrows show the general direction of the view from each point. The base map has been compiled from official sources.

lagoon. In the lagoon are two anchorages: Kobasang harbour, between Arakabesan and Ngargol; and Koror harbour, a pocket in the reef north-west of Koror island. This harbour, with its pier stretching into deep water, should not be confused with the open anchorage of Koror road. The tidal range in the area is 5 ft. 1 in. between spring tides; the mean tidal rise is 3 ft. 7 in.

Wharves and Piers. On Malakal island several wharves have been built. They include one belonging to the South Seas Development Company, at which two 6,000-ton ships can be berthed. The reef has been converted into a breakwater by driving in steel piles. Large areas were being reclaimed and used as wharves. The shores of the western end of Koror island, which is known as Madalai, were being reclaimed to form wharf frontages. On the north-west side a wharf over 1,000 ft. long had been completed and was used by lighters and small craft. From the south-west corner of this wharf to the causeway (or bridge) on the site of the former German government pier, is a wharf area with about 400 ft. of berthing space. The area south-east of this, extending to the site of the former Japanese pier (about 1,500 ft. south-eastward), is being reclaimed, probably to form a wharf with deep water facing the Lebugol channel. The old pier

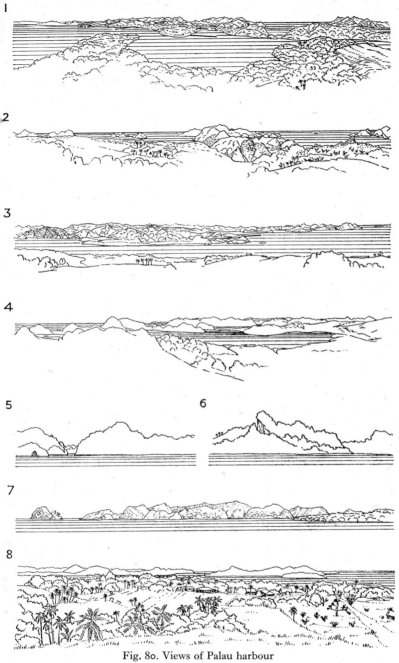

Fig. 80. Views of Palau harbour

1, Lebugol channel, Koror island and Malakal harbour from Arakabesan: 2, view south-eastward from mount Ked-ra Tund, Arakabesan: 3, view south-westward from mount Ked-ra Tund, showing Koror island: 4, view west-south-westward from mount Malkrabisck showing Airai bay, Airai causeway and Korak island: 5, view of Gongolungel channel from the east: 6, view of Ngatkip cliff on the south-west of Babelthuap, from the south-west: 7, view south-westward from Airai causeway showing Pkulapnei, off the south coast of Babelthuap: 8, view westward from mount Tukur, Koror island (the area shown here is now largely built over). Based on the same source as Fig. 76, Teilband I, pp. 189, 192, 195, Teilband II, p. 200 (Hamburg, 1917, 1919).

forms the south-east side of this reclaimed area. There is about 400 ft. of berthing space for small craft along it. An old pier further south in the Lebugol channel is apparently derelict. At Ngarmid in Songel A Lise (Iwayama bay) there is a small pier (Fig. 81). A concrete pier projects from Ebaduls on the north-east side of Koror to deep water at the reef edge, where it divides to form a circular basin. A road 30 ft. wide has been built on this pier.

Fig 81. Ngarmid cove, Koror island, showing boat houses and outrigger canoes.

A view from the landward side of the cove, looking towards the short, narrow channel which cuts through a steep ridge and gives access to Toagel Mid. The bridge shown in the centre background is near the entrance to this channel. Based on A. Krämer, *Ergebnisse der Südsee Expedition, II (Ethnographie), B (Mikronesien)*, Band III, Teilband II, p. 253 (Hamburg, 1919).

Bunkering and Water Supplies. In 1936 there were at least two oil tanks with a combined capacity of 2,500 tons on Malakal and a small one of 20 tons capacity on Koror. Further tanks were said to be under construction in 1941. There is a coal dump containing 20,000 tons on Malakal. There are also large tanks for the storage of water on each side of Malakal.

Repair Facilities. There is a small landing slip on Koror, where vessels up to 100 tons can be hauled up for repair; and it has been suggested that the channel cut through the north end of Auluptagel could be converted into a dry dock.

The Towns of Koror (Plate 100) *and Malakal*

Used by the Germans before 1914 as a government station, western Koror has been developed by the Japanese into a large settlement with modern buildings. Included among these are the Nanyo Cho office (headquarters of the administration), the Palau Branch Bureau office, an observatory, the post office (with W/T station), and the hospital. There are also an agricultural experimental station, a pearl culture station and a fisheries experimental station, and several schools. The north-east of Malakal has many modern houses, factories and warehouses. These two settlements formed the headquarters of the local fishing industry. Some thirty fishing vessels are normally based here and all fishing vessels in the mandated islands come in for repairs. The bauxite mined in Babelthuap comes to Malakal by causeways for export.

Communications

Malakal harbour is the principal port of call for all overseas shipping (p. 369), as well as for local services such as the ferry service which runs from the north-east of Koror to Babelthuap. A narrow-gauge railway has been built from the government pier to the W/T station, and on the west of Koror there is a network of roads. One road stretches eastward to Pipiroi inlet. Both Arakabesan and Malakal are linked with Koror by causeways. The Malakal causeway, which is partly of masonry over coral and partly of piles, stretches from the west end of Koror across to the north end of Auluptagel.

During recent years air communication was developed and Palau became an important base. The main airfield is on Arakabesan, and there are seaplane anchorages off-shore. There was a telephone system on Koror island with an extension to Malakal, and a powerful W/T station.

URUKTHAPEL

Urukthapel, the second largest island of the Palau group, is shaped like a bracket open to the west. The northern arm of this bracket bounds the western side of Malakal harbour. The distance between the arms of the bracket is about 8 miles. The width of the island varies between about 200 yd. and roughly a mile. The surface formations consist wholly of raised coral, and the island reaches a maximum height of about 680 ft. The hills, which are densely wooded, slope down steeply to the sea. The island is surrounded by very narrow coral reefs. It is apparently uninhabited except for possible Japanese naval and military personnel.

EIL MALK

Eil Malk, also known as Amototi, lies immediately south of Uruk-thapel, from which it is separated by Yar (Sar) passage. This passage provides an anchorage area $4\frac{1}{2}$ miles by $2\frac{1}{2}$ miles among several islets. The island is roughly crescentic and encloses a bay which appears to be similar in character to Songel A Lise (p. 369). Its east-to-west length is 3 miles and its north-to-south length is about $3\frac{1}{2}$ miles. The whole island is of rugged limestone and is thickly wooded. The east coast is fronted by a fringing reef which can apparently be crossed, at any rate by native canoes. Behind the reef is a narrow sandy beach under limestone cliffs which have been undercut by wave action. At the southern end there are caves which were formerly used for temporary shelter by native fishermen. Detailed information concerning other coasts is lacking. Everywhere they are rugged and the west side is fronted by a wide reef and numerous dome-shaped islands.

PELELIU

Peleliu is the southernmost island on the main reef system of Palau. It is about 6 miles long from north-east to south-west and has a range of hills about 100 ft. high on its north-western side. The southern and eastern sides are only a few feet above sea level and provide a relatively wide plain which has been levelled and is used as an airfield. The island is composed of limestone and is well wooded. Two tidal creeks overgrown with mangroves run inland from a bay on the north-east coast and probably extend right through the island. There are discrepancies in the various accounts of the form of the island. Peleliu is surrounded by coral reefs which divide north of it. That to the west forms the barrier reef which borders the whole of the lagoon to the west of the group. That to the east runs northward as a very incomplete barrier reef. Shonian harbour, which is used as an anchorage, lies to the north between Peleliu and Eil Malk. There are sandy beaches behind the coral reef on the west side of the island, except where steep hills come down to the sea, or where there are low cliffs. On the west coast surf is light to moderate.

During the German administration there were five native villages connected by tracks. The villages were all destroyed by a hurricane in 1927, but were apparently rebuilt, since there were about 650

Plate 98. Hemp field at Airai on Babelthuap
A view showing the gently undulating country near the south coast.

Plate 99. Malakal harbour, Palau
The view shows the steep, narrow islands which lie within and around the harbour.

Plate 100. A street in Koror settlement, Palau

A view looking towards the W/T station. Traders' stores and houses are often largely of wood with roughly tiled roofs.

Plate 101. Akalokul, Peleliu

The view shows the refinery and loading jetty on the north coast of Peleliu.

native inhabitants in Peleliu in 1930. At a later date, the natives were all removed from the island. Phosphate deposits in the centre near Asias were developed, roads were built, and a phosphate refinery was set up at Akalokul on the north coast (Plates 92, 101–2). Here loading piers were built. In 1935 the export of refined phosphate was 5,486 tons. Between 50 and 100 Japanese were employed by the South Seas Development Company, which worked the phosphate. An airfield and seaplane base and a small subsidiary naval base were established on the island. At the Akalokul phosphate plant a concrete pier with a square loading platform at its outer end, two wooden piers and a slipway have been built.

ANGAUR (Fig. 82)

Angaur, the southernmost island of the Palau group, is some 6 miles south-west of Peleliu, and lies outside the complex of reefs which surrounds the main islands. It is composed of raised coral, and is shaped like a half-moon with the slightly concave side to the west. It is about $2\frac{1}{2}$ miles in length and $1\frac{1}{2}$ miles in breadth, with an area of about 4 sq. miles.

Hills rise to a height of about 200 ft. near the west coast, and to about 90 ft. on the east side of the island. The remainder of the island is almost flat, being lower in the centre than near the coasts. Beds of phosphate rock lie over the greater part of the island and vary in depth from 3 to 7 metres, according to one report, and from 1 to 3 ft. according to another. There is no natural supply of fresh water. Water is obtained by catchment. It is said that vegetables will not grow on the island and that, together with other provisions, they have to be imported from other islands in the group.

A reef, which lies close in-shore, fringes the island from half-way down the east coast to the south-west corner. From this point it extends about $\frac{1}{2}$ mile to seaward, and then returns to the coast off the village of Saipan in the centre of the west coast. (This village should not be confused with the island of Saipan in the Marianas.) For the most part, low cliffs surround the coast except where it is fringed by the reef. There are shelving beaches which are unprotected by a reef on the north-east coast and midway down the east coast.

Piers have been built on the north-east coast and in the middle of the west coast at Saipan, where a channel has been cut in the coral to allow large steamers to come alongside. The latter pier is equipped with an appliance for the rapid loading of phosphate. The loading capacity of the plant is 180 tons per hour or 3,500 tons per day. There

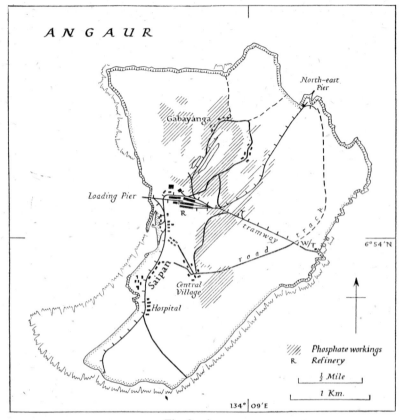

Fig. 82. Angaur

Light railways are shown leading from the loading pier to the phosphate workings and thence to the north-east pier, and also from the loading pier to the south-west coast. Based on: (1) Admiralty chart no. 977; (2) other official sources.

are four mooring buoys off the pier. The anchorage is not safe in westerly winds and ships must be ready to leave at any moment.

In 1933 there were some 300 Japanese, a few Chinese and Chamorro and a floating population (about 400) of indentured labourers, usually recruited for a year from the islands of Truk or Yap. The population is said to have increased to 400 Japanese and 800 natives by 1941. A government hospital, a school, a post office and a W/T station are situated at Saipan village. There are two other villages on the island—Gabayanga (North village) and Central village.

Sea communications are maintained direct with Japan by freighters which call to load phosphate about 10 times a year; by N.Y.K. liners on the West-Round line (p. 356); and with the rest of Palau by small motor sampans which do not draw more than about 3 ft. 6 in.

Narrow-gauge railways run along the south-west coast and from the phosphate refinery at Saipan in three branches across the island to the various phosphate workings.

There are altogether about 7 miles of road on the island. Though the roads are flat and their surface is good they are not more than 12 ft. wide. There is a telephone line from the post office to the W/T station.

ISLANDS SOUTH OF PALAU

SONSOROL

Sonsorol, also known as Sonsol and as St Andrews, lies approximately in lat. 5° 19' N, long. 132° 13' E, 150 miles south-west of Angaur. It is a single island of coral, densely wooded and surrounded by a reef from 200 to 600 yd. wide. It is only about 1 mile long from north to south. There were 153 natives and 7 Japanese living on the island in 1935, in a village on the west side. There are three wells containing brackish water. Drinking water is obtained by catchment. An auxiliary schooner from Palau called four times a year before the war. A W/T station communicating with Angaur was built in 1941.

BANNA

Banna is a small islet surrounded by a fringing reef immediately north of Sonsorol. Strong currents flow through the intervening strait. Banna is uninhabited.

PULO ANNA

Pulo Anna (lat. 4° 40' N, long. 131° 58' E) is a small coral island about 42 miles south-south-west of Sonsorol. It is densely wooded and was, in 1935, inhabited by 19 natives. The schooner visiting Sonsorol included Pulo Anna in its itinerary.

MERIR

Merir (lat. 4° 20' N, long. 132° 19' E), also known as Warren Hastings island, is a flat coral island about 1¼ miles long, surrounded by a fringing reef. Anchorage can be obtained on a bank extending northward from the island and boats can land over the reef on the south side at high water and possibly also on the west side. The only water supply is that obtained by catchment. The population in 1935 comprised 171 natives and 9 Japanese. Copra is prepared in small quantities for export.

TOBI

Tobi, also known as Lord North island, lies in lat. 3° 00' N, long. 131° 10' E, about 104 miles west of Merir, which it closely resembles. A channel cut through the fringing reef provides access to a small pier and there are two or three mooring buoys. Water is collected in cisterns.

The normal population is under 200, including a few Japanese. Phosphate deposits were being worked in 1940. Small quantities of copra are produced.

Nippon Yusen Kaisha steamers of the West-Round line (p. 356) called about

4 times a year, and there are numerous native canoes. The construction of a W/T. station was authorized in 1940.

HELEN REEF

Helen reef (lat. 2° 52′ N, long. 131° 47′ E), about 35 miles east of Tobi, is an atoll about 13 miles long from north to south, consisting of a single thickly wooded but normally uninhabited island on a narrow reef, which is awash at half-tide and encloses a lagoon. A pass on the western side gives access to the lagoon which has possibilities as an anchorage. The island was uninhabited in 1935, but there are a few buildings.

THE YAP AREA

The islands described in this section include the major island, or cluster, of Yap and a number of atolls and small coral islands lying between long. 137° and 148° E (Fig. 83). The most westerly of these lesser islands is Ngulu and the most easterly is Pikelot. Copra is the principal export.

YAP

Yap (Fig. 84) lies between lat. 9° 25′ and 9° 46′ N and long. 138° 03′ and 138° 14′ E. It is made up of four principal islands—Yap, Map,

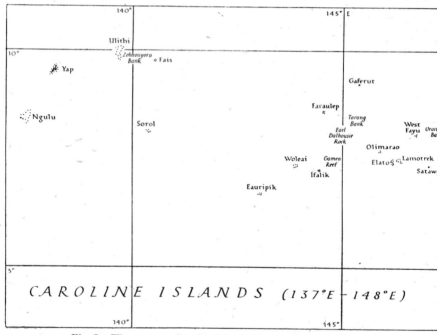

Fig. 83. The western Caroline islands between long. 137° E and 148° E
Based on Admiralty chart no. 763.

Gagil and Rumung—and ten smaller islands. These islands are grouped together on a triangular reef.

Physical Geography

The geological history of the island is obscure. Apparently dis-

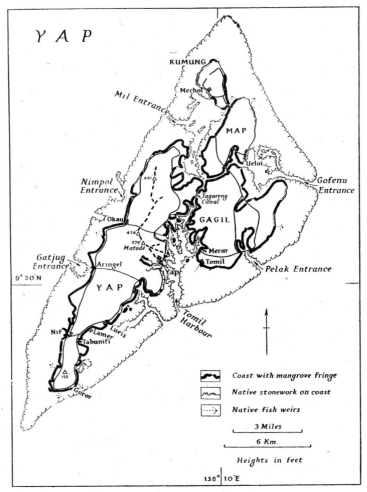

Fig. 84. The Yap group: coastal features

Tracks are shown by continuous lines and the ridge trends of the hilly northern half of Yap by broken lines. The south-west of Yap is largely low, fertile land. The coastal areas in the neighbourhood of the Tagareng canal and east of Tomil harbour are of lateritic lavas. The stone-built native causeways largely antedate the entry of Europeans into the area. Based on official sources.

turbances upheaved a triangular mass of igneous and metamorphic rocks which, after a long period of erosion, was reduced to a peneplane, the edge of which is indicated by the edge of the present reef. Later, subsidence with some fracture occurred, and certain areas were again elevated, giving rise to a series of terraces at different levels. The lowest region consists of a beach deposit derived from crystalline schists.

All the islands lie in a compact mass, 16 miles long by 8 miles wide. Yap itself, lying on the west side of the cluster, is about 12 miles long and about 3 miles wide, narrowing to about a mile at the south-west end. Most of the southern part of the island is low-lying, and marshy in places, but in the north there is a range of wooded hills rising to heights of between 400 and 600 ft.; and low hills rise on the west from a very narrow coastal flat immediately behind the mangrove belt. Gagil island (the southern part of which is known as Tomil) lies immediately east of Yap, being separated from it by Tomil harbour and the Tagareng canal. It has a north-south length of about 5 miles. Rising from the east coast is a series of low rounded hills rising to about 200 ft., and most of the western part is a plateau with a height of from 100 to 200 ft., with hills sloping to the west coast. Immediately north of Gagil and separated from it by a narrow channel is the island of Map. It is about 3 miles long and rises to a height of 200 ft. Immediately north-west of Map and about 2 miles north-north-east of Yap is Rumung. Most of the hills in the four islands are grass-covered, with scattered pandanus trees, not unlike the savannah country on parts of Palau. Coconuts grow on the low land near the coast, which is mainly fringed with mangroves. There are few streams and none of any size.

The reef on which the islands stand extends up to $1\frac{1}{4}$ miles from the shore. In character it is midway between a true barrier reef and a fringing reef. Its outer edge and shore edge are dry at low water, but in between there is a depth of from 3 to 6 ft. The shore line itself is deeply embayed in the east and north; and Tomil harbour (p. 382) is formed by a series of drowned river valleys.

Except for small stretches of sandy beach the whole coastline is fringed by a dense belt of mangrove swamp. There are two short stretches of sand near the village of Gillifitz on the west of Yap, a 2-mile stretch on the east of Map and two short stretches on the east of Gagil. At many points round the coast stone walls or embankments, jetties for the landing of canoes, and fish-weirs have been built near native villages.

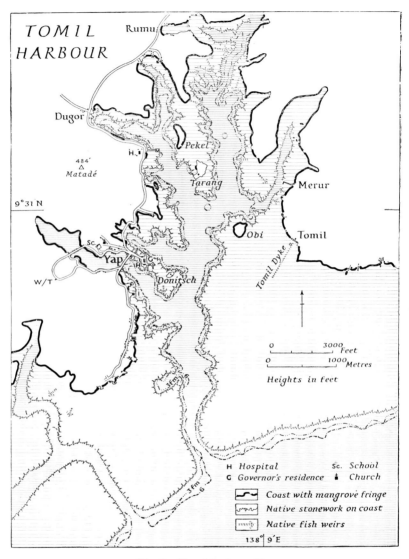

Fig. 85. Tomil harbour, Yap

The lighter horizontal shading shows reefs which dry or are awash at low water; the heavier shading shows deeper water. Based on official sources.

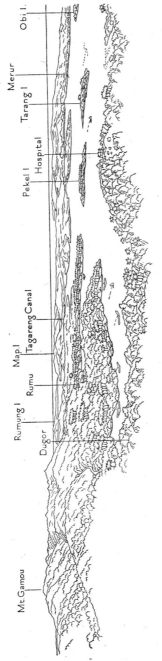

Fig. 86. The north end of Tomil harbour

A view from Matante (behind the hospital on Yap island), looking across the northern part of Tomil harbour. Native fish-weirs are shown in the harbour and its inner branches. Based on A. Krämer, *Ergebnisse der Südsee Expedition, II (Ethnographie), B (Mikronesien), Band III, Teilband IV,* p. 17 (Hamburg, 1919).

Passes, Anchorages and Landings

The main pass through the reef leads to Tomil harbour. It is only 100 yd. wide between 3-fathom lines. On the north-east of the islands is the Gofenu entrance which can be navigated by schooners; it leads, *via* a pocket in the reef, to the narrow strip of water between Gagil and Map. Mil entrance is a narrow passage through the reef giving access to the west coast of Map. With a shallow patch in mid-channel, it leads to a sheltered lagoon between Yap, Map and Rumung islands. This lagoon is connected with Tomil harbour by the Tagareng canal, which has a reported depth of 1 ft. at low water and a width of 21 ft (Plate 105).

Landing for boats is difficult anywhere except in Tomil harbour, owing to the exposed nature of the reef and the presence of native fish-weirs; but native canoes use the stone causeways or piers, some of which project into comparatively deep water.

Tomil Harbour (Figs. 85, 86; Plate 103)

Situated east of the centre of Yap, Tomil harbour is a deep, narrow harbour in the reef, protected on all sides except the south-east by the high land of Tomil and Yap and on the south-east by the barrier reef. It has been described as the best harbour in the Carolines. Entrance is through a channel in the reef, about 100 yd. wide between 3-fathom lines and with a least depth in mid-channel of 16 fathoms. The land areas bounding the harbour lie about 2 miles apart and the length of the harbour is about 3 miles, but the fringing reef projects from both sides, leaving a deep-water area only about 500 yd. wide. This forks into various branches and creeks shallowing gradually to 2 fathoms or less. The main deep-water area could provide anchorages for large vessels only if mooring buoys were put down, but small craft or launches can use the smaller creeks. The reef dries to depths of from 1 to 6 ft. at low water.

The principal piers where landing is normally effected are by the settlement on the Blelatsch peninsula, which projects south-eastwards from the west side of the harbour. None of these reach deep water but boats can come alongside at all states of the tide. The usual landing is at the middle of three piers on the south side of the settlement. There are also piers on the north side. On Tarang island there is a wharf with a depth of 27 ft. alongside, which is used for coaling, but is only suitable for vessels under 250 ft. in length. Apparently there are neither facilities for repairs nor lifting apparatus. There is, how-

Plate 102. Mining phosphate, Peleliu
The phosphate deposits are intermittent and working may be preceded, as here, by forest clearance.

Plate 103. Tomil harbour, Yap
A jetty at the main settlement, Yap town, which lies on the west side of Tomil harbour.

Plate 104. A Chamorro town house, Yap
The Chamorro seen here display various stages in the adoption of Western dress.

Plate 105. The Tagareng canal, Yap
This waterway cuts through the narrow isthmus between Yap and Gagil islands.

ver, a small supply of coal, which is kept on Tarang island, where drinking water is also stored in tanks with a capacity of 1,000 tons. The town contains certain official buildings, including the local Branch Bureau administrative buildings, a post office, a hospital, and an observatory. There are also two schools for natives and one for Japanese children. Houses, some of considerable size, are built along the west side of the harbour north and south of the town of Yap which stands on Blelatsch peninsula.

Social and Economic Conditions

The population of the island in 1935 amounted to 4,016, made up of 3,713 natives, 392 Japanese and 11 foreigners. For many years the native population of Yap has been declining. In 1783 it was estimated at 40,000, which was probably an exaggeration. In 1862 it was about 10,000; since then it has fallen to 7,156 in 1903, 6,328 in 1910, and to 3,713 in 1935. Tuberculosis, venereal diseases and dysentery were apparently the prime causes of depopulation. A new factor has been added with the recruiting of natives of Yap for work in the phosphate mines on Angaur.

The only important Japanese settlement is the town of Yap. Villages are mostly littoral, though a few are situated inland. At the time of German occupation there were 84 inhabited villages and traces of about 150 deserted village sites. It is probable, in view of the further decline in population, that there are fewer to-day. Villages are not built to any definite pattern but usually consist of a men's club house (p. 328) built on a stone platform by the sea shore and several scattered thatched dwelling houses among the trees inland. In many villages there are native-built causeways, embankments, paths or narrow roads paved with flat stones, and sometimes raised stone platforms. The last are used for dances or on other ceremonial occasions.

The people live by fishing and subsistence agriculture based primarily on the growing of yams, taro and fruits. Some coconuts are collected and copra is exported. The Japanese are said to have discovered bauxite and nickel in the islands in 1937 and to be mining these metals.

Communications

Nippon Yusen Kaisha ships on the West-Round line made 40 calls per year on their service from Japan to the Philippines, and smaller ships based on Yap served the islands immediately east of it, while one ship made annual trips to and from Angaur. Native traffic about the islands is very largely by canoe. Good, though narrow, roads have been built by natives, by the Germans and by the Japanese. About 40 miles of such roads exist, encircling the island of Yap and crossing creeks by causeways and bridges. As late as 1935 there were no motor-cars in the island, and the normal means of transport was by hand cart. Flying boats on the service from Palau to Ponape called at Yap; an airfield has been constructed on the plateau in the west-centre of Gagil.

A W/T station is situated about ½ mile south-west of the settlement of Yap; and there is another on the south side of Gagil. Submarine cables were laid to connect Yap, *via* Guam and Honolulu, with the United States, and with Manado, but have been out of use for some years. Another cable connects Yap, *via* the Ryukyu islands, with Japan. This system serves among other functions to relay W/T messages from other islands in the mandate. There is also a local telephone system, the wires of which follow the more important roads.

NGULU

Ngulu (lat. 8° 18′ N, long. 137° 29′ E) is an atoll with about eight islets on the reef. It lies about 90 miles south-west of Yap. The largest islet in Ngulu, situated at the extreme south, which has an area of less than ⅓ sq. mile. All the islets are wooded. The reef is roughly triangular in shape, enclosing a lagoon about 19½ miles from north to south, 12 miles from east to west and about 100 sq. miles in extent, with a depth from 11 to 24 fathoms. The eastern side of the reef is sunken but the other two sides dry out at low water.

There are gaps with deep water in the sunken reef on the east side of the lagoon but it is exposed to the prevailing trade winds and the water is generally rough. Anchorage can, however, be found in the south of the lagoon north of Ngulu island or in the northern part of the lagoon. Landing is difficult owing to the presence of surf both within and outside the lagoon and to the wide fringing reefs which surround most of the islands. There are one or two wells on Ngulu island but their water is unfit for drinking. Water is obtained by catchment. In 1935 the population consisted of 53 natives, all of whom lived on Ngulu island. The soil is too saline to permit of much cultivation, but breadfruit and coconuts are grown and some poultry is kept. Fish are abundant in the lagoon. The only regular communications were by a Nanyo Boeki Kaisha steamer, which called four times a year.

ULITHI (Fig. 87)

Ulithi atoll (lat. 10° 05′ N, long. 139° 43′ E, approximately, at Mogamog) has an irregular and broken rim, with about 30 small islands. It is also known as the Mackenzie islands. There are four main parts: the main lagoon; an isolated island, Falalop, off its north-eastern corner; a small detached reef with four islets east of the main atoll; and Zohhoiiyoru bank, an incomplete atoll with two islets, to eastward. The main atoll is about 24 miles long from north to south and about 15 miles across at its widest point from east to west, and of irregular shape with large parts of the eastern side submerged. The islands are all small and have sparsely forested interiors. The most important is Mogamog on the northern side of the atoll. Other important islands are Asor, Fassarai and Lossau. There are several passes into the lagoon on both east and west sides. The best is immediately north of Mangejang island. This has a depth of over 5 fathoms and is clear of dangers. Anchorage can be obtained ¾ mile north-west of Asor island and in most of the north-eastern part of the lagoon. Before the war there were no wharves or jetties. The most usual places to land are opposite the trading station on Asor island and at the northern end of Fassarai. Small boats could make landings over the reefs which surrounded most of the islands.

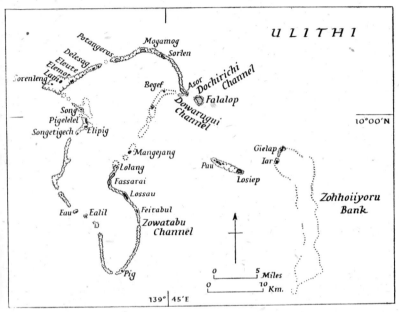

Fig. 87. Ulithi atoll and off-lying islets
Based on official sources.

Falalop, outside the main atoll and about 1 mile from Asor, is about ½ mile long, entirely surrounded by a fringing reef, and has a swampy depression in the centre. The islands of Pau, Bulubul and Losiep are on a detached reef about 5 miles south-east of Falalop. Zohhoiiyoru bank is about 3 miles east of Losiep and has two islets on the north end, but is otherwise submerged.

Water is obtained from wells dug in the higher parts of some islands. There are said to be wells on Falalop, Asor, Mogamog, Lam and Pigelelel. Water from them is drunk by the natives but the Japanese consider it unsuitable for drinking. In 1935 there were 443 natives and one Japanese in the group. On Falalop there were 160; on Mogamog 95; on Fassarai 67; on Lossau 39; and on Asor 47. Some alteration in this distribution has probably been caused by the arrival of native labour brought from Palau by the Japanese to construct fortifications. In former times Mogamog, as the seat of the chief of the group, was the most important island. A curious differentiation in the diets of the inhabitants of the various islands used to exist. The people of Asor and Falalop subsisted primarily on vegetables and fruit, while the inhabitants of the other islands in the group depended largely on fish.

There is no regular industry, but the Nanyo Boeki Kaisha had a trading station. Regular communication was maintained by a vessel which called from Yap four times a year. A W/T station was established in 1938.

FAIS

Fais (lat. 9° 46′ N, long. 140° 31′ E) is 48 miles east of the Ulithi group and about 135 miles to the east of Yap. It is also known as Tromelin island. It is roughly 1½ miles in length and ¾ mile wide, and is a good example of a raised atoll. The level interior, which once formed the lagoon floor, is about 60 ft. above sea level. Except at its north-eastern and south-western ends, which are cliffed and free of coral, the island is protected by a fringing reef. Anchorage can be obtained in 19 fathoms off the south-west and in 23 fathoms on the east side; in 6 fathoms on the north-east, and also on the south side; but nowhere is there much protection. Landing is difficult, but small boats can cross the reef and make a landing on the south-west end of the island at high water. In view of the quantities of phosphate exported it is probable that some facilities for loading must exist, though there were none in 1936. Water is obtained from wells, but the supply is limited. The island is thickly wooded and cultivated in parts of the interior, where mushrooms are grown. In 1935 there were 334 inhabitants. The principal exports of the island, apart from phosphate, are mushrooms, coconuts and copra. To handle this traffic, the South Seas Trading Company (Nanyo Boeki Kaisha) have established a depot on the south-west of the island. Phosphate deposits have been discovered and considerable quantities have been exported. A Nanyo Boeki Kaisha vessel, probably an auxiliary schooner, visited the island four times a year and a W/T station was also established.

SOROL (PHILIP) ISLANDS

The Sorol islands (lat. 8° 08′ N, long. 140° 25′ E) lie about 109 miles south of Fais and roughly 170 miles in a south-easterly direction from Yap. They consist of the main island of Sorol and about ten islets grouped on an atoll. The reef which forms the northern side of the atoll is awash at high water; that on the southern side is submerged and is cut by a broad passage 4 ft. deep. The enclosed lagoon is lozenge-shaped. There is no safe anchorage. Landing can be affected by boat on the lagoon side of Sorol and in calm weather on the seaward side. The islands are all on the north side of the reef. The largest, Sorol, is some 2 miles long, and varies in width from 200 yd. to about ⅓ mile. The islands are well wooded. In 1935 there were 8 natives living on Sorol island.

EAURIPIK

Eauripik (lat. 6° 41′ N, long. 143° 05′ E) lies about 180 miles south-east of Sorol and 320 miles south-east of Yap. It consists of a closed atoll about 5 miles long and 2 miles wide, with its major axis lying east and west. It has six small islands.

The two principal islands, Eauripik in the east and Oao in the middle of the north side of the reef, are not more than ¼ mile across. The former is ½ mile long, while the latter is circular. There is no anchorage and no entrance to the lagoon, but there is a small jetty on the southern side of Eauripik at which boats can land at high tide. The reef is steep-to. All islands except Edarepe, which is awash at high tide, are covered with coconut palms. There were 110 natives on the atoll in 1935.

WOLEAI

Woleai (Anangai islands) (lat. 7° 21′ N, long. 143° 55′ E, at its eastern end), lying 32 miles west of Ifalik and 60 miles north-east of Eauripik, is a group of disconnected islets, 21 in all, on a double atoll of figure-8 shape, and about 6½ miles in length,

Most of the reef is submerged but detailed information is lacking. Parts of the exposed reef reach a width of about 600 ft. All the islands are well wooded, coconuts and breadfruit trees predominating.

The eastern lagoon is entered through Raur channel (750 yd. wide, with a minimum depth of 10 fathoms in the fairway) or through a channel north-west of Motegosu island 500 yd. wide and 12 fathoms deep. There is also a shallow pass in the north-west part of the lagoon.

The western lagoon is entered through three channels, South opening, West channel and North channel. South opening, between sunken reefs, has a width of only 125 yd. and has a 2-fathom patch in the middle. West channel is about 500 yd. wide, with general depths of 5 to 6 fathoms but with a 3½-fathom patch. North channel is only 200 yd. wide, with a minimum depth of 3¼ fathoms. The western lagoon can also be entered from the eastern lagoon.

Anchorage in the eastern lagoon is about 900 yd. west of Raur island. The western lagoon is large and deep but the shallow entrances make it difficult for large vessels. Landings can be made at two wooden piers in the middle of the south side of Woleai island. Most of the beaches fronting the lagoon slope easily but a beach-crest runs along the seaward beaches. Water is generally obtained by catchment. In 1935 the population consisted of 570 natives and 1 Japanese. The natives dwell in villages scattered round the inner shores of the lagoon. They live mainly on a subsistence basis but collect large numbers of coconuts and sell copra to the Japanese. Their gardens produce bananas, breadfruit and various tropical vegetables, and they are expert canoe-builders and fishermen. The most plentiful fish are mackerel, bonito and horse mackerel. Trade is mostly with the Japanese who have trading stations on Woleai island and Mariaon island, but they also trade in turmeric with the natives of Truk, receiving meat and ornaments in exchange. Raur island was formerly the chief trading centre of the islands but was devastated by a hurricane in 1922. There are, in addition to the trading station and the native villages, a police station and a typhoon observatory, constructed in 1936. An auxiliary steamer visited the atoll four times a year, and in 1935 a W/T station was built on Woleai island.

IFALIK

Ifalik (lat. 7° 15′ N, long. 144° 27′ E) is a Q-shaped atoll about 30 miles east of Woleai. The reef is continuous, except for one entrance in the south, and encloses a lagoon about 1¼ miles in diameter with depths of from 6 to 11 fathoms. Three islands, Ifalik, Flalap and Ella lie on the east side of the lagoon; they vary in length from 900 to 1,800 yd. and have a total area of rather less than 1 sq. mile. The only entrance is a small channel 125 yd. wide, 6 fathoms deep at the entrance but between ¼ and 2¼ fathoms inside. Inside the lagoon there is good anchorage for any trading schooners or other small craft able to enter. Drinking water is probably obtained by catchment. In 1935 there were 288 natives inhabiting the atoll. Communications were maintained by an auxiliary schooner calling four times a year.

FARAULEP

Faraulep (lat. 8° 35′ N, long. 144° 33′ E) lies about 80 miles northwards from Ifalik. It is a small atoll, consisting of three islets on a reef surrounding a lagoon with an area of about ½ sq. mile and depths of from 8 to 11 fathoms. The islets are all low, small and wooded. The tops of the trees on the largest, Faraulep, reach a height of 78 ft. Small steamers can enter the lagoon and find good anchorage but the entrance is narrow, tortuous and dangerous. Landing can be effected over the reef at half tide. Water is obtained by catchment. In 1935 the total population amounted to 291 natives and 1 Japanese, who managed a trading post belonging to the Nanyo Boeki Kaisha.

GAFERUT

Gaferut (lat. 9° 14′ N, long. 145° 23′ E) lies about 60 miles north-east of Faraulep. It is also known as Grimes island. It is a single low coral island about 600 yd. long and 300 yd. wide, covered with trees and surrounded by a fringing reef which extends about 600 yd. from the northern point of the island. Its only importance is as a source of phosphate, which was being worked immediately before the war. There is a small lagoon in the northward extension of the reef. There is a small boat passage in the north-western part of the reef, but in 1935 there were no piers or jetties. It is, however, possible that some facilities for loading phosphate have subsequently been built. In 1935 the island was uninhabited, though occasionally visited by natives from Faraulep who came to catch birds. Since then labourers have been imported to work the phosphate deposits. The only communication with other islands is provided by the vessels which call occasionally to collect phosphate.

OLIMARAO

Olimarao (lat. 7° 41′ N, long. 145° 51′ E) lies 95 miles south-south-east of Gaferut. It is a small atoll consisting of two islets on a reef surrounding a triangular lagoon, with an area of rather less than 2 sq. miles. The larger of the two islets, Olimarao, in the northern corner, is covered with coconut palms. The other island, Falifi, has few trees. In the south side are two shallow boat passages. Landing is difficult and there were no permanent inhabitants in 1935, although a trading schooner visited the island occasionally.

ELATO

Elato (lat. 7° 28′ N, long. 46° 10′ E) consists of two small atolls lying about 20 miles south-east of Olimarao and 5 miles west of Lamotrek. The northern atoll consists of a reef enclosing two narrow lagoons. The southern atoll, Toas, is 2 miles long. Elato, the northern atoll, has a lagoon from 6 to 11 fathoms deep and 1½ sq. miles in area. The islets on the reef are Elato (about ½ mile long), Oletel, Kari and Falipi. Elato is wooded and rises to a height of about 100 ft. A small pass leads into the northern lagoon and another into the southern. Landing can be made on a sandy beach on the south-west side of Elato.

The southern atoll consists of two islands, Toas and Ulor, on a penannular reef surrounding a lagoon with an area of about ½ sq. mile. There is a narrow boat passage leading into the lagoon. Water is obtained from wells and also probably by catchment. Mangroves growing on the lagoon side of Elato provide useful timber and are a good source of firewood.

In 1935 there were 71 natives in the group. A schooner from Yap visited the atoll four times a year.

LAMOTREK

Lamotrek (lat. 7° 30′ N, long. 146° 20′ E), 5 miles east of Elato, consists of three wooded islands at the corners of a triangular reef surrounding a lagoon 8 miles long by 3 miles wide, with depths of from 10 to 23 fathoms.

Lamotrek island, at the south-east end of the atoll, about 1,500 yd. long by 900 yd. wide, is the largest island and the tops of the trees reach a height of 107 ft. The other islands are Falaite and Pugue. There are several passes into the lagoon; the widest and best is ¾ mile southward from Pugue on the north-east side. It has a minimum depth of 6½ fathoms. Ample anchorage may be found in the lagoon on the west side of Lamotrek island, and it is suitable for all types of ships, but in south-westerly winds there is little protection. Landing can be made on a sandy beach on the west of Lamotrek. Water is obtained by catchment.

In 1935 there were 192 natives and 1 Japanese, all of whom lived on Lamotrek.

Sea communication was maintained by canoe voyages to Elato to connect with the schooner from Yap.

SATAWAL

Satawal (lat. 7° 21′ N, long. 147° 02′ E), 40 miles eastward from Lamotrek, is a small crescentic coral island surrounded by a fringing reef. It is also known as Tucker island. It is slightly over ½ mile long and rises from 10 to 15 ft. high. The east side, which is stony, is covered by low scrub and coconut palms and the west side is thickly wooded. In 1935 there were 287 natives and 3 Japanese. The Nanyo Boeki Kaisha had a trading store there, and an auxiliary schooner called four times a year.

PIKELOT

Pikelot (lat. 8° 05′ N, long. 147° 38′ E) is a small island about 500 yd. long, fringed by an extensive reef and covered with trees and bushes. It is also known as Coquille island. There is a landing for boats on the west side. The island is uninhabited but natives occasionally come from other islands to hunt for turtles.

WEST FAYU

West Fayu (lat. 8° 05′ N, long. 146° 44′ E) is a small, densely wooded islet, about ¼ mile in length, on an extensive reef. A detached reef curves north-eastwards from it; the main reef opens up westwards to form a roughly oval lagoon 2 miles long and about 1½ miles wide. There is a wide but shallow passage into the south-east of the lagoon. Landing can be made on the west of the island from the lagoon. The natives of Satawal occasionally visit it.

THE TRUK AREA

The islands described in this section include Truk, which is of great importance owing to the wealth of good anchorages available within its lagoon, and a number of atolls and small coral islands stretching approximately between long. 148° and 154° E (Fig. 88). Truk alone is heavily populated and well developed economically.

TRUK (Figs. 89–91)

Truk (lat. 7° 25′ N, long. 151° 53′ E) lies in the centre of the Japanese mandated islands. It is about 680 miles from Saipan, about 1,300 miles from Palau, and 440 miles from Ponape. In 1914 it was made the headquarters of the Japanese naval forces occupying the area. It is the centre of one of the three administrative districts into which the mandated islands are at present divided (p. 339). Truk was formerly often known as the Hogolu islands.

Physical Geography

The Truk group is an atoll of unusual form with groups of volcanic islands in the middle of the lagoon, in addition to numerous low coral islands on the atoll rim. The reef encloses a roughly triangular lagoon

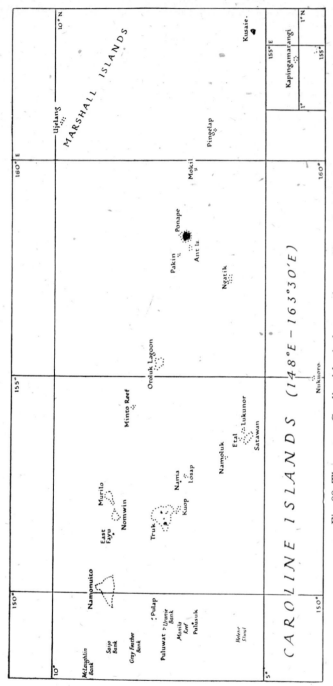

Fig. 88. The eastern Caroline islands, between long. 148° E and 163° 30′ E
The inset shows the Kapingamarangi group which lies south of Nukuoro. Based on Admiralty chart no. 762.

about 34 miles across from east to west and from north to south, with an area of about 500 sq. miles. Immediately south, and separated from the main atoll, is the roughly rectangular atoll about 11½ miles

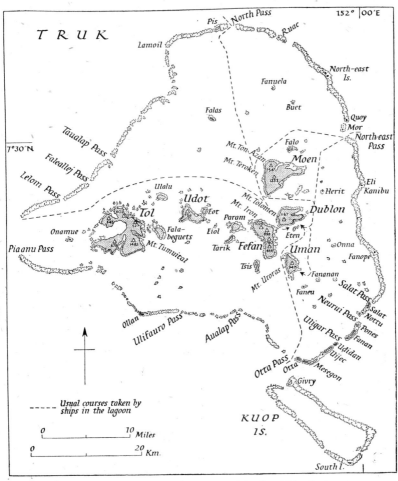

Fig. 89. Truk atoll: the barrier reef and islands within the lagoon.

The encircling reef has a maximum height of 10 to 15 ft. The higher peaks of the volcanic islands are indicated by spot heights. These conical islands are largely of olivine basalt. Truk atoll represents a late stage in the submergence of a volcanic mass. Only the peaks remain above sea level, and no great heights are attained. The barrier reef is low, narrow, and frequently broken. The drowned valleys of rivers form considerable embayments in individual volcanic islands, e.g., Tol and Moen. Ponape (Fig. 94) represents an intermediate stage, and Kusaie (Fig. 95) an early stage in the series showing submergence of volcanic islands. Based on official sources.

long known as the Kuop islands. The larger islands in the Truk lagoon are basaltic and rise steeply to heights of between about 800 ft. and 1,440 ft.; the smaller islands rise to about 100 ft. In addition there are many low coral islets.

The unique combination of small high volcanic islets and low atoll formations can be explained by the subsidence theory: a large volcanic mountain with a fringing reef underwent considerable submergence over a long period, leaving only a small portion of the summit above water. This has subsequently been eroded into the present numerous islands.

The Japanese divide the islands into two groups—the Shiki shotō, or eastern group, which includes Moen, Dublon, Fefan and Uman, as well as many smaller islands; and the Schichiyo shotō, or western group, which include Fala-beguets, Tol, Onamue, Ulalu and their surrounding smaller islands.

The volcanic islands are basaltic and number about 14; they vary from 1½ to 5 miles in length. Some reach heights of nearly 1,500 ft., but many of the smaller islets are only about 100 ft. high. The volcanic islands are densely wooded and steep and have little flat ground. The shores are fringed with coral reefs which are mainly studded with coral heads along the outer edge. There are many mangrove swamps. There are beaches of sand (Fig. 90) on some islands, notably Moen and Uman. Tol, the largest and most westerly, is considerably embayed, but most of the other islands have even coastlines with few inlets.

The reef is everywhere steep-to on the outside and well developed on the east side of the atoll. The north-west and south-west sides are not so well developed, especially the latter, which is submerged in places. Nowhere is the reef more than about 600 yd. wide. It is not continuous, and there are numerous passes into the lagoon. The islands on the reef rim are small, rarely more than 1½ miles long, and some are mere islets. They are mostly thickly wooded with coconut palms. The larger ones are all situated in the south-east corner. Mesegon, Uijec, Fanan and Salat are the largest.

Entrances to the Lagoon. Of the many entrances into the lagoon, twelve (Fig. 89) are suitable for large vessels. North-east pass, a break in the reef 5 miles north-east of Moen island, is ¾ mile wide, but obstructed by a reef to 750 yd., with a depth of 19 fathoms. There is a heavy swell in north-east winds and strong tide-rips occur. North pass is about a mile wide, but there are several shoal patches immediately inside the lagoon. Pis island pass, also on the north side,

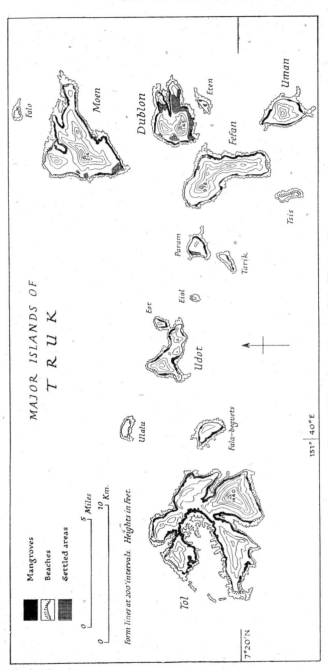

Fig. 90. The major islands of the Truk atoll

The islands show the irregular forms characteristic of partly submerged mountain peaks. Each island has a fringing reef. The summit of Eten has been truncated to provide an airfield. Based on official sources.

has deep water, but there are no clear landmarks on the western side. Piaanu pass, in the extreme west of the reef rim, is 1½ miles wide; it is deep, but has a shallow patch on the north side; there are no clear leading marks. Ulifauro pass on the south side of the atoll is ½ mile wide, with depths of from 7 to 10 fathoms. Other passes on the south side of the atoll are South pass, 800 yd. wide and not obstructed; Otta pass, which is deep and 1½ miles wide; Uligar pass; Neurui pass; and Salat pass. The last three have obstructions of coral or sand and Salat is liable to strong tide-rips at the entrance.

Anchorages and Channels in the Lagoon. The best and most used anchorage is Dublon harbour, between Dublon and Eten islands. There is also known to be good anchorage north of the foul ground between Fefan and Param islands; in Uola roads, off the west of Moen island, with good protection from trade winds; north of Falo island; in various places round Tol island; east of Udot island; and off the south-west of Uman island. The lagoon is so large that there are probably many other areas suitable for anchorage. The principal navigation routes in the lagoon are indicated on Fig. 89.

Water Supply. Water is obtained from two sources—the small streams in the volcanic islands, and catchment. Everywhere there are small storage tanks or cisterns. On Dublon, the chief area of Japanese settlement, there are three large cisterns near the main pier.

The Port

The main port (Dublon harbour) lies between Dublon island and Eten island.

Approaches. The normal approaches are through North-east pass or Otta pass. When approaching from North-east pass care must be taken when changing course to pass between Middle ground and the reef off Eten island.

Anchorage Area. The harbour, bounded in the east by a line drawn to the east of Middle ground, in the west by the northern end of Fefan island, and in the south by a line from the north-east corner of Fefan island through the summit of Eten island, is roughly 2½ miles by ½ mile. Depths in the eastern part of the harbour vary from 10 to 23 fathoms and in the western part, where there are coral patches, between 5 and 7 fathoms. The naval anchorage is west of Dublon island, outside the harbour limits.

Wharfage. Before the war, Dublon was well supplied with piers and wharves. At the east end of Dublon harbour was a large jetty equipped

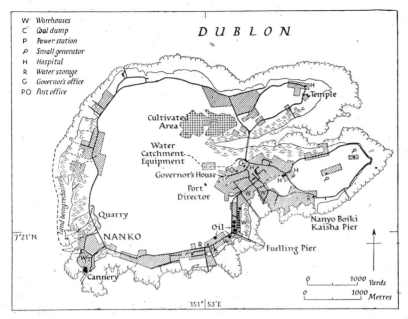

Fig. 91. Dublon island, Truk
The shaded sections show the settled areas which extend inland to the foot of the steeply rising basalt hills. (For the relief of the interior of Dublon, see Fig. 90.) Mangrove swamps are also present along the unsettled part of the north coast. For *Boiki* read *Boeki*. Based on official sources.

with narrow-gauge railway and water mains. In the main boat basin south-west of Lavalol bay there was a pier parallel to the north-east shore, and about 980 ft. long. There were about 2,000 ft. of wharves along the water-front, extended by a pier 260 ft. long. South-west of the harbour inlet was a fuelling pier equipped with an oil pipe-line. In the same area were two other piers of about 500 ft. long, serving repair shops and warehouses. There were also various piers, wharves and seaplane ramps by the seaplane base and various wharves and piers on the west of the island and three piers on the north side. Warehouses of ample capacity are situated along the shore of Dublon island, especially round the boat basin.

Bunkering and Water. Oil tanks are situated at the foot of the fuelling pier and there are probably underground tanks further inland. Coal is kept in a large dump north-east of the seaplane base. Water is supplied from two 25-ton tanks for boiler purposes and for drinking from a 280-ton tank.

Social and Economic Conditions

In 1935 the population of Truk included 1,978 Japanese and 10,344 natives. Of these 873 Japanese and 1,502 natives lived on Dublon island. In 1942 the native population had increased, clearly as a result of considerable immigration, to 15,292. The number of Japanese civilians in Truk at that time was reported to be 1,032. The native population is spread through all the volcanic islands and the larger islets of the atoll rim. The people are stated to differ considerably in physical type. Those living in the eastern islands are said to be considerably darker skinned than those of the western islands. Among at least a section of them there has been considerable and prolonged opposition to the Japanese administration. For many years it was impossible to collect taxes from them.

The principal Japanese settlement is on Dublon. It lies on the south side of the island and stretches for a short distance inland from Eten cove to the foot of mount Tolowan. It consists mainly of a line of buildings extending east and west along the south side of the island. The residential quarter is situated on Lavalol bay. There is another group of buildings in the Nanko area to the south-west. In the town itself there are the government offices, an electric power station, a post office, several barracks and a W/T station, together with the offices of the Nanyo Boeki Kaisha. Hospitals are situated on the north-east peninsula of Dublon and north-east of Lavalol bay. Dublon is also the site of the Roman Catholic Cathedral. This is the seat of the Vicar Apostolic of the Marianas, Carolines and Marshall islands.

The main Japanese settlements on other islands are on Eten, Moen and Uman. Among modern buildings on the west side of Moen are barracks and a naval hospital. There are other small Japanese settlements on Fefan, Param, Udot and Tol islands.

There is no large-scale industry on Truk, which is, from the point of view of the Japanese, of strategic, rather than economic, importance. There are some cultivated areas on Dublon, probably market-gardens for the supply of the Japanese population. The natives rely on subsistence agriculture, fishing, and coconut growing for copra production. Quite large quantities of copra and dried fish are exported.

Communication between the various islands of Truk has been maintained by a small steamer of about 300 tons and by launches (Plate 109). A seaplane base was formed in Dublon harbour, and airfields have been built on Eten, Tol and Moen islands. Roads

Plate 106. Dublon, Truk
The winding upper section of the road leading up-slope from the harbour.

Plate 107. The coast of Dublon
A view looking south-east from the government buildings. The road leads to the main jetty.

Plate 108. Basalt cliffs, Ponape
The high cliffs of Jokaj island on the north side of Ponape.

Plate 109. Moen island, Truk
An inter-island ferry at a native landing stage. Moen island is the most north-easterly remnant of the former land mass of Truk.

surround most of the larger islands and there are some short stretches in the interior. Those on Dublon (Plates 106–7) have a good surface; on most of the other islands the roads are narrow and are probably surfaced with broken coral.

A powerful W/T station on Dublon can communicate direct with Japan, but for commercial purposes messages are transmitted by W/T to Yap and then relayed by cable to Japan. There are also four other stations on Truk. Telephone lines link up important points on Dublon and possibly connected with other islands by submarine cable.

PULUWAT

Puluwat (lat. 7° 21′ N, long. 149° 11′ E) consists of the islands of Puluwat and Alet and three small islets. They are encircled by a reef. The two larger islands represent raised sections of the lagoon floor. The total length of the atoll is not more than 2¾ miles. Most of the atoll characteristics have disappeared, and the remains of the lagoon form a small harbour. This lies between Puluwat and Alet and has depths of from 1 to 6 fathoms. It is suitable for small vessels with local knowledge and the islands on each side have sandy beaches. A pass gives access to the harbour from the south. It is 2 fathoms deep and is suitable for small craft with local knowledge. There are also two boat passages. Anchorage might be possible on a bank from 7 to 10 fathoms deep off the south of the atoll. A pier about 90 ft. long stretches into the lagoon from the south-east end of Alet island, and a road leads across the island from here. Dense growths of breadfruit are found in the interiors.

In 1935 there were 355 natives in the Puluwat group. They lived in three villages on the lagoon side of Puluwat, which were joined by a road. The only external communication was by a small steamer which called three times a year to load copra, and by a W/T station on Puluwat.

PULUSUK

Pulusuk (lat. 6° 42′ N, long. 149° 19′ E) lies about 220 miles west-south-west of Truk. It is a low coral island about 1½ miles long and ½ mile wide. It is generally flat, with a central depression in which water collects. It is fringed by a coral reef about 100 yd. wide. The reef extends in a submerged form northward as an incompletely formed atoll with depths over the coral rim varying between 3¾ fathoms and 10 fathoms. Inside the reef rim there are depths of from 18 to 24 fathoms in an exposed anchorage. Water is obtained by catchment. In 1935 there were 194 natives.

PULAP

Pulap (Tamatam) islands lie in lat. 7° 36′ N, long. 149° 25′ E, approximately, about 150 miles in a westerly direction from Truk. They consist of three wooded islands on an atoll. Except for fringing reefs round the three islands, and an outlying reef, which projects 2½ miles south-west from Pulap, the reefs forming the atoll are submerged to a depth of about 5 fathoms.

The lagoon is about 6 miles long and about 3 miles wide at its widest part. Entry into the lagoon can be made over most parts of the eastern reef and at many places in the south-west between Fanadik and Tamatam where the depths vary between 5 and 17 fathoms. There are also two boat passes on the east side of Pulap. The lagoon offers little protection for anchorage but depths are suitable everywhere. Landing can be effected over the reef on both sides of Tamatam and, according to the Admiralty chart, there is a narrow stretch of water between the reef and the shore on the south-east side of Pulap.

Pulap, the most northerly island, is ¾ mile long and ½ mile broad. It is sandy and wooded. Fanadik, on the west, is small and uninhabited. Tamatam on the southern rim consists of a small western area ⅜ mile by ⅛ mile, from which projects eastward a sandy peninsula over a mile long and somewhat under 200 yd. wide. In 1935 the population of the group was 257, made up entirely of natives.

NAMONUITO

Namonuito (lat. 8° 35′ N, long. 150° 24′ E, at Pisaras island) lies about 140 miles north-west of Truk. It is also known as Onon islands. It consists of a triangular atoll rim, on which are situated the three islands of Ulul, Pisaras and Magur and numerous smaller islands. The reef, enclosing a triangular lagoon with an area of 500 sq. miles, is for the most part submerged to a depth of 5 fathoms or more, and offers little shelter. A passage 7 fathoms deep enters the lagoon at its south-western angle, and there are anchorages on the east and west of Ulul island. Ulul is roughly 3 miles in length, and at its greatest width about ½ mile. It is low and flat, surrounded by a fringing reef except for a small area on the eastern side of the island where there is a boat passage to a sandy beach. The island is covered with coconut palms and other trees. Pisaras is oval and about ¾ mile long; it lies at the east end of a V-shaped reef. There are a few coconut trees on the island. Magur is an oval island ¾ mile in length, with a fringing reef (but with a landing for small boats). The island is densely wooded. Water is obtained by catchment.

In 1935 there were 303 natives and 1 Japanese in the atoll. On Ulul there was a Nanyo Boeki Kaisha store. A road had been built across Ulul. Nanyo Boeki Kaisha vessels from Truk called occasionally.

EAST FAYU

East Fayu (lat. 8° 34′ N, long. 151° 22′ E) is a small low lying and uninhabited coral island about 68 miles east of Namonuito atoll. It is under a mile in length and surrounded by a fringing reef. It is visited occasionally by natives from the Hall islands who come to catch birds. Water collects in a central depression.

HALL ISLANDS

The name Hall islands is given to the two adjoining atolls of Nomwin and Murilo (Fig. 92), which lie about 70 miles north of Truk. Nomwin (also known as Namolipiafan), the western of the two atolls, is a fairly complete circuit of reef enclosing a lagoon 15 miles from east to west and 9½ miles wide, with an area of 85 sq. miles. The lagoon varies in depth from 16 to 28 fathoms, with many coral patches. There are numerous islands on the south-east side of the lagoon, the largest of which is Nomwin. Most are wooded, principally with coconut palms. On the south-east side there are also several passes through the reef. The best is South-west passage, ¾ mile wide between reefs, but narrowed by patches to 400 yd. with a depth of 8 fathoms. There is another deep pass north of Setoaneris island, and there are shallow passes suitable only for boats north-east of Elin island and 2½ miles south-west of Fananu island.

There is room in the atoll for large numbers of ships. The best anchorage is to be found in 20 fathoms, 1 mile north of Nomwin island, and in 13 fathoms west of Fananu. Landing can be made from boats on the beaches of most of the islands. Water is obtained by catchment. In 1935 there were about 130 natives on Fananu island.

Murilo, the eastern of the two atolls forming the Hall islands, is about 20 miles long and 10 miles wide. The lagoon has an area of about 100 sq. miles with general

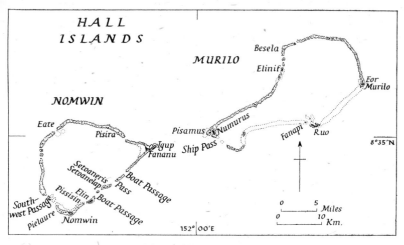

Fig. 92. The Hall islands
The land area of the islands on the bounding reefs of atolls in the Carolines is very
small. Based on Admiralty chart no. 970.

depths of from 14 to 25 fathoms, though there are some shallower patches. The reef
is well formed on the north side but the southern side is sunken to a depth of from
3 to 5 fathoms for the greater part of its length. Murilo, Ruo and Numurus are the
most important islands. There are sandy beaches on the lagoon side of most of the
islands. A pass south-east of Numurus island can take vessels of any draft. A pass
west of Ruo island has dangers immediately inside. Small vessels can cross the
sunken reef. There is probably suitable anchorage for several ships.

In 1935 there were roughly 100 natives on each of the larger islands. A small
Japanese steamer used to visit the atoll about three times a year to trade cheap
Japanese goods for copra, dried fish and possibly fruits.

NAMA

Nama (lat. 7° 00′ N, long. 152° 35′ E) is a densely wooded coral island. It is about
a mile long and rises to about 20 ft. It is surrounded by fringing reef, which is
steep-to. There is no suitable anchorage area. In 1935 there were 460 inhabitants.
Nama lies about 11 miles north-west of Losap.

LOSAP

Losap (lat. 6° 53′ N, long. 152° 44′ E) is a semi-circular atoll, with islands at the
two extremities. The largest island, Laol, is roughly triangular and under 1 mile
long. The soil of all the islands is poor but they are wooded, chiefly with coconut
and breadfruit. On the east side of the atoll is Morchan channel, crooked and with
a depth of only 3¾ fathoms. On the west side are five small passes; the second from
the north, with a depth of 4¾ fathoms, is probably the best. The anchorage inside
the lagoon is sheltered from the north-east winds. There are two wells, one on Losap,
and one on Pis, but these are brackish and drinking water is obtained by catchment.
The population in 1935 was 570, of whom 339 were on Losap and 196 on Pis. There
were two churches and a branch office of the Nanyo Boeki Kaisha. A small steamer
visited the atoll twice a year.

Namoluk

Namoluk (lat. 5° 54′ N, long. 153° 07′ E) is a small triangular closed atoll near the Nomoi islands. The larger islands are situated on the three corners of the reef. The largest, Toinom, is about 1 mile long. There is a narrow boat passage in the middle of the south-west side but this can only be used at high water.

In 1935 there were 225 natives on Namoluk island and 65 on Amas island. Each of these islands has a church. A Nanyo Boeki Kaisha steamer visited the atoll four times a year.

The Nomoi Islands (Fig. 93)

The Nomoi islands consist of the large atoll of Satawan and the two small atolls of Lukunor and Etal to the north of it. In 1935 the population of the three atolls amounted to 2,200 natives, 7 Japanese and 10 others. The group is also known as the Mortlock islands; it lies about 180 miles north of Truk. The group should not be confused with Tauu (Mortlock) island, north of Bougainville (vol. III, p. 668).

Satawan (lat. 5° 20′ N, long. 153° 45′ E, at its eastern end) consists of numerous islets on an atoll 20 miles long by about 8 miles wide. Satawan and Ta islands between them form an almost continuous land rim along the south-east side; the former is about 1¼ miles long and the latter 4½ miles long but only 600 yd. wide. Many

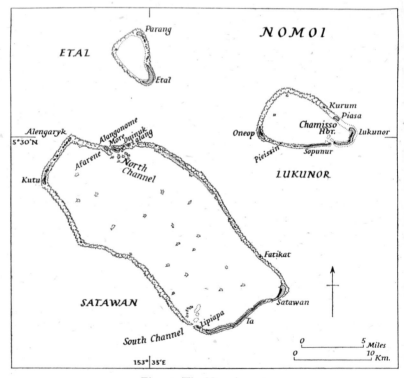

Fig. 93. The Nomoi group

Thin strips of mangrove swamps on the lagoon sides of the larger islands are indicated in solid black. Based on Admiralty chart no. 909.

of the smaller islets are on the northern rim. There are two deep navigable channels leading into the lagoon: South channel, west of Lipiapa island; and North channel, west of More island. North channel is crooked and difficult, and South channel is narrow. There is plenty of room for anchorage in from 16 to 18 fathoms west of Satawan, and in the lee of Ta island. Landing is generally possible on the lagoon sides of the islands. A trader's wharf of coral rock and coconut husks has been built on the west side of Satawan. Other piers are situated on Ta and Kutu islands. Water is collected in trenches and stored in cisterns.

In 1935 there were 291 natives and 1 Japanese on Satawan island, 275 natives and 25 Japanese on More island and 142 natives on Ta. The soil of Satawan is said to be suitable for the production of melons and potatoes. Copra is the principal export.

Lukunor lies about 5 miles north-east of Satawan. It is an oval atoll with an incomplete reef-rim enclosing a lagoon 7 miles long by 4 miles wide at its widest point. The principal islands are Lukunor, Sopunur and Oneop. Lukunor is 2 miles long and about 650 yd. wide. The pass into the lagoon is wide, but divided by a reef. Small steamers can use it and the anchorage is good. Protection from easterly winds is found in 11 fathoms in Chamisso harbour, and from westerly winds off Oneop, in 16 fathoms. There are two small boat piers on the west side of Lukunor. Water is obtained by catchment.

In 1935 there were 480 natives and 2 Japanese on Lukunor and 408 natives and 1 Japanese on Oneop. The Nanyo Boeki Kaisha had a station on Lukunor, where considerable trade was done in copra and other native produce in exchange for Japanese goods. The natives have been subjected to considerable missionary influence. Communication was by small steamer with Truk.

Etal lies about 8 miles west of Lukunor and about 5 miles north of Satawan. It is a small atoll consisting of a coral ring completely enclosing a small triangular lagoon. The lagoon is 3½ miles long and 2¾ miles wide. Altogether there are thirteen islets on the reef rim. The largest, Etal, is at the southern end of the lagoon; the remaining twelve are on the east side. Landing can be made on Etal at a pier projecting 100 ft. from the southern side. In 1935 the population was 255; it was made up entirely of natives.

THE PONAPE AREA

The islands described in this section comprise all the Caroline islands east of long. 154° E. There are in this area the two large islands of Ponape and Kusaie and numerous atolls. Many Japanese have settled on Ponape and Kusaie.

PONAPE (Fig. 94)

Ponape (lat. 6° 53′ N, long. 158° 14′ E) lies about 440 miles east of Truk and is one of the principal ports of call for the Japanese shipping services to the mandated islands. It has an area of about 145 sq. miles.

Physical Geography

Ponape is a volcanic dome; subsidence is less advanced than that of the Truk atoll. It is about 14 miles from north to south and 16 miles from east to west. It is surrounded by a barrier reef, which encloses a narrow lagoon containing numerous small islands. Some of these

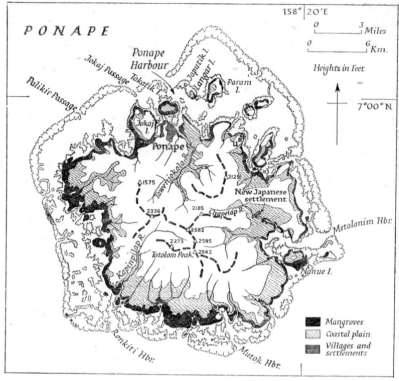

Fig. 94. Ponape: physical features and major settlements

The olivine basalt dome, although deeply dissected, has not suffered the same denudation or submergence as has that which now lies largely below sea level at Truk (Fig. 89). The culminating points of the Ponape lava dome are higher than those of Truk. The distance between the barrier reef and the main island is relatively small and, in the south, is restricted to narrow channels. Submergence of the lower valleys of rivers is characteristic, as at Truk, but the land mass is not yet so deeply entrenched by the sea as, for example, at Tol, in the west of the Truk atoll. Based on official sources.

islands are volcanic; others of coral. The interior of Ponape rises to a series of jagged and sharply eroded peaks. Totolom (2,542 ft.) south of the centre of the island, and two peaks rising to 2,595 ft. and 2,582 ft., north-west of it, are the highest. Deep valleys radiating from the centre of the island have been cut by numerous streams and give the island its characteristically rugged appearance. In places great scarps and cliffs of columnar basalt occur. Examples are found on Jokaj island, off the north coast (Plate 108). It falls away sheer from a height of about 900 ft. to sea level. In most places hill spurs run almost to the coast, and the only large flat areas are found along the south and east coasts and up some river valleys. In the interior, which is difficult of access, small areas of flat land are reported. There is a narrow belt of alluvial land round most of the coast.

For the most part the island is densely wooded, with a belt of mangroves along the swampy coastal strip. Inland these give place to nipa palms, tree ferns, and (higher up) to areca palms and many timber trees. Some of the plateaux are said to be grass-grown savannah country. There are many streams which flow for a few hours after rain and then disappear. Others, starting as mountain torrents, reach the sea in comparatively wide estuaries. The most important are the Tawenjokola in the north and the Kapinpilap in the south. Small boats can generally navigate the larger streams for a mile or two. The water in the higher reaches is drinkable; carp-like fish up to a foot long breed in the streams of the Kiti district in the south-west.

Coast. The coast is indented by the drowned valleys of the rivers. It is fringed everywhere by a belt of dense mangroves growing out of swampy ground, except for short stretches along the north and east coasts; and the whole island is encircled by a reef, the outer edge of which is steep-to. The reef extends 3 to 5 miles off the coast in the north and east, and a lesser distance in the south and west. The northern part encloses a lagoon which forms Ponape harbour and Jokaj harbour. The lagoon has depths up to about 30 fathoms, but is much encumbered with coral patches. Breaks in the reef provide entrances to small harbours and anchorages, and there are shallow channels in places between the reef-edge and the shore, notably from Tauak channel to Ronkiti harbour (in places this is only navigable by canoes), and from Metalanim to Ponape (which is suitable for launches).

Channels, Anchorages and Landings

On the north side of the island Palikir, Jokaj and Ponape harbours, entered by three passes, are all interconnected to form with the facilities at Ponape town the port of Ponape. On the south side of the island are Lot, Mutok and Ronkiti harbours. Lot harbour is about 6½ miles southwards along the coast from Metalanim. It is a narrow gap between the reefs, about ¾ mile long and from 300 yd. to 400 yd. wide. There is indifferent anchorage in 6 fathoms off Lot village on the west side of the harbour. Mutok harbour, 3 miles south-west of Lot, is another gap in the reef with a deep entrance and good shelter for small vessels. Ronkiti harbour is an opening in the reef divided into an inner and outer anchorage. The outer anchorage is not very well sheltered and is deep. The inner harbour, entered through a channel only 40 yd. wide, is well sheltered but rather limited, with a depth of about 7 fathoms.

Ponape Harbour (Plates 111–12)

Ponape harbour, on the north side of the island, consists of an anchorage in the lagoon, bounded by Japutik and Langar islands on the east and by Takatik island on the west. It is formed by the estuary of the Tawenjokola river, on the west bank of which Ponape town is situated. Lying immediately to the west of the anchorage, and connected with it by passes through the reef are Jokaj harbour and Palikir harbour, both lagoon anchorages with passes into the open sea.

The entrance is about 460 yd. wide between reefs, with a westerly current across it. The area between the entrance and the mainland is of very uneven depth and obstructed in places by coral patches. The best anchorage for small ships is near the south-west side of Langar island. The entrance to the port itself, between Takatik island and Not point is narrow, and in normal times marked by beacons; according to the Admiralty chart it has a depth of about 4 ft. It is, therefore, only suitable for lighters and small craft. There is considerable wharfage space along the waterfront of the town. Large stocks of coal are stored on Langar island and possibly on Takatik island. Drinking water can be supplied at the rate of 60 to 80 tons a day and river water at the rate of 120 to 130 tons a day. Schooners of up to about 50 tons have been built in the port.

Metalanim Harbour

Metalanim harbour, on the east coast of the island, is a small harbour in the reef with an inner harbour into which drain two streams from the interior. The entrance is about 400 yd. wide between reefs, and with considerable depths in mid-channel. The outer harbour is subject to heavy swell, being inadequately protected from the prevailing trade winds by the islands of Nanue, Nanmatol, Napali and Na. The inner harbour, entered by a channel between Nanue island and Pantieinu point with a width of about 600 yd. and a depth of about 8 fathoms, is much obstructed by coral and sand banks. Depths are generally shallow. In the mouth of the Chapelap river which drains into the harbour there are several wharves and a small jetty.

The function of the port is as a loading point for the tapioca,

Plate 110. Ronkiti factory, Ponape
This works processes copra and tuna and lies on the south-west side of Ponape.

Plate 111. Ponape town from the air
The settlement lies on the north coast of Ponape. The black areas along the coast and the shores of adjoining islands are mangrove swamps.

Plate 112. Ponape town
A view of part of the township from the harbour.

Plate 113. Megalithic remains, Ponape
Metalanim harbour has many immense coastal structures built largely of local columnar basalt. The ruins include breakwaters and substantial buildings and give evidence of considerable skill among the proto-historic Micronesians.

coconuts and sugar grown on the low-lying ground immediately behind the harbour. This produce is loaded into launches and taken through the passage inside the reef to Ponape harbour.

Social and Economic Conditions

In 1920 the native population of Ponape was about 6,500. By 1941 it had risen to about 9,000. The natives live mainly in villages round the coast. In 1942 the Japanese population was 5,000. It has reached this large figure since starch manufacture and bauxite mining were undertaken on the island.

The administrative centre is Ponape town, or Colony (from its Spanish name of Colonia de Santiago). The town was founded by the Spaniards in 1887. It has grown considerably during recent years. Buildings include administrative offices, a post office, several hospitals, schools, a prison, Roman Catholic and Protestant churches and a branch office of the Nanyo Boeki Kaisha. There are bakeries and stores. The town is supplied with electricity.

Ponape was visited before the war by Japanese vessels of 4,000 to 6,000 tons about three times a month. The principal exports are bauxite, copra, ivory nuts, starch and dried bonito.

KUSAIE (Fig. 95)

Kusaie (lat. 5° 20′ N, long. 163° 00′ E, approximately) is the most eastern of the Carolines. It is also known as Ualan and as Strong's island. It is a port of call on the main shipping route from Palau to Jaluit.

Physical Geography (Fig. 96)

Kusaie is of irregular shape, about 8½ miles from north to south and about 10 miles across from east to west. The main part of the island is made up of two rugged basaltic mountain masses with sharp knife-edge ridges, jagged peaks and steep-sided valleys characteristic of immature erosion. The northern one, mount Buache, rises to a height of 1,943 ft. and is of more or less circular form with radial valleys. The southern mass is separated from it by a low-lying valley which runs right across the island. It consists of a chain of peaks stretching in an irregular line over the whole of the southern part of the island with heights varying from about 1,200 ft. at each end to mount Crozer (2,061 ft.) in the centre. This range forms a compact mass in the centre of the island. Surrounding both masses is a low coastal flat which is alluvial and varies in width. It is rarely more than

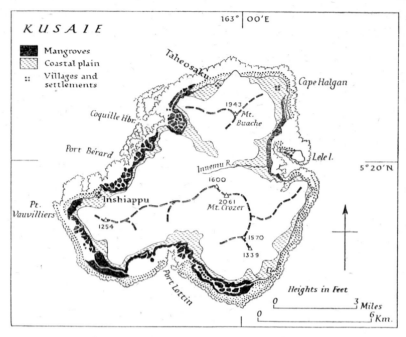

Fig. 95. Kusaie: physical features and settlements

Mount Crozer is relatively flat-topped. This island shows an early stage in the submergence and denudation of a volcanic mass. The lagoon is much narrower than that of Ponape; in some cases only a fringing reef is present and there is no lagoon. The sea has not entered the valleys of the basalt dome to any great extent. Based on official sources.

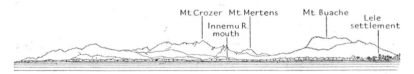

Fig. 96. Profile of Kusaie from Lele harbour

The sketch shows the sharp topography of the interior of Kusaie and the absence of well-developed coastal plains. The broad through valley partly occupied by the Innemu river lies between mount Mertens and mount Buache. Based on E. Sarfert, *Ergebnisseder Südsee Expedition, II (Ethnographie), B (Mikronesien)*, Band IV, Teilband II, p. 17 (Hamburg, 1920).

a mile wide. The coast flat is broken at a few points where spurs project from the mountain masses. Rocky foreshores occur there (Fig. 97), e.g., west of Port Lottin on the south coast, immediately to the north and south of Lele harbour, and at one point on the north coast. The rivers are mainly narrow and flow through gorges. Water-falls are common. The most important rivers are the Innemu and the Okaato which flow respectively into Lele harbour on the east and to Coquille harbour on the west coast. The greater part of the mountains is covered with dense tropical vegetation (p. 315). Coconut palms and mangroves grow profusely on the coastal flats.

Fig. 97. The coast of Kusaie

Basalt blocks lie off much of the coastline of Kusaie. Based on the same source as Fig. 96, Teilband I, p. 14, plate 3, fig. 2 (Hamburg, 1919).

Coasts. The whole island is surrounded by a fringing reef of a rather unusual type. For large areas on the north coast it is a normal shore-reef which dries out at low water or is only slightly covered. On the south-east and south coast, banks of sand and coarse pebbles have accumulated near the reef edge, and they stand sufficiently far away from the shore to allow the formation of channels which are suitable for native canoes between them and the shore. On the south coast, both sides of these channels are lined with mangrove swamps and penetration of the interior is difficult. Mangroves also front the greater part of the west coast and the east side of Lele harbour. Large caves up to 200 ft. long are said to occur on the west coast.

The main gaps in the reef are at Lele harbour, Port Lottin and

Coquille harbour. Owing to the difficulty of crossing the reef and penetrating the mangroves, landing is only practicable in the harbours, though native canoes thread their way through channels in the mangroves.

Anchorages

The most important anchorage area is Lele harbour, which is described separately below. The best of the other anchorages are Coquille harbour and Port Bérard. Both of these are pockets in the reef. The former provides good anchorage in from 13 to 15 fathoms and the latter in 8 fathoms. Both are exposed to westerly winds, but these are rare. Port Lottin, on the south side of the island, is another pocket in the reef which is suitable for anchoring. Its entrance is about 250 yd. wide. It is well sheltered but suitable only for small craft.

Lele Harbour

Lele harbour is situated off the Innemu river mouth. Like the other anchorages of Kusaie, it is formed by a pocket in the reef. Entrance is through a pass, with a depth in mid-channel of not less than 17 fathoms and a width of about 100 yd. Inside the entrance, the pocket broadens out and forks into two arms, the northern one with depths of about $6\frac{1}{2}$ fathoms and the southern one varying in depth from 7 to 12 fathoms. But there is not sufficient room for many vessels. The best anchorage is in 12 fathoms west of Eripou reef, an isolated patch immediately inside the entrance, or in 8 fathoms south of Lele island. There are no wharves or piers with deep water alongside and no lifting appliances, but there are several small piers or jetties suitable for boats.

The harbour is surrounded by coral reefs extending from a mangrove shore. Lele island, on the reef to the north, provides shelter. It is about 1 mile long by from 500 to 600 yd. wide, and rises in the east to a height of 351 ft. The western half is flat.

Social and Economic Conditions

In 1935 the population of Kusaie comprised 1,189 natives, 25 Japanese, and 25 others. The Japanese population is said to have increased recently to about 100. The native population is apparently increasing.

The natives live on Lele island and round the coast of the main island. They are all Christian. An American Congregationalist mission was active on the island many years before the establishment of Spanish control; and the Japanese have allowed it to continue its work. There is a mission school at Lele harbour; another mission station is situated on the west side of the island. Many of the natives have learnt English from the missionaries. Economically, the natives are still dependent primarily upon subsistence agriculture and fishing. Some copra is prepared for the market. The native houses are of rectangular form; the better ones are built on raised stone platforms.

The Japanese have started a small sugar plantation, and Japanese immigrants from the Ryukyu islands carry on fishing in motor sampans. Lele harbour is the base for these fishing expeditions. The only considerable Japanese settlement is at Lele. It includes a police station, a small hospital, and an office of the Nanyo Boeki Kaisha.

On Lele island there are the ruins of a native 'city'. These consist for the most part of walls built from gigantic basalt blocks, rising in places to a height of 20 ft., comparable with those at Metalanim in Ponape (Plate 113), and intersected by canals and channels obviously cut to facilitate transport of this building material.

Oroluk Lagoon

Oroluk lagoon (lat. 7° 31′ N, long. 155° 18′ E) lies about 170 miles west of Ponape. It is an atoll formed of an irregular chain of reefs enclosing a lagoon 18 miles long and about 15 miles wide. The only land is Oroluk island, a very small expanse of heavily wooded land on the north-west corner. There is a small rock, Baxo Trista, on the east side. Two channels lead into the lagoon, Keltie pass in the north, and Pioneer pass in the west. The former is extremely deep and the latter has a shallow patch in the middle but is 12 fathoms deep on the south side. There is anchorage in 11 fathoms about 1 mile south-east of Oroluk island. Until 1935 Oroluk lagoon was uninhabited, but in that year 5 Japanese and 38 natives settled on the island.

Ngatik

Ngatik (lat. 5° 49′ N, long. 157° 21′ E, at the south-east end) lies about 90 miles south-west of Ponape. It is an atoll, with three islands and several small islets. The largest, Ngatik island, is about 1 mile long and ½ mile wide; it is wooded and entirely surrounded by reef. A long and winding passage enters the south of the lagoon. The lagoon is about 11 miles long and 5 miles wide. It is suitable only for small sailing craft; it contains many coral patches. There is no anchorage outside. Landing can be made by boat at high water over the coral on the north side of Ngatik island. In 1935 there were 295 inhabitants, all living on Ngatik island. There is a church and also a branch office of the Nanyo Boeki Kaisha.

Pakin

Pakin (lat. 7° 02′ N, long. 157° 50′ E, at the south-east end) lies about 21 miles west-north-west of Ponape. It is an atoll, with five islands and several islets on the reef. The lagoon is 4 miles long and 1½ miles wide. There is one entrance suitable for small boats. Most of the islands are wooded. In 1935 the atoll was uninhabited.

ANT ISLANDS

The Ant islands (lat. 6° 47′ N, long. 157° 57′ E) are about 8 miles west of Ponape. They consist of several small islands on an atoll about 7 miles long and between 3½ and 5½ miles wide. A passage into the lagoon between curved reefs is suitable only for small craft. There are many detached heads of coral near the reef, but the centre of the lagoon is clear. In 1930 the population was about 40.

MOKIL (Fig. 98)

Mokil (lat. 6° 41′ N, long. 159° 47′ E, approximately) is a small atoll midway between Ponape and Pingelap, to the east. The atoll consists of a wide reef rim (300 to 1,300 yd. wide) surrounding three islets and a small lagoon; its total length is only about 2 miles. Mokil island in the north-east is hook-shaped, about 1½ miles long

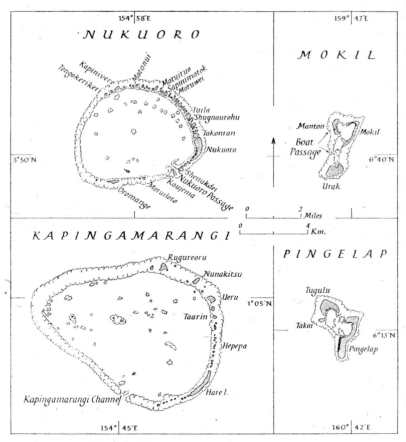

Fig. 98. Islands of the south-eastern Carolines

Thin strips of mangrove swamps are shown in solid black. Based on Admiralty charts nos. 978 (Mokil and Pingelap) and 979 (Nukuoro). The map of Kapingamarangi is based on other official sources.

and a few hundred yards wide. Urak in the south is about ⅜ mile long as also is Manton in the north-west. The lagoon is divided into two parts by a reef which is pierced by a boat passage. There are boat passages from the open sea into both parts of the lagoon. Landing can be made on Mokil by a stone wall on the west side. There is no proper anchorage but trading vessels sometimes drop anchor on the edge of the lee side of the reef in the trade wind season. In 1935 there were 258 native inhabitants, most of whom lived on Mokil island.

PINGELAP (Fig. 98)

Pingelap (lat. 6° 13′ N, long. 160° 42′ E) is a small wide-rimmed atoll, about 2 miles in extreme length, situated 60 miles east-south-east of Mokil and roughly midway between Ponape and Kusaie. There are two islands and one islet on the reef, which has an overall length of 2½ miles. Pingelap, the largest island, is about 1½ miles long and ⅓ mile wide. The lagoon, which has a length of 1 mile and a width of ⅓ mile, contains coral patches. There is a boat passage on the west side of the reef, between 3 and 6 ft. wide and about 1 ft. 6 in. deep. Native canoes are hauled through this by lifting the outrigger float out of the water and carrying it. Apparently there are no anchorages. Water is obtained by catchment.

The population in 1935 comprised 694 natives and 4 Japanese, mostly living on the westside of Pingelap island. There was a trader's store. The natives lived partly by exporting copra in exchange for Japanese goods and partly by subsistence agriculture and fishing. A small steamer called three times a year.

NUKUORO (Fig. 98)

Nukuoro (lat. 3° 51′ N, long. 154° 58′ E) lies about 300 miles south-west of Ponape. It is an atoll containing some 40 islands and islets grouped close together, principally on the east side of a circular reef. The enclosed lagoon is roughly 3½ miles in diameter. There is a narrow passage on the south side of the lagoon, obstructed by a bar with a depth of 4½ fathoms. (During the ebb the current reaches a speed of 4 knots. The passage should be attempted only at slack water.) Inside the lagoon anchorage can be found, but there are many coral patches. Water is obtained by catchment. There were 198 inhabitants in 1935.

KAPINGAMARANGI (Fig. 98)

Kapingamarangi (lat. 1° 04′ N, long. 154° 48′ E) lies about 480 miles south-south-east from Truk and about 440 miles south-west from Ponape. It is the most southerly island in the Japanese mandated islands and lies about 200 miles north-east of New Ireland. The atoll has been used by the Japanese as a seaplane base.

The atoll consists of an oval coral rim enclosing a lagoon 6½ miles long and 4½ miles wide. About 30 islets are set on the eastern rim. Of these Hare island, in the south-east, is the largest, with a length of 1 mile and a width of 300 yd. The only entry into the lagoon is through Greenwich passage, which is divided into two channels, apparently able to accommodate small vessels. There is a 5-knot stream in the channel during ebb tides. Most of the lagoon has depths of over 16 fathoms, but parts are obstructed by banks and coral patches. The lagoon shores at most of the islands are sandy, and the Japanese have built two temporary landings not less than 100 ft. long on Hare island, which they use as a seaplane station.

In 1935 the native population was 399. The people lived on Hare island and Nunakitsu island and on the islands between them. Nanyo Boeki Kaisha steamers called at Kapingamarangi five times a year before the war. A W/T station was built in 1935.

(For Bibliographical Note see Chapter XVI.)

Chapter XVIII

THE MARSHALL ISLANDS

Ralik Chain—Ujelang : Eniwetok : Bikini : Rongelap : Rongerik : Ailinginae :Wotho : Ujae : Kwajalein : Lae : Lib : Namu : Jabwot : Ailinglapalap : Jaluit : Kili : Namorik : Ebon

Ratak Chain—Pokaakku : Bikar : Utirik : Taka : Ailuk : Mejit : Jemo : Likiep : Wotje : Erikub : Maloelap : Aur : Majuro : Arno : Mili : Knox Islands

The Marshall islands (Fig. 99) comprise two separate chains of atolls, trending from north-west to south-east. The more westerly of the two is the Ralik chain, with which the two isolated atolls of Ujelang and Eniwetok are usually included. The more easterly is the Ratak chain. All the islands of the area are of coral formation. They include a number of very large atolls, of considerable importance as anchorage areas. The largest atoll is Kwajalein. The administrative centre of the group is at Jaluit.

THE RALIK CHAIN

UJELANG

Ujelang (lat. 9° 46′ N, long. 160° 58′ E, at the west end of Ujelang island) is also known as Areficos and as Providence island. It lies between Eniwetok and Ponape, in the Carolines. Together with Eniwetok it has not been treated for administrative purposes by the Japanese as part of the Jaluit District but as part of the Ponape District.

Ujelang consists of a lagoon 11½ miles long and 3 miles wide, surrounded by a narrow coral rim on which are scattered 26 small islands, covered with coconut palms. The largest, Ujelang, is in the south-east corner. The five main islands all lie along the south-west side, while the north-east side has small islets scattered along it at intervals. The longer axis of the atoll is from north-west to south-east.

There are two entrances to the lagoon, both on the south side. They are Wide passage, 250 yd. wide and 4 fathoms deep, and Narrow passage, 150 yd. wide and 2 fathoms deep. Both are difficult to navigate. There is also a small boat passage west of Einmlap island. There are no achorages outside the lagoon, but inside there is anchorage in 9 to 10 fathoms off the island of Ujelang. Landing can be effected by boat at a small wharf projecting into the lagoon, or on the beach on the lagoon side of almost all the islands. Brackish water is available from wells.

In 1934 there was a population of 40 natives and 12 Japanese, but the atoll is capable of supporting a much larger population. Before 1870 there were about 1,000 inhabitants ; but they migrated to Jaluit after a tidal wave had struck the island in that year. There was a Nanyo Boeki Kaisha trading post on Ujelang. Communication was maintained by a steamer from Ponape which called three times a year. A naval W/T and meteorological station had also been built.

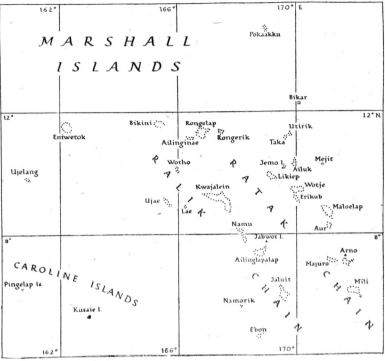

Fig. 99. The Marshall islands

All the islands shown on this map, except Kusaie, are of coral. Based on Admiralty chart no. 983.

ENIWETOK

Eniwetok (lat. 11° 21′ N, long. 162° 21′ E, approximately) lies 125 miles north-east of Ujelang. Like Ujelang it is administered from Ponape. It is also known as Brown island. It is a nearly circular atoll, 21 miles long and 17 miles wide, with a circumference of 70 miles. The coral rim varies in width from ¼ to 1½ miles. There are numerous islands scattered on the atoll rim, mostly on the east side. The largest are Eniwetok (3 miles long by ½ mile wide), Parry and Engebi (triangular and 1 mile along the south side). Palms grow thickly on the larger islands—especially on Eniwetok.

There are three gaps in the reef: Wide passage in the south, Deep entrance in the east, and South-west pass. The last is narrow and said to be dangerous, but Wide passage (between Eniwetok and Igurin islands) has a width of 5 miles, and, while it is partly obstructed by coral, there is a minimum depth of 13 fathoms and the channel can be used by large ships. Deep passage, to the north of Parry island, has a depth of 5 fathoms but can also apparently be used by large vessels. South-west passage is narrow and dangerous.

There is ample anchorage off the lagoon side of Eniwetok in from 20 to 30 fathoms, and good anchorage is also said to be found off Engebi island. There is a large pier on the lagoon side of Parry island, where vessels with deep draft can come alongside.

Boats can land anywhere on the sandy beach on the lagoon side of Eniwetok and also on the south side of Engebi.

Rain water is collected from roofs and stored in underground tanks, but there is an abundant supply of water of poor quality from a well on Eniwetok.

The population in 1935 amounted to 81 natives and 13 Japanese. The natives were all said to be Christians. Sea communication was by the steamer from Ponape, but the atoll has been a closed area and no visitors have been allowed in the islands, and no natives allowed to leave. Roads, about 7 ft. wide, have been built on Eniwetok and Parry islands, and a naval W/T and meteorological station is also reported.

BIKINI

Bikini (lat. 11° 30′ N, long. 165° 20′ E, approximately) is the northernmost atoll of the Ralik chain. It is also known as Escholti island. For a number of years the Japanese have excluded visiting natives from the island, which they regard as of considerable military value. The atoll is formed by an elliptical reef rim, the southern part of which is sunk to a depth of from 4¾ to 10 fathoms for a distance of 8 miles. It surrounds a lagoon 21½ miles from east to west and 13 miles from north to south, with an area of 170 sq. miles.

Altogether there are 23 islands and islets on the atoll rim. The longest is Bikini in the north-east corner, with a length of about 2 miles and width of ½ mile. This island is joined to Enyu on the south by a strip of sand always above high water. Both these islands are densely covered with coconut palms. Other islands in the north are lightly wooded, and many islets have few trees and very little sand. There are altogether eight passes into the lagoon, only three of which are of any value as ship passes. Enirikku pass between Enirikku and Eninman islands has a width of about 900 yd. with a depth of 29 fathoms. Enyu channel, over the sunken south-east portion of the reef, is a wide pass, with depths varying from 4¾ to 10 fathoms. Depths in the lagoon vary from 9 to 31 fathoms; and, though shelter from wind is not especially good, the lagoon provides ample anchorage for several vessels. The best shelter is found in 11 fathoms on the lagoon side of Bikini. Temporary anchorage can be found on the inner side of Enyu island, but ships here are liable to be disturbed by the swell. There are no wharves, but landing presumably can be made on the lagoon side of most of the islands. Water is obtained by catchment and stored in tanks. The population has been reported as being 60 in 1933 and 159 in 1935. On Bikini island there are several houses and at least one large building. Considerable developments have probably been undertaken, notably the provision of fuel and petrol supplies for ships. Fish are abundant in the waters near the atoll, but the supplies of coconuts are said to be barely sufficient for the inhabitants and offer no surplus for copra export. Sea communications include visits by steamer from Jaluit seven times a year. A W/T station is said to have been built.

RONGELAP

Rongelap (lat. 11° 09′ N, long. 166° 53′ E) is about 67 miles east of Bikini and about 18 miles west of Rongerik. It consists of an atoll enclosing a lagoon of irregular shape with an area of about 300 sq. miles; its greatest length (north-east to south-west) is 29 miles. The coral rim is narrow. On it are 50 small islands, some very small. The longest, Rongelap, in the south-east corner, is about 4 miles long. The soil is very poor and sandy and vegetation is limited to low scrub and a few coconut trees (Plate 73).

There are altogether nine entrances into the lagoon, several of them capable of taking large ships. South pass, between Rongelap island and Arubaru island, is most used. It has depths of 6 fathoms, but sunken dangers and no convenient leading marks. North-east pass, immediately west of Mellu, has deep water and no apparent dangers, Kaeroga pass, to the west of Enigan island, has a depth of at least 15 fathoms; a pass north of Enybarbar island has a depth of 10 fathoms. Accurate surveys of the lagoon are not available; but it varies in depth from 24 fathoms to 30 fathoms and in places there are coral patches, but there is ample anchorage. Specific points where good anchorage can be found are about 1,600 yd. off the inner side of Rongelap; westward of Enlaidokku island, on either side of a projecting sand-spit; and off the north-west of Arubaru island. Landing can be made by boats on sandy beaches on the lagoon side of most of the islands and on the north of Mellu island. The beach on Rongelap would be particularly suitable for hauling out seaplanes.

Drinking water is probably limited to that which can be obtained by catchment; other sources are said to be brackish. The population in 1935 consisted of 98 natives, most of whom lived on Rongelap and Enlaidokku islands. There is a native church near the lagoon on the south-east part of Rongelap, and the natives are said to be all Protestant. Health conditions are good. Before the war Nanyo Boeki Kaisha vessels visited the atoll twice a year. A W/T station has been built.

RONGERIK

Rongerik (lat. 11° 18′ N, long. 167° 28′ E, approximately, at Enyvertok island) is about 18 miles east of Rongelap.

The lagoon, which is of irregular shape, has an area of about 90 sq. miles, being 9 miles across from north to south and from east to west. For a distance of 2¼ miles on the west side the reef is submerged. Altogether there are 13 islands or sandbanks on the reef, the largest of which are Enyvertok (1 mile long and 250 yd. wide), in the south-east, and Rongerik island (triangular with each side about ½ mile), in the north-east. The former is unusual in rising to a height of 28 ft. on the lagoon side. Both islands are wooded with palms, but vegetation on the others is limited to low scrub.

The main entrance into the lagoon is Enyvertok pass, with a reported depth of 12 fathoms. Bock pass, over the sunken reef, is 2¼ miles wide but divided by shoals into several channels. The middle one has a depth of 12 fathoms but is hard to identify. Jedibberdeb pass, in the north, is suitable only for small craft and is subject to heavy seas. Though the lagoon is not so big as that of Rongelap, it still affords anchorage for several large ships. The only anchorages specifically indicated are in 15 fathoms, 600 yd. off the inner side of Enyvertok; in 9 to 10 fathoms, south-east of Bock island; north-west of Rongerik; and in Bock pass. The first of these is suitable only for small vessels, and the last is suitable only in calm weather. Landing can be made on beaches on the lagoon side of Enyvertok and Rongerik islands.

Water is probably obtained by catchment. In 1930 the population was 11; it had fallen to 6 by 1935. Health conditions are said to be bad. Few coconuts are obtainable, but turtles are plentiful in the lagoon and pearl oysters are found. Communication was maintained before the war by two visits a year by Nanyo Boeki Kaisha vessels from Jaluit.

AILINGINAE

Ailinginae (lat. 11° 07′ N, long. 166° 24′ E, approximately) lies 4½ miles off the south-west corner of Rongelap. The lagoon, which is generally shallow, is surrounded by a reef and is roughly rectangular. It is about 14 miles from east to west and 4½ miles from north to south, with small islets mostly on the east and south sides. The largest, Mogiri, is less than 1 mile long. Coconut palms grow on the islets of the western end, and casuarina trees on the eastern islets. There are two passes, one on each side of Mogiri island, leading into the lagoon. The longer one is 1,600 yd. wide, but both are obstructed by coral patches, and only small craft can enter the lagoon through them. There is no anchorage outside the reef, but inside small craft can anchor 600 yd. north of Mogiri island. Except in strong wind, boats can land on most of the islands from the lagoon. There are no permanent inhabitants, but natives visit the atoll from Rongerik and Rongelap. A few coconuts can be obtained and there are abundant supplies of fish in the lagoon.

WOTHO

Wotho (lat. 10° 02′ N, long. 166° 01′ E, at its southern end) is 66 miles north-west of Kwajalein. It is also known as Schane island. It consists of thirteen small islands on a reef, surrounding a roughly triangular lagoon, with a concave eastern side. The reef is continuous on the north and east sides, but broken up by shallows and boat-passages on the west. The three largest islets, Wotho, Kabben and Medyeron, are situated at the north-east, south and north-west corners respectively. All three are thickly covered with bushes and small trees, and the longest, Wotho, is roughly 1½ miles long and 1 mile wide. There are three shallow passes in the reef, but they are suitable only for small craft. Ombelim channel, which is the best, has a depth of about 3½ fathoms, but it is not well defined. The lagoon is much obstructed by coral in the north and south. The best anchorage is off Wotho island.

Rain water, collected in cisterns, provides the only supply of water fit for drinking.

In 1939 the population of the atoll comprised 47 natives. These people lived mainly by fishing and the export of small quantities of copra. A steamer of the Nanyo Boeki Kaisha called twice a year.

UJAE

Ujae (lat. 9° 02′ N, long. 165° 35′ E, approximately) is also known as Katherine island. It is of elongated lozenge shape, 22 miles long from north-west to south-east and about 6½ miles wide. The reef completely surrounds the lagoon but is sunken on its western side. In all there are fifteen islets on the reef rim; the largest are Enylamieg, Ebbetyu and Ujae. All are thickly wooded and Ujae and Enylamieg are said to be the most fertile in the Marshall islands. There are, in all, four passes into the lagoon, all on the west side. Only two can take ships, and these are only suitable for small craft: they are Bock channel and North pass. The former is narrow and tortuous with strong tidal streams; the latter is over a sunken portion of the reef, with a least depth of 3 fathoms. There is no anchorage in the lagoon suitable for ships with more than 16 ft. draft, but for small vessels anchorage may be found north of Bock island, west of Ebbetyu and north of Ujae. Landing can probably be effected from boats on the lagoon side of most of the islands. Water is obtained by catchment and stored in cisterns.

The total population in 1935 was 160. Communications with other islands were maintained by a Nanyo Boeki Kaisha steamer, which formerly called twice a year.

KWAJALEIN (Fig. 100)

Kwajalein (lat. 9° 23′ N, long. 167° 28′ E, at its northernmost point) is the largest atoll in the Marshall group. It has also been known as Menschikov island. The lagoon has been developed and used as a base for naval operations by the Japanese. The lagoon, surrounded by a reef rim which is not continuous, stretches roughly 75 miles from north-west to south-east, and is about 30 miles across at its widest point. The larger islands are Kwajalein in the south, Roi and Namur in the north, and Ebadon in the extreme north-west. The islands in the south are heavily wooded; Roi is more lightly wooded, and most of the remaining islands have few or no trees.

There are about 25 passes into the lagoon, either through or over the reef, but only about half-a-dozen are ship passes. Gea pass near the southern end of the south-west side, South pass, North pass, two passes east of Roi island, and two more

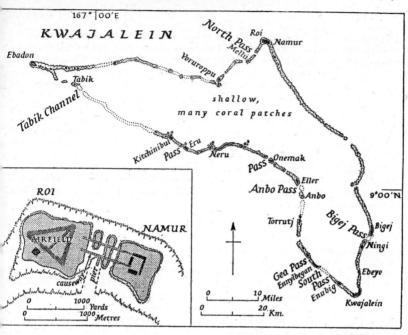

Fig. 100. Kwajalein atoll
Based on Admiralty chart no. 984. The inset is based on official sources.

on the south-west side of the atoll seem to be most used. Bigej channel, on the east side, is only suitable for small vessels. In the lagoon there is ample room for a large number of ships. Specific anchorage areas are just off Kwajalein island (7–15 fathoms), inside South pass, and south of Roi island.

Landing facilities consist of a jetty on the lagoon side of Kwajalein island, a ramp for hauling out seaplanes on Ebeye, and a pier or jetty projecting from the southern-most of two causeways joining Roi and Namur islands. There are wells on some islands, but the Japanese rely for water supply mainly on catchment, supplementing this source when necessary by importing water in ships.

In 1935 the native population amounted to 1,079, the principal villages being on Kwajalein, Roi, Ebadon and Neru islands. At that time there were only 6 Japanese, but considerable numbers must since have been brought in to undertake construction work in connection with the development of the atoll as a base. The native people are Protestants. Their chiefs still have considerable authority over them. Health conditions are poor. 'Marshall typhus' and dysentery are common, and the heat is considerable. The Japanese consider that it takes three months for the crews of their ships to become accustomed to local conditions.

Sea communications were maintained before the war by Nanyo Boeki Kaisha steamers calling four times a year. Airfields have been built on Roi island and on the south of Kwajalein, and an emergency landing ground has been built on Ennylbegan island. There are W/T stations on Enubig island and possibly elsewhere. Causeways have been built joining Namur island, where there are some administrative buildings, with Roi island.

LAE

Lae atoll (lat. 8° 55′ N, long. 166° 13′ E, at Lotj island) is about 40 miles south-west of the western end of Kwajalein atoll. It consists of a roughly circular reef enclosing a lagoon about 2½ miles from north to south and 3¼ miles from east to west. There are 14 islets, lying for the most part close together on the eastern side of the reef rim. Lae, the largest, is roughly 1 mile long, ½ mile wide, and 6 ft. high. There is one pass leading into the lagoon, but it has a depth of only 10 ft.

Anchorage is possible off the entrance in north-easterly winds. Inside the lagoon small craft can anchor on the west side of Lae island, but the anchorage is surrounded by reefs and the lagoon is unsurveyed. Landing by boats can be made on the lagoon side of Lae at high tide. Wells on Lae, Lotj and Ribong islands provide water which is slightly saline but is drunk by the natives.

The total population in 1935 amounted to 88 people, most of whom lived on Lae. All of them were Protestants, and there was one native missionary. Many could speak English. The Nanyo Boeki Kaisha steamer from Jaluit called twice a year before the war.

LIB

Lib island (lat. 8° 19′ N, long. 167° 24′ E, approximately) lies about 30 miles south-west of Kwajalein. It is a quadrangular raised atoll ¾ mile from north-west to south-east, and about ½ mile wide. The island is low and sandy with a central depression behind a beach crest which encircles the island. There is a fresh-water pond in the centre, surrounded by a thick clump of trees. The coast is fringed by coral reef extending from ¾ to 1¼ miles from the coast, on all sides except the west, where it extends only about ¼ mile. Landing is possible only on this side, and then only at high tide. There is no anchorage. The natives drink the water from the pond. In 1935 there were 68 inhabitants, who lived by producing copra, breadfruit, pumpkins and pineapples from the very fertile soil of the island. There are no regular communications with the outside world.

NAMU

Namu (lat. 7° 45′ N, long. 168° 13′ E, at Leuen island) is about 34 miles south-east of Kwajalein. It has sometimes been known as Mosquillo. It is a long irregular atoll, 32 miles from north-west to south-east, with a lagoon area of 110 sq. miles. There are over 50 islands and islets, nearly all of which are on the north-east rim. The largest islands are Leuen, in the extreme south, Namu at the north-west point, and Kaginen. Leuen is of crescentic form following the shape of the reef; it is about 2 miles long and nowhere more than 400 yd. wide. The others are each about a mile long.

There are three openings into the lagoon, all on the west side. Bock channel, a deep but tortuous passage only 160 yd. wide, and Anil channel are both too difficult for large ships to negotiate. The latter is apparently the better entrance of the two. The third opening, situated between them, is suitable only for boats. Outside the lagoon there is anchorage for small craft on a shoal off Namu island. Landing can be effected on the west side of Namu island and probably almost anywhere on the lagoon side of the other islands. Water is obtained by catchment and stored in cisterns.

The population in 1935 consisted of 276 natives and 3 Japanese. The latter were presumably the staff of the Nanyo Boeki Kaisha store on Namu island. There were several native houses on the western end of Leuen island and wide areas were cultivated. Health conditions are good, but cases of venereal disease are not uncommon. Communication by sea was maintained by steamer or schooner with Jaluit. Travel between the islands is by canoe, and on some islands there are roads surfaced with coral and pebbles.

JABWOT

Jabwot island (lat. 7° 44′ N, long. 168° 59′ E) is a small island about ¾ mile long. There is no lagoon. The coast is surrounded by reefs which extend ⅜ mile on the north and east sides, and ¼ mile on the south and west sides. In 1930 there was a native population of 48. Deposits of phosphate are said to have been found on the island.

AILINGLAPALAP

Ailinglapalap lies in lat. 7° 26′ N, long. 165° 45′ E, at Enyebing. It is 90 miles south-east of Kwajalein and 68 miles north-west of Jaluit. It is also known as Elmore and as Odia island.

The lagoon is roughly triangular, with a greatest length of about 27 miles from north-east to south-west. It is 15 miles wide at its widest point. The reef rim is practically continuous and there are altogether 49 islands scattered at intervals on it. None is more than ½ mile wide, though some are of considerable length. The largest are Wotja, on the west side; Ailinglapalap, on the south; and Jeh on the east. The height of the land varies from 3 to 10 ft. All the islands are palm-covered.

There are altogether seven entrances into the lagoon. The only two which can take small craft are South pass, between Bigatyelang and Ailinglapalap islands, and East pass, between Ailinglapalap and Kubar islands. The former has deep water and is probably the best entrance, but owing to its twisting nature and the presence of a reef at its inner end, it is only useful for small vessels. The latter is about 400 yd. wide and is suitable for small vessels, though tidal currents attain a speed of about 2 knots within it.

Outside the lagoon there is anchorage sheltered from the prevailing north-east wind to the west of Wotja island, in 10 to 12 fathoms, and also outside the entrance to South pass, though here the coral bottom does not give good holding ground and the depths increase rapidly 200 yd. from the shore. Inside the lagoon there are said to be anchorages at the east end of Ailinglapalap island, north of Bigatyelang island, south and west of Jeh island, and in South pass. There are no wharves or jetties. Landing can be made only inside the lagoon when the wind is favourable. Water is collected and stored in cisterns; it is said to be in short supply during the winter months.

In 1935 there were 682 native inhabitants and 5 Japanese. The most important villages were on Ailinglapalap and Wotja islands. On Wotja the Boston mission had a church and school and the Nanyo Boeki Kaisha a store. The paramount chief of the Ralik chain lives at Enyebing, on Wotja. Copra is exported. Vessels of the Nanyo Boeki Kaisha formerly called twice a year.

JALUIT (Fig. 101; Plate 114)

Jaluit (lat. 5° 55′ N, long. 169° 40′ E, at Jabor island) lies near the southern end of the Ralik chain. It was the former German administrative centre for the group. There has been some commercial and considerable military development.

Physical Geography

Jaluit is a roughly lozenge-shaped atoll, with a greatest length (north-west to south-east) of 33 miles and a maximum width of 18 miles. The lagoon has an area of about 200 sq. miles. The reef rim is well developed with almost continuous chains of islands on the east side and several islands on the west side. The majority of the islands on the east side are long and narrow, being only about 400 yd. wide. The main island is Jaluit on the south side. Enybor island, immediately north of South-east passage, is of somewhat similar form. This characteristic of a thin continuous or semi-continuous land rim is typical of the southern two-thirds of the

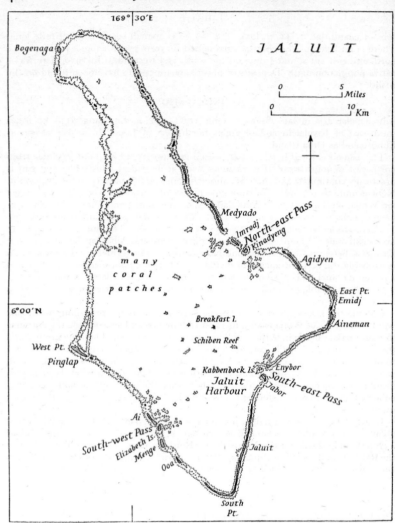

Fig. 101. Jaluit atoll

Those parts of the atoll rim which are above high water mark are stippled or shown in solid black. The land area of this group, and of Ebon atoll (Fig. 102), is greater than the average for the atolls of the Marshall islands. Based on Admiralty chart no. 988.

east side of the atoll. The northern third has a chain of very small isolated islets. There are only a few islets on the western side. The total land area of the whole atoll does not exceed 6½ sq. miles and nowhere is the land more than 12 ft. high. Along the narrow strips of land the seaward side reaches a height of about 5 ft., forming a crest of coral boulders, and slopes gently towards a flat beach on the lagoon side. Vegetation consists of palm trees, scattered shrubs and grasses.

Entrances, Anchorages and Port Facilities

There are three ship passes into the lagoon; the best known (South-east pass) is immediately north of Jabor island. At the entrance it is about 700 yd. wide, narrowing to 200 yd. between Jabor and Kabbenbock islands. There is a depth of at least 9 fathoms in the fairway, but currents setting northwards across the entrance make it difficult for sailing vessels to enter. North-east pass, between Kinadyeng and Imrodj islands, has a width of 500 yd. and a depth of 16 fathoms. South-west pass, between Ai and Elizabeth islands, is deep and tortuous, but only 200 yd. wide. Soundings are not available for the whole lagoon, but between the above passes the depth varies from 15 to 25 fathoms. In parts of the lagoon there are detached coral heads. In general, however, the lagoon offers facilities for the anchorage of large numbers of ships. While the area immediately inside the harbour entrance is unsuitable owing to strong currents and lack of protection from winds, the whole of the eastern side of the lagoon is said to be available for anchorage. Specified anchorage areas are: in 8 to 9 fathoms, 400 yd. off the government pier on Jaluit island; in 6 to 20 fathoms, anywhere west of Jaluit island; and between Ribong and Imrodj islands.

On Jabor island there are three wharves or jetties, the principal (Government) one being a stone or concrete jetty about 600 yd. long, opposite the Nanyo Boeki Kaisha warehouse. This has a depth of from 18 to 25 ft. alongside at high water and is equipped with three mobile cranes and two railway trucks. The other two are the Nankai jetty, on the north-west corner, and the Nanyo Boeki Kaisha jetty about 200 yd. north of the main jetty. Both of these are suitable only for boats, as also is the Sydney town jetty, a long jetty extending from a point about a mile south of Jabor to the reef edge. About 20,000 tons of coal are kept near the Government jetty, and oil is stored in tanks on an islet midway between the Government jetty and Sydney town jetty. Other storage tanks are situated near the airfields on Enybor island. Water is obtained by catchment. There are also some wells, but their water is probably unsuitable for drinking purposes. On Enybor island the Mitsubishi Engineering Company have built a small workshop with lathes and drilling machines, and there is a boat-building yard where boats up to 100 ft. over-all have been built.

Social and Economic Conditions

Before 1941 there were about 2,000 natives in the atoll, but they have since all been moved to other islands. In 1940 there were also two missionaries, one of them German. The major industry was copra production; small quantities of coffee were also produced; and a quite extensive fishing industry had grown up. The principal settlement is the town on Jabor island. It is well laid out with two main streets. There are many well-built Japanese buildings, including several Japanese hotels, a post office, a government school, a police station, and three government hospitals, in addition to numerous wooden houses. There are a refrigeration plant, a small power station and a cannery.

Communications

Jaluit was the terminal point of the East-Round line and the East-West Connecting line of the Nippon Yusen Kaisha; and the local services of the Nanyo Boeki Kaisha were based on the atoll. Some of the latter company's vessels went south to the Gilbert islands. There is a naval air station on Enybor island, and there are two airfields—one on Enybor and the other on Emidj. There are good roads, suitable for motor traffic, on Jabor island. The main W/T station, on Jabor, maintained communication with Truk, Ponape and Palau. A telephone system linked government buildings and those of the Nanyo Boeki Kaisha.

KILI

Kili (lat. 5° 29′ N, long. 169° 07′ E) is a low island with no lagoon, about 1 mile long and ¼ mile wide, lying 35 miles south-west of Jaluit. It is surrounded by a fringing reef which extends submerged at a depth of from 5 to 15 fathoms from the south-west point for a distance of 1½ miles. Anchorage may be obtained on the reef, though the position is much exposed. Landing can occasionally be effected from surf-boats on the western side in calm weather. The island is apparently inhabited, since pigs are said to be exported to Jaluit. It was devastated by hurricanes in 1874 and 1911. It was planted with coconut palms by the German Jaluitgesellschaft.

NAMORIK

Namorik (Baring) atoll (lat. 5° 36′ N, long. 168° 06′ E) is a small rectangular atoll about 94 miles west-south-west of Jaluit. It is roughly 3 miles across, and there are no breaks in the reef rim. On the reef are two low islands, Namorik, which covers the whole of the east and south sides, and Matamat, in the north-west corner. Although there are no passes into the lagoon small boats can, with difficulty, cross the reef rim at high water, if care is taken to avoid rocks which are scattered about on it. The lagoon is shallow and there are numerous coral heads inside. Boats can land on the west side. There is no anchorage.

In 1935 there were 368 natives and 8 Japanese. The people have had many contacts with Europeans, principally missionaries. Some are possibly able to speak

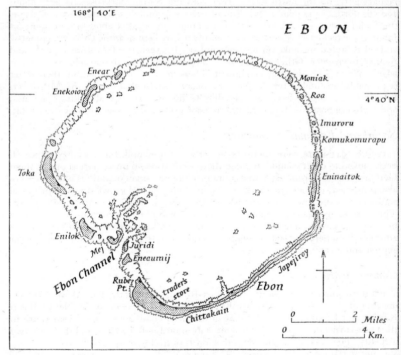

Fig. 102. Ebon atoll
For explanation and source see Fig. 101.

English. There are two churches served by native missionaries. Copra and bananas are the principal resources, but there are also pigs and chickens. Overseas communication was by Nanyo Boeki Kaisha steamers twice a year.

EBON (Fig. 102)

Ebon (lat. 4° 35′ N, long. 168° 41′ E, at Rube point) is the southernmost atoll of the Ralik chain and lies 85 miles south-west of Jaluit. It has also been known as Boston island. The reef rim is roughly circular, enclosing a lagoon with a diameter of about 7 miles. Altogether there are 23 islets on the reef rim, mostly on the south; Ebon island, the largest, has a length of 6 miles but is nowhere more than ½ mile wide. There are thick growths of trees, mostly coconut palms, pandanus, breadfruit and casuarina.

The only pass into the lagoon is deep (its minimum depth is 9 fathoms) but it is narrow and crooked, being 150 yd. wide where ships have to alter course and 130 yd. wide at its narrowest point. Tidal currents are very strong, reaching 7 knots on the ebb tide during springs. Large vessels are said to anchor outside. Inside, anchorage can be found off Ebon island in 14 fathoms. The reef dries out inside the lagoon and launching is difficult except at high water. Boats can land outside the lagoon south of Rube point in calm weather only. Water is obtained by catchment.

In 1935 there were 650 natives, all of them Protestant; many know some English and German. There were also 4 Japanese. A mission station is situated on the south end of Ebon and there are villages on Ebon and the other two large islands. Deposits of phosphate have been discovered and are said to be worked by the South Seas Colonization Company. Communications were maintained by Nanyo Boeki Kaisha vessels calling twice a year.

THE RATAK CHAIN

POKAAKKU

Pokaakku (lat. 14° 43′ N, long. 168° 57′ E, approximately), also known as Taongi, is the most northerly atoll of the Marshall islands. It lies 150 miles north-north-west of Bikar. It is low and crescentic, with the convex side to the east, 9 miles long from north to south and about 5 miles wide in the middle. The lagoon is shallow, varying probably from 4 to 5 fathoms, and encumbered with coral heads. There are altogether ten islands or islets on the reef rim, all grouped along the southern half of the eastern side. The largest, Sibylla island, is about 2½ miles long and 300 yd. wide, with a maximum elevation of about 15 ft. There is a dense growth of trees on the southern part of Sibylla island and on the most southerly island. On the others there are some trees and low sandy patches with scrub.

There is only one boat pass into the lagoon on the western side. This is only 25 ft. wide, and very crooked; but it is said to be deep enough to take a motor launch. There is a strong current reaching a speed of 6 knots in the pass during ebb tides. This is caused by water breaking in over the reef rim in heavy weather and building up the level of the lagoon above the sea outside. The Japanese were dredging another channel north of the southernmost island. There is no known anchorage inside, or outside, the lagoon, but boats can land on the beaches on the lagoon side of the southern islands, which are steep and offer no difficulties. Those further north offer some encumbrances in the form of coral reefs.

There are normally no regular inhabitants, but Japanese visited the atoll to collect bird-skins from the numerous sea birds which nest there. There is a corrugated-iron hut. Recently, considerable constructional work has been undertaken, possibly for a seaplane base. Flies and mosquitoes are said to be absent, but there are numerous sharks in the waters round the atoll.

BIKAR

Bikar (lat. 12° 15′ N, long. 170° 07′ E) lies near the northern end of the Ratak chain and is the nearest point in the Japanese mandated islands to the Hawaiian islands, being 1,900 miles distant from Pearl harbour. It is also known as Dawson island. The atoll is of irregular shape, 7 miles long and 4⅛ miles wide. There are 8 small islands on the reef rim. The largest, Bikar, is 800 yd. long, with a maximum altitude of 10 ft. There is a miscellaneous growth of trees but few, if any, palms. There are numbers of scattered islets in the lagoon itself. A single pass leads into the lagoon. It has a width of 100 ft. at the entrance, but it is split into two narrow crooked passes by a reef in the middle. Tidal currents up to 5 knots are experienced in these, and they are only suitable for small craft. There is probably anchorage room within for vessels which could negotiate the passage, but nothing is known definitely. Landing can be made on beaches on the lagoon side of most of the islands. The atoll is uninhabited, but natives visit it from time to time to catch fish and birds, which are plentiful.

UTIRIK

Utirik (lat. 11° 14′ N, long. 169° 51′ E) is approximately 60 miles south-south-west of Bikar. It has also been known as Kutusov island. It is an atoll with a reef rim enclosing a roughly triangular lagoon, 8 miles from north to south and 6 miles wide. There are 8 islands, mostly on the eastern and southern sides of the reef. The largest is Utirik, about 1½ miles long and ¾ mile wide. There is a narrow pass leading into the lagoon but there is no further available information about it. The lagoon is encumbered by coral patches, but soundings show depths of from 13 to 23 fathoms. Altogether there are at least ten wells on the atoll; one provides drinkable water. In 1935 the population consisted of 126 natives, most of whom lived in Utirik, where the settlement included a church. Moderate quantities of copra and dried fish were exported, and a steamer from Jaluit called at least 7 times a year. A naval W/T station has been established.

TAKA

Taka (lat. 11° 07′ N, long. 169° 40′ E) is separated from Utirik by a deep channel 4 miles wide. It has been known to Europeans as Suvorov island. The atoll is about the same size as Utirik, and has 8 islands on the reef. The longest is Taka, with a length of about ½ mile. The only pass into the lagoon, on the western side, is narrow and suitable for small vessels only. The lagoon has an area of about 25 sq. miles, and is fairly deep but encumbered by coral and subject to swells. There are no permanent inhabitants; the atoll is visited by natives who come to collect copra.

AILUK

Ailuk (lat. 10° 13′ N, long. 169° 59′ E, approximately) is 41 miles south-south-east of Taka and 45 miles north of Wotje. It is a triangular atoll about 15 miles long from north to south and about 7 miles across at the southern end. The eastern rim is thickly studded with islets, none of which exceeds ½ mile across. Ailuk island lies at the south-east corner. Most are densely wooded, with coconuts predominating on the lagoon sides.

There are various passes into the lagoon, all are suitable only for small craft. The best are Erappu channel, which is about 200 yd. wide and very deep, but also very crooked. Marok channel north of it is deep and straight but narrow. The lagoon has an area of over 50 sq. miles but is obstructed by coral heads, small islands and submerged rocks. Depths vary from 6½ to 27 fathoms according to the few available soundings. Anchorage for small craft can be found off the lee (lagoon) side of

Kapeniur island in the north, and about 1½ miles from Ailuk in 12½ fathoms. There are two good wells on Ailuk and a 3-ton water storage tank.

The population in 1935 was 293 natives and 2 Japanese. Most were living on Ailuk, where there is a Protestant church served by a native missionary, and a Nanyo Boeki Kaisha store. Copra is the only regular export. Bonito, tuna and flying fish are plentiful in the lagoon. Nanyo Boeki Kaisha ships visited the atoll 7 times a year before the war and the lagoon could probably be used as a seaplane anchorage.

Mejit

Mejit (lat. 10° 17′ N, long. 170° 53′ E, approximately) is a small island lying 53 miles east of Ailuk. It is low and sandy, well cultivated and wooded with coconut and breadfruit trees. A shallow inlet divides it into two regions, the northern being flat and the southern uneven. A reef 400 yd. wide at the south-east end and 1 mile to 1½ miles wide at the north-east, surrounds the island. There is a landing place on the south part of the west side but this is usually inaccessible from December to April.

In 1935 there was a native population of 424, mostly Protestant. There was a Japanese trading station and schooners called regularly.

Jemo

Jemo (or Temo) is charted as lying about 27 miles south-west of Ailuk in lat. 10° 06′ N, long. 169° 30′ E; but it is reported that it is 10 miles west of the charted position. It is a small, sandy, thickly wooded island, surrounded by reefs, which extend for about 5 miles off-shore on the east side. The island is uninhabited but visited occasionally by natives from Ailuk and Likiep, who come to hunt turtles.

Likiep

Likiep (lat. 9° 40′ N, long. 169° 18′ E, approximately) is 35 miles north-west of Wotje and 20 miles south-west of Jemo. The north-west end is reported to extend beyond its charted position. The atoll is of irregular shape, about 23 miles long from north-west to south-east, with a maximum width of 9 miles. The reef which surrounds the lagoon varies in width from ½ mile to 1½ miles. There are altogether 44 small islands distributed fairly evenly along the reef, though they are most numerous in the south and south-east. All the islands are low and have a thick cover of coconut palms.

Several passes lead into the lagoon, but the only one suitable for large ships is South pass, with a minimum depth of 8 fathoms. The inner end is divided into three by an island and a sand-spit. The eastern channel is said to be the best; it has tidal currents reaching 2·1 knots on the flood and 1·5 on the ebb. Two other passes on the west side of the lagoon are both encumbered with reefs and only suitable for small craft. Other passes are only suitable for small boats. The lagoon, with an area of about 75 sq. miles, should provide reasonable anchorage accommodation, but adequate surveys are not available. It is much encumbered by coral reefs. There is anchorage in 10 fathoms, on good holding ground and with good shelter, north of Likiep island, and in 8 fathoms off the south-west side of Roto island. Outside the lagoon there is anchorage north-west of Kapenor island.

There are four rain-water tanks, with a total capacity of 35 tons, and also a number of wells. In 1935 the population was 499. The majority was native; but there were a considerable number of mixed-bloods and 2 Japanese. Most of the people are Protestant, but there are some Roman Catholics. The atoll is 'owned' by 2 Germans, who act as heads of the two clans into which the people are divided. Before the war these two men administered the atoll for the Japanese, engaged in copra trading and had a small boat-building yard capable of building boats up to 25 tons. Over 100 tons of copra are produced annually. The island is also rich in breadfruit and papaya. Pigs and chickens are kept, and fish are plentiful in the lagoon. Health conditions are bad; skin diseases and venereal and respiratory diseases common, and amoebic dysentery is not infrequent. Communication was maintained by Nanyo Boeki Kaisha vessels, which called 7 times a year.

WOTJE (Fig. 103)

Wotje (lat. 9° 28′ N, long. 170° 15′ E, at Wotje island) is a large atoll with ample accommodation for a large fleet. It was formerly known as Romanzov island. The maximum length of the atoll is 26 miles in an east-west direction and the width 11 miles. The reef is well formed on the east but submerged in the west. On it are altogether about 56 islands, mostly in the east and south-east. The largest and most important, Wotje island, lies in the middle of the eastern side. It is crescent-shaped, about 2 miles long from north to south and rather over ½ mile wide. It is low and

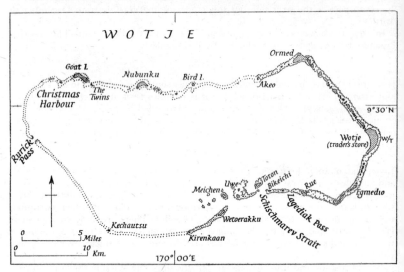

Fig. 103. Wotje atoll

Much of the northern and western reef rim is submerged. Based on Admiralty chart no. 988.

sandy and covered with coconut trees. Considerable developments have taken place on this island since 1938.

The best entrance to the lagoon is Schischmarev strait (called Toton pass by the Japanese) on the south side of the atoll. The minimum width is 300 yd. and the least known depth is 15 fathoms. Tidal currents are not strong. Lagediak pass (a short distance east of Schischmarev) and Rurick pass on the extreme west are also fairly wide. The former is about 100 yd. wide and apparently 4 fathoms deep, but has strong currents. The latter is wide and deep but has 3-fathom shoals on either side. The lagoon has an area of 190 sq. miles and a tidal range of 5 ft. 9 in. Though it contains several coral heads, it can provide shelter for many ships. Specific anchorages are: 400 yd. west of Wotje island, in 8 fathoms increasing to 19 fathoms 1 mile off-shore; 1,200 yd. off Ormed, in 16 fathoms (though this is not recommended by the Japanese); in 10 fathoms in Christmas harbour at the extreme north-west of the atoll; and off Goat island. Landing can be made on the beach on the lagoon side of Wotje island, or at either of the recently constructed jetties. Wells are numerous, and a few supply water which is drinkable if boiled. Fresh water is also said to collect in pits in the sand. In 1935 the population consisted of 590 natives and 10 Japanese, most of whom lived on Wotje and Ormed islands. A Japanese public school and a Nanyo Boeki Kaisha store then existed on the atoll. But since 1938 the native population has been removed and 1,000 convicts have been imported to work on military construction. This work included two landing jetties on the lagoon side of Wotje island (one running into deep water), fuel tanks, various hangars, barracks, etc., and an airfield with two runways. A road which has been built round Wotje island also joins the three islets immediately to the north by bridges or causeways, and projects half-way over the reef between the third and fourth islands to the north of Wotje. Before the war Nippon Yusen Kaisha steamers on the East-Round line called about 16 times a year; schooners carry on the local trade.

ERIKUB

Erikub (lat. 9° 11′ N, long. 169° 54′ E, approximately) lies immediately south of Wotje, from which it is separated by a channel 5 miles wide. The southern end is reported to be 8 miles north of its charted position. The atoll is elliptical in form, roughly 17 miles from north-west to south-east and 5 miles wide. Altogether thirteen small islands stand on the reef rim, the largest is Erikub, in the extreme south, with a length of about a mile. Vegetation is scanty, consisting of low scrub with a few coconut palms on Erikub.

Four openings give access to the lagoon, three on the south-west and one on the north-east. The pass on the south-west side, between Enego island and Log island, is said to be the best, but is suitable only for small craft. The pass on the east side is described as being narrow but deep, and as suitable for small boats but difficult to use on account of tidal currents. The lagoon has an area of 72 sq. miles and is free of reefs, but no information is available about depth of water. It is not likely to afford much protected anchorage.

There is no known water supply. The atoll is uninhabited, though natives visit it occasionally to gather coconuts. There are two or three huts to afford temporary shelter on Erikub island.

MALOELAP (Fig. 104)

Maloelap (lat. 8° 43′ N, long. 171° 14′ E, approximately at Taroa) is 85 miles south-east of Wotje and is said to be 3 miles north-west of its charted position. It is triangular, with its greatest length, of 32 miles, from north-west to south-east. The lagoon is 250 sq. miles in area. More than 60 islets are scattered round the reef rim: the largest one Taroa, at the east corner; Airik, at the south-east corner, and Kaven island, at the north-west corner. All the islands are thickly covered with coconut palms, breadfruit trees, etc., and are very fertile.

Several passes lead into the lagoon. The three best are: Enijun pass, ½ mile wide and very deep, but with a 5-fathom patch; South opening, divided inside by a sand bank, but with a channel 20 fathoms deep; and Torappu channel (north of Bogen island), wide and of unknown depth, but said to be navigable. The lagoon has general depths of from 30 to 40 fathoms, except for isolated patches, and should provide anchorage for very large numbers of ships. Good anchorage is found off Taroa island in from 6 to 15 fathoms, in deep water east of Kaven island and off Airik. Until recent construction was undertaken, landing was made on the beach on the lagoon sides of islands. Rain water obtained by catchment is the principal source of drinking water, but there are wells containing dirty water in several places.

The population in 1935 consisted of 460 natives and 3 Japanese, a decline of nearly 50% from the total of 900 in 1917. The most important settlement in 1935 was on Taroa island, which was the residence of the native chief who was regarded as the overlord of the islands of the Ratak chain. There were also two traders' stores. The natives were all Protestant, and there were native missionaries. Health conditions are poor. Mosquitoes are numerous, and skin and venereal diseases common. Communication was by Nanyo Boeki Kaisha ships, which formerly called 7 times a year.

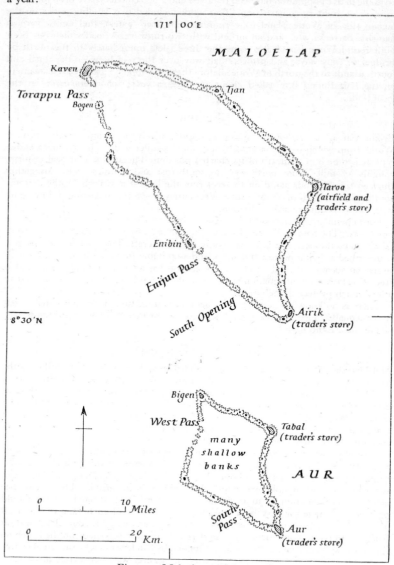

Fig. 104. Maloelap and Aur atolls
Based on Admiralty chart no. 984.

The Japanese have undertaken considerable work to convert Taroa into an important air station. A powerful W/T station has been installed, and an airfield and a seaplane base, oil tanks and two wharves have been constructed. One is situated in the middle of the lagoon side of Taroa and the other projects seawards from the south-east side.

AUR (Fig. 104)

Aur atoll (lat. 8° 07′ N, long. 171° 19′ E, at Aur island) lies about 9 miles south of Maloelap. It is also known as Ibbetson island. It contains a lagoon of roughly rhomboid shape about 17 miles from north-west to south-east and 10½ miles from north-east to south-west. The reef rim is narrow and on it are situated 32 wooded islands, of which the largest are Aur and Tabal, both on the east side.

The best entrance to the lagoon is on the west side, about 2½ miles south of Bigen island. It has a width of 400 yd. and a depth of 13½ fathoms, but reefs in the fairway make navigation difficult. South pass, in the middle of the south-west side of the atoll has a width of 100 yd. and depth of 2½ fathoms. Two other passes on the west side are said to be suitable for vessels not drawing more than 12 ft. The lagoon, with an area of 5 sq. miles, has depths varying from 20 to 45 fathoms but is encumbered with coral heads, especially in the north. Specific anchorages are: off the lagoon side of Tabal, in 21 fathoms; west and north-west of Aur; and off the lagoon side of Bigen island, in 10 fathoms.

In 1935, 279 natives and 1 Japanese were living on the atoll, mainly on Tabal and Aur islands, where there are churches. Overseas communication was by Nanyo Boeki Kaisha vessels, which called 7 times a year.

MAJURO (Fig. 105)

Majuro (lat. 7° 08′ N, long. 171° 10′ E) lies about 60 miles south of Aur atoll. It has been sometimes known as Arrowsmith island. It is near the southern end of the Ratak chain, and was considered as a potential base by the German navy before the war of 1914–18.

It is an oval atoll with an east-west length of 21 miles and a width of 6 miles. Majuro island, lying along the reef rim on the whole of the south side, has a length of 22 miles, but is extremely narrow. Some 50 or more islands and islets are scattered along the northern and east sides; all are thickly wooded with coconut palms and breadfruit trees.

There is only one entrance into the lagoon. This is on the north side, west of Calalin island. It is 2¼ miles wide but divided into two channels by a coral bank. It can, however, take large vessels. The lagoon has an area of about 90 sq. miles, but the western half is unsuitable for navigation or anchorage owing to the presence of coral patches; the eastern half affords good opportunities for anchorage for an almost unlimited number of ships. Specific anchorages are off Ejit island in 12 fathoms, close to the west of Djarrit island, and off the western end of Majuro. There are small jetties, on the south shore of Ejit island and on the west coast of Djarrit island, but both of these are suitable only for small boats. Rain water is collected in cisterns for drinking purposes. In the event of this supply failing, there are several wells, but the quality of the water in them is not good.

In 1935 there were 782 natives. They were all Protestant. Native missionaries maintained a church on Roneron island. There were 3 Japanese trading stations in the atoll at that time—probably on Djarrit, Roneron, and the western end of Majuro. The principal exports were copra and dried fish. Nanyo Boeki Kaisha vessels called 7 times a year before the war. Recently a W/T station has been installed.

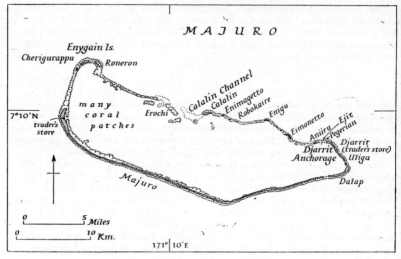

Fig. 105. Majuro atoll

Those parts of the atoll rim which are above high-water mark are stippled. Majuro, in the south of the Ratak chain, is remarkable for the length of Majuro island. As in Jaluit and Ebon atolls, in the south of the Ralik chain, long stretches of the reef rim are above high-water mark. This feature is uncommon further north in the Marshall islands. Based on official sources.

ARNO

Arno (lat. 6° 59′ N, long. 171° 42′ E, at Ine island) lies 10 miles east of Majuro. It is a large atoll of irregular shape resembling a D. The two horns of the D extend northwards and eastwards, and each expands slightly to enclose a small lagoon, which is cut off from the main lagoon.

The total land area of the atoll, though small, is greater than that of any other atoll in the Marshall islands. The bulk of it consists of one island, which occupies 13 miles of the southern reef rim but rarely exceeds about 600 yd. in width. There are also 100 other islands and islets scattered round the reef rim. On most there is a dense growth of coconut palms, casuarina and breadfruit trees. Four passes lead into the main lagoon and one into the detached eastern portion. The main entrance is Dodo passage with a depth of from 21 to 23 fathoms; tidal currents make navigation difficult. To the south-east of this is Tagelib pass, which is divided into two by Enirikku island; the western channel has a depth of 14 fathoms but is narrow; the eastern channel has a depth of $3\frac{1}{2}$ fathoms. Two miles further east, the reef is submerged to a depth of $3\frac{1}{4}$ fathoms, with a $1\frac{3}{4}$-fathom patch. There is also a passage into the eastern lagoon, but depths are not available. Outside the atoll there is anchorage on a shelf off the island in from 15 to 20 fathoms. It is safe in easterly winds, but not at other times. Anchorage can also be found off the north-west point. Inside the main lagoon most of the area is encumbered with coral, but specific anchorages used are as follows: south of Tagelib island; and on a 15-fathom bank between Tagelib island and Ine island. In the eastern lagoon there is anchorage in from 6 to 7 fathoms. There were no wharves or jetties in 1935, but landing can be made on the outside of Ine island through a cut in the coral reef and probably on the lagoon side of most of the islands.

There are several wells supplying brackish water, and there is a 20-ton tank on Ine island. It is likely that further supplies are obtainable by catchment.

In 1935 there were 942 natives and 5 Japanese on the atoll. The natives are mostly Protestant, and there are some native missionaries. The inhabitants are divided into two groups, each with its own chief. Under the German administration the Jaluit-gesellschaft had a trading station. Now there are three Japanese trading stations—one on Terranova island and two on Ine island. Native economy is mainly on a subsistence basis. Pigs and chickens are kept, and fish are plentiful. The only regular export is a small quantity of copra. Formerly sea communication was maintained by Nanyo Boeki Kaisha vessels, which called 7 times a year.

MILI

Mili (lat. 6° 14′ N, long. 171° 48′ E, at Tokowa island), the southernmost atoll in the Ratak chain, lies about 43 miles southward from Arno. It is roughly rectangular, 23 miles from east to west and 11 from north to south. It contains numerous islands and islets. Most, including Enajet, the largest, lie along the southern rim; all are very narrow. Mili in the south-west corner, however, is over ½ mile wide. Coconut palms, casuarina and other trees occur on most of them, but the sandy soil is of very poor quality and discourages cultivation.

Numerous passes, some suitable for large vessels, cut through the reef on the north side; one, for small craft only, on the northern part of the east side; and one on the south side. The best entrance is Tokowa channel, 150 ft. wide at its narrowest point, with depths of from 9 to 20 fathoms; tidal currents flow straight in and out, on the flood at 3 knots and on the ebb at 2½ knots. East of this is the crooked Reiher pass with a width of 400 yd. and a depth (except for one ½-fathom patch) of over 13 fathoms. Ennanlik channel has a clear passage of 14 fathoms depth, but there is a submerged coral bank on the south side, and the approach is said to be difficult. North-east passage, nearly a mile wide, is shallow and suitable only for small craft, as also are the passages on the east and south sides.

The lagoon, with an area of 220 sq. miles, and depths from 13 to 25 fathoms, is partly obstructed by coral, especially in the south, and complete surveys are not available, but all classes of ships could find accommodation. Tokowa anchorage (Port Rhin) offers anchorage on a mud bottom, in depths of from 1 fathom to 19 fathoms, and is moderately protected. Other specific anchorages are: off Mili island, in 16 fathoms (except in north-easterly gales); east of Lukunor island; off Enajet island; and in the north-eastern part of the lagoon. A pier about 100 yd. long, extending into the lagoon, has been built on Mili island, and landings can be made on the southern point of Tokowa and probably on the lagoon side of most of these other islands.

Fresh water can be obtained from pits dug to a depth of from 6 to 12 ft. in the sand, and there are also wells; but the principal supply of drinking water is by catchment. Supplies are sometimes short between January and March.

In 1935 the population amounted to 515 natives and 4 Japanese. The majority lived on Mili, which is the residence of the chief and two sub-chiefs; but a few lived on Burrh, Tokowa and other islands. The natives are nearly all Protestants, and there are churches staffed by native missionaries. The Japanese have established trading stations on Mili, Tokowa, Alu, Lukunor and Jobenor islands, but the only export consists of small quantities of copra and dried fish. Health conditions are generally good, but the incidence of venereal disease is high. Sea communications were maintained by Nanyo Boeki Kaisha vessels, which visited the atoll 7 times a year. The Japanese have built an airfield on Mili island capable of accommodating numerous aircraft; a powerful W/T station has been installed.

KNOX ISLANDS

The Knox islands form a small atoll south-east of Mili and separated from it by a channel about 2 miles wide. They consist of about ten islets on a reef. There is a boat passage leading into the lagoon on the west side. The atoll is about 4½ miles long and about 1 mile wide.

(For Bibliographical Note see Chapter XVI.)

Plate 114. The hotel, Jaluit
This building was erected during the German occupation of the Marshall islands.

Plate 115. Cape Banaderu, Saipan
This view was taken from Matansa and shows the forested coastal shelf which
surrounds the northern hills.

Plate 116. Garapan town, Saipan
The settlement built by the Japanese on the west of Saipan.

Plate 117. Houses in Mutcho
Mutcho forms the northern part of the settlement of Garapan on the east side of
Saipan harbour.

Chapter XIX

THE MARIANAS

Saipan: Rota: Tinian: Agiguan: Farallon de Medinilla: Anatahan: Sariguan: Guguan: Alamagan: Pagan: Agrihan: Asuncion: Maug: Farallon de Pajaros

The Marianas (Fig. 106) are a group of fifteen islands stretching northward from Guam (lat. 13° 26′ N) to Farallon de Pajaros (lat. 20° 33′ N). With the exception of Guam, all the islands lie between long. 145° and 146° E. Guam is under American administration and is described separately (Chapter XXI). The remaining islands of the group, which are described in this Chapter, have been administered since 1920 by Japan under mandate from the League of Nations. The southern islands of Saipan, Rota and Tinian have been developed extensively by the Japanese as centres of sugar production. The northern islands are small; several of them are active volcanoes; and a number are uninhabited.

SAIPAN (Fig. 107)

Saipan (lat. 15° 12′ N, long. 145° 43′ E) is, after Guam, the largest island in the Marianas. It is the administrative and commercial centre of the Japanese islands in the group. It is of considerable strategic importance, since it is situated near the southern end of the Marianas chain. Economically it is of great value, being the headquarters of the sugar industry. Very large numbers of Japanese have migrated to the island, and considerable sums have been spent on harbour improvements, probably for naval requirements.

Physical Geography (Plates 74, 115, 118)

The island is about 14 miles long from north-east to south-west, with widths varying from about 3 to 6 miles. It has an area of 71 sq. miles. It is of volcanic formation, but the original volcanic mass subsequently subsided. During this period, coral grew over the original andesitic core. Subsequent elevations raised the whole island again, leaving an incomplete limestone covering which, in places, shows terraces which indicate various stages of elevation. A Japanese geologist claims to have identified no less than 13 terraces at heights of 2, 5, 20, 45, 60, 80, 90, 130, 200, 250, 300, 350, and 470 metres respectively. A ridge of high hills runs down the long axis of the

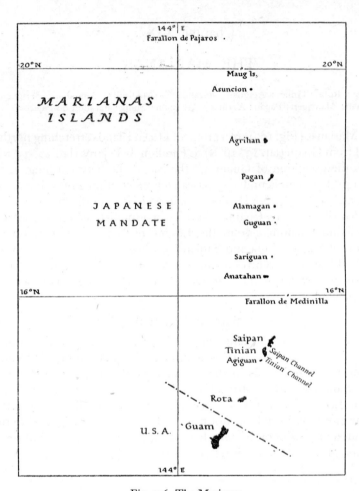

Fig. 106. The Marianas

The islands form two arcs concentric to the curve of the Nero deep which lies to eastward. The first arc includes the islands between Guam and Farallon de Medinilla. The second stretches from Anatahan to Farallon de Pajaros. Both have the slight curvature characteristic of island arcs of relatively recent origin, though the more recent Iwo and Bonin arcs (Fig. 110) have even less curvature. The islands of the southern arc of the Marianas have well-developed terraces of raised coral on their east coasts which front on to the Nero deep. Extinct volcanoes are found behind their western coasts. Active volcanoes and a smaller development of raised coral terraces are characteristic of the newer, northern arc of the Marianas. Based on official sources.

island, from mount Marpi (832 ft.) in the north to a point about 4 miles from the south end of the islands. The highest point is mount Tapotchau (1,554 ft.), near the centre of the island. A belt of low-lying land about 1,000 yd. wide separates the base of the central ridge from the coast round the northern part of the island. Southwards from mount Tapotchau the range fans out, merging into more gently sloping foothills, which reach almost to the coast. Most of the hills are thickly wooded; and parts of the low-lying land are thickly set with coconut palms and casuarinas, notably the west coast southwards from Garapan and round the south coast to Obiam, and also the east coast round Magicienne (Raurau) bay. In places coconuts extend some way up the lower slopes.

Rivers are few. Two small streams flow into the sea on the west side, north-east of Tanapag, and two on the east side near Inai Fahan and Donnay respectively. There are swampy areas up to about a mile inland from Agigan point and Mutcho point.

Coasts. Coral is not particularly well developed, being almost absent on the east coast except in Raurau bay. Uncharted coral reefs are reported off the south coast. Along the west coast a barrier reef extends from Agigan point to Mutcho point, with passes opposite the town of Garapan. North of Mutcho point, where the coast trends north-eastward, there is a comparatively wide gap in the reef which swings eastwards in an arc embracing Maniagassa island, to form Tanapag harbour. It then joins the coast at Tanapag, about 4 miles eastward, whence it continues for a further 3 miles as a fringing reef.

Sandy beaches occur along most of the west coast, and in many places along the northern part of the east coast, but heavy surf breaks in most places. Most of the southern part of the east coast is cliffed. The land rises steeply inland from Raurau bay, and the coast round Obiama bay is thickly wooded.

Anchorages and Landings

Tanapag harbour (Fig. 108) provides ample anchorage. Vessels can also anchor about 1½ miles off Garapan in from 12 to 14 fathoms in north-easterly winds or in Raurau bay, the only place in the island which is suitable when the wind is north-westerly. Large ships can anchor here in 30 fathoms.

Tanapag harbour is a stretch of water naturally protected by barrier reefs on the west coast of the island north of Garapan town. The Japanese have spent large sums of money on its improvement.

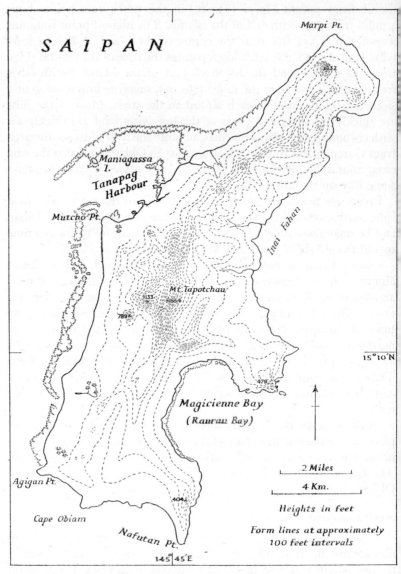

Fig. 107. Saipan : physical features

Spot heights are approximate. On the east coast fringing reefs are slightly developed and barrier reefs are absent. This is the emerging coast which fronts on to the Nero deep. The west coast has less deep water off-shore and a well-developed barrier reef. The peaks of the mount Tapotchau massif are extinct volcanoes. The lava is hypersthene andesite. Based on official sources.

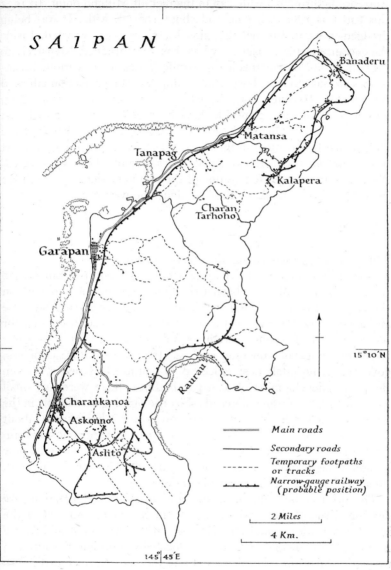

Fig. 108. Saipan: settlements and communications
Towns and villages are indicated by squares. Based on official sources.

Entrance is through a wide gap in the reef off Mutcho point. In 1932 this gap was 1,800 yd. long and about 100 yd. wide. It was being dredged to 25 ft. Further dredging has since been reported. Inside the entrance is a large lagoon, which has been dredged extensively to provide an anchorage area about 1 mile in diameter. Various breakwaters are said to have been built to improve the protection afforded by the reef. Two new concrete jetties from 1,000 to 1,500 ft. long, with a depth of 28 ft. alongside, have been built about 1,000 yd. east of Mutcho point. One of these has a rectangular stone wharf at the end, with a face parallel to the shore 225 ft. long. In the eastern part of the harbour there are two small jetties, one of which is L-shaped. A 5-ton crane is reported on one of the two new piers, and both are joined by railway tracks to the line along the west coast.

Social and Economic Conditions

The population in 1938 is said to have included 25,000 Japanese. This is a large increase on the figures for 1935, when there were 20,280 Japanese and 3,282 'natives' (mostly Chamorro). Since 1920 Japanese immigrants have been arriving in large numbers to work on the sugar plantations. Garapan (Plates 116-17) with 7,492 Japanese and 2,444 natives in 1935, is the only town of any size. It consists for the most part of wooden dwellings built close together with a few larger buildings of concrete, such as the Branch Bureau offices, government hospital, post office, W/T station and police station. Before the development of Tanapag harbour, there were two small jetties with 6 ft. of water alongside. Electric lighting is available in the town, but the generating station is of low power. Charankanoa, about 4 miles south of Garapan, contains two sugar mills and a hospital run by the sugar company (Nanyo Kohatsu Kaisha). There are a few isolated villages and hamlets in other parts of the island (Fig. 109). Most of these are on the sugar plantations.

The primary industry is sugar planting (p. 351). Plantations are developed round the north coast, and in the south and east of the island. Quantities of molasses obtained in the process of milling are converted into alcohol for export or local consumption, flavoured to resemble whisky or other liquors. In all there are thirteen distilleries in Saipan. Considerable areas of the coastal lowlands are under coconuts. There is also one coffee plantation situated between Inai Fahan and Charan Tarhoho. A few cattle are kept and there is a little general farming or fruit growing, including such produce as taro, rice, yams, cassava, bananas and papaya. An agricultural experimental station is

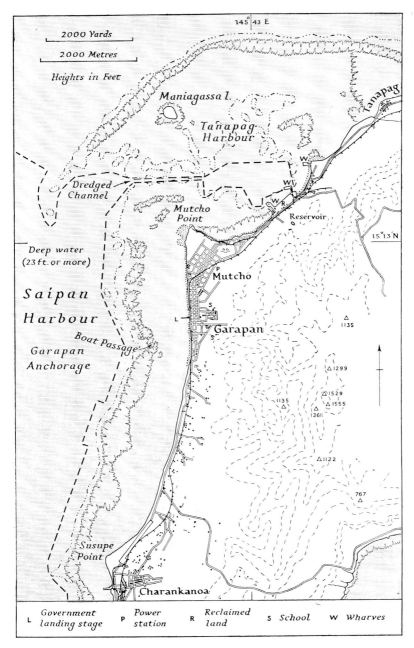

Fig. 109. Saipan harbour

Form lines are at approximately 200-ft. intervals. The heavy pecked line represents
the inner limit of deep water. Based on official sources.

situated near Raurau bay. The island is not self-supporting in food-stuffs, and quantities of rice and canned foodstuffs are imported.

There are three Roman Catholic churches and the Catholic church also maintains a school for Chamorro girls. Education is also provided by the Japanese public schools (p. 346). Health conditions are said to have improved since Japanese occupation. The prevailing diseases are yaws, tuberculosis, dysentery and eye diseases. Typhus was formerly frequent as was hookworm. The medical staff at the hospital at Garapan consisted before the war of 5 doctors and several pharmacists and nurses, and that at Charankanoa of 1 doctor and 5 nurses. Three dentists in private practice live in Garapan.

Communications

Nippon Yusen Kaisha ships running on the Western and Eastern lines (p 356) called at Saipan. Launches and small steamers link Saipan with Tinian and Rota. A narrow-gauge railway, owned by the Nanyo Kohatsu Kaisha, follows the coast northwards from Garapan round to Kalapera, and also southwards to near Agigan point, whence it crosses to the east coast to serve the plantation there. The total track mileage is said to be about 55 miles, and the gauge 2 ft. 2 in. or 2 ft. 6 in.—probably the latter. From Garapan to Charankanoa a third rail had been laid down outside the other two, to accommodate wider-gauge vehicles. In 1936 there were only narrow-gauge locomotives, but there were about three hundred wagons, some narrow-gauge and some broad-gauge. Apparently draw-gear on the locomotives was suitable for coupling to the broad-gauge wagons.

There is a fairly extensive network of roads, mostly with powdered coral surface, the principal road being that following the west coast from Charankanoa through Garapan to Matansa. Extensions of inferior quality serve the plantation areas and the west coast, and three branches cross the island. An airfield has been built on the flatter southern hills, and seaplanes use Tanapag harbour. It is a calling place on the route between Japan and Palau.

There are two W/T stations—one on a ridge north-west of Garapan, and the other immediately behind the town. A wireless receiving station is situated in the town of Garapan. There are no submarine cable facilities except a line connecting the Saipan telephone system (which has about 1,000 subscribers) with Tinian.

ROTA

Rota (lat. 14° 08′ N, long. 145° 09′ E, at Rota village) lies about 38 miles north-east of Guam and is the southernmost of the Marianas under Japanese administration.

It is chiefly important for the sugar refineries on the island, and the anchorage in Sosanjaya bay, off the south-west coast.

Physical Geography

The island is about 13 miles long and for the most part about 4 miles wide, rising near the middle of the western end to a height of 1,613 ft. A spit of land with a steep terraced hill (which looks like a detached island) projects about 2 miles from the west end. The island is volcanic in formation, but most of the volcanic rock has been overlaid by coral, which has been elevated at various dates, producing a series of clearly marked limestone terraces. The highest one forms a central plateau 800 ft. high. There is a small stream on the east side of the island, and probably others elsewhere. The coast is steep and for the most part cliffed, but landing can be effected on beaches on each side of the isthmus at the west end of the island.

Anchorages and Landings

Sosanjaya bay is the best anchorage, giving fairly good protection in north-east winds. Depths vary from 13 to 16 fathoms. In winds from south-east to south anchorage is probably possible for a few ships in from 20 to 25 fathoms in Sosanlagh bay on the north side of the isthmus. A landing stage or jetty is situated on this side of the isthmus, and it is probable that wharf facilities have been constructed in Sosanjaya bay to handle sugar traffic.

There are two or three wells in the village on the shores of Sosanjaya bay, but they are unsuitable for drinking. Good drinking water can, however, be obtained from the stream on the east of the island, and quantities are collected by catchment and stored in concrete cisterns, with capacity varying from 5 to 15 tons.

Social and Economic Conditions

In 1935 the population consisted of 764 natives, probably all Chamorro, and 4,841 Japanese, mostly living in Rota village. The village is a remarkably clean settlement at the base of the isthmus on the west of the island. Buildings include a police station, a post office, a church, and a school and many dwelling-houses. Numbers of the latter are of bamboo construction. The principal industry is sugar growing and refining. The main mill is situated south-east of the village and has a capacity of about 800 tons of sugar cane a day. A smaller and newer mill has a capacity of about 300 tons a day. Attached to both mills are distilleries for the production of alcohol from molasses, some of which is converted into imitation whisky or wine. The plantations, which absorb most of the labour, are apparently in the eastern part of the island. Electric power is generated for the mills, and there is a small generator used in connection with the W/T station.

Communication was maintained by Nippon Yusen Kaisha steamers on the Saipan line (p. 356), which called 24 times a year. There are also a number of small craft. Narrow-gauge railway tracks have been built round the sugar mills and probably extend to the plantations. Some good roads have been built. A W/T station is situated near the police station in Rota village.

TINIAN

Tinian (lat. 14° 58′ N, long. 145° 38′ E, at Sunharon) is about 56 miles north-north-east of Rota and 2½ miles south-west of Saipan. Off the south coast, separated from Tinian by a channel 5 miles wide, is Agiguan island. Naftan rock lies ¾ mile to the south-west of Tinian.

Physical Geography

The island has a total area of 32 sq. miles, and rises to heights of 557 and 530 ft. in the south, and 456 ft. in the north-west. It is composed of volcanic rocks, largely overlain with coral limestone. Successive upheavals have produced a series of limestone terraces. The high ground at each end is joined by a ridge near the east side of the island from which the land slopes steeply to the coast on the east side and more gradually to the west, where there are expanses of low-lying plain or downland. In the centre of the island there is a small lake. Most of the low-lying land is given over to the cultivation of sugar cane. The higher ground is thickly overgrown with forest and scrub. The greater part of the coastline is fronted by limestone cliffs undercut and eroded into caves in places. Sandy beaches also occur, notably in the bay fronting Tinian harbour (Sunharon roads). There is little evidence of erosion except by wave action.

Anchorages and Landings

Sunharon roads is the only anchorage, but it is not safe in the south-west monsoon. In front of the town of Sunharon there is a concrete pier with a length of 450 ft. This extends over the reef, but is suitable only for small craft, as water is very shallow at the end of it. Another pier was being built in 1935, and there is a pier capable of accommodating vessels up to 4,000 tons north-west of the harbour, near Gurguar point. There are numerous wells scattered through the island, but drinking water is obtained by catchment and stored in cisterns.

Social and Economic Conditions

Before occupation by the Spaniards, Tinian was thickly populated. Some evidence of this is to be found in the double rows of curious square-section stone pillars with hemispherical capitals (Plate 86), which occur in the island and which are believed to be the remains of house structures. But a process of concentration of the population by the Spanish authorities on Guam led to the gradual depopulation of the island, and when Anson visited Tinian in 1742, on his voyage round the world, he found it almost deserted and over-run by wild cattle and pigs. In 1935 the population consisted of 25 Chamorro and 14,108 Japanese, almost all engaged on the sugar plantations or in the sugar mills (Plate 95). The main settlement is Sunharon, where the two mills are situated close together. There are also a hospital, an administrative office, police station, post office, W/T station, school and numerous dwelling-houses. In the east side is the village of Moropo. The mills have a capacity of about 1,320 tons of sugar cane a day, and produce alcohol as a by-product from molasses. A few oranges, breadfruit, coconuts and other fruits are grown, and there were between 6,000 and 7,000 cattle in the island in 1935, as well as a few deer and goats. Many Nippon Yusen Kaisha steamers calling at Saipan called also at Tinian, and there was a local service of launches linking the two islands.

A narrow-gauge railway, with a gauge variously reported as 2 ft. 2 in. and 2 ft. 6 in., encircles the island, using small coal-burning steam locomotives or petrol engines having a weight of about 10 tons. There are a few roads and tracks, but they are of poor quality. Facilities have been provided at Sunharon for seaplanes, and the lake might be used as an alighting area. A W/T station has been built near the sugar mills, and there is a local telephone system linked with that on Saipan by a submarine cable. A visual system of signalling is also used between the two islands.

AGIGUAN

Agiguan (lat. 14° 51′ N, long. 145° 34′ E) is a small island about 2 miles long, some 6 miles southward from Tinian. There are steep cliffs on the north side but landing can be made on the west where the beach is sandy. There is said to be an anchorage off the south-west. It was uninhabited in 1935, but was occasionally visited by people wishing to hunt the wild pigs which abounded on the island.

FARALLON DE MEDINILLA

Farallon de Medinilla (lat. 16° 01' N, long. 146° 04' E) is about 54 miles north-north-east of Saipan. It is a barren mass of terraces of raised coral limestone. It is 1½ miles long and ⅓ mile wide at its widest point. It reaches a height of 265 ft. The greater part of the coast consists of steep cliffs with numerous caves. Landslides are frequent. The southern part of the island is separated from the north by a deep chasm.

There is no protected anchorage but small craft can anchor on a shelf off the west coast; and larger vessels on a reef about ¼ mile off the northern end. Landing is difficult and there is no water supply. The only inhabitants are flocks of sea birds.

ANATAHAN

Anatahan (lat. 16° 22' N, long. 145° 38' E) lies about 35 miles north-westward of Farallon de Medinilla. It is an oval volcanic island, about 5 miles long and 2 miles wide. The highest point is 2,504 ft. above sea level, and the centre of the island is occupied by the oval crater of an extinct volcano. This has a grassy floor surrounded by a high rim. The land on the outside slopes steeply to the sea. Anchorage can be found 600 yd. to the west of the north-west corner of the island. Landing can be effected on a pebble beach opposite the anchorage or on a beach near the south-west of the island. Water collects in the crater, forming a lake in the wet season, but in dry weather water is probably scarce.

In 1935 there were 37 natives and 3 Japanese living in a village near the anchorage. A few coconuts are grown. The island is largely over-run by rats. An auxiliary schooner called 5 times a year.

SARIGUAN

Sariguan (lat. 16° 43' N, long. 145° 47' E) is 24 miles north of Anatahan. It is an extinct volcano, roughly conical in shape, and about 1½ miles across. The highest point (1,800 ft.) is rather to the south of the centre of the island. The land slopes steeply from the crater to the coast, especially on the south side. In places there are steep gullies, with streams in wet weather. There is a little comparatively flat land on the north-west coast. Dense tropical vegetation, including numerous creeping plants, fills the valleys, and there are a few palm trees near the north-west coast. The whole island is said to be surrounded by perpendicular cliffs, but the Admiralty chart shows two short stretches of beach on the east side and one on the south-west side. Landing can be effected on the latter beach and ¾ mile from the northern point of the island. Boats can anchor off the latter landing in north-west winds.

In 1935 there were 21 natives and 8 Japanese on the island. Communications were maintained by an auxiliary schooner calling 5 times a year.

GUGUAN

Guguan (lat. 17° 20' N, long. 145° 51' E) is about 42 miles north of Sariguan. It is of oval shape, about 1½ miles from north to south and 1 mile from east to west. There are two peaks, a northern one, which is an active volcano, and a southern one, which is extinct. They have heights of 813 ft. and 987 ft. respectively. The land is cut up into deep ravines with many breadfruit trees, but no coconuts. The outer slopes are steep and cliffed or lava-covered in places. Much of the coast is cliffed; large areas of water round the island are of suitable depth for anchorage, but there is no shelter. Landing is difficult. There were no inhabitants in 1935.

ALAMAGAN (Plate 119)

Alamagan (lat. 17° 35′ N, long. 145° 50′ E) is 18 miles north of Guguan. It is a quiescent volcano of oval shape, about 5½ miles from north to south and 3½ miles from east to west. The highest point, variously given as 2,440 ft. and as 3,165 ft., is near the middle of the island, and is on a crater rim breached to the west. The south-eastern side of the island consists of a steep barren slope of lava. There is a small plateau on the south-western side. Deep ravines cut the western slopes. There are steep cliffs on many parts of the coast, but beaches are shown on the Admiralty chart on the south-west and north sides. There is anchorage off the south-west side of the island, and landing can be effected opposite the anchorage or further up the west coast. There are hot springs near the north-west corner; drinking water is presumably obtained by catchment. In 1935 there were 20 natives and 4 Japanese who had come to collect copra. They dwelt in a village on the plateau. The Nanyo Boeki Kaisha had a store on the island. Alamagan was visited 5 times a year by an auxiliary schooner.

PAGAN

Pagan (lat. 18° 08′ N, long. 145° 46′ E) is 32 miles northward from Alamagan, and is the largest island in the northern part of the Marianas. It consists of two volcanoes joined by an isthmus. The island is about 10 miles long from north-east to south-west. The last eruption of mount Pagan occurred in 1922. The northern volcano reaches a height of 1,869 ft. and consists of a large caldera, in which there are numerous craters and cinder cones. The southern one, though smaller, also consists of a caldera, with three craters inside. The chief difference between the two is that the northern volcano is largely composed of basalt while the southern one is predominantly of andesite. Except in Apan bay and Eastern roadstead, on either side of the isthmus, the coast is steep and fringed with casuarina trees.

Anchorage may be found in Apan bay in 10 fathoms, with shelter from north-east and east, or during northerly winds in Eastern roadstead, where Graf von Spee anchored his squadron in August and September 1914. The only good landings are in Apan bay and opposite Eastern roadstead. Over most of the rest of the coast landing is difficult owing to the steepness of the cliffs. There are two freshwater wells on the north-west of the lagoon, but the water is not potable. Drinking water is obtained by catchment. Small numbers of both natives and Japanese have been brought to the island to collect copra. In 1935 there were 131 natives and 89 Japanese on Shomushan plateau. The Nanyo Boeki Kaisha have established a trading station and small quantities of sugar cane, vegetables and cotton have been cultivated experimentally, as well as tropical fruits. A few pigs and chickens are also kept. Sea communication was maintained by an auxiliary schooner from Saipan, calling 5 times a year. In 1938 the construction of a W/T station was authorized.

AGRIHAN

Agrihan (lat. 18° 44′ N, long. 145° 39′ E) lies 39 miles northward from Pagan. It is a dormant volcano rising to a height of 3,165 ft. The last eruption occurred in 1917. It consists of one major irregular conical mass with small subsidiary craters on the south, south-east, and south-west sides. Most of the island is steep, but there is a relatively gentle slope on the south-west, where there is a small stream. Except on this side, where there is a beach of black sand, the coast is for the most part steep and rocky.

Anchorage may be found off the south-west corner of the island on a narrow shelf, but it is not safe during strong south-west winds when there is a heavy swell. Landing is possible on the beach mentioned above or possibly on a stretch of sand about 500 yd. long on the north-west side. There are wells, but the water is unsuitable for drinking. Rain water is obtained by catchment.

A few natives are brought to the island from time to time by the Nanyo Boeki Kaisha to grow sugar or to work the phosphate deposits. Mangoes and pineapples are grown in small quantities. A village is situated on the south-west side near the beach.

Sea communication was maintained by an auxiliary schooner from Saipan, calling 5 times a year.

ASUNCION

Asuncion (lat. 19° 39′ N, long. 145° 24′ E) lies about 53 miles north-north-west of Pagan, and is an active volcanic cone from which white smoke can be seen rising on occasion. The island is roughly circular, about 2 miles in diameter, rising steeply on all sides to the crater, which is about 2,900 ft. high. The sides of the cone, especially near the summit, are covered with deposits of volcanic ash. The northern and eastern sides are steeply cliffed and fissured near the coast, and smoke may sometimes be seen issuing from the crevices. On the west side is a small area of flatter ground with palm trees. Ships can anchor off the southern end of the island, and boats can land on a pebble beach on the south-western tip. In 1935 there were no inhabitants, but natives sometimes visited the island to collect copra. There are a few huts near the beach.

MAUG

Maug (lat. 20° 02′ N, long. 145° 19′ E), about 27 miles north-westward of Asuncion, consists of three rocky islands, North island, East island, and West island. It is uninhabited, but the lagoon around which the islands lie, about 1 sq. mile in area, offers the only protected anchorage in the northern Marianas. The three islands form a circle, suggesting that they are the remnants of an eroded crater. All are steeply cliffed. Columnar basalt rocks can be seen on both North island and West island, on both of which there is a scrubby vegetation of coarse grass and low stunted bushes. East island has scrubby bushes and coconuts on the steeper slopes. There are three entrances to the lagoon, one between each pair of islands. The southern entrance is best. The north-west, with a depth of 4¾ fathoms, is the shallowest. Most of the lagoon is of considerable depths, but it is believed that the Japanese have improved the lagoon by putting down mooring buoys. In 1935 there were no inhabitants, but, in view of its military and air possibilities, the Japanese may have developed the group.

FARALLON DE PAJAROS

Farallon de Pajaros (lat. 20° 33′ N, long. 144° 54′ W, approximately) is the most northerly of the Marianas, lying 42 miles north-west of Maug. It is also known as Uracas. It is an active cone of volcanic ash, with an isolated rock off the south-east side. Except along the south side, where there are a few trees and some grass, the island is entirely barren. There are no anchorages and no good landings, but it is possible to land in cracks between rocks in calm weather.

(For Bibliographical Note see Chapter XVI.)

Plate 118. A Saipan cove

The coast south-east of mount Tapotchau is the most rugged in the island. This cove is the entry to a steep ravine and like it has high limestone walls honeycombed with caves.

Plate 119. Alamagan island, Marianas

An island of the northern arc of the Marianas. The view shows the dormant volcano with steep lava slopes largely devoid of vegetation.

Plate 120. An active volcano, Bonin islands

Some of the smaller Bonin islands contain active volcanoes and are uninhabited.
Steep shoreward slopes are characteristic of the whole group.

Plate 121. Cultivated land on Haha shima

This view, taken on the slopes of Chibusayama, shows small irregular-shaped fields
protected by windbreaks, such as are typical of most of the cultivated areas of the
Bonin islands.

PART THREE

THE BONIN ISLANDS, MARCUS ISLAND, GUAM AND WAKE ISLAND

Chapter XX

THE BONIN ISLANDS AND MARCUS ISLAND

Bonin Islands—Physical Geography: History: Social and Economic Conditions:
Ports and Settlements: Communications
Marcus Island
Bibliographical Note

THE BONIN ISLANDS

The Bonin islands and Volcano islands, which are here treated together, form the southern part of a chain of islands stretching south from Japan and known collectively by the Japanese as the Nanpō shotō (Fig. 110). The Japanese names for the two groups respectively are Ogasawara guntō and Kazan rettō. Geologically, the chain is continued to the south of the Kazan rettō by the Marianas (Chapter XIX). The Bonin islands have a total land area of only 27 sq. miles. They consist of three groups—the Mukoshima rettō; the Chichishima rettō; and the Hahashima rettō. The northernmost is the Mukoshima rettō, lying between lat. 27° 30′ and 27° 45′ N, long. 142° 05′ and 142° 13′ E. It comprises the main island of Muko shima, together with Nakōdo shima (some 3½ miles southward), the nearby islets of Kitano shima, Nakano shima, Sasago shima and Harino shima, and Yame shima, which lies some 10 miles to the south of Nakōdo shima.

The Chichishima rettō, between lat. 27° 01′ and 27° 11′ N, and long. 142° 09′ and 142° 14′ E, containing the main harbour of Futami kō (Port Lloyd), is the principal cluster. The main island is Chichi shima; north of it are Ani shima and Otōtō shima and numerous off-lying rocks and islets. The southern cluster of the Bonins, the Hahashima rettō, between lat. 26° 32′ and 26° 43′ N, and long. 142° 06′ and 142° 15′ E, consists of one large island and several off-lying islets. The Kazan rettō (Volcano islands), lying to the south of the Bonins, consist

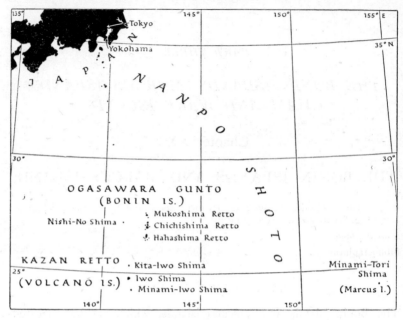

Fig. 110. Nanpō shotō

The map shows the islands of the Bonin and Iwo arcs, two of a series of young mountain arcs which form part of the main andesite zone south of Japan. Active volcanoes are present in both arcs, which have only slight curvature, owing to their geologically recent formation. To the east of the islands lies the south Japan trough which, further northwards, is over 29,500 ft. deep. It is a southward continuation of the Tuscarora deep. Kita Iwo shima and Minami Iwo shima are steep lava domes of augite andesite. Iwo shima is composed of beds of volcanic tuff. This rugged island is the largest, and geologically the most recent, of the Kazan rettō. The Bonin islands are composed of andesitic lavas, tuffs and agglomerates. Based on National Geographic Society, *Map of Japan and Adjacent Regions of Asia and the Pacific Ocean* (Washington, 1944).

of Iwo shima (lat. 24° 47′ N, long. 141° 18′ E) which is the largest, Kita Iwo shima (lat. 25° 25′ N, long. 141° 16′ E) and Minami Iwo shima (lat. 24° 14′ N, long. 141° 28′ E) (Figs. 111–12).

Certain islands of the central group (the Chichishima rettō) were named by Beechey, but local usage applied other names to them. Otōtō shima, Ani shima and Chichi shima were called respectively Stapleton, Buckland and Peel island by Beechey, and North island, Hog island and The Main island by local inhabitants. Futami kō was called Peel harbour by Beechey, and the name is still frequently used.

For administrative purposes the islands form two districts (*gun*) of the Prefecture of Tokyo.

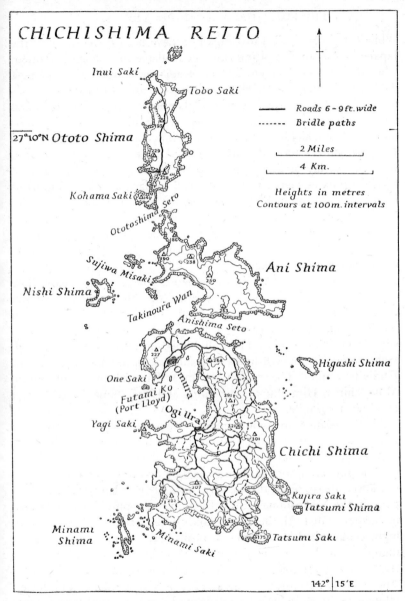

Fig. III. Chichishima rettō: physical features, settlements and communications
The coasts are heavily cliffed. Off the west coast of Chichi shima stacks composed of andesitic lava are common off-shore. Precipitous slopes in the interior are indicated by cliff symbols. Spot heights are approximate. Based on official sources.

PHYSICAL GEOGRAPHY (Plates 120, 122–3)

While certain geological investigations have been undertaken by the Japanese, the amount of information available in English is limited. The whole group is made up of volcanic rocks outpoured amongst older sedimentary beds. Haha shima is mainly formed of coarse-textured andesitic lavas. At the higher levels there are horizontal layers of limestones and fossiliferous calcareous tuffs rich in nummulites. The Chichishima and Mukoshima clusters are, according to Japanese sources, formed of massive boninite, tuffs and agglomerates, with an overlay of limestone. Captain Beechey described parts of Chichi shima as being formed of small upright angular columns of basalt each only an inch or so in diameter and reminiscent, in miniature, of the Giant's Causeway. The basalt is greyish-green in colour and traversed by veins of olivine and hornblende. None of the islands is of any great size. In the northern group (Mukoshima rettō) none is more than 2 miles long.

The Chichishima rettō is the greatest compact land mass. The three main islands lie so close together that the channels between them, which are about 1¼ mile wide, are not visible out at sea. From north to south they are under 10 miles long and a little over 3 miles wide at the widest point. The only big island of the southern group, Haha shima, is about 8 miles long and varies in width from about ½ mile to 2 miles. The majority of the outlying islands of this group, Muko shima, Hira shima, Ane shima and Mei shima, have areas of less than 1 sq. mile.

All the islands are mountainous with steep slopes, bare eroded peaks and few areas of flat ground. In the Chichishima rettō, peaks over 1,000 ft. high are found in the main island; in the islands north of it heights are lower, seldom exceeding 800 ft. Generally speaking the lower areas are on the western sides of the islands. The highest point in the Mukoshima rettō is Byobu yama (approximately 500 ft.) in Nakōdo shima. All the other islands in this group are under 300 ft. high. Haha shima has a range of peaks between 1,000 and 1,500 ft. high running down the east side of the middle of the island, with steep slopes to the east coast and easier slopes and small hills to the west. The northern extremity is high and rocky. The southern end is lower, falling away in steep cliffs to the sea on the east side and sloping more gently on the west. Small streams are frequent. Iwo shima (Sulphur island), the only island of importance in the Kazan rettō (Volcano islands), consists of two volcanoes, Moto yama in the north-east and

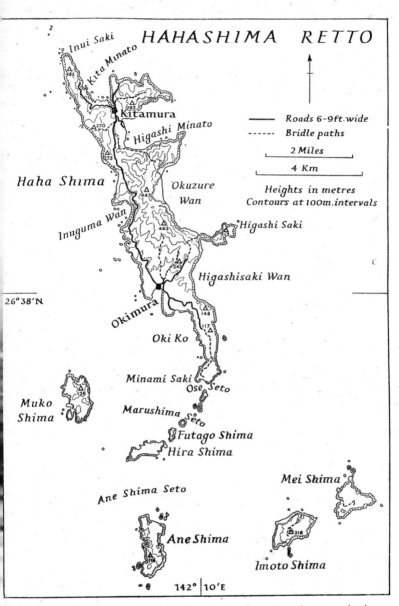

Fig. 112. Hahashima rettō : physical features, settlements and communications
The east and south coasts have terraces of limestone containing Tertiary fossils.
Based on official sources.

Suribachi yama in the south. The former is a large flat-topped, dome-shaped hill, 377 ft. high, on the south-west side of the island. The land slopes away gently to a sandy isthmus joining it to Suribachi yama, which rises as a truncated cone to 546 ft.

Rivers, or small streams, are plentiful on the larger islands, as might be expected from the ample rainfall distributed fairly evenly throughout the year.

The coasts of the small islets, as well as of the larger islands, are steep, consisting for the most part of high cliffs. Rocky promontories, with deep bays between them and many off-lying rocks, characterize the Chichishima rettō and Haha shima especially. Short stretches of shingle or sandy beaches occur in some of the bays. Coral reefs are found but they are not much developed.

Anchorages and Landings

Apart from Futami kō (Port Lloyd), there are few anchorages offering more than temporary shelter. Off Chichi shima anchorage can be found only in Futami kō (p. 457). Temporary shelter can be found in Takinoura wan on the south side of Ani shima except in south-westerly winds. The only landing stages or wharves in this cluster are in Futami kō. Possible landing beaches on Chichi shima are south of the headland known as Fukuro misaki, on the west side; north-west of Tatsumi saki, in the south-east corner; on two beaches in the head of Tatsumi wan and on the east coast north-east of Chuo san (opposite Higashi shima).

In the Mukoshima rettō anchorage can be found in a bay on the north side of Muko shima by small vessels with local knowledge, and off a bay on the south side known as Minamihama. There are many off-shore rocks in the vicinity of these anchorages. Landing can be made on a small beach at the head of Minamihama. On Yame shima landings can be made on beaches in small bays on either side of the south end, or on a beach in a small bay in the north of the island.

Off Haha shima, the only important island in the southern cluster, the principal anchorage is in Oki kō, a small indentation on the west side of the island. It is divided into an outer anchorage and an inner harbour suitable only for boats. The latter is a narrow shallow inlet about $\frac{1}{2}$ mile long with the village of Okimura, the principal settlement of the island, at the head of it. Good protection can be had in all winds except those from the east in Higashi minato. This is a large bay on the east side of the north end of the island. The water, however, is deep, and anchorage can only be found near the shore. Kita

minato, to the north-west of it, is protected from winds between
south-east and south-west, but it is not recommended for anchorage.
The southern part of Okuzure wan and Higashisaki wan offer temporary anchorage. Landings can be made on beaches in Kita minato,
in the bay known as Inuguma wan, and at various points on the rocky
shores of Oki kō. At Okimura a wooden pier about 150 ft. long has
been built. There are also two small wooden piers at Higashi minato,
and at Kitamura there is a stone sea-wall against which boats can
come at high water. In the Kazan rettō anchorage can be obtained off
Minami mura on the east side of Iwo shima, and also on the west side
of the same island. There are no piers or jetties but landings may be
made on beaches on both sides of the island. In Kita Iwo shima the
only landing is on the west side near the village of Ishino. Steamers
anchor off Ishino village.

Climate

The Bonins, lying further north than the majority of the Pacific
islands, have greater temperature ranges and a more stimulating
climate, though rain is fairly frequent and summer days are rather
sultry.

The group is to the north of the north-east trade wind belt but
within the influence of the monsoon winds of Asia. These are relatively weak when they reach the Bonins and there is thus no marked
preponderance in any one month of winds from any one direction.
Seasonal variations in wind direction are, however, noticeable. From
November to February northerly monsoon winds of the western
north Pacific predominate. They are often strong, though they seldom
reach gale force. During March there is only a slight predominance of
northerly winds and in April these give place to winds from the east
and north-east. In May, June and most of July light southerly winds
are most frequent; roughly 50% of winds experienced at Chichi
shima in June are from the south or south-west. During August,
September and October winds increase in strength and those from an
easterly direction predominate. Winds become more northerly towards the end of the latter month, prior to the establishment of the
winter monsoon. Gales are rare, but from August to January typhoons
may pass close to, or over, islands in the group. Tracks and frequencies
vary annually, though October is the most likely month for typhoons.

The average annual rainfall over a period of 23 years is about 62 in.
Rain is spread fairly evenly throughout the year. In no month is there
an average fall of less than 3 in., and in May, the wettest month, it

amounts to about 8 in. Fig. 113 shows the mean monthly rainfall of
Chichi shima together with mean daily maximum and minimum temperature over a period of 23 years. Temperatures are highest in
August when they reach about 88° F. by day, falling only to about
75° by night. January and February, with 69° and 58° F., are the
cooler months.

Relative humidity varies from 70% in January to 85% in June.
There is a secondary maximum of 83% in August–September. Cloud

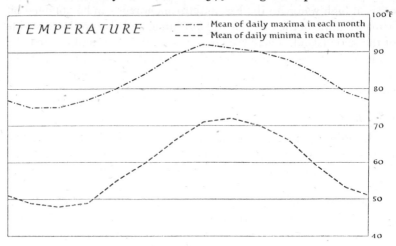

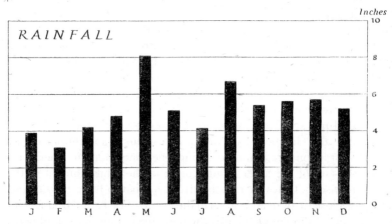

Fig. 113. Chichi shima: temperature and rainfall

The station of Chichi shima is in lat. 27° 05′ N, long. 142° 11′ E, at a height of 13 ft.
The period of observation was from 1907 to 1935. Based on statistics in the
Admiralty *Japan Pilot*, vol. II, p. 675 (London, 1940).

cover varies from month to month. Cloudy days (with 8-tenths or more of the sky covered) occurred on an average of 140 days a year at Chichi shima during the period 1907–29; months with most cloudy days were March (average 12 days), April (average 16 days), May (average 19 days), June (average 14 days) and August (average 13 days). The lowest number of cloudy days (8 in each month) was experienced in July, September and October. Days with a clear sky averaged 21 a year; they were usually about two per month, except from February to May, when there was one a month. Fogs are rare between July and January, though an average of two days of fog occurs between April and June.

Vegetation and Fauna

The Bonin islands, though lying considerably to the north of the Tropic of Cancer, have an essentially tropical vegetation, for which their warm oceanic climate is responsible. The forests which originally covered most of the land area are evergreen and may be classified as sub-tropical rain forest. A large proportion of the plants are similar to, or identical with, those of Malaya and Polynesia—that is to say, the flora is predominantly Indo-Malayan and has little resemblance to that of Japan. Along with many typically tropical species, however, various plants of northern origin are native to the group and serve as reminders of the nearness of the temperate zone. The commonest and most conspicuous of these is a kind of juniper, *Juniperus taxifolia* (or a nearly related species), a small tree or shrub which is the only native conifer in the islands. About 14% of the flora is endemic—a comparatively small proportion, which is probably a consequence of the geologically recent origin of the group.

Near the coasts the vegetation is much like that of the more southerly Pacific islands. Herbaceous plants such as the goat's-foot convolvulus (*Ipomoea pes-caprae*), and shrubs such as *Scaevola frutescens* and *Tournefortia argentea* are common, while characteristic trees of the coast include *Calophyllum inophyllum*, *Hernandia ovigera*, *Hibiscus tiliaceus* and *Terminalia catappa*. On exposed rocky coasts there are few trees, and the vegetation consists of laurel-like and myrtle-like shrubs together with the native juniper. A remarkable feature is the complete absence of any kind of mangrove vegetation.

The early colonists on the islands cut down the forests recklessly to clear land for cultivation and to-day there is little woodland left. In some places, as on Haha shima, the Japanese government has tried to preserve the remaining forests as a protection for the soil. Though few large specimens are left a considerable variety of trees is found in these forests. As well as various broad-leaved evergreen trees, the chief forest constituents are an endemic pandanus, which is abundant up to a height of over 650 ft., and two species of palm, *Ptychosperma elegans* and *Livistona chinensis*; these palms are much taller than most of the other trees and stand out well above them. The numbers of the *Ptychosperma* have been much reduced by felling, but *Livistona*, easily recognized by the tattered flexible tips of the leaves which flutter in the wind, is still plentiful and its leaves provide the islanders with their chief roofing material. Ferns are very common and varied; two kinds of tree fern sometimes grow in pure groves. With increasing height above sea level the proportion of tropical species decreases, but none of the islands is high enough to have a true alpine or mountain vegetation.

The volcanic rock weathers to a fertile red soil and, but for the scarcity of level land, the islands would be very productive. The chief crop is the sugar cane, which formerly gave good yields, but owing to the careless methods of cultivation and the ravages of locusts and other pests the harvest is poorer than it used to be. The next most important crops are bananas and pineapples; maize, coffee, coconuts and tropical fruits such as lemons, oranges, mangoes and papaya are also grown. Various plants have been introduced from other countries for use or for ornament; some of these—e.g., the tobacco plant and the American agave—have run wild and are now thoroughly naturalized. The fibres from the leaf of the agave are extracted and made into good string.

So far as animal life is concerned, the Bonins are typical oceanic islands. The only native land mammals are flying foxes (fruit bats). Many animals have been introduced. Pigs were brought to the islands in 1827 and have since multiplied and run wild. Other introduced mammals include rats, mice, goats, sheep, Californian oxen, and dogs. The last were brought from Hawaii by the early colonists. Birds are few in species, the commonest being *Hypsipetes squamiceps* (a kind of bulbul); *Cettia diaphone* (a warbler); *Monticola cyanus solitaria* (the blue rock-thrush); and *Fringilla kittlitzii* (a finch). Swallows arrive in March or May and leave in August or September. Among sea birds a gannet, *Sula leucogastra*, and a puffin are very numerous. Albatrosses formerly visited the island every year, but in recent years have come only rarely to Muko shima. Reptiles include a small brown spotted lizard. Crabs are said to be numerous. Turtles are plentiful. The commonest is the green turtle, which arrives in the early months of

Plates 122, 123. Vegetation on Chichi shima
Plate 123 (right) shows a pure stand of the palm *Livistona chinensis.*

Plate 124. Omura, Chichi shima

A view taken in 1917. The Anglican church can be seen in the foreground. The main settlement is behind the ridge beyond it. Much of Omura has recently been destroyed by Allied bombing.

Plate 125. A street in Omura

The buildings are nearly all of wood, unpainted, and many of the roofs are thatched.

the year and leaves by August. Sharks abound in the coastal waters; they are caught and the oil and fins are sent to Japan.

HISTORY

The Bonin islands were possibly first sighted by the Spaniard Villalobos in 1542. The Japanese claim that they were discovered by the Japanese voyager Ogasawara Sadayori in 1593; but the account of Ogasawara's activities appears to be a forgery concocted in the eighteenth century. The earliest apparently well-authenticated visit is that of a Japanese merchant, Chozaemon, in 1670. Following this visit they were named the Munin (or Uninhabited) islands; the later Western name of Bonin is probably a corruption of this. Among later visits one of the most important is that of Captain Beechey, of H.M.S. *Blossom*, in 1826. Beechey was in the group for six days, and his account long remained one of the principal sources of information regarding the islands. During his visit he proclaimed British sovereignty over the group.

Before Beechey's visit, however, the Bonins had begun to be visited by whalers. Among the earliest of such visits recorded are those of two British ships—the *Transit*, Captain James Coffin, in 1823, and the *William*, which was wrecked in the islands not long afterwards. Their history during the next thirty or forty years is broadly similar to that of a number of other Pacific islands previously uninhabited and now made important by their proximity to sperm whaling grounds (e.g., compare the Kermadec islands and Lord Howe island, vol. III, pp. 390–1, 410–1). In 1830 Richard Charlton, British Consul in the Hawaiian islands, sent a party of 5 Europeans and about 30 Polynesians to settle in the Bonins. They developed a trade in provisions with visiting whalers. This prospered considerably, and from time to time more settlers joined the community. The principal difficulty, as in other settlements similarly isolated, was in maintaining order among the crews of visiting ships. Charlton and others apparently hoped to see the establishment of a regular British administration; and Alexander Simpson, acting-consul in Honolulu during Charlton's absence, in 1842 took the step of giving a letter to Matteo Mazarro, the nominal head of the colonists, expressing the desire that Mazarro's authority be recognized by all pending the appointment of a British administrator.

New importance was temporarily given to the islands when Commodore Perry forced the Japanese authorities to open two of their ports to Western commerce in 1853. Perry actually visited the Bonins on his epoch-making voyage, and, disregarding the British claim to sovereignty, purchased land for an American coaling station. He also drew up for the settlers a simple code of laws, which provided, amongst other things, for the election of a chief magistrate and two councillors. This was accepted by the people, and the leading American settler, Nathaniel Savory, was made chief magistrate. Perry's actions led to some consideration of the question of sovereignty, but neither Britain nor the United States took any decisive action. In 1858 the maritime Powers secured from Japan the right to establish depots of naval supplies in Japanese open ports, and the Bonin islands again sank into obscurity.

In 1861 a Japanese expedition was sent to the islands, consisting of a commissioner and staff to administer them and a party of about 100 colonists. The new authorities sought to obtain the co-operation of the existing inhabitants. But despite their efforts, the colonizing venture was not a success. In 1863 the commissioner and the last of the Japanese colonists left the Bonins. In 1875 a second Japanese expedition visited the islands and made a renewed declaration of Japanese sovereignty. Two years later they were formally annexed. Neither Britain nor the United States disputed the Japanese action. The settlers in the islands were offered Japanese nationality, and no new settlers other than Japanese were allowed to come to the group. With the development of fishing and sugar-cane production many Japanese colonists went to the islands.

In 1877 the Anglican church in Tokyo became interested in the welfare of the original colonists. In that year and on a number of subsequent occasions pastoral visits were made to the islands, and in 1909 a church was built at Omura, in Chichi shima.

SOCIAL AND ECONOMIC CONDITIONS

After 1875 the original population of mixed European and Polynesian descent was gradually out-numbered by Japanese. By 1930 the population of the islands had risen to 5,743. By 1940 it was well over 7,000. Of this latter number about 3,100 were females, showing that there was a likelihood of considerable further growth by natural increase.

The Table on page 457 shows recent growth in total population and the distribution of population among the islands of the group.

Roughly 78% of the land is covered with forest, and is too hilly and too badly watered to be profitable agriculturally. About 11% is good arable land. Agriculture is the principal industry (Plate 121). An attempt to cultivate indigo was made in the early days of Japanese

Growth of Population in the Bonin Islands, 1930–40

Island	1930	1935	1940
Chichi shima	2,730	3,692	4,302
Haha shima	1,731	1,782	1,905
Iwo shima	1,028	1,065	1,051
Kita Iwo shima	124	92	103
Other islands	130	98	?
Total population	5,743	6,729	7,361 (plus that of 'other islands')

occupation, but climatic conditions were unsuitable. Attention was turned to sugar production, with successful results. A stimulus was thus given to colonization. Small mills driven by cattle were set up, and in 1919 the total value of the sugar crop had reached 800,000 yen. It has increased further since then. Some refining is carried out in the islands. Exports include not only molasses and raw sugar but also small quantities of refined sugar. Papaya, bananas, lemons and other tropical fruits and vegetables are also grown and exported in small quantities. In spite of the large proportion of the islands which is wooded, forestry does not seem to have been undertaken seriously. After agriculture, fishing is the most important industry. Whales and tuna are caught from November to May, and bonito from June to October.

PORTS AND SETTLEMENTS

The only important harbour in the Bonins is Futami kō (Port Lloyd), a large bay on the west of Chichi shima (Fig. 114). It is protected by high land against winds from the north, east and south. The bay is entered between the two capes of One saki and Yagi saki. The distance between these points is about 1,500 yd., but the effective width of the entrance is reduced to about 800 yd. by shoals. The bay has an east-west width of about 1,800 yd. and a length from north to south of about 2,300 yd., with depths for the most part between 10 and 23 fathoms. Most of the bay is sheltered and affords plenty of room for anchorage. Vessels generally anchor off the breakwater in the north. Telegraph cables occupy part of the harbour, and anchorage is forbidden near them. Most of the shores of the bay are cliffed or have coral growing off them. There are a few sandy beaches and several settlements line the shore. The principal wharf is a break-water mole projecting about 300 ft. into the harbour from the north shore. It adjoins the settlement of Omura. The water alongside is

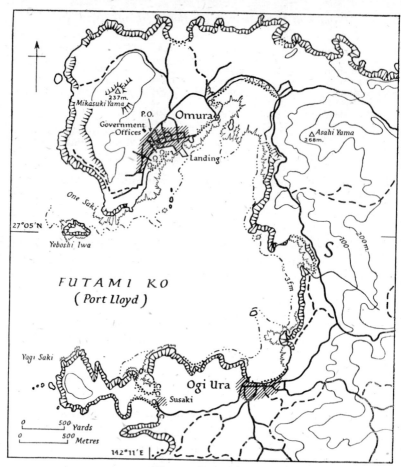

Fig. 114. Futami kō

Form lines, at 100 m. intervals, are approximate. Continuous lines show roads
from 6 to 9 ft. wide and broken lines show bridle paths. Settled areas are shaded.
S denotes the approximate site of the new settlement of Sakae Ura which is reputed
to be larger than Omura. Based on official sources.

shallow and suitable only for lighters and small craft. A flight of steps
on the inner side is used by passengers from small boats. About
500 yd. from this wharf is a wooden pier about 120 ft. long used by
a whaling company. There are also a small wooden pier and a small
jetty at Byōbu Tani and Ogi Ura respectively. Water can be obtained
from two water barges in the harbour, and the town has a good
supply, piped from a reservoir at Byōbu Tani. Coal is kept in small
quantities.

The town (or village) of Omura (Plates 124–5) is a small settlement behind the wharf on the north side of the harbour. It is supplied
with electric light, and equipped with a small hospital and an ice-
making plant. The government offices are situated on the outskirts of
the town on the west side. Of the other settlements round the bay the
most important until recently was Ogi Ura, on the south side. Now,
however, it seems that a large new settlement, named Sakae Ura, has
been created on the east side of the bay.

There are few other settlements on Chichi shima. On Haha shima,
to the south, the principal village is Okimura (Plate 126), at the head
of Oki kō, where the population is between 1,000 and 1,500. In the
Kazan rettō there are settlements on Iwo shima and Kita Iwo shima.
On the former, the villages are Hiyashi, the most important, where
there is a mill; Moto yama, to the south of the mountain of that name;
and Minami mura, near the south-eastern shore at the north end of
the isthmus. The only village of importance on Kita Iwo shima is
Ishino, on the east side of the island.

COMMUNICATIONS

Sea communication is maintained by ships on the services between
Tokyo and Saipan, which call at Futami kō, in Chichi shima, and on
occasions anchor off some of the more important of the other islands.
Before the arrival of the Japanese in 1875 the settlers used outrigger
canoes basically of a Hawaiian pattern but with European sails. It is
possible that craft of this sort are still used for fishing. On many of the
smaller islands there are no roads, but on the more important short
stretches of rough roads have been constructed.

There is probably a telephone system on Chichi shima; and the
island is also a station on the submarine cable system from Yap to
Japan.

MARCUS ISLAND

Marcus island (lat. 24° 34′ N, long. 153° 58′ E) lies about 1,200 miles
south-east of Yokohama. It is known by the Japanese as Minami Tori
shima and is administered by them as part of the Bonin islands.

PHYSICAL GEOGRAPHY

Marcus island is a small coral island, roughly triangular in shape. It
has an area of about 740 acres. The coastline has a length of 4 miles.
The island is surrounded by a fringing reef which varies in width

from 100 to 200 yd. The east side of the island, which is exposed to the force of the prevailing winds and is in the path of occasional typhoons, has been built up of lumps of coral detached from the reef. They form a bank which rises to a maximum height of 70 ft. On the south and north-west sides of the island, which are more protected, the beach is lower and composed of fine coral shingle and sand. It is probable that coral formations grew on the cone of a submerged volcano, and a depression in the centre of the island is probably a former lagoon filled with dead coral and humus.

Soundings about ¼ mile from the reef edge show a depth varying from 8 to 14 fathoms but nowhere is there a really satisfactory landing. The whole of the south coast is composed of a coarse coral shingle. There are two boat passages through the middle of the reef, the only two on the island, and opposite these some slight distance inland and about 15 ft. above sea level is a shelf of conglomerate exposed by the greater amount of water action through the gaps in the reef. The slopes of this conglomerate were occasionally disturbed in heavy storms and carried some way inland. There are former beaches as much as 20 ft. above sea level. On the east coast the beach is made up of six successive steps some 12 ft. deep and fairly wide, and consists of rounded lumps of coral about as big as a man's head on the upper levels, decreasing in size nearer the water's edge.

Trade winds blow steadily from the north-east from October to March. During the remainder of the year the wind is generally strong enough to cause heavy breakers on the reef and to render landing dangerous. Rainfall is said to be scanty. During a visit by an expedition from the Bishop Museum, of Honolulu, for a few days in August 1902, there were frequent tropical rain storms. Temperature during the same short period varied between 72° F. and 82° F. The minimum temperature on the island is said to be about 65° F. and the maximum 99° F. The average temperature during summer is about 89° F.

There are no streams on the island, and water is obtained mainly by catchment. Prior to the construction of an airfield the island was densely wooded. Marcus island is frequented by sea birds. Amongst those recorded are the noddy, frigate bird, tropic bird and a number of different kinds of terns.

OCCUPATION

During the latter half of the nineteenth century Marcus island was frequently visited by American whalers and Japanese bird-catchers. In 1896 the collection of the skins and feathers of the birds frequenting the island was developed by Japanese interests on a regular basis. An American group formed a company to consider the possibility of obtaining phosphate and of growing coconut palms on the island. The island was variously claimed as American and as Japanese territory. The Japanese enforced their claim by landing a small force. At the Washington Treaty of 1921 Marcus was excluded from the *status quo* area and the Japanese have built a military air station which occupies most of the island, with runways parallel to each side. A small pier has been built in the south gap in the reef. There is no information about population or communications.

BIBLIOGRAPHICAL NOTE

A general account of the Bonin islands is given in Willard Price, 'Springboards to Tokyo', *National Geographic Magazine*, vol. LXXXVI, pp. 385–467 (Washington, 1944). Geological details for parts of the Bonin group will be found in Johannes Petersen, 'Beiträge zur Petrographie von Sulphur Island, Peel Island, Hachijo und Mijakishima', *Proceedings of the Third Pan-Pacific Science Congress*, pp. 24–54 (Tokyo, 1927). The coasts of the Bonins (and also of Marcus island) are described in the Admiralty *Japan Pilot*, vol. II (4th edition, London, 1940). The climate of the Bonins is dealt with in the Air Ministry Meteorological Office *Weather in the China Seas and in the Western Part of the North Pacific Ocean*, vol. II (London, 1937). There is much information on vegetation, and some on fauna and other aspects of physical geography, in: O. Warburg, 'Eine Reise nach den Bonin- und Volcano-Inseln', *Verhandlungen der Gesellschaft für Erdkunde zu Berlin*, vol. XVIII, pp. 248–68 (Berlin, 1891); F. H. von Kittlitz, *Twenty-four Views of the Vegetation of the Coasts and Islands of the Pacific*, translated by B. Seemann (London, 1891); and H. Hattori, 'Pflanzengeographische Studien über die Bonin-Inseln', *Journal of the College of Science, Imperial University, Tōkyō, Japan*, vol. XXIII, article 10, pp. 1–65 (Tokyo, 1907–8). The visit of Captain Beechey to the Bonins is described in F. W. Beechey, *Narrative of a Voyage to the Pacific and Beering's Strait* . . . , vol. II (London, 1831). Later history is dealt with in L. B. Cholmondeley, *A History of the Bonin Islands from the Year 1827 to the Year 1876* . . . (London, 1915). A good general picture of the history of the Bonins, with much accurate factual material, is given in Robert Standish, *Bonin, A Novel* (London, 1944).

For maps see Appendix I.

Chapter XXI

GUAM AND WAKE ISLAND

Guam—Physical Geography: History: People: Government and Social Services:
Economics: Ports and Settlements: Communications

Wake Island—Physical Geography: History and Recent Occupation

Bibliographical Note

Guam, which is the southernmost island of the Marianas, and Wake
island, a small atoll between Guam and Midway (vol. II, pp. 447–9),
are both American possessions. Both are administered by the United
States Navy Department, and both are points of call on the American
air route across the north Pacific from San Francisco to Manila.

GUAM

Guam (lat. 13° 26′ N, long. 144° 39′ E) has a length of about 30 miles
from north-north-east to south-south-west. It is about 7 to 9 miles
wide, but narrows to a central neck about 4 miles across. It has an
area of about 225 sq. miles. Since the close of the Spanish-American
war of 1898, Guam has been an American naval station.

Physical Geography (Plates 128–30)

The northern part of the island—i.e., to the north of the central neck
—is formed of raised coral limestone, while the southern half is of
volcanic formation. The northern plateau is generally flat, but has a
downward tilt towards the south-west so that the northern and eastern
parts of the island are high, ending in sheer cliffs and bluffs. While the
land slopes away gently to the south and west, a few hills rise from
this plateau, notably Barrigada (674 ft.) near the southern end, Santa
Rosa (870 ft.) on the east coast, and Machanao (610 ft.) at the extreme
north-west (Fig. 115).

The south part of the island, a mass of augite andesite, is rugged,
showing signs of considerable erosion. There is a complex mountainous belt immediately south of Agaña, which stretches right
across the island. A ridge with a general height of about 1,000 ft. runs
south from this about a mile from the western shore, leaving steep
slopes on the west side with a narrow belt for cultivation, while on the
east side, after an unusually steep slope down to 400 ft., the land falls

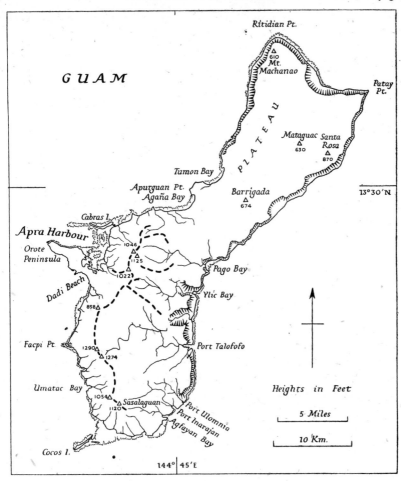

Fig. 115. Guam : physical features

As in the more northerly island of Saipan (Fig. 107), fringing and barrier reefs are better developed on the west coast, which is less steep-to. The western ridge is made up of a series of extinct volcanoes. The lava is augite andesite, but much of it is covered by a raised reef capping. Based on Admiralty chart no. 1101.

away gently to the east coast where it terminates in cliffs about 200 ft. high. The western peaks are all extinct volcanoes.

In the limestone area to the north, owing to the porous nature of the soil, there are no perennial streams except round mount Santa Rosa, where short water courses disappear into the ground at the foot of the hill. The low-lying neck of ground south of the plateau is drained by the Agaña river, a small stream which rises in the centre of the island and after approaching to within a few hundred yards of the shore turns parallel to the coastline and runs about a mile westward through a swamp before discharging into the sea. In the southern (volcanic) part of the island, there are five principal streams, all rising east of the main watershed and flowing across the island into the sea. There are also a few short streams on the west side of the ridge.

Coasts

Coral is poorly developed round the coasts of Guam. Along most of the west coast, the southern part of the east coast, and most of the north coast it takes the form of a narrow fringing reef. Off the south coast it extends outwards for about $2\frac{1}{2}$ miles to enclose the off-lying Cocos island. In the centre of the west coast a spur of reef projects westward to form, with Cabras island, the north side of Apra bay. Low-lying and sandy beaches are rare, occurring at only a few places on the southern part of the east coast and along the south coast, where the rivers have cut into the cliffs. There are gaps in the fringing reef caused by the outfall of fresh water at several points on the southern part of the east coast, and at one or two places on the west side of the island. The northern part of the west coast, the north coast and the east coast are all steeply cliffed, though on the north and east coasts the cliffs recede a short distance from the shore, leaving small amphitheatre-like areas open to the sea. The southern part of the west coast is low and comparatively flat.

Anchorages

On the west coast, apart from Apra harbour (p. 479), there is anchorage $2\frac{1}{2}$ miles south of Ritidian point in from 4 to 5 fathoms; in Umatac bay (with little room, and from November to May only) in $7\frac{1}{2}$ fathoms; and in Agat bay (off Dadi beach) during north-easterly winds. On the east coast the only anchorages are off the river mouths of the southern half. They are mostly suitable only for small craft. The best is Port Talofofo, an indentation between steep cliffs about $\frac{1}{2}$ mile long and $\frac{1}{4}$ mile wide. Here, there are depths of from 2 to 8 fathoms, and the inlet is protected in all weathers. There is a short stretch of beach about 300 yd. long south of the mouth of the Talofofo river, which flows into the head of the bay. Anchorage is also possible in Agfayan bay in $2\frac{1}{2}$ to 3 fathoms, and at Port Inarajan in a restricted space in 2 to 3 fathoms, but the latter is exposed and dangerous. Pago bay, a semi-circular inlet, can only take small craft owing to the narrowness (50 ft.) of the pass through the reef, and Port Ulomnia is also suitable only for boats.

The best landing beach for boats on the east coast seems to be Talofofo bay, whence there is a road leading to Inarajan and Agaña. Landing may also be possible in Agfayan bay, where there is apparently no reef, or in Inarajan bay over a reef. On the west coast, there are boat passes through the reef in Tumon bay and at Dadi beach, where there is clear sand, with apparently no reef, south of the Orote peninsula.

Climate

Climatic conditions in the Marianas have been outlined in Chapter XV (pp. 308–13). The climate of Guam is similar to that of Saipan. Between November and June north-east trade winds usually predominate, with an average strength over the sea of 13–24 m.p.h. (force 4–5 on the Beaufort scale). The summer season has variable winds, because Guam lies close to the divide between the spheres of the summer monsoon and north-east trades. In August and September the wind may be predominantly north-easterly in one year and southwesterly in the following year. Westerly winds are not uncommon during the period of atmospheric instability (July to October) in which most typhoons occur. Calms tend to occur mainly in summer. Winds of gale force are very rare throughout the year, although an extreme case of three days with gale has been recorded in July alone. Rainfall is heavy, especially from July to October. The mean monthly figures (in inches) over 23 years at Sumay are shown below:

J	F	M	A	M	J	J	A	S	O	N	D	Year
2·6	3·1	3·1	2·0	4·2	5·7	14·3	15·6	15·2	13·2	7·6	4·9	91·5

Rain is also frequent, being likely to occur at all hours of the day. The total number of rain-days in an average year is 212. February may be almost rainless, and less than 1 in. may occur in each of the months January to April. Rainfall is very variable from year to year. The maximum fall in 24 hours (16 in.) occurred in October, whilst a typhoon was passing.

The mean monthly temperature is high and fairly constant, varying from 79° F. in January to February to 82° F. between April and June. Extreme maximum and minimum temperatures vary between 94° F. and 71° F. in May and 89° F. and 68° F. in February. Relative humidity is high with a mean annual value of 80%. The maximum cloud amounts are recorded from July to September and the minimum in April or May.

Water Supply. In the north of the island there is an artesian well (depth 291 ft.). Near Agaña there is a reservoir which also supplies Asan, Piti and Cabras island. Water can be obtained from the streams in the southern part of the island.

Vegetation

The vegetation of Guam is similar to that of the Carolines and of the other large islands in the Marianas group. Over 550 species of flowering plants and ferns are known to grow in the island, but of these about 314 are believed to have been introduced by man, intentionally or otherwise. The introduced plants include a large number of weeds and useful plants found in all parts of the tropics, but it is interesting to note that many of the introduced species are of American origin, some of them being unknown outside tropical America, except in Guam. A large proportion of these American plants were probably brought to the island between its discovery by Magellan in 1521 and the beginning of the nineteenth century; during most of this period a galleon called yearly at Guam on the voyage from Acapulco in Mexico to the Philippines. Guam has probably served as a centre from which many American plants have spread to other Pacific islands. The native flora, consisting of about 230 species, as in other Western Pacific islands, is mainly or entirely of Malayan origin; about 61 species are endemics, not known from anywhere else.

Before the coming of man, Guam was probably completely covered with trees, but now the forest has been much reduced in area, much of the island being cultivated or covered with secondary grassland and scrub. The remaining natural vegetation may be divided into coastal vegetation, consisting mainly of beach vegetation and mangrove swamps, and inland vegetation, consisting of forest, scrub and grassland.

The mangrove swamps are found at the mouths of streams and consist of trees such as *Rhizophora*, *Bruguiera* and the red-flowered *Lumnitzeras*. A short distance up-stream, where the water is less salt, there are thickets of nipa palms, the leaves of which are used for thatching the better-class houses. The nipa, like all the other palms of the island, is probably not native and is believed to have been introduced from the Philippines in quite recent times.

The sandy beaches are in many places fringed with a strip of beach forest, with a carpet of the goat's-foot convolvulus to seaward. In the beach forest there is the usual mixture of trees such as *Barringtonia*

Plate 126. Okimura, Haha shima

The principal settlement in the Hahashima rettō. Windbreaks of trees and shrubs, which border all canefields and gardens in Haha shima, can be seen on the surrounding hill sides. Tall trees grow only on sheltered slopes.

Plate 127. Kitamura, Haha shima

A village in the north of the island. The narrow bay, with a beach at its head (on which fishing boats can be seen drawn up), is typical of the Hahashima rettō.

Plate 128. The south side of Cabras island, Guam

Cabras island flanks Apra harbour on its northern side. The vegetation includes Cycads and is developed on eroded raised reefs.

Plate 129. Orote point, Guam, looking southward

The Orote peninsula is a great bluff of raised coral reefs. The volcanic cliffs of Facpi point are seen in the distance.

Plate 130. Volcanic hills east of Agaña, Guam

The grassy slopes of much of the interior of Guam are steep and heavily eroded. Scrub is here confined to gullies.

racemosa, Hernandia, Hibiscus tiliaceus, etc., with two kinds of purple-flowered convolvulus and other creepers climbing over them. A handsome lily, *Crinum asiaticum*, grows beneath the trees. Coconut palms are abundant on the west coast, but there are hardly any on the east. *Casuarina equisetifolia*, which also grows inland scattered over the grassland, forms groves on the sandy beaches on the windward side of the island and near the southern end of the lee side. On the cliffs grows, among other plants, the palm-like *Cycas circinalis*, called *fadang* by the islanders; the fruit was at one time one of their staple foods.

In the inland forest the chief trees include species such as the *nonag* (*Hernandia ovigera*), the Indian almond (*Terminalia catappa*) and the *daog* or *palo maria* (*Calophyllum inophyllum*), which also grow in the beach forest. Many of the commonest Polynesian trees are completely absent, e.g., the paper-mulberry, the candlenut and *Metrosideros*. The wild, seed-producing breadfruit, a giant banyan (*Ficus* sp.) and two kinds of pandanus are common. The areca-nut palm sows itself and is plentiful in damp places. *Calophyllum*, the *ifil* (*Intsia bijuga*), the *paraiso* (*Melia azedarach*) and other trees provide good timbers. On abandoned clearings masses of introduced plants of all kinds spring up and form dense thickets. On the sites of former gardens various cultivated plants persist for a long time; some seed themselves, others such as the cashew-nut tree seem unable to do so.

On the uplands there are stretches of bare grassland with very few trees. The chief plant here is the grass *Miscanthus floridulus*, which grows higher than a man; the sharp-edged leaves are used for making thatch.

Fauna

At the time of discovery, there were no four-footed mammals in Guam, and only two species of bats. The Norway rat, introduced later, does great damage to crops, as also do deer. Cattle, horses, mules, cats, pigs, and goats have all been introduced. Sea birds are plentiful. They include noddies, terns, and boobies. The latter nest on Orote peninsula. Land birds are also plentiful, including a megapode, a short-eared owl, and several species of dove. Reptiles include a black and yellow snake about 4 ft. long and a gecko. The former is a pest which does great damage to poultry. Wasps and several species of ants are plentiful, one of the latter stings severely. It marches in long columns and will sting any animal it encounters. Small scorpions are common but, while their stings are painful, they are not dangerous. Also included in the fauna are mosquitoes, centipedes, and large brown spiders which, however, are harmless.

HISTORY

The history of Guam from its discovery by Magellan in 1521 up to its occupation by American forces in 1898 has been described in Chapter XV (pp. 319–23). At the end of the Spanish-American war of the latter year, American possession was made permanent by formal cession. Like eastern Samoa, which was acquired by the United States a year later (vol. II, pp. 598, 601), Guam was valued principally as a potential naval base and coaling station. It was, therefore, placed under naval administration, and its internal history has continued to be conditioned largely by that fact. Money has been spent freely on the development of social services, and the people have been given full freedom to continue their traditional way of life.

PEOPLE

Population Distribution and Trends

In 1901, when the first American census was taken in Guam, the population was 9,676; all but 46, out of this number, were Chamorro. By 1940 the number of native Chamorro had increased to 21,502; and there were 787 non-native residents (comprising Americans, Filipinos, and a few Japanese and mixed-bloods), and 778 officers and ratings of the United States navy. The total population was thus 23,067.

A large proportion of the people maintain a house in one of the towns and also one in the country, where their farmland is situated. Thus, figures of population density in different areas give a somewhat generalized picture of a situation whose detailed outlines are subject to frequent, though only temporary, change. According to official figures 10,861 people live in Agaña, the capital, and a further 4,088 in the neighbouring municipalities of Sumay, Piti, Asan and Sinajaña. The remainder of the island is rather thinly peopled. The distribution and density of population are shown in Fig. 116.

Physical Type

The Chamorro of Guam, like their kinsfolk in other islands of the Marianas, are of mixed Micronesian, Filipino and Spanish origin. During the eighteenth century mortality among Chamorro men was extremely high, owing to the frequent revolts against Spanish rule; and, as a result, a large number of Chamorro women married

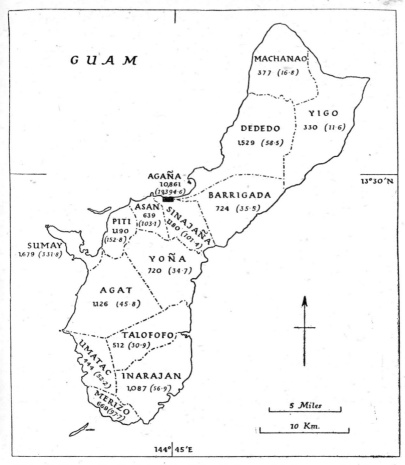

Fig. 116. Guam: distribution of population in the municipal areas and in the town of Agaña

Figures in brackets denote density per square mile. Other figures show total population. Based on Laura Thompson, *Guam and its People; A Study of Culture Change and Colonial Education*, pp. 18 and 34–5 (San Francisco, 1941).

Spaniards or Filipinos. The people are generally of good physique. They are not homogeneous, and their skin colour varies from that of a south European to the brown of pure Micronesians. Their hair is black and generally either straight or wavy.

Language

Many of the younger people speak English, which they have learnt in the American-controlled schools. The older people, however, generally speak only Chamorro. This is basically Micronesian in structure and vocabulary, but it incorporates many Spanish and Tagalog words. It has many affinities with Malay and with Polynesian. Thus *niyog* (coconut) has its counterpart in the Samoan *niu*. On the other hand, there are many Chamorro words with Malayan affinities only such as *apu* (ashes), a Malayan form of which is *habu*, while the corresponding Polynesian word is *lefulefu*; or *tolang* (bone) for which the Malayan word is *tulang* and the Polynesian *ivi*. Many other words have no apparent connection with either group.

In common with Polynesian and Malay, Chamorro has no copulative verb, and two forms of the first person plural, but, unlike Polynesian, it expresses tenses, number and mood by prefixes, suffixes or infixes, and possession is indicated by suffixes. Thus : *tata*, father; *tata-no*, my father; *tata-mo*, thy father; *tata-ña*, his father. Some vowels too are modified after the use of the definite article : *a* becomes *ä*; *o*, *e*, and *u* become *i*. Thus : *lahe*, man; *i lähe*, the man: *guma*, house; *i gime*, the house. The plural of nouns is formed by placing the word *siha* after them, by reduplicating the tonic syllable, or, as in the case of all adjectives, by adding the prefix *man*. Spanish and Filipino words adopted follow Chamorro syntax, thus *santos* (saint) becomes *manantos* in the plural.

Social Organization

In the present-day social organization, the family has displaced the clan as the chief unit. Descent is now, by American law, through the male line. The family in Guam usually consists of a man and his wife and children, and some near relatives, who form a household which usually acts as an economic unit. The members also have certain outside ties and obligations, such as the *compadre* relationship (that of god-parents). The father is the nominal head of the family and is responsible for the economic well-being of the family, but the mother partially represents the tradition of the ancient matrilineal descent of the Chamorro. She usually holds the purse-strings and has great influence with the children even after they have grown up. For social, religious and economic purposes, families group themselves into units of mutual assistance. Groups of families living in outlying farms, form themselves into rural communities, usually with a common school, chapel, and cockpit, and help each other in planting, harvesting, fishing, and so on. They also act as groups on political occasions, and form processions on saints' days. In the larger villages, the same thing happens, but there is less economic co-operation. In the same way a group of households living near together in Agaña are called a *barrio* and each has its own chapel, etc.

Traces of the 'caste' system of the Chamorro still survive in Agaña, though they are now much less significant. In Spanish times a wealthy class of Spanish Chamorro, about 12 families in all, arose as a property-owning class and would not mix with the common people; but with the advent of American rule, a monetary economy and compulsory common education, their exclusiveness broke down. However, they still survive as large landowners. Most of the land is held in the form of comparatively small estates owned by individual families. Under American law, estates should be divided among all of a man's children at his death. But in practice, estates are often registered in the joint names of all the heirs, and then administered by one of them. Thus a form of communal ownership of land within family groups continues.

Housing and Food

The houses of the richer people are large adobe dwellings of Spanish style, with tiled or thatched roofs. Many of the smaller dwellings have thatched roofs and some corrugated iron. Houses in the country, *ranchos*, vary from well-built houses to simple huts with plaited fibre sides and thatched roofs.

There is some good fertile land in Guam, particularly on the alluvial soil of the inland valleys. Before the coming of Europeans the diet of the natives consisted chiefly of fish, fruit, coconuts, yams, taro and breadfruit. Some rice was grown and eaten as a luxury on special occasions. There was neither maize nor sweet potatoes; and the Tahitian chestnut has only been introduced very recently. Now, maize is the chief crop; and much rice is grown in marshy ground, though some is imported. Taro and yams are now eaten only when other food is scarce. Sweet potatoes, tobacco and many other crops are grown. Cattle, horses, pigs and buffaloes are kept, and leaves (particularly of the breadfruit) are used as forage.

Religion

To-day the greater part of the people are Roman Catholics. Early Jesuit missionaries were responsible for the original colonization of the island, and Catholic influence has remained the dominant religious force in the group ever since, but there are still some survivals of the original Chamorro religious ideas, notably in the belief in *taotaomara* (ancestral spirits), *maligna* (evil spirits) and *duhende* (goblins).

At present the clergy are mostly Spanish Capuchin monks. In 1939 a Roman Caholic bishop, about nine Capuchin fathers, two brothers and one native priest resided on the island. Resident missionaries were stationed in Agaña and the other more thickly populated municipalities. With the arrival of the Americans, the American Board of Commissioners for Foreign Missions established a station near Agaña, but they withdrew in 1910. In 1911 American Baptists established a mission, which has succeeded in gaining about 400 supporters. There is some slight friction between the two churches, characterized by occasional stone-throwing during Baptist services or ceremonies.

In general, religion plays a very large part in the daily life of the people. People living on isolated farms go into the villages on Sundays and saints' days, when they take part in solemn processions. Each village has its own special saint's day.

Occupations

In 1930 about 50% of males and 11% of females in the total population were gainfully employed. Of the men about 63% were farmers or farm labourers, 10% unskilled labourers (principally in the towns), 4% army or navy personnel, 4% domestic servants, 2% book-keepers, clerks and messengers, and a very few are employed as government officials, policemen, etc. Among women who are in paid employment, 68% are in domestic service, 7% are teachers, and 5% are nurses or midwives; the remainder are either dressmakers or shop-assistants.

GOVERNMENT AND SOCIAL SERVICES

Central Administration

The office of Governor of Guam is held by an American naval officer, appointed by the Secretary of the Navy for a two-year period. To assist him, he has an aide for civil administration, a military aide and a secretary. Under him there are various departments headed by naval officers and staffed in part by Chamorro. They include an executive department, concerned with native officers and general administration; a department of records and accounts (vital statistics, land records, finance and cadastral survey); a department of industries (public works and utilities generally); a department of education; a department of health; a police department; a military department (supervising the Guam Militia); a judiciary department; a customs and immigration department; and a department of agriculture.

The Governor is advised on matters of general policy by the Guam Congress. This body was formed in 1917 and at first consisted of the commissioners and deputy commissioners of the various municipalities into which the island is divided. It met every month. In 1931 it was reorganized. It was then divided into two houses—a House of Council, with 16 members; and a House of Assembly, with 27 members. Both houses are popularly elected. The functions of the congress remain purely advisory, but it has provided a fairly effective platform from which the political ideas of the people can be made known.

Local Administration

During the time of Spanish rule, Guam was divided for purposes of local government into municipalities, each under a *gobernadorcillo*, with a subordinate staff. Both the *gobernadorcillo* and his assistants were elected by the people of the municipality. This system was taken over by the American administration. Popular election of officers has, however, not been continuously maintained. It has been replaced for several periods by official appointment. The principal officers of the municipalities are now termed commissioners. Their function is to act as intermediaries between the government and the people, to interpret the laws, and to explain government policy. In addition, they have limited judicial powers (p. 474). In 1939 there were 14 rural municipalities in the island and the urban municipality of Agaña. In Agaña, the chief municipal officer bore the title of Chief Commissioner.

The commissioners hold public meetings once a month. These are attended by at least one member of every family group living in the municipality and, in addition, by all municipal officials and by a representative of the central government.

Law and Justice

The Spanish legal and penal system was only gradually changed. Laws were codified and slightly modified in 1908, and the courts were partially reorganized between 1905 and 1910. In 1932, a major reorganization of the whole legal system was undertaken, and laws based on those of California were promulgated in 1932. The courts set up at this time consisted of a Court of Appeals, an Island Court, a Justice Court, a Police Court, and a Special Court. The Court of Appeals is the supreme legal tribunal of the island. It is presided over by a naval officer with legal training and four associate judges, usually two other naval officers and two Chamorro lawyers. Sentences of the Island Court exceeding one year's imprisonment are reviewed in this court. The Island Court, with a Chamorro lawyer as judge, deals with major criminal cases and all civil cases not specifically allotted by law to the Justice Court. It also deals with cases of probate, guardianship, trusteeship, etc., and hears appeals from the Justice Court. The Justice Court, also under a Chamorro lawyer, deals with criminal cases of a less serious nature than those coming under the scope of the Island Court and with minor civil cases. The Police Court, under a naval officer, deals with minor criminal cases. Petty offences in out-lying municipalities involving not more than $5 are dealt with sum-marily by the commissioners.

There is a prison in Agaña. Prisoners are employed cleaning streets, cutting copra, or catching fish. There are also a prison farm and a small tile factory, worked by prison labour, outside Agaña. Juvenile delinquents do not appear in the courts, but are treated individually by the chief of police and generally put on probation.

Laws governing land tenure are designed for the protection of native interests. Land held by the Spanish Crown has become govern-ment property, and may be leased at low rentals for periods up to 25 years to natives, or up to 5 years to foreigners. Purchase of land by foreigners is forbidden. Under American inheritance laws, land should be divided among all the heirs, but in practice kinship groups tend to register their various holdings jointly, and thus to some extent to continue the kinship group ownership prevalent in ancient times. A few rich families acquired large tracts of land in Spanish times, and still own them.

Finance

The principal taxes are a poll tax of $2 (U.S.) per head per year and a property tax. The former was originally a commutation of a labour tax by which males between 18 to 60 were liable to provide 10 to 15 days' labour a year. This was commuted to $8 (Mexican), later to $5 (Mexican) and then to the present figure. The property tax is levied at a rate of 3% of the assessed value with additions in cases of improved land values. In Agaña 3% is also collected on the assessed increase in value, but in the rural municipalities only 1% is so collected. Small taxes are also collected in respect of the use of water, on domestic liquor, and of the ownership of dogs, motor-cars, and firearms.

Health Services

The health of the people of Guam was seriously undermined by European contacts in former times. In particular, the establishment of a hospital for seamen, during the whaling period in the nineteenth century, led to the spread of many diseases. In 1849 and again in 1856 epidemics of influenza swept the island. Leprosy also gained a hold. Since the American occupation of the island, health conditions have much improved. They are now reasonably good. During the five years 1933–7 the most prevalent diseases and the number of cases of each were as follows: dysentery, 633; pneumonia, 388; bronchitis, 276; tuberculosis, 275; gonorrhoea, 199; yaws, 165.

Health services are administered by the department of health and the medical department. Medical staff in 1940 consisted of 9 medical officers, 46 pharmacists' mates, 7 native hospital apprentices, 14 native nurses, and 16 native probationer nurses. In 1939, native boys were being trained as native medical practitioners, on lines similar to those adopted by the Central Medical School in Fiji. Hospitals in Guam are the Naval Hospital, which deals not only with service personnel but also with civilians, and the Susana Hospital, a private establishment controlled by the naval authorities, which takes paying patients. There are also dressing stations in six of the outlying villages. The Guam branch of the American Red Cross has a staff of about six nurses, and usually has funds available for the relief of distress. Among the Chamorro the use of traditional herbs still survives to some extent, and a class of professional herbalists (*suruhana*), made up mostly of old women, still practises clandestinely.

Education

Education is under the control of the Naval Chaplain, who is head of the Department of Education. Under him he has a native superintendent of public instruction. In the island there are altogether 28 public elementary schools. Secondary education is provided by the Washington High School and the Washington Junior High School, a nurses' training school, and the agricultural school in Piti.

Education is compulsory between the ages of 7 and 12, and children showing sufficient aptitude can continue their education in the secondary schools. All teachers are recruited from the Chamorro, who undergo a course in pedagogy, physiology, hygiene, craftwork, arithmetic, English, history, and geography. All teaching is in English, and the use of the Chamorro language is forbidden in the schools. Textbooks similar to those in use in California are used. The curriculum is designed to pay special attention to handicrafts and agriculture. In the rural schools this last aspect of the training takes the form of agricultural clubs. Religious instruction in the public elementary schools is forbidden, but most children attend schools run by the Catholic clergy for an hour or so in the evenings, when they receive religious instruction.

ECONOMICS

Guam possesses no known mineral deposits. The people depend primarily upon agriculture for their livelihood, and there is some fishing. The only considerable export is copra. The land is generally fertile, but soil composition and drainage vary considerably in different parts of the island. In the north, where there is a shallow infertile soil cover, the land is largely planted with coconut palms, but there are many small clearings used for gardens. In the lower river basins of the south, rice is cultivated. Land utilization is shown in greater detail in Fig. 117. The following Table gives an estimate of production of the principal agricultural crops in 1939:

Principal Agricultural Crops, 1939

Crop	Approximate yield	Acreage
Coconuts	2,500 tons †	12,000–13,000
Maize	30,000 bushels	1,500
Rice	12,500 bushels	640
Sweet potatoes	295,000 lb.	200
Tapioca	500,000 lb.	150
Taro	665,000 lb.	100
Sugar cane	—	10

† The figure for coconuts represents the amount of copra exported only. Based on Laura Thompson, *Guam and Its People*, p. 123 (San Francisco, 1941).

An estimate of production of minor crops in 1939 is as follows: bananas, 917,000 lb.; mangoes, 500,000 lb.; avocados, 300,000 lb.; papayas, 86,000 lb.; oranges, 20,000 lb.; lemons, 20,000 lb.; pineapples, 10,000 lb.; limes, 10,000 lb.; tangerines, 10,000 lb.; kapok, 500 lb. About 500 acres were at that time devoted to the cultivation of various vegetables. There were about 5,000 head of cattle (including *carabao*, used for draft purposes) and 7,000 pigs.

Copra

Coconut plantations were developed by the large land-owners in

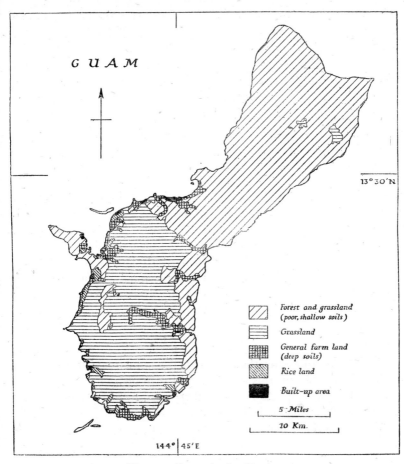

Fig. 117. Guam: land utilization

The north and south-east of the island have shallow soils derived from the raised reef terraces. They provide a contrast with the south-western volcanic area with its richer soils derived from andesitic lava, and its alluvial coastal pockets and valley bottoms which provide the best agricultural land on the island. Based on the same source as Fig. 116, p. 112.

the nineteenth century, and in 1900 560 tons of copra were exported to Japan. The greatest quantity ever produced was in 1929, when nearly 3,000 tons were exported. Production has varied with world prices, but has also been affected by the incidence of hurricanes and coconut scale (*Aspidiotus destructor*). The sale of copra in the United States has been handicapped by a processing tax of 3 cents per pound. This tax differentiates against Guam copra in comparison with Philippine copra, because in the latter case the tax is refunded to the Philippine government.

Rice

Rice has always been a staple crop in the island. It is usually cultivated by groups of male relatives who own a stretch of alluvial land, but no very large area has been cultivated. Up to about 1930 rather less than 200 acres were producing rice; but, as a result of government encouragement in the form of a free supply of building materials for the construction of dams, advances for the purchase of land, and the purchase of home-grown rice in preference to the cheaper Japanese imported rice, the area under cultivation rose to 640 acres in 1937, and the yield per acre rose from about 20 bushels per acre to between 27 and 59 bushels per acre, according to locality.

Very heavy demands are made on labour at planting and harvest times, and on these occasions all available relatives assist. Even so labour is scarce, and this is probably the main reason why larger crops are not produced. The present supply is inadequate for local requirements and large quantities are imported.

Maize

Even more important than rice is maize, which is grown on small farms. Cultivation in this case is by all members of a family; even young children help. As in most other ventures in Guam, there is a good deal of mutual assistance between neighbours. The chief difficulties facing the maize growers have been lack of storage equipment and an inadequate water supply. The former has been overcome by the use of petrol drums for storage, and, to meet the latter, an irrigation scheme for the area south of Agaña was started in 1940. Total acreage in 1930 amounted to 1,500 and the yield to 30,000 bushels. The high yield is due to the fact that two crops can be grown in a year.

Sugar

In contrast with the neighbouring island of Saipan and with Hawaii, sugar is hardly grown at all. In 1939 there were only 10 acres under cultivation. While soils and climatic conditions are similar to those of Saipan, the short-term leases, high freight rates, high price of local labour, and scarcity of transport, have all combined to discourage the investment of capital in sugar growing.

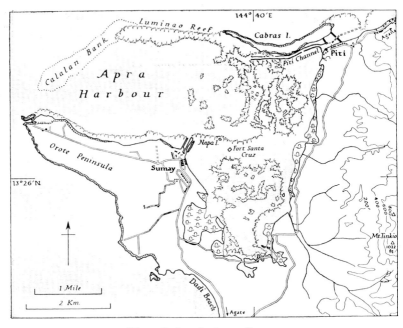

Fig. 118. Apra harbour, Guam

Form lines are at approximately 200-ft. intervals. Based on official sources.

Fishing

Deep-sea fishing is hardly practised at all in spite of the former employment of Japanese deep-sea fishermen as instructors. Lack of suitable vessels and gear is a major factor impeding this development. In-shore fishing from canoes with seine nets is regularly undertaken by small groups of men, sometimes assisted by all the inhabitants of the village. Fishing with rod and line, and the use of stupefacients, are also practised; the latter is illegal. Most of the fish caught are consumed locally, by the relatives and neighbours of the fishermen, but some are caught by groups of fishermen who catch fish primarily for sale in Agaña.

Trade

Even in Spanish times, Guam was not self-supporting economically and to-day large quantities of maize and rice are imported, together with supplies and equipment for the naval personnel and their families. The only export of any importance is copra. In 1929, the peak year for copra, nearly 3,000 tons were exported. The principal destinations of Guam produce are Manila, the Hawaiian islands, and the United States, though small quantities have been exported to Japan.

Up to 1911 about 64% of all imports came from Japan, but in 1912 Apra was closed to foreign ships, and since that date American goods have gradually captured more and more of the market from the Japanese. During the last 30 years there has always been a large excess of imports over exports.

PORTS AND SETTLEMENTS

Apra (Plate 132)

Apra (Fig. 118) is the only port in Guam. It is situated on the west side of the island, between the Orote peninsula and Cabras island; it affords good protection in all weathers, though a swell may be experienced in westerly winds.

The entrance is between Orote island and the southern end of Calalan bank, a south-easterly extension of Luminao reef. The least depth is 11 fathoms and the width about 400 yd. The harbour itself is L-shaped, but the western and southern extensions are much encumbered by coral reefs, which extend along the southern shore of the harbour and along the north side close to Cabras island. This with the projecting tongue known as Luminao reef, forms the northern side of the harbour and acts as a natural breakwater. The harbour area available for anchorage is limited by coral to the area between the Orote peninsula and Luminao reef. Ships anchor in the north and seaplanes in the south, off Sumay. Anchorage is in from 17 to 36 fathoms on sand. Low cliffs occur on Cabras island and on the western part of the Orote peninsula, and mangroves fringe the eastern and south-eastern shore. The land to the east rises steeply from a narrow plain.

There are no wharves with deep water, and all cargoes are landed by lighter against a wharf at Sumay, on the south side of the harbour, or at a small pier at Piti. A dredged channel, about 3 ft. 6 in. deep, leads to Piti and extends east-north-eastwards. Another channel leads to Sumay, beside which is a ramp for hauling out seaplanes.

There is a coal dump on Cabras island. Oil used to be stored in a tanker with a capacity of 2,000 tons. A reasonable water supply can be obtained between June and December, but at other times of the year it is difficult to obtain water.

There is no large town round the harbour, the only settlements being the villages of Sumay and Piti. The former, with a population in 1939 of about 1,200 inhabitants, is the local headquarters of the Pacific Cable Company and of Pan-American Airways. There are also barracks for marines, a church, a school, and a number of native dwellings. Some of them are built of adobe. Most of the inhabitants make a living by fishing. Piti, with a population in 1939 of about 1,000, is the official port of entry. There are one naval and some commercial warehouses, in addition to native dwellings. A good road running round the harbour joins the villages and continues north-west along the coast to Agaña.

Agaña (Plate 131)

With a population of 10,861 (mostly Chamorro) Agaña is the only town of any size in the island. It has a frontage along the shore of about a mile. The sandy beach is protected by a fringing reef. It consists for the most part of small but well-built native dwellings, some of timber and thatch, others of adobe with tiled roofs in Spanish style. The chief public buildings are the Government House, administrative offices, marine barracks, militia barracks, court house, post office, gaol, and Roman Catholic church. There is a small soap works and a refrigeration plant. Water is supplied from a reservoir behind the town, and from artesian wells. There is also a small power station providing electric current, and there are two cinemas.

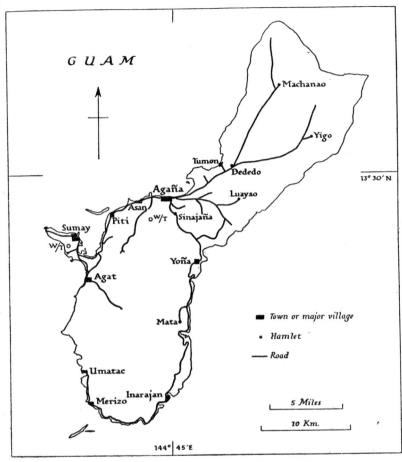

Fig. 119. Guam: settlements and communications

The rugged volcanic area of the south-west restricts habitation and roads, so that settlements are mainly coastal. The north-eastern limestone area is lower, slopes are less abrupt, and settlements are more widely diffused. Coastal villages are exceptional in the north-east of Guam. Based on the same source as Fig. 117, p. 18.

COMMUNICATIONS

Sea communication with Guam is provided in normal times by United States navy and army transports and by a cargo liner of the American President line, calling every six months. Commercial cargoes are carried by the transports as well as by the American President line ship. Since 1912 the port of Apra has been closed to foreign shipping. Since 1936 Apra has been a point of call on the Pan-American Airways service from San Francisco to Manila.

Guam has about 85 miles of road (Fig. 119). The more important stretches have a macadam surface; the remainder have one of powdered limestone. A local telephone service links Agaña and Sumay and extends to several of the other settlements in the same part of the island. The United States Navy Department maintained a high-power W/T station; there was also a commercial broadcasting station.

WAKE ISLAND

Wake island (lat. 19° 18′ N, long. 166° 35′ E) is an isolated atoll lying about 1,500 miles from Guam and about 1,180 miles from the western end of the Hawaiian chain. It is a United States possession. In view of its strategic importance the island was declared a naval defence area and a naval air station was established.

PHYSICAL GEOGRAPHY (Fig. 120)

The atoll consists of a quadrangular coral rim pointed towards the south-east but square in the north-west, enclosing a lagoon roughly 4 miles long and 1½ miles wide. The southern and north-eastern sides of the atoll are occupied by three islands. The largest, Wake island, is V-shaped and forms the south-eastern end of the atoll. Its two arms are about 3 miles long and about ½ mile wide. Wilkes and Peale islands, forming continuations of the south and north arms respectively, are about 1½ miles long and less than ½ mile across. The channels between the islands had a depth of about 3½ ft., but it was proposed to deepen these. The lagoon itself is shallow, varying from 6 to 12 ft. and is in places obstructed by coral. It shelves at its eastern end into a wide beach of firm white sand, but part of this has been cleared to provide a seaplane alighting area. The reef, varying in width from 500 ft. (on the south of Wake island) to ½ mile on the western end of the atoll, makes landing difficult except from boats inside the lagoon. Anchorage can be obtained outside, off the south-east end of Peale island in 15 fathoms in the trade wind season.

Plant life is limited to about twenty species. Bush forest rose to about 20 ft. and covered much of the surface of the islands before recent development took place. The dominant tree was a heliotrope (*Messerschmidia argentea*). Other trees included *Pisonia grandis* and a few *kou* (*Cordia subcordata*), of very immature development. Morning-glory vine (*Ipomoea grandiflora*) grew in tangles in all directions and obstructed movement. The goat's-foot convolvulus (*Ipomoea pes-caprae*) was also growing, but rather less abundantly.

Plate 131. Agaña, Guam

A view of part of the town from the slopes behind. The photograph was taken at low tide and shows the reef partly uncovered.

Plate 132. Sumay and Apra harbour

The township of Sumay is in the foreground, and Cabras island, which forms the northern shore of Apra harbour, is seen in the background.

Plate 133. Landing stores at Wake island

Since nothing is produced on Wake island all the requirements of the airways station have to be brought in by sea or air.

Plate 134. Landing pier, Wake island

This is one of two piers built at Peale island by Pan-American Airways as part of their establishment at Wake.

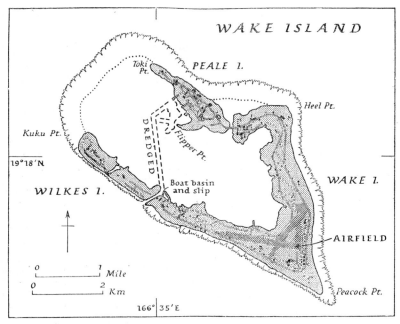

Fig. 120. Wake island

The dotted line shows the approximate inner limit of the atoll rim. The parallel broken lines show the dredged channel across the lagoon. Based on official sources.

There were also several kinds of low shrubs and grasses; notably plentiful was *Sesuvium portulacastrum*.

The only mammal found on the island by the *Tanager* expedition in 1923 was a rat, closely related to the Hawaiian rat. Hermit crabs were then plentiful. Sea birds, which were present in great numbers, included terns, boobies, petrels, frigate birds, and red-tailed tropic birds. Migratory birds visiting the island were found to include the golden plover and the bristle-thighed curlew. The only land bird permanently on the island was a flightless rail (*Rallus wakensis*), about 9 in. high, with wings about 4 in. in length.

HISTORY AND RECENT OCCUPATION

Wake is almost certainly the island sighted by the Spaniard Mendaña in 1568 and named by him San Francisco. Its existence and approximate position were finally made known, however, by William Wake, of the schooner *Prince Henry*, who rediscovered it in 1796. It was charted and its exact position ascertained by the United States Exploring Expedition in 1841. It became better known when the barque *Libelle* with a valuable cargo was wrecked there. The survivors set out in a long-boat and gig in an attempt to reach Guam 1,508 miles away. The voyage was accomplished successfully by the long-boat in 13 days, but the gig was lost without trace; later several vessels visited the atoll to salve the *Libelle*'s cargo. During the Spanish-American war several ships called and raised the American flag, but it was not formally annexed until 1899. After this no serious interest was taken in the island until 1923, but during this interlude Japanese parties visited Wake to collect birds' feathers and established two temporary camps. In 1923 the American *Tanager* expedition made a scientific examination of the island. Pan-American Airways made it a stopping place in 1935, building a rest-house and pier on Peale island. In the same year the island was placed under the jurisdiction of the United States Navy Department as a defence area. In the opening stages of the Pacific war the island was captured by the Japanese after strong resistance.

The population from 1935 to 1941 was limited to Pan-American Airways personnel and to the American garrison. Pan-American Airways had built a hotel on Peale island, and various barracks and other buildings, including a dispensary, were erected on the atoll. An airfield suitable for land planes was constructed on Wake island, and roads were built on all three islands; Peale and Wake islands were linked by a bridge. On Peale island there were two landing piers (Plates 133-4) and a ramp for hauling out seaplanes.

Communications were maintained by air and by occasional ships. There was a W/T station on the atoll and a telephone service.

BIBLIOGRAPHICAL NOTE

General works on Guam include: L. M. Cox and others, *The Island of Guam* (Washington, 1925); and Laura Thompson, *Guam and Its People: A Study of Culture Change and Colonial Education* (San Francisco, 1941), which gives an account of administration and social and economic conditions. Physical geography is dealt with, to some extent, by the Admiralty *Pacific Islands Pilot*, vol. I (London, 1933; with supplement, 1944). W. E. Safford, 'Useful Plants of the Island of Guam', *Contributions from the United States National Herbarium*, vol. IX (Washington, 1905) is not only useful as a work of botanical reference, but includes sections on physical geography, history, ethnology and the Chamorro language. A further work dealing more specifically with linguistic problems is E. R. von Preissig, *Dictionary and Grammar of the Chamorro Language of the Island of Guam* (Washington, 1918). Some general references will be found in Henry E. Crompton, 'A Journey to the Mariana Islands, Guam and Saipan', *Natural History*, vol. XXI, pp. 126-45 (New York, 1921). Brief reference is made to current developments in the United States Federal Government *Annual Report of the Secretary of the Navy* (Washington, 1933-40). Wake island is described in E. H. Bryan, *American Polynesia and the Hawaian Chain* (Honolulu, 1943).

For maps see Appendix I.

Appendix I

MAPS AND CHARTS OF THE WESTERN PACIFIC (NEW GUINEA AND ISLANDS NORTHWARD)

GENERAL

Although the area covered in this volume has been described above under three headings, it may for cartographic purposes be more conveniently discussed under two, viz. New Guinea and the islands near to it, including the Bismarck archipelago on one hand, and the greater part of Micronesia (including the Japanese mandated islands and Guam) and the out-lying Bonin islands, Marcus island and Wake island on the other. (Maps of the remaining parts of Micronesia have been treated in vol. III.) The New Guinea area includes large land masses. A few general maps cover the whole of it and there are also numerous sketch maps indicating routes followed by District Officers, the findings of surveys for mining purposes, and several good maps published by German authorities. Since the outbreak of hostilities in the south-west Pacific numerous maps have been produced by Australian and United States military authorities from aerial reconnaissance photographs. These latter maps provide a more complete and detailed cover than is usually obtainable in maps of the Pacific. Both Micronesia and the Bonin islands on the other hand are very poorly mapped. Among those available are a few from Japanese sources, sketch maps published in scientific works, and a few maps produced by the United States Army Map Service.

Both areas are covered by Admiralty charts, United States Hydrographic Office charts and American aeronautical charts. General remarks on these are appended below. Further notes on material available for each area will be found under subheadings. These notes are not intended to provide an exhaustive list, but merely as a broad indication of maps and charts which are generally available.

For most purposes charts are produced on Mercator's projection, and plans and charts of small islands (as opposed to small-scale charts of large areas) vary in scale from roughly 1 : 5,000 to 1 : 600,000. Lists of British Admiralty charts (including scale and dates of publication of original and latest editions) are given in the *Catalogue of Admiralty Charts and other Hydrographic Publications*; and for American charts in the *General Catalog of Mariners' and Aviators' Charts and Books*, published by the United States Hydrographic Office. Index sheets will also be found in the various *Sailing Directions*. Charts, of necessity, cannot always be reliable or detailed in matters of topography. Hills, for example, if indicated, are almost invariably shown by hachuring and rarely by contours. In many cases the ordinary published charts are based only on sketch surveys, some of considerable age, and while new editions incorporating the latest corrections are constantly being issued, they have sometimes been found to be inaccurate in some respects.

The United States Army Map Service issue a series of World Pilotage Aeronautical charts on a scale of 1 : 1,000,000 showing settlements, communications, etc., and also isogonic lines. They are suitably coloured for use by white, ultraviolet, red, or amber light. The series is designed to cover the world in sheets covering 4° of latitude and, for sheets on the equator, 5° of longitude, with a greater number of degrees of longitude with increasing distance from the equator. On the reverse side of every sheet is an index of these charts, which are numbered consecutively. For certain areas the service produces approach charts on a scale of 1 : 250,000 which cover one-sixteenth of the area covered by the World Pilotage sheets. These bear corresponding numbers to the World Pilotage charts and a secondary number and letter indicating their position on the corresponding small-scale chart.

NEW GUINEA, THE BISMARCK ARCHIPELAGO AND NEIGHBOURING ISLANDS

Admiralty Charts. A large general chart on a scale of 1 : 1,700,000 covers the whole area from the Dutch frontier to the northern Solomons. A series of charts on a larger scale (1 : 190,000) covers the coast of Papua and the Louisiade archipelago. Three charts on a scale of 1 : 750,000 cover the coast of north-east New Guinea and the Bismarck archipelago. Charts and plans on scales varying from 1 : 100,000 to 1 : 750,000 cover most of the ports and anchorages in the area. The Papuan coast series are for the most part based on British surveys made in the period 1845–50, or between 1885 and 1888. Two sheets for the north-eastern coast of Papua are, however, based on recent Australian charts. Those for north-east New Guinea are based primarily on German charts bearing dates up to about 1933. A few of the harbour and anchorage charts depend on recent surveys. For example, the charts for Kanapapa anchorage are dependent on surveys made by U.S.S. *Susquehanna* in 1943 and that for Dedele anchorage on a survey by H.M.A.S. *Moresby* in 1929.

Australian Survey Corps and Corps of Engineers, U.S. Army, Maps. Maps on various scales have been produced by the Australian Survey Corps and the Corps of Engineers, U.S. Army, since 1942. They are the most detailed maps of eastern New Guinea and the surrounding areas. While they vary slightly in type, they may be regarded as interchangeable, some series being made up of maps of both authorities. They are all based primarily on reconnaissance photographs by the R.A.A.F. or U.S.A.A.F. On parts of some sheets ground distances may be slightly inaccurate owing to lack of ground control. The degree of reliability is indicated in the margin of each sheet so constructed.

While maps on a small scale cover practically the whole of New Guinea, large-scale maps are limited to areas of particular military significance. Relief is shown where possible by contours, or more frequently by form lines, and elsewhere by hachuring. Vegetation, plantations, settlements and communications are indicated. All maps are gridded, though some sheets have only an arbitrary grid. Individual sheets produced by the Australian Survey Corps are named and numbered. The names of adjacent sheets are indicated by a locality diagram. Sheets made by the United States Corps of Engineers are similarly named and localized, but many also bear index numbers on the system adopted for the International 1 : 1,000,000 series. All bear an index number giving the position of the top left-hand corner and the number of minutes covered by the sheet, e.g., S411-E15210/5 indicates that the position of the top left-hand corner is in lat. 4° 11′ S, long. 152° 10′ E and that the map covers 5′ in each direction. S145-E14600/60 × 120 indicates that the top left-hand corner is in lat. 1° 45′ S, long. 146° 00′ E and that the map covers 60′ of latitude and 120′ of longitude. In October 1944 the two series of maps were as follows :

(i) 1 : 20,000. Maps on this scale have been produced both by the Australian Survey Corps and by the Corps of Engineers, U.S. Army. The series was not complete in October 1944, and covered only a few parts of New Guinea, notably the Aitape, Wewak, Manam and Saidor areas, the Gazelle peninsula, and one or two other areas in New Britain, together with some of the islands of the Bismarck archipelago. The reverse sides of sheets in this series have photo-maps of the areas depicted.

(ii) 1 : 25,000. Maps on this scale are produced only by the Australian Survey Corps. The areas covered are scattered. By October 1944 sheets had been produced for Port Moresby, Milne bay, Buna, and further north, Salamaua, Lae, Finschhafen, Madang, Wewak and Merauke.

(iii) 1 : 63,360. Maps on this scale are produced by the Australian Survey Corps and by the Corps of Engineers, U.S. Army. The combined series covers a good deal of New Guinea and many off-lying islands. Some of the American sheets are supplemented by photo-maps.

(iv) 1 : 126,720. There are two sheets covering Buna and its vicinity on this scale. They are produced by the Corps of Engineers, U.S. Army. Other sheets on this scale may have been produced.

(v) 1 : 253,440. Maps on this scale are produced both by the Australian Survey Corps and by the Corps of Engineers, U.S. Army. The combined series is planned to cover the whole of New Guinea and extends as far east as Buka and Bougainville.

G.S.G.S. Maps. G.S.G.S. have produced several maps covering New Guinea and the Bismarck archipelago; they include No. 3860 (East Indies, Sheet 2) and No. 4283 (New Guinea and Papua). The first map will be found in the folder at the end of this volume. It is the best small-scale relief map of the area which is generally available, and is on a scale of 1 : 4,000,000. The second map, on a scale of 1 : 2,640,000 is, like the first, on Mercator's projection and was printed in 1942 from a map made in 1934 by the Property and Survey Branch of the Department of the Interior, at Canberra. It covers the area from the British-Dutch boundary to the Solomon islands, and shows political boundaries, government stations, missions, plantations, towns and villages. G.S.G.S. No. 4345 shows the Kavieng District of New Ireland and is on a scale of 1 : 1,000,000. It was copied in 1942 from a map made in 1921 by the Department of Lands, Surveys, Mines and Forests of the Mandated Territory of New Guinea. It shows major plantations, settlements and communications.

A.M.S. Maps. Apart from a few maps in the Corps of Engineers series described above, which are catalogued by the U.S. Army Map Service, there are two published series:

(i) No. T 691 (New Ireland) is in 4 sheets on a scale of 1 : 100,000 and is compiled from the same source as G.S.G.S. No. 4345. Further information has been added from aerial photographs and from intelligence reports. The map is gridded.

(ii) No. T 401 is a series covering New Guinea and nearby islands on a scale of 1 : 500,000. It is drawn on a polyconic projection, and is compiled from various sources including American, British and French charts, and Australian Survey Corps 1 : 253,440 maps of New Guinea. They show relief by hachuring and spot heights, together with roads, settlements, airfields and anchorages. They also show isogonal lines and are gridded.

Maps Made by Australian Government Departments. A few maps have been made by Australian government departments. The most useful is a 1 : 2,264,000 map by the Property and Survey Branch of the Department of the Interior (G.S.G.S. No. 4283 is copied from this map). A geological map of Papua from surveys made by E. R. Stanley and others was produced on a small scale in 1923 by the Northern Territories Branch of the Department of Home and Territories. There are also various sketch maps of particular areas, such as those based on patrols made by District Officers. An example is the map of the land between the Purari delta and Yule island on a scale of 1 : 125,000. This is based on surveys made in connection with Dr. Wade's petroleum expedition of 1913, and was published by the commonwealth government at Melbourne.

Maps of the Royal Geographical Society, London. Maps have been published at intervals in the *Geographical Journal* (London), to illustrate patrol reports forwarded by District Officers to the Royal Geographical Society. Details of these reports are given in the Bibliographical Note at the end of Chapter II of this volume. In addition to the maps thus published, the findings of these patrols have been incorporated on a base map held by Royal Geographical Society. The value of these maps lies mainly in providing information on areas not particularly well covered by the recent Australian and American Army maps.

German Maps. In addition to charts published by the German Admiralty there are a few maps produced by the Imperial Survey Office of German New Guinea prior to 1914; maps were also published in *Mitteilungen aus den Deutschen Schutzgebieten* and in other journals. The Imperial Survey Office maps include a map of New Ireland in four sheets, showing roads and settlements, and a similar general map of Lavongai.

In *Mitteilungen aus den Deutschen Schutzgebieten,* Erganzungsheft no. 3, 1910, there are several maps by Dr Karl Sapper. These cover New Ireland, Lavongai and the Anir (Feni) islands. They are as follows: (i) a contoured map of Lavongai on a scale of 1 : 200,000 in 7 layer tints, with an inset on a scale of 1 : 200,000 showing geological formations; (ii) a similar map, in two sheets, on a scale of 1 : 200,000 with geological insets; (iii) a geological map of the Anir islands on a scale of 1 : 150,000 showing heights and the position of raised reef terraces studied by the author; (iv) a map of New Ireland on a scale of 1 : 1,000,000 showing the same features as the map of the Anir islands; (v) a map of New Ireland on a scale of 1 : 1,000,000 showing distribution and approximate density of population. A map in the same publication for 1903 shows the north of the Gazelle peninsula on a scale of 1 : 100,000 with insets of Rabaul and the German capital Herbertshöhe (Kokopo). Another published in 1912 shows part of the south-east corner of German New Guinea mapped in connection with the Anglo-German frontier expedition.

The same publication (Erganzungsheft no. 11, 1914) has maps of the Sepik river in two parts by Dr Leonhard Schultze of Jena. Part I consists of a single sheet on a scale of 1 : 200,000 showing the lower course of the river. Part II, consisting of three sheets on a scale of 1 : 100,000, shows the previously unexplored upper reaches. These maps indicate only the river and its immediate surroundings, but they are of considerable value. They give soundings taken in the river and details of topography and vegetation on the banks. This information is shown partly by symbols and partly by notes on the maps.

Petermanns Mitteilungen aus Justus Perthes' Geographische Anstalt has published various maps. Among these are:

(i) A map by W. Behrmann of the Sepik river on a scale of 1 : 250,000. The river is shown in blue; form lines are in brown. The map shows topographical features, native settlements and swamps. It was published in 1924.

(ii) A map by W. Behrmann of the Sepik area on a scale of 1 : 800,000, layer tinted, with two insets to show population and linguistic divisions, and plantations respectively. Also published in 1924.

(iii) A map of the island of Manus by A. Leben on a scale of 1: 300,000. Published in 1923.

Miscellaneous. A useful general map is the *Schetskaart van Nieuw-Guinea* produced by the Topografische Dienst at Batavia in 1938. This map covers the whole of New Guinea and the Bismarck archipelago (with the exception of the south-east of New Ireland and the islands which lie off it). It is on a scale of 1 : 2,500,000 and shows relief by hachuring. Major shipping routes and settlements are indicated. An inset on a scale of 1 : 10,000,000 shows political boundaries and divisions in both Dutch and British New Guinea.

MICRONESIA AND THE BONIN ISLANDS

Charts. For this area there are large Admiralty charts on comparatively small scales. Two charts on scales of 1 : 1,500,000 cover the Caroline islands, one on a scale of 1 : 2,000,000 cover the Marshall islands, and one on a scale of 1 : 1,510,000 covers the Marianas. Almost all the individual islands and atolls in the area are covered by separate charts (on various scales), and there are insets of the harbours and anchorages of the larger islands on larger scales. For example, the chart for Palau is on a scale of 1 : 250,000 and has an inset of Malakal harbour on a scale of 1 : 50,000. The chart for Ponape is on a scale of 1 : 100,000 and has insets of Lot harbour (1 : 12,500), Metalanim harbour (1 : 36,000), Ponape harbour (1 : 25,000), and Ronkiti harbour (1 : 25,000).

With a few exceptions, notably the charts of Guam and Apra harbour (which are from American sources), the charts of Lot harbour and Mokil island (which are from German sources), and the chart of Woleai (which is from a sketch survey made by Captain F. Lütke of the Russian Imperial Navy in 1828), the charts covering the Japanese mandated islands discussed in this volume are all based on Japanese surveys. These have been conducted since about 1920. Topography is extremely sketchy and hydrographic information is inadequate. More adequate Japanese charts have been produced, but they have not been generally available. Charts of the Bonin islands and Volcano islands are based on Japanese surveys made before 1914 and show rather more detail than the charts of the Carolines, Marshalls and Marianas.

In spite of the inadequate nature of the surveys on which these charts are based, they are the most complete sources of readily available cartographical information in the area.

Maps are few and are produced by American, German or Japanese authorities.

American Maps. The principal American authority is the Army Map Service. Among maps produced by this authority are the following:

(i) Ogasawara guntō (Bonin islands), on a scale of 1 : 50,000, in 21 sheets; these maps were published in 1943 from Imperial Land Survey sheets produced at various dates between 1912 and 1936. They cover all the islands between lat. 24° and 34° N. All are gridded. They show considerable detail and are contoured at intervals of 20 metres. They are difficult to read. Names in Japanese script are transcribed according to the modified Hepburn system.

(ii) Ogasawara guntō, on a scale of 1 : 250,000, in 5 sheets. These maps were prepared in 1943 from the same source as the above but were modified from intelligence reports. The series is gridded; it is in colour and the size of settlements is indicated on the maps.

(iii) Saipan, on a scale of 1 : 50,000. This map consists of one gridded sheet in colour showing settlements, communications and Japanese place-names transliterated. Elevations are indicated by heavier stippling than that covering the whole of the island. The heavier stippling gives no very definite indication of the margins of the higher land, and no precise indications of height are given.

(iv) Ponape, on a scale of 1 : 50,000. This map is generally similar in form to that of Saipan.

(v) Yap, on a scale of 1 : 88,000.

(vi) A map of Saipan and Tinian, on a scale of 1 : 245,000.

(vii) A map of Rota, on a scale of 1 : 206,000, with an inset of Sosanjaya bay on a scale of 1 : 50,000.

(viii) The Marianas, on a scale of 1 : 3,100,000.

Various maps have been produced by the United States Marine Corps. They include a series of 1 : 20,000 sheets, 15 in number, which cover the island of Guam.

Japanese Maps. Japanese maps include a series of 1 : 50,000 sheets for the islands south of Japan. They extend as far south as Minami Iwo shima, and have been published at various dates up to 1934. The A.M.S. 1 : 50,000 Ogasawara guntō sheets are based on this series. There is also a 1 : 1,100,000 sheet covering the Bonin islands. Many maps, especially for the Bonin islands, have been produced by the Japanese general staff. The *Geological Atlas of Eastern Asia*, published in 1929, has a map of the Bonin islands in one sheet.

German Maps. The German maps of the area are mostly found in scientific journals, but a few other maps have been produced. Among the latter are 3 maps produced by Dietrich Reimer of Berlin in 1909. They are a map of Ponape on a scale of 1 : 63,000, a map of the Marianas on a scale of 1 : 3,000,000 (with an inset of Saipan and Tinian on a scale of 1 : 1,500,000), and a map of the Marshall islands (1 : 3,000,000), with insets of Jaluit and Arno atolls, on a scale of 1 : 1,000,000. Other maps of varying quality will be found in the numerous volumes of *Ergebnisse der Südsee Expedition*, published by the Hamburg Museum under the editorship of G. Thilenius (see pp. 359–60).

Appendix II

PLACE-NAMES IN THE WESTERN PACIFIC (NEW GUINEA AND ISLANDS NORTHWARD)

Place-names in the area covered by this volume present a number of problems. As in other parts of the Pacific, native names predominate. But the number of native languages involved is large; in New Guinea the full number of separate linguistic stocks is so far undetermined. The problem of reducing these names to writing is thus a difficult one; and so far no standard system of orthography has been universally adopted, even within a single group of islands. Similarly, owing to the conditions of European contact with the area from the time of the explorers to the present, the place-names given by Europeans are in a number of different languages —English, German, French, Spanish and Dutch. Finally, in the islands under Japanese sovereignty or held by Japan under mandate, there are also large numbers of Japanese place-names. (The Japanese also gave names, of course, to many of the places which they occupied during the earlier stages of the present Pacific war; such names, however, seem to be of purely ephemeral importance, and they are nowhere noted in the present Handbook.) For a single geographical feature there are in many cases several different names, both native and non-native, from which a choice has to be made.

General Situation: Native Names and Non-native Names

The modern tendency has usually been to substitute a native place-name, where one can be ascertained, for a non-native name. This is especially so if, as often happens, no single non-native name has ever gained complete acceptance. For example, Kusaie has replaced the alternatives of Strong's island, Hope island, and Armstrong island; Ponape has replaced Ascension; Guam has replaced San Juan; Lavongai has replaced New Hanover; Bogadjim has replaced Stephansort; and Madang has replaced Friedrich Wilhelmshafen. In some instances the substitution is still not complete. Thus, Murua is used in this Handbook in place of Woodlark, but the latter name has not yet fallen wholly out of use. A complication is added where no native name is known to apply to the whole of an island or to a group of adjacent islands. Frequently the name of a part (probably the most important part) is extended to the whole. Thus, most of the atolls in the Caroline islands and the Marshall islands are known by the name of one of the islands on the atoll rim. Sometimes, however, a non-native name is adopted to refer to the whole. Thus, the adjacent atolls of Nomwin and Murilo, in the Carolines, are known jointly as the Hall islands.

In the New Guinea area German names have sometimes been anglicized. Thus Seeadlerhafen is sometimes called Sea Eagle harbour and Seichte bay, Shallow bay. More frequently the geographical term only is translated and not the name. Thus Lindenhafen is now usually known as Linden harbour, not as Limes harbour; and, in this volume, the form Seeadler harbour is used in preference to Sea Eagle harbour. The full German form is retained, however, in some instances, where it has become established as the conventional name of a settlement. Thus the name Alexishafen is used for the settlement centred round the German mission station at Sek harbour (Alexis harbour). Non-native names in other languages have sometimes been similarly translated. Thus, the former-Spanish settlement on Ponape named Colonia de Santiago and known familiarly as Colonia has been sometimes known in English as Colony. This name, incidentally, has been adopted by the

Japanese, and the Japanese form has been transliterated in reports and maps in English as Koroni. Similarly, the Japanese adopted the older English name of Greenwich island for Kapingamarangi, and the Japanese form has been transliterated as Gurinitchi.

Terms for Geographical Features

As in other volumes of the Handbook, the general practice has been to adopt the geographical terms used in maps and reports issued by the governments of the territories concerned but, where they are not in English, to translate them. Difficulties occur, however, in some cases where geographical terms are used with native names, since the latter often incorporate such a term. The use of an English geographical term thus causes reduplication. Instances of this were given for Polynesian names in the Eastern Pacific (vol. II, p. 687). Recent British and American official practice has been to avoid pleonasm, either by using only the native geographical term or by translating it. In the area dealt with in this volume it has often not been possible to take either of these courses, owing to the lack of study of place-names which has been discussed above.

An exception to the general practice has been made in respect of the Bonin islands, in order to achieve consistency with the usage of the Admiralty *Japan Pilot*. On maps and in the text relating to these islands Japanese geographical terms have been retained. The Japanese terms used, with their English equivalents, are given below:

guntō	archipelago	*seto*	strait, channel
kō	harbour	*shima*	island
minato	harbour	*shotō*	archipelago
misaki	cape	*tani*	valley
rettō	chain of islands	*ura*	creek, bay
saki	cape	*wan*	bay

The words for the four cardinal points of the compass, which commonly occur in place-names, are as follows:

higashi	east	*minami*	south
kita	north	*nishi*	east

Orthography, Spelling and Transliteration

The difficulties encountered in the writing and spelling of native names in this area are similar to those which have been described for the Eastern Pacific (vol. II, pp. 688–90). The position is particularly difficult in the Carolines, Marshalls and Marianas. There, not only has there been no official action to standardize orthography and spelling (as the Japanese use characters, not an alphabet), but Western linguists and anthropologists have been unable to work there since the establishment of Japanese control. As a result, it is often possible to obtain only the most imperfect clues as to the actual pronunciation of native names, and it becomes necessary to accept the commonly recognized spelling, however imperfect that may seem to be. Transliterations from Japanese forms of native names are particularly unsatisfactory from this point of view. Many of these Japanese forms contain not only sounds which do not exist in the native language but additional syllables which have been introduced by Japanese-speakers. Apart from these basic difficulties, there are variant forms of an immense number of names: e.g., Kayangel and Ngajangel; Ngeream and Garayamu; Salamaua, Salamoa, Salamua, Somoa and Samoa. The reasons for these differences are numerous: recorders have followed varying systems of orthography, they have failed to follow their own system consistently, they have had to deal with sounds which they could not satisfactorily represent by any simple combination of letters, and, often, they have failed to apprehend exactly the native pronunciation. At the present stage, it is sometimes impossible to choose with certainty between several variants.

Japanese names have been transliterated, following the usage of the Admiralty *Japan Pilot*, according to the modified Hepburn system. *Sh* is used in preference to *j* (e.g., *shima* instead of *jima*); *s* instead of *z* in some words (e.g., *saki* instead of *zaki*); and *sh* instead of *sy* (e.g., *shoto* instead of *syoto*). Again in accordance with Admiralty *Japan Pilot* practice, where a place-name and its attached geographical term are used jointly in an adjectival sense they are run together as one word: e.g., Chichi shima (Chichi island), when used adjectivally, becomes Chichishima, as in Chichishima rettō (Chichi-island chain).

Appendix III
NEW GUINEA SINCE 1939

This volume is primarily concerned with conditions before the outbreak of the present war. It contains incidental references to conditions since 1939 to show where a description no longer applies, or to bring Tables for exports, etc., up to date. The purpose of this Appendix is to give a brief general picture of events in Papua and the Mandated Territory of New Guinea since September 1939. Information is too scanty to permit a comparable account for the Japanese mandated islands. Military operations in the area are briefly summarized in vol. I, Appendix VI. Here they are mentioned only when they have a direct bearing on political and economic conditions.

Political Conditions

Political conditions in the two territories have altered considerably during the present war. Changes that took place in administrative structure and personnel before December 1941 were mainly independent of war conditions. Since that date the many sweeping changes are directly attributable to the war.

On 27 February 1940 Sir Hubert Murray, the Lieutenant-Governor of Papua, died in office. The Australian commonwealth government did not immediately appoint a successor. When, in December 1940, the Hon. H. Leonard Murray was appointed, the title of Administrator was substituted for that of Lieutenant-Governor. With this change the administrative structure of Papua was assimilated to that of the mandated territory. The relative freedom from control from Canberra which the administration of Papua had enjoyed, as compared with that of the mandated territory, came to an end. Thenceforward, the Administrator of Papua was not to have the power to select his own staff.

In the mandated territory (as has been indicated in Chapter IX) the proposal to shift the administrative capital from Rabaul to Lae was acted upon late in 1941. The Administrator took up his residence at Lae on 1 December. But only a few of the government departments had been moved by the time that the Japanese attacked the area.

The outbreak of war in Europe found the mandated territory wholly unprepared militarily. The terms of the mandate had forbidden the military training of the native population and the establishment of military bases or fortifications of any kind. The government sought to modify this situation by bringing into force certain defence measures that had been proclaimed in Australia. In March 1940 the territory began to recruit a small force of men for the Australian Expeditionary Force.

The entry of Japan into the war on 7 December 1941 caused no immediate political changes of consequence in either territory. As a precautionary measure, an order was made on 17 December for the evacuation of all European women and children from both territories. But the great speed of the Japanese advance, which carried them to Rabaul on 23 January 1942, soon brought normal administration to an end. On the mainland martial law was proclaimed and European officials of military age were co-opted for active service; all other Europeans were evacuated to Australia. Despite this measure, many European civilians, both official and non-official, were captured or killed in the Japanese advance.

Early in 1942 both territories were placed under a single military administration. The European officers of the former civil administrations who had remained at

494

their posts were incorporated in the military forces and formed into the 'Australian New Guinea Administrative Unit', generally known by its initials as ANGAU. This unit is under the command of the New Guinea Force. Its main function is to carry on the general administration that was formerly in the hands of the civil authorities; but it also has the important military functions of providing an intelligence service and of acting as a liaison with native populations in combat areas. In charge of ANGAU is Major-General Basil Morris, who was the military commander in Papua at the time of the Japanese invasion. His staff has been greatly expanded so that he now has charge of some 1,500 European officers and men, with native police forces and large bodies of native labourers. As the liberated parts of New Guinea have grown in area, the civil duties of ANGAU have also extended in scope. For purposes of local administration it has divided the former territories into three districts: the Southern district (the whole of Papua, including the eastern islands); the Northern district (north-east New Guinea); the Island district (the Bismarck archipelago and Bougainville). The headquarters of these three districts are respectively at Port Moresby, Lae and Finschhafen. A District Officer, with Assistant District Officers, is in charge of each headquarters.

All the judicial and administrative functions of the former civil governments have been assumed by ANGAU. Each headquarters has a detachment of native police, maintains medical services, carries out patrols and recruits native labour. Besides the normal tasks of maintaining law and order and health services, many additional burdens have been thrown on the organization. The native populations of whole districts have suffered acutely from the direct effects of the war. Many natives have been killed or ill-treated by the Japanese; many others have fled in panic from their villages and cultivations. Crops and domesticated animals have been looted by the Japanese. In some areas all the able-bodied men have been conscripted as road-builders, stretcher-bearers or porters; native food production has therefore suffered from a shortage of labour. Many of ANGAU's problems are therefore concerned with the re-habilitation and re-settlement of natives in the areas affected by military operations. In many areas food is so scarce that the District Officers are empowered to issue rations to all natives who ask for them.

The military administration of the two territories is now drawing to a close. On 9 March 1945 the Minister for External Territories announced in the commonwealth Parliament that the government had decided to restore civil administration in Papua and in the mandated territory south of the Markham river. It had decided to set up a single provisional administration, but to continue to apply the respective laws of the two territories, subject to such modifications as might be necessary. The separate Legislative Councils would not be restored; the power of legislation would for the present be exercised by the Governor-General.

Economic Conditions

Until the Japanese invasion, the effects of the war on economic conditions in Papua and the mandated territory were generally similar to those in other Pacific islands territories (vol. II, pp. 691–3; vol. III, pp. 710–12). From September 1939 many of the accustomed markets in Europe for copra and other island products were closed. And by the early months of 1940 the British reorganization of shipping services on a war basis was causing a serious shortage of shipping for the collection of copra. Stocks rapidly accumulated on plantations and at ports of shipment. By August 1940 there were over 4,000 tons awaiting shipment at Port Moresby. The industry gained some relief in 1941 from the establishment of a copra shipping and marketing pool for the Western Pacific territories.

Other products for which there was a local market in Australia and New Zealand began to enjoy a boom. The growing shipping shortage made it easier to import rubber and cocoa from New Guinea than from the main sources of supply further afield. The small rubber industry and the still smaller cocoa industry thus prospered. By February 1940 New Guinea cocoa beans were much in demand at £26 to £28 per ton. Gold production during 1940 and 1941 declined by about a third in Papua but increased slightly in the mandated territory.

The Japanese occupation of so much of New Guinea brought nearly all European economic activity to an end in 1942: European planters and miners were hurriedly evacuated to Australia or joined the defence forces; and some of the indentured labourers were repatriated to their homes, but the speed of the Japanese advance seldom permitted so orderly a withdrawal. Many of the copra sheds and loading installations and some of the gold-mining machinery were destroyed by enemy action. The only plantations to survive more or less intact were those on the south coast of Papua.

With the loss of Malaya and the Netherlands East Indies, most of the world's copra and rubber-producing areas fell into Japanese hands. Every effort was therefore made to increase output of these two vital war materials in such areas of production as remained under Allied control. From its inception, one of the tasks entrusted to ANGAU was the maintenance and expansion of production in the parts of New Guinea free from the Japanese, to meet the needs of the army and of Australian industry. Native labour was recruited to work the plantations, which now, in the absence of civilians, were managed by ANGAU officials. This side of the unit's activities expanded rapidly and with the extension of the liberated area of New Guinea it was entrusted on 1 July 1943 to a civil organization responsible to the Minister for External Territories, and known as the Australian New Guinea Production Control Board, or ANGPCB. The work of this organization is closely co-ordinated with that of ANGAU. It has taken over all the plantations and other civilian undertakings in New Guinea. By 1943, when all Papua had been cleared of the enemy, a few of the civilian owners and managers were allowed to return to their plantations, but the whole system of production and marketing has remained in government hands. Considerable success has attended the efforts of ANGPCB. More rubber than ever before is now being produced in Papua. In all its operations it works in close co-operation with ANGAU, from which it draws the necessary equipment, transport and labour supplies.

INDEX

Printed under the Authority of HIS MAJESTY'S STATIONERY OFFICE
by Butler & Tanner Ltd., Frome and London